PROGRESS IN FIBRINOLYSIS — VII

The international committee for fibrinolysis

PROGRESS IN FIBRINOLYSIS
VOLUME VII

Editors

John F. Davidson
Department of Haematology,
Royal Infirmary,
Glasgow, Scotland

Maria Benedetta Donati
Istituto di Ricerche Farmacologiche 'Mario Negri',
Milan, Italy

Sergio Coccheri
Associate Professor of Medical Pathophysiology,
Istituto di Patologia Spec. Medica II,
University of Bologna, Italy

**Under the auspices of the
University of Bologna, Italy**

CHURCHILL LIVINGSTONE
EDINBURGH LONDON MELBOURNE AND NEW YORK 1985

CHURCHILL LIVINGSTONE
Medical Division of Longman Group Limited

Distributed in the United States of America by Churchill
Livingstone Inc., 1560 Broadway, New York, N.Y.
10036, and by associated companies, branches and
representatives throughout the world.

© Longman Group Limited 1985

First published 1985

ISBN 0 443 03435 4
ISSN 0262-0790

British Library Cataloguing in Publication Data
Progress in Fibrinolysis.——Vol. 7
  1. Fibrinolysis——Periodicals
  612'.115   QP93.5

Printed in Great Britain
at the University Press, Oxford

Preface

This volume is a record of selected papers and posters presented at the 7th International Congress on Fibrinolysis held in Venice between 27th and 30th March 1984, under the Presidency of Sergio Coccheri and Maria Benedetta Donati. It was, regretfully, impossible to publish papers from all the presentations at the Congress and after very careful consideration it was decided to publish the main lectures, the five official symposia and all communications and posters on topics relating to these symposia.

Again owing to the need for the editors to contain the size of this volume, authors were required to restrict the size of their manuscripts. This has made it necessary to curtail bibliographies.

Fibrinolysis continues to advance on a wide front. This was reflected in the presentations at the Congress. The recognition of the fast inhibitor(s) of plasminogen activator appears to be a significant advance in our understanding of fibrinolysis. This concept is well represented in this proceedings.

Finally the continuation of the series is under review. The stage has now been reached when it is not possible to publish all presentations. The International Committee is considering this very carefully but it is likely that Volume VII will be the last in the series.

It has been a great privilege to edit the seven volumes.

Glasgow, 1984   J.F.D.

Acknowledgements

The Editors gratefully acknowledge support from the following who have contributed to the publication of this volume:

Department of Public Health, Regione del Veneto, Italy
Ciba Geigy PLC, UK
CISR — Centro Italiano per lo Sviluppo della Ricerca, Bologna
Immuno Ltd, UK
Lers-Synthelabo-Lirca, Paris–Milano
Upjohn Ltd,UK

Contents

Section 11 Plasminogen activators from different sources

Section 1
INTERNATIONAL COMMITTEE FOR FIBRINOLYSIS 1984 AWARD LECTURE

(supported by KabiVitrum, Stockholm)

1. Tissue plasminogen activator induced fibrinolysis: historical landmarks and present achievements

P. B. Wallén

The first observations related to fibrinolysis were made in the 18th century when it was found that blood from cases of sudden death or collected from animals, who were stressed to exhaustion was incoagulable. At the turn to the 20th century it was realized that such blood could destroy added fibrin or fibrinogen and that it was an enzymatic process. A short review of the early observations of fibrinolysis has been given by Marsh (1981).

The modern history of fibrinolysis began about 50 years ago when Tillet & Garner (1933) reported that certain strains of streptococci release a substance, which is able to dissolve blood clots. Their results aroused great interest and stimulated strongly the research on fibrinolysis. It was found that the streptococcal factor, subsequently called streptokinase, activated a proenzyme, plasminogen, to plasmin, 'a proteolytic enzyme (Christensen & MacLeod 1945). This discovery of the central reaction in fibrinolysis was of great importance for the research to follow.

THE DISCOVERY OF THE TISSUE PLASMINOGEN ACTIVATOR AND STUDIES ON THE DISTRIBUTION IN ANIMAL TISSUES

At the turn of the century it was noticed that cells grown on media containing fibrin (coagulated blood or blood plasma) often cause a liquefaction of the medium. It was early believed that the degradation of fibrin was a property of the living cell although the release of proteolytic enzymes became a more common explanation. Some scientists even suggested that that fibrinolytic activity was generated from a precursor in blood activated by an activator released from the cells (Demuth & Riesen 1928, Fischer 1946). These early studies have been reviewed by Astrup (1956).

In the 1940s the research group of A. Fischer to which T. Astrup had joined were actively exploring the fibrinolytic activity of tissues in culture. An assay for quantitation of fibrinolytic activity in tissues was developed imitating the conditions for cultivation on media containing fibrin. This was the basis for 'the fibrin plate method' which in different modifications subsequently should become a widespread method for the assay of fibrinolytic activity (Astrup & Kok 1970). Using this technique Astrup & Permin (1947) clearly showed that the compound in tissues causing fibrinolysis was not a proteolytic enzyme but an activator to a proenzyme present as a contaminant in the fibrinogen preparations. It was subsequently shown to be identical with plasminogen the precursor of the fibrinolytic enzyme plasmin discovered a few years earlier. The activator was at first called fibrinokinase but is now generally recognized as *'tissue plasminogen activator'*. A few years later Williams (1951) demonstrated that the earlier known fibrinolytic activity of urine also could be accounted for by an activator, which is now called urokinase. Thus in the early nineteen-fifties many of the components which constitute the fibrinolytic enzyme system were known. An important exception is the specific inhibitors to fibrinolysis (antiplasmin and antiactivator(s)), the discovery of which has occurred during the last 10 to 15 years.

Early determinations of the fibrinolytic activity of tissue suspensions indicated a high degree of variability between tissues from different organs and from different species. The content of the tissue activator in various tissues was systematically studied especially by Astrup & Albrechtsen. A problem encountered in these studies was the difficulty to solubilize the activator, which binds firmly to the insoluble tissue residue. An efficient extraction method, based on the stability of tissue plasminogen activator in 2 M KSCN and at low pH was developed and the extracts were analyzed with the fibrin plate method. Extensive reviews of these studies have been published by Albrechtsen (1959) and Astrup (1966). Table 1.1 is a selection of data from the review by Astrup and shows the

Table 1.1   Content of tissue plasminogen activator in different organs from man and various animals expressed in arbitrary units/gram. The data are selected from results published by Albrechtsen and Astrup and reviewed by Astrup (1966)

	Man	Pig	Ox	Dog	Rabbit	Guinea pig	Cat
Uterus	720	145	3	41	48	45	22
Prostate	335	5	4	133	0	—	—
Lung	225	0	0	9	+	24	0
Ovary	210	173	12	29	22	—	6
Muscle	110	24	0	0	0	0	0
Heart	80	216	28	0	0	39	0
Liver	1	—	—	—	—	—	—
Spleen	20	—	—	—	—	—	—

activator content in various organs from different mammalian species. Man has the highest content whereas some species such as rabbit, guinea pig and cat in general have a very low content of activator in their tissues. Pig takes an intermediate position. A striking feature is however the great variability both between different organs in the same species as well between the same organ in different species. There is certain correlation between high vascularization and concentration of the activator. Exceptions are however, liver spleen and placenta, which are highly vascularized organs with virtually undetectable fibrinolytic activity. In view of the present belief that the tissue plasminogen activator is of great importance for normal hemostasis and intact blood flow, the great variability between different species is rather remarkable. The presence of cell derived activator inhibitors could be one cause of variability. The existence of such inhibitors has been reported. (Noordhoek & Brakman 1974, Loskutoff & Edington 1977).

ISOLATION OF TISSUE PLASMINOGEN ACTIVATOR. ITS IMPORTANCE FOR THE FIBRINOLYTIC ACTIVITY IN BLOOD

In spite of much effort it took about 30 years from the discovery before pure preparations of tissue plasminogen activator were obtained. Three circumstances have helped to the slow progress. The very low content in tissues, the firm binding to insoluble matter of tissue suspension and especially in late stages of purification the marked tendency to aggregate and to adsorb both to plastic and glass surfaces.

In view of the low concentration of the activator in tissues the choice of a suitable source was very important. The pioneering work by Astrup, Albrechtsen and co-workers indicated that human uterus and pig heart should be suitable sources for the preparation of human and animal tissue plasminogen activator. Either of these tissues have also been used by most investigators.

In order to solubilize the activator, solution of chaotropic agents are generally used. One of the most effective solvents, 2 M KSCN was introduced by Astrup & Stage (1952) and used for the exploration of the distribution of tissue plasminogen activator in different tissues. Bachmann et al (1964) introduced 0.3 M sodium acetate pH 4.2 as extraction solvent, which is more selective but also less effective than thiocyanate. With regard to the human tissue activator the situation has considerably changed by the use of cell cultures. A melanoma cell line (Bowes) producing large amounts of a plasminogen activator was isolated by Rifkin et al (1974) and found by Collen to release the tissue type plasminogen activator (Rijken & Collen 1981). This cell line has been generously distributed to different laboratories.

Around 1980, preparations of pure tissue plasminogen activator were obtained in several laboratories. Largely using conventional fractionation techniques Cole & Bachmann (1977) and Kok (1984) isolated the porcine activator and Rijken et al (1979) the human activator. By applying specific affinity adsorbtion as main steps Wallén et al first purified porcine activator (Wallén et al 1981, 1982) by adsorbtion on fibrin and then the human activator utilizing the immunological cross-reactivity between human and porcine tissue activator (Wallén et al 1981). The melanoma cell activator was subsequently purified by applying methods used for purification of the activator from human tissues (Rijken & Collen 1981, Wallén et al 1983).

The fibrinolytic activity in blood is normally low but a significant increase may occasionally occur. It was found a long time ago that post mortem blood especially from cases of sudden death often had a high fibrinolytic activity, which as Müllertz (1953) could demonstrate is due to the release of a plasminogen activator into the blood. During the 1940s and 1950s it was observed that a marked increase of fibrinolytic activity is provoked by a variety of stimuli such as physical or mental stress, vasoactive drugs, venous occlusion and ischemia (for references, see Astrup 1978). An opinion grew more and more strongly that the increase of activity in these conditions was due to the release of an activator, probably related to the tissue plasminogen activator. This view was supported by the finding of Aoki & von Kaulla (1971) that an activator, the *'vascular plasminogen activator'* can be isolated from saline perfusates of human blood vessels. In an extensive study Rijken et al (1980) could substantiate the earlier suggestions to a large extent using immunological techniques.

THE PRIMARY STRUCTURE OF TISSUE PLASMINOGEN ACTIVATOR

The access to highly purified preparations has made it possible to determine the complete primary structure of the tissue plasminogen activator and to start discussions on structure function relationships.

Early electrophoretic analyses on highly purified preparations suggested that both porcine and human tissue plasminogen activators consists of two disulfide-linked chains (Wallén et al 1978, Rijken et al 1979). By using a protease inhibitor, aprotinin, in the purification procedure it was shown that both the porcine and the human activators were obtained as one-chain compounds which however, by cleavage with plasmin were transformed into the two chain forms (Wallén et al 1981 and 1982). Similar results have been obtained with the activator obtained from human melanoma cells provided the inhibitor is present in the culture medium (Rijken & Collen 1981 Wallén et al 1983). These results suggest that the tissue plasminogen activator is synthesized as well as released as a one chain compound.

Studies of the separated chains from the two chain form of the melanoma cell activator show that the two chain structure is generated by the cleavage at a single peptide bond (Arg-Ile) and that the light (B) chain, which contained the active site, originates from the C-terminal part of the native activator whereas the heavy (A) chain constitutes the N-terminal part (Edlund et al 1983, Pennica et al 1983, Wallén et al 1983). The structural studies have furthermore shown that the B-chain of the two chain activator is highly homologous with the B-chains of other mammalian serine proteases (Fig. 1.1.).

Thus from a structural point of view the generation of the two chain form of the activator is equivalent at a serine protease zymogen. A unique feature of the tissue activator is the lysine residue in position 2 of the B-chain. The positive

t-PA	I	K	G	G	L	F	A	D	I	A	S	H	P	W	Q	A	A	I
u-PA	I	I	G	G	E	F	T	T	I	E	N	Q	P	W	F	A	A	I
Plasmin	V	V	G	G	C	V	A	H	P	H	S	W	P	W	Q	V	S	L
Thrombin	I	V	E	G	S	N	A	E	I	G	M	S	P	W	Q	V	M	L

Fig. 1.1 The N-terminal sequence of the B-chain of two-chain human tissue plasminogen activator in comparison with the B-chains of some other serine proteases.

6

charge provided by this residue may speculatively induce a reactive conformation of the one chain activator ('the proenzyme form'), which could explain the high activity especially in the presence of fibrin (Wallén et al 1983, Rånby et al 1983).

Recently Pennica et al (1983) were able to deduce the complete amino acid sequence of the tissue plasminogen activator from c-DNA data. Besides the sequence corresponding to the 527 or 530 amino acids of the mature enzyme, they found a preceeding DNA-sequence which probably codes for a preprosequence of 35 amino acids. The first about 25 amino acids of this sequence seem to constitute a hydrophobic signal peptide. Contemporaneous and subsequent studies by protein sequence techniques are in full agreement with the data published by Pennica et al (Pohl et al 1984, Wallén et al 1983) and provide in addition explanations for the different types of heterogeneities, which have been described for tissue plasminogen activator (Jörnvall et al 1983).

The human tissue plasminogen activator contains 35 cystein residues. So far all attempts to deduce the disulfide arrangements are based on homologies with other proteins. Thus Pennica et al (1983) suggested a disulfide arrangement for the B-chain part of the molecule similar to the B-chain of other serine proteases and found sequence homologies in the C-terminal part of the A-chain indicating two 'kringle structures' a structure first described in prothrombin by Magnusson and coworkers. Recently Banyai et al (1983) showed that the A chain part of tissue plasminogen activator contain one domain (within residues 1–50), homologus with the finger-domains of fibronectin and one domain (within residues 51–100), homologous with the epidermal growth factor. They proposed that the finger-domaine may be involved in the binding of the activator to fibrin. Figure 1.2 is based on present knowledge of primary structure, disulfide alignement and sites of cleavage with plasmin of tissue plasminogen activator referred to above. It describes the long (L) form of the one chain activator (Jörnvall et al 1983).

ENZYMATIC PROPERTIES OF TISSUE PLASMINOGEN ACTIVATOR. THE EFFECT OF FIBRIN

Like all activators of the fibrinolytic enzyme system, tissue plasminogen activator cleaves the Arg_{560}-Val_{561} bond in the plasminogen molecule generating the two chain structure of plasmin.

Already in the 1930s it was postulated that the fibrinolytic process in the blood could be regulated by adsorbtion of active components to fibrin. The report by Müllertz (1953) that the blood activator discovered by him had a high affinity to fibrin supported this view. Twenty years later it was shown that the activator isolated from tissues in contrast to urokinase has a high affinity to fibrin and furthermore that this complex was a far more effective plasminogen activator than pure tissue activator (Camiolo et al 1971, Thorsen et al 1972, Wallén & Wiman 1975, Wallén 1977). Since it also was known that plasminogen binds to fibrin (Thorsen 1975) it was postulated that the stimulating effect was due to the assembly of a ternary complex on the fibrin surface. These observations prompted thorough kinetic studies under controlled conditions. Hoylertz et al

Fig. 1.2 Primary structure of human tissue plasminogen activator produced by melanoma cells. The disulfide arrangement is deduced from homologies with other proteins. Arrows indicate sites of cleavage by plasmin.

(1982) using a dried film of ^{125}I-labelled fibrin both as substrate and as stimulator found in the absence of fibrin a Michaelis constant (K_m) of 65 uM and a catalytic rate constant (Kc) of 0.06 s^{-1}. In the presence of fibrin these parameters changed to 0.16 and 0.12 respectively. Rånby (1982) determined plasmin generation by measuring accumulated paranitroaniline in a mixture of plasminogen, the plasmin substrate D.Val-Leu-Lys-pNA and activator. The calculated values for K_m and Kc were 8 uM and 0.006 s^{-1} in the absence of fibrin and 0.18 uM and 0.12 s^{-1} when fibrin was present. The data in both these studies refer to activation of Glu-plasminogen with two chain activator. The stimulation factor estimated from the kinetic data in both these studies is about 100–200 fold at physiological concentrations of plasminogen and up to 1000-fold at very low concentrations indicating a a considerable increase of enzymatic efficiency induced by fibrin.

Using a sensitive technique in which the rate of plasmin generation is measured continuously, Norrman et al (1984) recently found that the activation of Glu-plasminogen with tissue activator in the presence of fibrin proceeds in two phases with different kinetics. The initial phase (K 1 uM, Kc 0.17 s^{-1}) changes to the second phase (K 0.06 u M, 0.13 s^{-1}) when the plasmin concentration has reached a certain level. The decrease of K_m indicates a significant increase of affinity between the components in the ternary activation complex, which will keep the activation rate at a high level even at lowered plasminogen concentrations. These results suggest a proteolytic modification of reagents (e.g., fibrin or plasminogen) in the early stages of fibrinolysis and are in agreement with recent reports, which show that slightly digested fibrin stimulates the tissue activator induced activation much more efficiently than native fibrin (Suensen et al 1984).

CONCLUDING REMARKS

Finally I want to mention two lines of research which during the last few years have contributed to shed light on the importance of the tissue activator in haemostasis i.e. thrombolysis experiments and the discovery of a new inhibitor to the activator.

In vitro and in vivo studies have shown that the tissue plasminogen activator is more efficient than urokinase or streptokinase for dissolution of thrombi. As can be expected from the enzymological properties fibrinolysis induced by the tissue activator will cause much less damage to other proteins, e.g., fibrinogen, than the other two activators (Matsuo et al 1981, Mattson et al 1981). A few clinical trials have been performed with promising results (Weimar et al 1981). There is only one hindrance for the clinical use of the tissue activator – the limited supply. It is to be hoped that the efforts to produce the tissue activator in the large scale by gene cloning will be successful.

Tissue activator/vascular activator has been long known to be of importance for the prevention of thromboembolism (Isacson & Nilsson 1972). The presence of inhibitors to activators has been discussed. Quite recently a rapidly acting inhibitor to the tissue activator was detected in human blood. It was furthermore found that the concentration in blood is highly variable (Kruithof et al 1983, Chmielewska et al 1983). It seems clear that elevated levels of this inhibitor may cause a tendency to thrombosis. Further studies on this inhibitor will certainly be of interest for the understanding of 'idiopathic thrombosis'.

It is not possible in this small review to give a full account for all contributions to our knowledge about the tissue plasminogen activator which have emerged during the last about 40 years. It is also inevitable that many very important studies have been omitted from the reference list. There are however several other, more comprehensive reviews available. Some of them are included among the references (Astrup 1966, Collen 1980, Marsh 1981, Bachmann & Kruithof 1984).

REFERENCES

Aoki N, von Kaulla K N 1971 The extraction of vascular plasminogen activator from human cadavers and a description of some of its properties. American Journal of Clinical Pathology 55: 171–179

Albrechtsen O K 1959 Fibrinolytic activity in the organism. Thesis. Acta Physiologica Scandinavica 47: Suppl 165

Astrup T 1956 Fibrinolysis in the organism. Blood 11: 781–806

Astrup T 1966 Tissue activators of plasminogen. Federation Proceedings 25: 42–51

Astrup T 1978 Fibrinolysis: an overview. In: Davidson J F, Rowan R M, Samama M M, Desnoyers P C (eds) Progress in chemical fibrinolysis and thrombolysis (Glasgow 1976), vol 5. Raven Press, New York p 1–57

Astrup T, Kok P 1970 Assay and preparation of a tissue plasminogen activator. Methods of Enzymology 19: 821–834

Astrup T, Permin P M 1947 Fibrinolysis in the animal organism. Nature 159: 681–682

Astrup T, Stage A 1952 Isolation of a soluble fibrinolytic activator from animal tissue. Nature 170: 929–930

Bachmann F, Kruithof E K O 1984 Tissue plasminogen activator: Chemical and Physiological Aspects. Seminars in Thrombosis and Haemostasis 10 (1): 6–17

Bachmann F, Fletcher A P, Alkjaersig N, Sherry S 1964 Partial purification and properties of the plasminogen activator from pig heart. Biochemistry 3: 1578–1585

Bányai L, Varadi A, Patthy L 1983 Common evolutionary origin of the fibrin-binding structures of fibronectine and tissue type plasminogen activator. FEBS Letters 163: 37–41

Camiolo S M, Thorsen S, Astrup T 1971 Fibrinogenolysis and fibrinolysis with tissue plasminogen activator, urokinase, streptokinase-activated human globulin and plasmin. Proceedings of the Society for Experimental Biology and Medicine

Chmielewska J, Rånby M, Wiman B 1983 Evidence for a rapid inhibitor to tissue plasminogen activator in plasma. Thrombosis Research 31: 427–436

Christensen R L, MacLeod C M 1945 A proteolytic enzyme of serum: characterization, activation and reaction with inhibitors. Journal of General Physiology 28: 559–583

Cole E R, Bachmann F W 1977 Purification and properties of a plasminogen activator from pig heart. Journal of Biological Chemistry 252: 3729–3838

Collen D 1980 On the regulation and control of fibrinolysis. Thrombosis and Haemostasis 43: 77–89

Demuth F, von Riesen I 1928 Eiweisstoffwechsel normalaer and Bösartiger Gewebe in vitro. Biochemisches Zeitschrift 203: 22–49

Edlund T, NyT, Rånby M, Heden L O, Palm G, Holmgren E, Josefsson 1983 Isolation of cDNA sequences coding for a part of human tissue plasminogen activator. Proceedings of the National Academy of Science 80: 349–352

Fischer A 1946 Mechanism of the proteolytic activity of malignant cells. Nature 157: 442

Hoylertz M, Rijken D C, Lijnen H R, Collen D 1982 Kinetics of the activation of plasminogen by human tissue plasminogen activator. Role of fibrin. Journal of Biological Chemistry 257: 2912–2919

Isacson S, Nilsson I M 1972 Defective fibrinolysis in blood and vein walls in recurrent 'idiopathic venous thrombosis Acta Chirurgica Scandinavica 138: 313–319

Jörnvall H, Pohl G, Bergsdorf N, Wallén P 1983 Differential proteolysis and evidence for a residue exchange in tissue plasminogen activator suggest possible association between two types of protein microheterogeneity. FEBS Letters 156: 47–50

Kok P 1984 Purification of a plasminogen activator from porcine ovarian tissue. Polypeptide chain structure, and unitage. Submitted for publication

Kruithof E K O, Ransijn A, Bachmann F 1983 Inhibition of tissue plasminogen activator by human plasma. In: Davidson J F, Bachmann F, Bouvier C A, Kruithof E K O (eds) Progress in fibrinolysis (Lausanne 1982) vol 6. Churchill Livinstone, Edinburgh, p 365–369

Loskutoff D J, Edington T S 1977 Synthesis of a fibrinolytic activator and inhibitor by endothelial cells. Proceedings of the National Academy of Science USA 74 3903–3907

Marsh N 1981 Fibrinolysis. Wiley, Chichester, ch 1, p 1–17

Matsuo O, Rijken D C, Collen D Thrombolysis by human tissue plasminogen activator and urokinase in rabbits with experimental pulmonary embolus. Nature 291: 590–591

Mattsson C, Nyberg-Arrhenius V, Wallén P 1981 Dissolution of thrombi by tissue plasminogen activator, urokinase and streptokinase in an artificial circulating system. Thrombosis Research 21: 535–545

Müllertz S 1953 A plasminogen activator in spontaneously active human blood Proceedings of the Society for Experimental Medicine 82: 291–295

Noordhoek Hegt V, Brakman P 1974 Histochemical study of an inhibitor of fibrinolysis in the human arterial wall. Nature 248: 75–76

Norrman B, Wallén P, Rånby M 1984 Plasminogen activation with special reference to early events. Submitted.

Pennica D, Collen D et al 1983 Cloning and expression of human tissue type plasminogen activator c-DNA in E. coli. Nature 301: 214–221

Pohl G, Källström M, Bergsdort N, Wallén P, Jörnvall H 1984 Tissue plasminogen activator: Peptide analyses confirm an indirectly derived amino acid sequence, identify the active site residue, establish glycosylation sites and localize variant differences. Biochemistry in print.

Rifkin D B, Loeb J N, Moore G, Reich E 1974 Properties of plasminogen activators formed by neoplastic human cell cultures. Journal of Experimental Medicine 139: 1317–1328

Rijken D C, Collen D 1981 Purification and characterization of the plasminogen activator secreted by human melanoma cells in culture. Journal of Biological Chemistry 256: 7035–7041

Rijken D C, Wijngaards G, Zaal-de Jong M, Welbergen J 1979 Purification and partial characterization of plasminogen activator from human uterine tissue. Biochimiea et Biophysica Acta 580:140–153

Rijken D C, Wijngaards G, Welbergen J 1980 Relationship between tissue plasminogen activator and the aactivator and the activators in blood and vascular wall. Thrombosis Research 18: 815–830

Rijken D C, Hoylertz, Collen D 1982 Fibrinolytic properties of one-chain and two-chain human extrinsic (tissue-type) plasminogen activator. Journal of biological Chemistry 257: 2920–2925

Rånby M 1982 Studies on the kinetics of plasminogen activation by tissue plasminogen activator. Biochimica et Biophysica Acta 704: 461–469

Rånby M, Bergsdorf N, Norrman B, Suenson E, Wallén P 1983 Tissue plasminogen activator kinetics. In: Davidson J F, Bachmann F, Bouvier C A, Kruithof E K O (eds) Progress in Fibrinolysis, vol 6. Lausanne 1982 Churchill Livingstone, Edinburgh, p 182–184

Suenson E, Luetzen O, Thorsen S 1984 Initial plasmin degradation of fibrin as the basis of a positive feedback mechanism in fibrinolysis European Journal of Biochemistry. 140: 513–522

Thorsen S 1975 Difference in the binding to fibrin of native plasminogen and plasminogen modified by proteolytic degradation. Influence of omega-amino acids. Biochimica et Biophysica Acta 393: 55–65

Thorsen S, Glas-Greenwalt P, Astrup T 1972 Differences in binding to fibrin of urokinase and tissue plasminogen activator. Thrombosis et Diathesis Haemorragica 28: 65–74

Tillett W S, Garner R L 1933 The fibrinolytic activity of hemolytic streptococci. Journal of Experimental Medicine 58: 485–502

Wallén P 1977 Activation of plasminogen with urokinase and tissue activator. In: Paoletti R, Sherry S (eds) Thrombosis and urokinase (Rome 1975) Academic Press, London, p 91–102

Wallén P, Wiman B 1975 Purification of tissue plasminogen activator using adsorbtion on fibrin and hydrophobic interaction chromatography; effect of fibrin on the enzymatic properties of the activator. 5th International Congress on Thrombosis and Haemostasis, Paris, Abstr no 331

Wallén P, Kok P, Rånby M 1978 The tissue activator of plasminogen. In: Magnusson S, Ottesen M, Foltman B, Danö K, Neurath H (eds) Proceedings of the 11th FEBS Meeting Copenhagen 1977. Pergamon Press, Oxford, vol 47, p 127–135

Wallén P, Rånby M, Bergsdorf N, Kok P 1981 Purification and characterization of tissue plasminogen activator: on the occurrence of two different forms and their enzymatic properties. In: Davidson J F, Nilsson I M, Astedt (eds) Progress in fibrinolysis, vol 5. (Malmö 1980) Churchill Livingstone, Edinburgh, p 16–21

Wallén P, Bergsdorf N, Rånby M 1982 Purification and identification of two structural variants of porcine tissue plasminogen activator by affinity adsorbtion on fibrin. Biochimica et Biophysica Acta 719: 318–328

Wallén P, Pohl G, Bergsdorf N, Rånby M, Ny T, Jörnvall H 1983 Purification and characterization of a melanoma cell plasminogen activator. European Journal of Biochemistry. 132: 681–686

Weimar W, Stibbe J, van Seyen A J, Billau A, DeSomer P, Collen 1981 Specific lysis of an iliofemoral thrombus by administration of extrinsic (tissue-type) plasminogen activator. Lancet 2: 1018–1020

Williams J R B 1951 The fibrinolytic activity of the urine. British Journal of Experimental Pathology 32: 530–536

11

Section 2
INVITED LECTURE

2. The fibrinolytic system of cultured endothelial cells: deciphering the balance between plasminogen activation and inhibition

D. J. Loskutoff

Abnormal thrombus formation and dissolution are associated with several cardiovascular diseases including atherosclerosis and both thromboembolic and hemorrhagic conditions. The walls of blood vessels undoubtedly contribute to the pathogenesis of these disorders. More specifically, vascular endothelial cells appear to have the potential to participate in the hemostatic process through the synthesis of molecules which may function either to promote thrombosis (e.g., Faction VIII, von Willebrand factor), or to maintain vessel patency (e.g., plasminogen activator; PA). The fibrinolytic system of endothelium thus assumes pivotal importance in maintaining this hemostatic balance.

We have been studying cultured bovine aortic endothelial cells (BAES) as a model of endothelium (Loskutoff et al, 1982). The overall fibrinolytic activity of these cells changes with their growth state (Levin & Loskutoff, 1980), and in response to the presence of a variety of factors (Levin & Loskutoff, 1979; Levin & Luskutoff, 1980; Levin & Loskutoff, 1982a). Although it has been suggested that such changes reflect changes in PA, our recent and unexpected finding that these cells also synthesize an unusually stable antiactivator (Loskutoff et al, 1983; van Mourik et al, 1983), makes accurate interpretation of such results difficult. For example, do the altered fibrinolytic states of these cells following various treatments, or in blood in certain human diseases, reflect changes in PA, inhibitor or both?

This review will emphasize the concept that the fibrinolytic 'state' of endothelial cells, or of any cell or individual for that matter, is really a reflection of the balance between the activities of PAs and that of their natural inhibitors (Fig. 2.1). Thus, agents which alter the fibrinolytic state may do so by changing PA, inhibitor or both. The fibrinolytic system of cultured BAEs will be discussed to illustrate these ideas.

ENDOTHELIAL CELL-MEDIATED FIBRINOLYSIS

The first suggestion that the vascular activator might originate from the endothelium came from the work of Todd (1959) who incubated tissue sections on plasminogen-rich fibrin films and demonstrated a fibrinolytic activity which

15

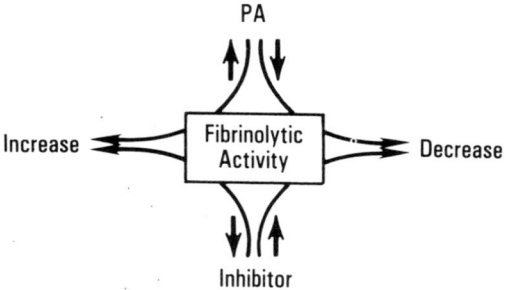

Fig. 2.1 Fibrinolytic balance. A measured increase in the total fibrinolytic activity of the blood after strenuous exercise, may result either from an increase in PA or from a decrease in inhibitor. Similarly, decreases in the fibrinolytic activity of a cell, perhaps in response to steroids, may reflect decreased PA or increased inhibitor.

seemed to be localized to the luminal (endothelial) surface of blood vessels. These observations have now been confirmed by many investigators employing the Todd technique. Although this approach localized PA to certain structures, it did not demonstrate the origin of this activity. Thus, it was unclear from these studies whether the PA was actually synthesized by endothelial cells or simply adsorbed to them from plasma. We attempted to verify these activity localization studies by demonstrating that pure populations of endothelial cells were fibrinolytically active. Cultured rabbit (Loskutoff & Edgington, 1977), and human and bovine (Levin & Loskutoff, 1979) endothelial cells indeed were able to digest iodinated fibrin in a plasminogen-dependent manner. Fibrinolytic activity was a constant feature of these cells even after prolonged growth in culture, indicating that this activity was produced by the cells. The fibrinolytic activity of these cells was enhanced by a number of agents, and in a way that required new protein synthesis, consistent with this conclusion.

Endothelial cells produce multiple PAs
The fibrinolytic activity of cultured BAEs results from the production of multiple PAs (Fig. 2.2). For example, when cell extracts or conditioned media (CM) from confluent BAEs was fractionated by SDS-PAGE and analyzed by fibrin autography, a complex lysis pattern developed with major zones at M_r 52 000 and 74 000. In addition, there was a rather distinct form with a M_r of approximately 120 000 daltons, as well as a characteristic smearing of activity between the two high M_r forms. The high M_r forms appear to be a family of related molecules since they share an isoelectric point of approximately 7.5 (Levin & Loskutoff, 1982b) and all bind to concanavalin A-Sepharose, and to fibrin (Loskutoff & Mussoni, 1983). In addition, their activity depends on fibrin, and can be quenched by antiserum to human melanoma 'cell tissue-type PA (t-PA) but not by antiserum to urokinase. Thus, these molecules are t-PA-like in nature.

The origin of this family of t-PA-like molecules has been the subject of considerable speculation. The M_r 74 000 form is rapidly inactivated by DFP (Levin & Loskutoff, 1982b), suggesting that it is an active enzyme. Surprisingly, the M_r 120 000 molecule is quite resistant to DFP, suggesting that it may be a zymogen form of t-PA. However, the structure of the t-PA (Pennica et al, 1983)

16

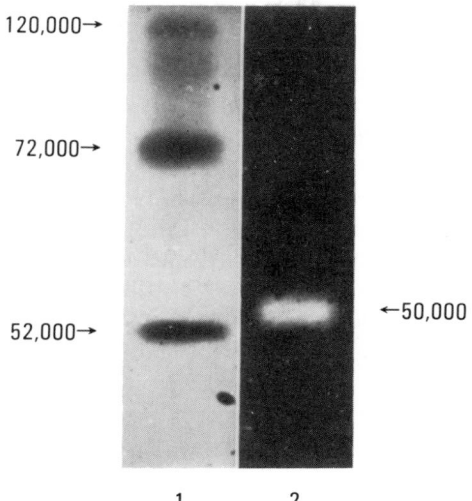

120,000→

72,000→

52,000→

←50,000

1   2

Fig. 2.2   PA and inhibitor profile of CM. The PA (lane 1) and inhibitor (lane 2) profile of cultured BAEs as revealed by fibrin autography (Levin & Loskutoff, 1982b) and reverse fibrin autography (Erickson et al, 1984), respectively.

argues against the existence of a large M_r proenzyme form of t-PA. Thus, this form may be a relatively inactive complex between t-PA and another molecule (Levin, 1983). In contrast to these results, the urokinase-like form (M_r 52 000) is quite clearly a zymogen. It is not only relatively resistant to inactivation with DFP (Levin & Loskutoff, 1982b), but when carefully isolated, is devoid of PA activity (Conforti & Loskutoff, unpublished observation). Like other cellular urokinase-like PAs (u-PAs), this molecule can be converted to a potent PA by treatment with trace amounts of plasmin.

Endothelial cells produce an antiactivator
The successful use of fibrin autography to delineate the PAs produced by cultured BAEs, prompted us to develop a similar approach to detect fibrinolytic inhibitors. This approach, which we've termed 'reverse fibrin autography' (Loskutoff et al, 1983; Erickson et al, 1984) was used to analyze CM from confluent BAEs after fractionating it by SDS-PAGE (Fig. 2.2). A single inhibitor zone of M_r 50 000 was revealed when CM was analyzed in this way. The inhibitor was an unusually stable molecule in that it not only survived exposure to SDS, but also was unaffected by treatment with 5% β-mercaptoethanol or incubation for 30 minutes at pH 12, in the presence of 1M acetic acid, 4M guanidine hydrochloride, or 6M urea (Loskutoff et al, 1983). Considerable activity could be detected after heating to 70°C or boiling for 30 minutes.

The inhibitor was purified from BAE CM by a combination of concanavalin A affinity chromatography and preparative SDS-PAGE, and further characterized (van Mourik et al, 1983). It is a single-chain glycoprotein of M_r 50 000 and has an isoelectric point of between 4.5 and 5. It differs from other characterized serum and cellular inhibitors in that it is not inactivated by treatment at low pH, or upon exposure to denaturants. Antisera to the purified inhibitor does not recognize protease nexin (not shown), a molecule with some properties in common with the endothelial cell inhibitor (Scott & Baker, 1983). Most importantly, the endothelial cell inhibitor is an antiactivator (Fig. 2.3) which blocks the activity of both t-PA and urokinase. Inhibition of t-PA is associated with the formation of an enzyme-inhibitor complex which can be detected after polyacrylamide gel electrophoresis in the presence of SDS (Fig. 2.3, inset). Preliminary studies suggest that the inhibitor is not an antiplasmin. Finally, the inhibitor is actually synthesized by endothelial cells and is not simply a contaminating serum protein. Interestingly, immunoprecipitation experiments indicate that it is a major secretory product of cloned BAEs, representing between 2.5–12% of the ^{3}H-leucine-labelled proteins released by the cells in a 24 hour period. These results indicate that the inhibitor is produced in at least a 100-fold molar excess over the PAs.

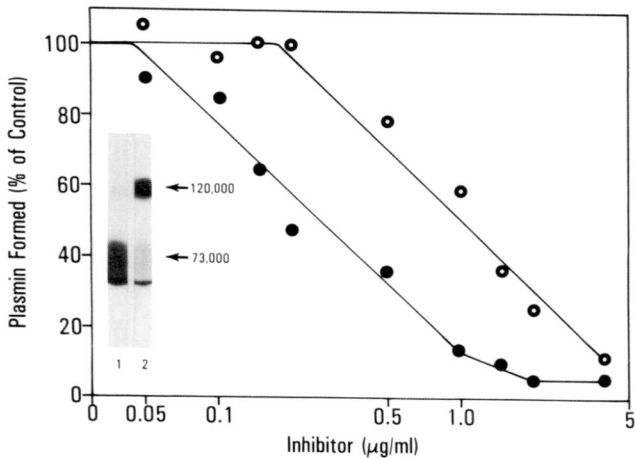

Fig. 2.3 Inhibition of PA activity by the BAE inhibitor. The effect of the purified inhibitor on the ability of urokinase (● and t-PA (o) to cleave ^{125}I-labeled plasminogen (Mussoni & Loskutoff, 1984) was assessed. The inset is an autoradiogram showing ^{125}I-labeled t-PA in the absence (lane 1) or presence (lane 2) of inhibitor.

QUESTIONS

Two questions, each central to our understanding of the fibrinolytic system of endothelial cells, have been raised by these findings. First of all why is the fibrinolytic profile of these cells so complex (Fig. 2.2)? And second, how can the cells be fibrinolytically active in the presence of a large excess of an inhibitor which has the potential to block this activity. The answers (see below) indicate that endothelial cell-mediated fibrinolysis is an extremely complex process, regulated not only by PAs and their inhibitor, but also by factors that modulate the activity and interaction of these molecules.

The complexity of the PA profile, especially the multiple, high-molecular t-PA-like forms, was unexpected. The gene for t-PA was recently cloned and the resulting sequence data (Pennica et al, 1983; Ny et al, 1984) do not support the idea that a large M_r precursor for t-PA exists. Thus, the large M_r, DFP-resistant form (Fig. 2.2) is probably not a proenzyme in the classical sense, but instead may be a complex between t-PA and another molecule. To test the possibility that this form is a complex between the active M_r 72 000 form and the BAE antiactivator, we attempted to demonstrate that both t-PA and antiactivator were present in this material (Fig. 2.4). BAE CM was fractionated by SDS-PAGE, the proteins in the gel were transferred electrophoretically to nitrocellulose sheets and stained with antibodies to either t-PA or the antiactivator. The t-PA staining pattern resembled the activity pattern (Fig. 2.2), although the majority of the antigen was associated with the highest M_r form, and not the form containing the majority of activity (M_r 72 000; Fig. 2.2). Thus, the specific activity of the 120 000 M_r form is low compared to that of the 72 000 form. This result is consistent with the conclusion that the highest M_r form is a relatively inactive enzyme-inhibitor complex. The majority of staining with antibody to inhibitor occurred in the position of the native molecule (compare Fig. 2.4, lane 2 with Fig 2.2, lane 2). However, it is clear that inhibitor is also present at a higher molecular weight. In fact, it is detected in the same position of the gel as the highest M_r material which

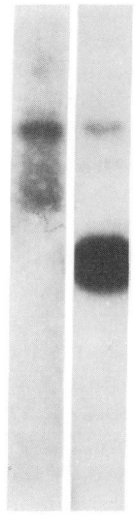

Fig. 2.4 Detection of t-PA and inhibitor in CM electroblotting. CM from BAEs was fractionated by SDS-PAGE, transferred to CN sheets by electroblotting, and stained by the double antibody technique. The autoradiograph shows the transferred proteins stained with the antibodies to t-PA (lane 1) and antiactivator (lane 2).

1   2

stained with anti-t-PA. Thus, the high M_r, DFP-resistant material contains both inhibitor (Fig. 2.4, lane 2) and t-PA (Fig. 2.4, lane 1). Finally, when purified t-PA was mixed with inhibitor, complexes of similar M_r were formed (Fig. 2.3, inset). These results indicate that the complexity of the PA profile of BAEs arises, at least in part, from the interaction of t-PA and inhibitor. Similar results were obtained when CM from human umbilican vein endothelial cells (HUEs) was analyzed (not shown). Why the cells would release t-PA apparently in complex with this inhibitor remains to be determined. The u-PA was not detected in complexes with inhibitor, presumably because it is a proenzyme. It is curious that most, if not all of the PA produced by these cells, is produced as an inactive form either because of its association with antiactivator, or because it exists as a zymogen.

I'd like to end now with a brief discussion of the second question I raised earlier. That is, how can these cells still be fibrinolytically active in the presence of a large molar excess of an inhibitor that blocks this activity? The answer to this question is related to the observation that the majority of the antiactivator elaborated by the cells exists in an inactive form which does not recognize PAs (Table 2.1). In these experiments, antiactivator activity was determined by adding increasing amounts of CM to mixtures of urokinase and plasminogen, and measuring the resultant decrease in fibrinolytic activity. No inhibitor activity could be detected in the untreated but dialyzed control. In fact, untreated CM stimulated the fibrinolytic activity of the mixture, presumably because of the additional PAs present in CM that were added to the urokinase. As expected, CM treated with β-mercaptoethanol to inactivate the PAs, no longer stimulated the assay. However, very little inhibitor activity was revealed in these samples.

This observation was unexpected because the sample also was analyzed by reverse fibrin autography and shown to contain considerable inhibitor. One of the major differences between CM analyzed by the ^{125}I-fibrin plate assay (Table 2.1) and by reverse fibrin autography (Fig. 2.2), is that with the latter technique, the sample is subjected to electrophoresis in the presence of SDS. To test whether the SDS itself was somehow stimulating or activating the inhibitor, we treated CM with CM with 0.1% SDS and after exhaustive dialysis, reassayed it. Surprisingly, a potent inhibitory activity was now revealed. Although SDS is notoriously difficult to remove from samples, especially by dialysis, the controls suggested that this result was not an artifact of the SDS. Thus, when the medium itself, that is MEM that had not been conditioned by the cells, was treated with β-ME and SDS and dialyzed in parallel, no inhibitor activity was detected. Moreover, a number of other agents, including guanidine hydrochloride, urea, potassium thiocyanate, and decyl sodium sulfate all stimulated activity, whereas treatment with high concentrations of sodium chloride and sodium sulfate were without effect (not shown). We were able to quantitate the amount of 'active' versus 'latent' inhibitor in CM by determining the amount of inhibitor that could bind to t-PA. We found that 24 hour BAE CM contains approximately 50 ng/ml of active inhibitor, and 1–2 μg/ml after treatment with SDS. Since this assay measures the actual interaction between t-PA and inhibitor, it seems clear that

Table 2.1 Inhibitory activity of BAE CM after various treatments

Sample	Treatment	cpm released	% of control
MEM	—	4677	100
CM	—	6445	138
CM	β-ME	3400	73
CM	β-me, SDS	554	12
MEM	β-ME, SDS	4170	101

One ml aliquots of MEM or CM were incubated as indicated for 60 min at 37°C, dialyzed extensively against 0.1M tris-HCl containing o.5% TX-100 and tested for inhibitor activity by the ^{125}I-fibrin plate assay. In each case, 5 μl of the dialyzed material was added to the standard assay containing in 1 ml, 4 μg human plasminogen, 0.5% TX-100, 0.1% gelatin, and 0.025 units of urokinase. There were 21 000 counts in each well.

SDS is changing the inhibitor in such a way that it interacts more efficiently with t-PA. Guanidine, thiocyanate and urea stimulate this interaction in a similar way, and in all cases, the 'activating' concentration for inhibition and for t-PA binding were identical. We are using this approach to determine kinetic constants for this interaction.

CONCLUSIONS

These observations indicate that cultured endothelial cells have a relatively complex fibrinolytic system, one responsive both to the physiological state of the cell itself, and to a variety of agents added to the culture medium. The fibrinolytic activity of these cells results from the production and interaction of both urokinase-like and tissue-type PAs, and of an antiactivator capable of inhibiting their respective activities. Interestingly, the inhibitor is immunologically and biochemically related to the rapidly acting antiactivator detected in human platelets (Erikson et al, 1984) and in the plasma of some patients (Erikson et al, Chapter 00; Wiman et al, 1984). Thus, the inhibitor may represent a novel class of fibrinolytic inhibitors (the antiactivators), likely to play a critical role in modulating the fibrinolytic potential of tissues, blood, and the vascular wall itself.

Preliminary experiments indicate that there is at least 100 times more potential antiactivator than PA in BAE CM. And yet, we can readily demonstrate that the cells are fibrinolytically active under most conditions. At least part of the explanation for this apparent inconsistency is the finding that the majority of the inhibitor exists in a latent form which can be activated with denaturants like SDS. The active inhibitor in CM (less than 10% of the potential inhibitor) readily forms complexes with cellular t-PA but not with cellular u-PA, presumably because this latter PA is a proenzyme. Understanding the mechanism of this 'activation' event, and the nature of the biological equivalent to SDS, will be central to our understanding of this system, and remains to be elucidated.

REFERENCES

Erickson L A, Lawrence D A, Loskutorf D J 1984 Reverse fibrin autography: a method to detect and partially characterize protease inhibitors after sodium dodecyl sulfate-polyacrylamide gel electrophoresis. Analytical Biochemistry 137: 454–463
Erickson L A, Ginsberg M H, Loskutoff D J 1984 Detection and partial characterization of an inhibitor of plasminogen activator in human platelets. The Journal of Clinical Investigation (in press)
Levin E G 1983 Latest tissue plasminogen activator produced by human endothelial cells in culture: evidence for an enzyme-inhibitor complex. Proceedings of the National Academy of Science USA 80: 6804–6808
Levin E G, Loskutoff D J 1979 Comparative studies of the fibrinolytic activity of cultured vascular cells. Thrombosis Research 15: 869–878
Levin E G, Loskutoff D J 1980 Serum-mediated suppression of cell-associated plasminogen activator activity in cultured endothelial cells. Cell 22: 701–707
Levin E G, Loskutoff D J 1982a Regulation of plasminogen activator production by cultured endothelial cells. Annals of the New York Academy of Sciences 401: 184–194

Levin E G, Loskutoff D J 1982b Cultured bovine endothelial cells produce both urokinase and tissue-type plasminogen activators. Journal of Cell Biology 94: 631–636

Loskutoff D J, Edgington T S 1977 Synthesis of a fribinolytic activator and inhibitor by endothelial cells. Proceedings of the National Academy of Science USA 74: 3903–3907

Loskutoff D J, Levin E G, Mussoni L M 1982 Fibrinolytic components of cultured endothelial cells. In: Nossel H L, Vogel H J (eds) Pathobiology of the endothelial cell. Academic Press, New York, p 167–182

Loskutoff D J, Mussoni L M 1983 Interactions between fibrin and the plasminogen activators produced by cultured endothelial cells. Blood 62: 62–68

Loskutoff D J, van Mourik J A, Erickson L A, Lawrence D A 1983 Detection of an unusually stable fibrinolytic inhibitor produced by bovine endothelial cells. Proceedings of the National Academy of Science USA 80: 2956–2960

Mussoni L M, Loskutoff D J 1984 A direct, plasmin-independent assay for plasminogen activator. Thrombosis Research 34: 241–254

Ny T, Elgh F, Lund B 1984 The structure of the human tissue-type plasminogen activator gene: correlation of intron and exon structures to functional and structural domains. Proceedings of the National Academy of Science USA (in press)

Pennica D, Holmes W E, Kohr W J, Harkins R N, Vehar G A, Ward C A et al 1983 Cloning and expression of human tissue-type plasminogen activator cDNA in E. Coli. Nature 301: 214–221

Scott R W, Baker J B 1983 Purification of human protease nexin. Journal of Biological Chemistry 258: 10439–10444

Todd A S 1959 The histological localization of fibrinolysin activator. Journal of Pathological Bacteriology 78: 281–283

Towbin H, Staehelin T, Gordon J 1979 Electrophoretic transfer of proteins from polyacrylamide gels to nitrocellulose sheets: Procedure and some applications. Proceedings of the National Academy of Sciences USA 76: 4350–4354

van Mourik J A, Lawrence D A, Loskutoff D J 1983 Characterization of a novel fibrinolytic inhibitor synthesized by bovine aortic endothelial cells in culture. Thrombosis and Haemostasis 50: 281

Wiman B, Chmielewska J, Rånby M 1984 Inactivation of tissue plasminogen activator in plasma. The Journal of Biological Chemistry 259: 3644–3647

Section 3
THROMBOLYSIS FOR ACUTE MYOCARDIAL INFARCTION AND INNOVATIONS IN THROMBOLYTIC THERAPY

3. Even if the efficacy of intracoronary thrombolysis is proven, this approach is a death issue in terms of public health

M. Verstraete

The rationale for thrombolytic treatment of acute myocardial infarction is based on two established facts and three reasonable assumptions:

1. The first fact is that a thrombus obstructing an atherosclerotic coronary artery is the most frequent precipitating cause of acute transmural infarction
2. The second fact is that intracoronary administration of streptokinase or urokinase can reopen the occluded coronary artery within one hour and that reperfusion of ischemic myocardial tissue is in general well tolerated

The three assumptions are:
1. Does timely reopening of an acutely occluded coronary artery actually save more myocardial tissue and therfore improve myocardial function, reduce the reinfarction rate and decrease early and late mortality?
2. Does a high, single dose of streptokinase administered intravenously in the first few hours after the clinical onset of infarction symptoms offer a similar chance to reopen the coronary artery as a lower dose of streptokinase, infused in the coronary artery?
3. Does the intravenous injection of human plasminogen tissue activator have the same thrombolytic potential without the hematological hazards (systemic fibrinogenolysis) of streptokinase and urokinase?

Thrombosis of an atherosclerotic coronary artery is the most frequent cause precipitating a transmural myocardial infarction
The long-standing debate among assertive pathologists and cardiologists as to whether coronary thrombosis is the immediate cause rather than a consequence of myocardial infarction, has been based mainly on analysis of pathologic findings. There is now a general consensus based on the results of coronary angiography and surgery that, in the early stages of transmural myocardial infarction, thrombotic occlusion of a coronary artery is present in well over 80% of patients (DeWood et al, 1980). Intracoronary arteriography has hereby ended a long-running dispute and prompted cardiologists to re-examine their concepts concerning the significance of coronary thrombosis in and optimal treatment of acute myocardial infarction. In particular, the question of recanalization of an

25

occluded atherosclerotic artery with thrombolytic agents or with angioplasty, has been re-examined.

Intracoronary infusion of low-dose streptokinase can safely reopen a thrombosed coronary artery

After the pioneering work of Rentrop et al (1981), cardiologists of many coronary care units have clearly demonstrated that patients with acute myocardial infarction tolerate intracoronary administration of streptokinase or urokinase and that acute coronary occlusions occurring less than four hours before treatment, can readily be lysed in as much as 67% to 90% of the cases.

There is now satisfactory evidence that thrombolysis induced within the first four to six hours after the onset of myocardial infarction, is much less frequently associated with uncontrollable reperfusion tachyarrhythmias and hypotension than in experimental animal models. Reperfusion of the right coronary artery apparently carries a substantially higher risk. As it is likely that the risk of myocardial hemorrhage and edema due to microvascular damage probably increases with the duration of ischemia, a strict limitation of the time interval between the onset of clinical symptoms and attempted thrombolytic treatment is imperative as well for reasons of efficacy as for safety.

Does timely reopening of a thrombosed coronary artery result in a greater salvage of contractile myocardium, decrease early and late mortality and improve the quality of life?

While intracoronary thrombus dissolution is a respectable achievement, it is not a goal in itself; the immediate aim is to prevent necrosis and dysfunction of jeopardized myocardial cells.

Severely ischemic cells inevitably progress to necrosis within 20 minutes. There is only hope to save myocardial cells which are incompletely deprived of blood, a twilight state maintained through collateral channels. Consequently, the interval between the sudden reduction of blood flow and reopening of the supplying coronary vessel is a critical factor.

There is satisfactory evidence in animals that infarct size is smaller and myocardial function better when an occluded coronary artery can be reopened within the first three to four hours. The evidence that timely reopening of a coronary artery in man leads to an improved myocardial function is limited and most often indirect. Relief of chest pain is a welcomed but complex and subjective criterion, and even when associated with a reduction in ST-segment, changes may not correlate with early improvement of the left ventricular ejection fraction (Anderson et al, 1983). Indeed, not all authors could correlate relief of pain and improvement of ECG-changes with the left ventricular ejection fraction determined by contrast or radionuclide ventriculography, which remain most often at the same low level before and just after recanalization (Khaja et al, 1983). One should, however, envision the possibility that an improved ventricular ejection fraction could result rather from compensatory hyperkinesia of healthy segments than from the restoration of damaged ischemic segments. Whatever the correct interpretation, left ventricular function assessed by radionuclide angiography, was found by some (Markis et al, 1981) but not all authors (Khaja et al, 1983), better by the time of discharge from hospital in those patients whose coronaries recanalized as compared to those whose arteries remained blocked. Similarly, the immediate and short-term (3 months) uptake of thallium-201 by the human myocardium, which requires an intact membrane Na^+-, K^+-ATPase, is improved after coronary thrombolysis. A method indicating myocardial viability which is independent of blood flow per se, is positron emission tomography; metabolic recovery after coronary reperfusion has been demonstrated by increased accumulation of ^{11}C-palmitate emission tomography.

The yardsticks to determined whether myocardial reperfusion is of benefit to the patient are long-term contractile recovery and reduced mortality. Proof is not yet available. Although there is limited evidence that in-hospital mortality is lower in those patients with reopened coronary arteries than in those in whom reperfusion could not be obtained, the data demonstrating that reinfarction rate, angina, heart failure, arrhythmia, and long-term survival substantially improve after flow restoration in the coronary circulation, are still lacking. To this end, well-mounted large-scale multicenter trials are required.

Has the systemic administration of a single, high-dose of streptokinase a similar chance to reopen a briefly occluded coronary artery as the intracoronary infusion of streptokinase?

Many catherization laboratories have administered with very significant success, low-dose streptokinase (2 000 U/min during 60 to 120 minutes) through standard coronary catheters close to the ostium of the occluded coronary artery or through a smaller catheter placed in the vicinity of the thrombus. However, in less experienced hands, complications such as coronary dissection or perforation will be more frequent. Maximal benefit from thrombolytic treatment will be obtained by the earliest possible reperfusion. There is considerable time loss before a catheter can be placed in the coronary artery (minimum 1 hour?), which admittedly is shorter than the time required to mobilize an operating theatre team to perform an urgent aortocoronary bypass. Finally, not all hospitals have a catherization laboratory and in many of those that do, the technical staff most often is not on permanent stand-by. Furthermore, at times of economic restrictions it is unrealistic to equip, staff, and maintain round-the-clock facilities for intracardiac catheterization. For all these reasons it is obvious that the widespread application of coronary thrombolysis will depend on the development of simple therapeutic regimens that do not require coronary catherization.

Schröder et al (1983) and others have demonstrated by coronary angiography performed before and immediately after systemic administration of respectively 0.5 million streptokinase within 30 minutes or 1.5 million streptokinase within 60 minutes, that re-establishment of coronary blood flow was obtained in 52 to 80% of the patients with evolving infarction. These results are comparable to those obtained with intracoronary streptokinase in patients with acute myocardial infarction (occurring less than five hours before treatment). Furthermore, there is some evidence that reocclusion of the coronary artery is less frequent within the first three to four weeks after intravenous administration of streptokinase than after intracoronary administration. These results suggest that systemic thrombolytic therapy initiated sooner (compared to intracoronary administration) after the onset of infarct pain, may enhance the lysis of the fresher thrombus, maximizing efficacy, safety and practicability of this procedure.

A prospective German-Swiss controlled double-blind multicenter trial (coded ISAM), evaluates the effect of 1.5 million units of streptokinase administered intravenously over 60 minutes within six hours after onset of clinical symptoms of myocardial infarction. The primary endpoint is mortality; coronary angiography is also being performed after four weeks in the majority of patients.

It is recomforting that another European multicenter trial in patients with acute myocardial infarction (ISIS: Intravenous Streptokinase Intervention Study), will investigate the effects of a maximally practicable regime of minimal toxicity on mortality and a few easily assessed major morbid events. The plan is to administer 1.5 million streptokinase or placebo in patients with myocardial infarction of less than 12 hours duration. In a multifactorial design anticoagulation (1000 units of heparin/hour for 2 to 4 days followed by oral anticoagulants during four weeks) and/or aspirin (300 mg enteric-coated tablets in alternate days during four weeks) will or will not be added to the streptokinase or placebo treatment.

Does the intravenous injection of human plasminogen tissue activator have the same thrombolytic potential without the hematological hazards (systemic fibrinogenolysis) of streptokinase?

Specific thrombolysis will only be possible if the activation process of plasminogen can be localized at and confined to the fibrin surface (Collen, 1980). According to the present knowledge, this can only adequately be achieved with the use of a tissue-type plasminogen activator which, like the physiological activator, adsorbs to the fibrin surface and becomes active in loco. The production of tissue-type plasminogen activator from human tissue culture fluids is possible but prohibitively laborious and expensive (Rijken & Collen, 1981), but can now be produced in large scale by recombinant DNA technology (Pennica et al, 1983).

Coronary thrombolysis was induced within 19 to 50 minutes with intravenous or intracoronary tissue-type plasminogen activator in six out of seven patients with evolving myocardial infarction and confirmed angiographically in each case (Van de Werf et al, 1984). Circulating fibrinogen, plasminogen and α_2-antiplasmin were not depleted in these patients.

None of the thrombolytic agents, whether applied directly in the coronary artery or intravenously, will influence atherosclerotic narrowings or prevent coronary spasm. Transluminal angioplasty and coronary surgery are and will remain second-step therapeutic interventions, but hopefully applied in better prepared patients.

In order to offer the benefit of an effective thrombolytic treatment to a greater number of patients with myocardial infarction, short and simple therapeutic schemes must be developed. In our opinion the odds are in favour of the intravenous route of the safest of these drugs.

REFERENCES

Anderson J L, Marshall H W, Bray B E, Lutz J R, Frederick P R, Yanowitz F G et al 1983 A randomized trial of intracoronary streptokinase in the treatment of acute myocardial infarction. The New England Journal of Medicine 308: 1312–1318

Collen D 1980 On the regulation and control of fibrinolysis. Edward Kowalski Memorial Lecture. Thrombosis and Haemostasis 43: 77–89

Collen D, Verstraete M 1983 Systemic thrombolytic therapy of acute myocardial infarction. Circulation 68: 462–465

DeWood M A, Spores J, Notske R, Mouser L T, Burroughs R, Golden M S et al 1980 Prevalence of total coronary occlusion during the early hours of transmural myocardial infarction. The New England Journal of Medicine 303: 897–902

Khaja F, Walton J A Jr, Brymer J F, Lo E, Osterberger L, O'Neill W W et al 1983 Intracoronary fibrinolytic therapy in acute myocardial infarction. Report of a prospective randomized trial. The New England Journal of Medicine 308: 1305–1311

Markis J E, Malagold M, Parker J A, Silverman K J, Barry W H, Als A V et al 1981 Myocardial salvage after intracoronary thrombolysis with streptokinase in acute myocardial infarction. Assessment by intracoronary thallium-201. The New England Journal of Medicine 305: 777–782

Pennica D, Holmes W E, Kohr W J, Harkins R N, Vehar G A, Ward C A et al 1983 Cloning and expression of human tissue-type plasminogen activator cDNA in E coli. Nature 301: 214–221

Rentrop P, Blanke H, Karsch K R, Kaiser H, Köstering H, Leitz K 1981 Selective intracoronary thrombolysis in acute myocardial infarction and unstable angina pectoris. Circulation 63: 307–317

Rijken D C, Collen D 1981 Purification and characterization of the plasminogen activator secreted by human melanoma cells in culture. The Journal of Biological Chemistry 256: 7035–7041

Schröder R, Biamino G, v Leitner E-R, Linderer T, Brüggemann T, Heitz J et al 1983 Intravenous short-term infusion of streptokinase in acute myocardial infarction. Circulation 67: 536–548

Van de Werf F, Ludbrook P A, Bergmann S R, Geltman E M, Tiefenbrunn A J, De Geest H et al 1984 Clot-selective coronary thrombolysis with tissue-type plasminogen activator in patients with evolving myocardial infarction. The New England Journal of Medicine (in press)

4. The clinical relevance of opening a coronary artery in patients with acute myocardial infarction

W.H. Bleifeld, D.G. Mathey, J. Schofer,
K.H. Kuck, R. Montz and P. Stritzke (with help
from W.O. Siftung)

Acute myocardial infarction might be a model not only to analyse the underlying pathophysiologic mechanism, but also to derive new concepts for the therapy of left ventricular failure. Accordingly, three topics will be reviewed:

1. The analysis of the underlying mechanisms, leading to an acute myocardial infarction.
2. Methods used for reperfusion.
3. The results of thrombolytic treatment, especially with regard to rate of re-opening, ventricular function and post-thrombolytic treatment.

It is generally accepted (Fig. 4.1) that the size of an acute myocardial infarction is of major importance in the development of left ventricular failure (1). Accordingly, it is of the utmost importance to limit infarct size (2). The prevention of the initiation of ischemia and also of the progression from ischemia to infarction may be achieved by the improvement of the myocardial-O_2-supply/demand ratio. Research has been focused during the last 10 years to decrease the O_2-demand (3) without general clinical application and moreover, by metabolic interventions to improve the anaerobic metabolism (4). Direct intervention for the re-establishment of flow by spasmolytic compounds, thrombolysis, transluminal dilatation or aorto-coronary bypass-surgery, only recently have been investigated.

1. Thrombosis as the cause of acute coronary occlusion

Several observations showed that the cause of an acute occlusion of a coronary artery was usually a blood clot, which was found immediately after acute myocardial infarction (AMI) by coronary arteriography in 87% of cases and which had already resolved after 24 hours in one third of the patients (5). The thrombosis is usually found, as predicted by previous fluid dynamic investigations (6) distal from the stenosis rather than extending proximally. The rational consequence of these observations was the application of a thrombolytic agent (7).

Although several investigators like Chazow et al (8), Houck et al (9) and Boucek (10) pioneered the technique in individual patients through angiography, of re-opening coronary vessels occluded by a thrombus using streptokinase, this technique received worldwide attention when Rentrop et al (11), demonstrated the effect of intracoronary streptokinase systematically in a series of patients. A number of reports followed soon (12, 13).

WHY LIMIT INFARCT SIZE?

Infarct size is related:

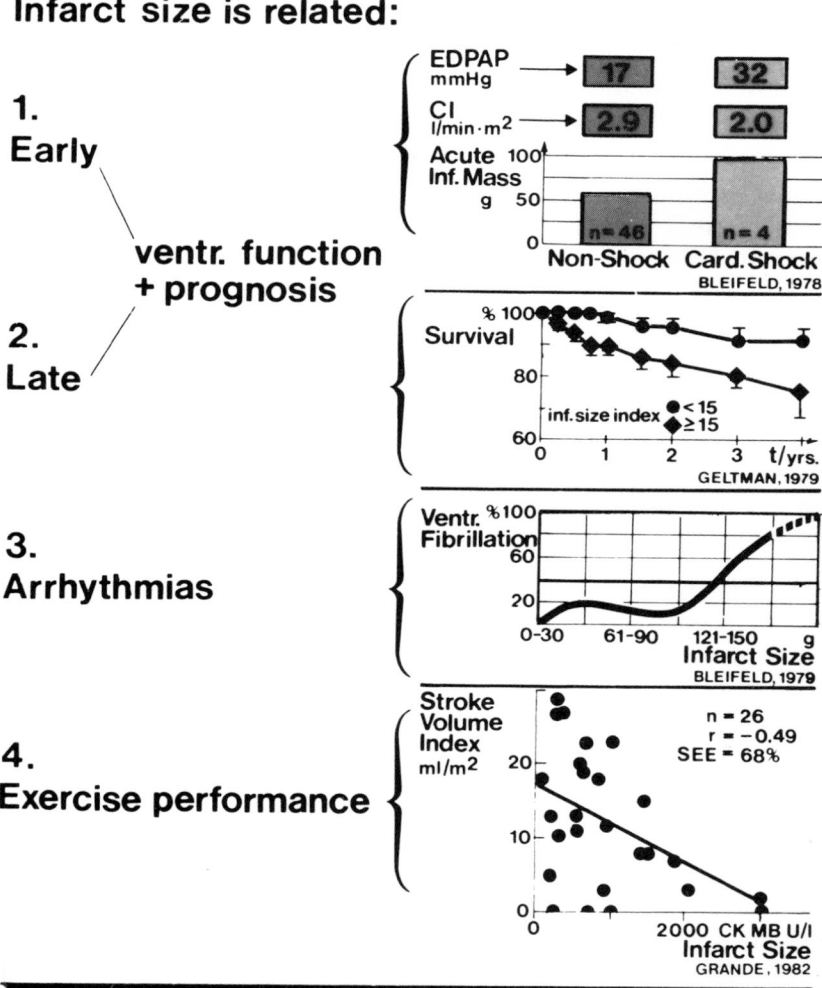

1.
Early

ventr. function
+ prognosis

2.
Late

3.
Arrhythmias

4.
Exercise performance

Fig. 4.1 The relation between infarct size and early response and late ventricular function, prognosis, arrhythmias and exercise performance.

Panel 1: Infarct size is related to the decrease in cardiac index response the increase in end diastolic pulmonary artery pressure (edpap).

Panel 2: Larger infarctions have a poorer late prognosis than smaller as taken from the survival curves.

Panel 3: The incidence of ventricular fibrillation rises markedly with increasing infarct size above 80 g.

Panel 4: The increase of stroke volume index during standardized exercise tests is inversely related to infarct size.

2. Methods for reperfusion by thrombolytic drugs

At present thrombolytic drugs are used in two ways:

1. The intracoronary way, beginning with 4000 U/min followed by 2000 U min up to a total dosage of 2.5 million units.
2. The intravenous way either
    (a) with streptokinase administered over 20 minutes (14) or
    (b) recently by urokinase as a 2 million units bolus (15), or
    (c) by recombinant — tissue-plasminogen activator (16).

3. Results of thrombolytic therapy on the reperfusion rate, myocardial function, clinical outcome and mortality

Reports from different groups have demonstrated that with i.v. application there is a dose dependent percentage of coronary artery reperfusion (17), which cumulates with high dosages of units to about 70% (14), while with intra-coronary streptokinase the reperfusion rate was 80–85% (18). Our own experience with urokinase resulted in a reperfusion rate of about 60% (15). Tests using the tissue plasminogen activator in seven patients led to reperfusion in six of these (16).

It has been shown by different investigators that after re-opening, a high degree residual stenosis is usually present (19), which results in a mean of about 15–20% re-occlusion with or without re-infarction (20). Thus, after reperfusion of an occluded vessel, it is of major importance, first, to know whether jeopardized myocardium (21) has been salvaged and second, to establish therapeutic methods such as effective anti-coagulation, balloon dilatation or coronary bypass to maintain the reperfusion of this jeopardized area. Since myocardial function after an occlusion of more than 60 minutes improves only within 8–10 days (22), the immediate evaluation of wall motion by angiography or echo-cardiography is too early and thus not rational.

Maddahi et al (23) have demonstrated in animal experiments that the uptake of [201]thallium correlates with the viability of myocardial cells. This has been confirmed by clinical observations from Schofer et al (24). They demonstrated that patients who had an immediate [201]thallium uptake after reperfusion showed usually an improvement of the regional myocardial function in the control angiogram after 10 days in contrast to those, who had no [201]thallium uptake. If jeopardized myocardium is still present, to avoid re-occlusion either a balloon-dilatation of the residual stenosis or coronary artery bypass surgery should be performed in addition to strict anticoagulation. With this concept in mind, the analysis of the clinical relevance of re-opening a coronary artery has to focus on the effect on myocardial function, to the clinical outcome and to the complications.

One of the parameters for the evaluation of myocardial function might be the alteration of ejection fraction, which has been used in several reports. The ejection fraction is, however, completely unable to reflect the changes in wall motion of the infarcted area following thrombolytic treatment, since compensatory hyperkinesis in the non-infarcted myocardium may outbalance the regional akinesis in the infarction (26).

In our experience the centerline method of Dodge et al (25) (Fig. 4.2) has been shown as the most favourable of all available angiographic valuation techniques.

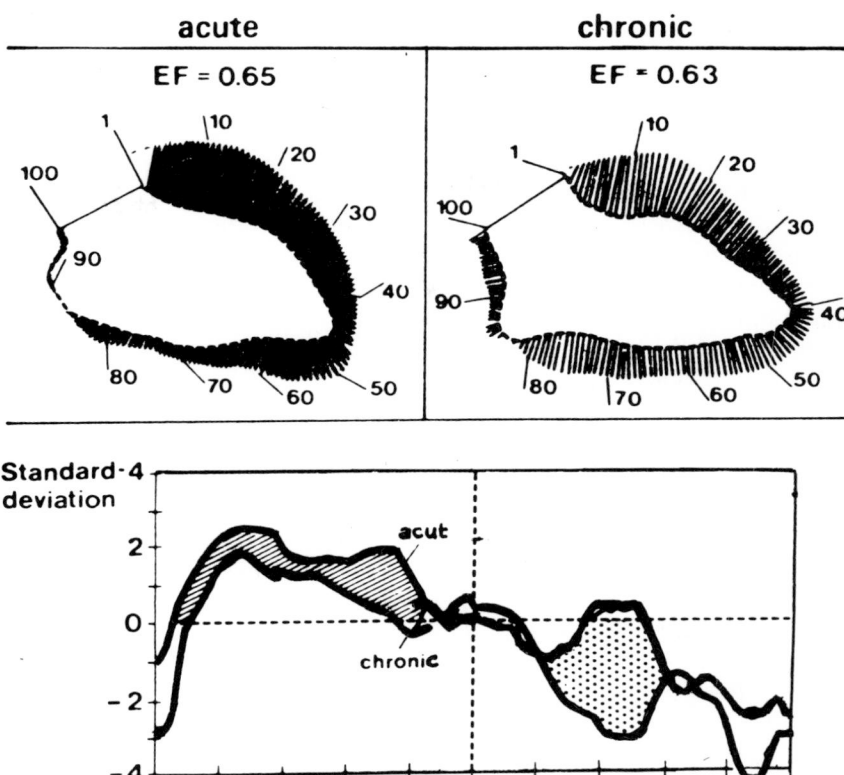

Fig. 4.2 Evaluation of regional myocardial function by the ejection fraction (EF) and the centerline method by Dodge (25) taken from a left ventricular angiogram in acute posterior myocardial infarction. A midline is drawn between the end diastolic and end systolic contours. The alterations of 100 segments perpendicular to this midline are compared to the mean values of ± 1 SD of the wall motion in healthy subjects. The lower panel shows the deviations from normal (0-line) in the different segments and demonstrates that in this posterior AMI the anterior wall (segments 0–50) were hyperkinetic in the acute phase, while the posterior wall was in the segments 60–80 severely hypokinetic and returned to normal, when studied later. This shows definitely an improvement in the infarcted area and explains the unchanged EF (from 26).

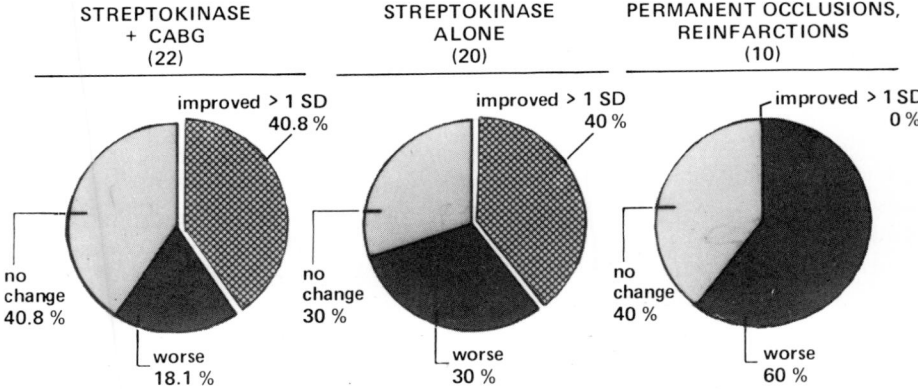

Fig. 4.3 Results of regional wall motion (r.w.m.) (% of patients in whom r.w.m. changed). 1 SD from normal (see Fig. 4.2) in patients.

When using this method the following results were obtained (Fig. 4.3) (26). Patients, who had no successful recanalization had in 37% of cases no alteration, but were worse in 63%. 40% of patients with a reopened coronary artery exhibited improvement of their regional wall motion with infarcted area, which is similar to the percentage in patients who have been acutely treated by a coronary bypass graft. This is certainly not in agreement with other investigators. Their results are listed in Table 4.1 (25, 27–31). It can be seen from this table that three of the studies used mainly global ejection fraction. Moreover, the study by Kajha et al (27) has to be criticized for two reasons:

1. They used global ejection fraction evaluated by radionuclid-ventriculography.
2. The value at the 12th day was compared to that of the 2nd day, when possibly following thrombolysis already residual wall motion may have occurred.

Thus, the results with regard to myocardial function are quite controversial and the reasons can only be suspected. First, the ejection fraction – used by some of the investigators – is not a measure to evaluate the improvement in myocardial function (25); second, the time, when the thrombolytic therapy was applied ranged in the different studies by up to 24 hours; third, the postoperative treatment was extremely varied and the effect of coronary bypass surgery was not considered in some of the studies. Using the evaluation mentioned above (25) 40% of our patients successfully reperfused either with or without aorto-coronary bypass surgery, exhibited significant improvement of myocardial wall motion in the infarcted area (26) (Fig. 4.3). Looking to the clinical outcome, it is the general experience of most investigators that not only pain is relieved immediately after reperfusion, moreover the incidence of left ventricular failure and cardiogenic shock (32) decreases markedly.

With regard to mortality, which has been defined as the endpoint of this new type of treatment by some investigators (14). Table 4.2 lists the data, available at present (35, 21, 28, 36, 29, 33, 34, 35). Only three of these studies were randomized. All randomized examinations showed a marked decrease in mortality. The additional non-randomized studies showed also a significant reduction in mortality. One could take from this data that in more than 1000 patients, thrombolytic therapy was relevant in decreasing the immediate mortality. However, it should be pointed out that only the study of Kennedy et al (36) followed the patients up to six months. All other studies regarded only in – patient mortality, which does not necessarily mean a decrease in two or five year mortality, a question which is still unresolved.

The main clinical complications are bleeding (19) followed by arrhythmias and those which are due to the acute invasive procedure (37). Bleeding complications resulting in the need for transfusion have been reported in about 7% of cases. Reperfusion arrhythmias, which occur in 75% of the patients, may be divided into ventricular fibrillation (20%) rapid ventricular tachycardia (20%) and are probably due to a re-entry mechanism and accelerated ventricular tachycardia (60%), demonstrating itself as ichioventricular tachycardia due to enhanced ventricular automaticity (38).

34

Table 4.1 Results of six studies using intracoronary thrombolysis on ejection fraction and regional wall motion as evaluated from cine-angiograms or radionuclid-ventriculograms

Investigator	No.	randomized	Method	Parameter	Results thrombolysis	controls
Khaja et al (1983)	40	+	Cine-Angio	EF, reg. wall movement	no change	no change
Anderson et al (1983)	50	+	Nuclear-Ventr.	EF	no change	no change
			Nuclear-Ventr.	EF	+ 3.9%	− 3.0%
			Echo	Reg. wall movement		no change
Rentrop et al	55	∅	Cine-Angio	EF	+ 4.0%	− 3.0%
				Reg. wall movem. (score)		no change
Gould et al (1983)	136	∅	Nuclear-Ventr.	EF	+ 7.0%	+ 1.0%
Schwarz et al (1982)	27	∅	Cine-Angio	EF	CK<1000 CK>1000 +8.0% +0.5%	− 4.4%
				Reg. EF	+14.0% +2.0%	− 6.0%
Sheehan et al	52	∅	Cine-Angio	EF	no change	no change
				Reg. wall	↑↑ in 40%	no change

Table 4.2 Results from six studies with intracoronary streptokinase application on mortality

Investigator	No.	Rando-mized	Controls (n =)	% Mortality thrombolysis	controls
Kennedy et al (1983)	250	+	116	3.7	11.2
				(AWI) 7.9	18.9
				(PWI) 0	4.8
				3.7	14.7
Khaja et al	40	+	20	1/20	2/20
				0/19	2/18
Anderson et al (1983)	50	+	26	1/24	4/26
Merx et al (1981)	204	Ø	37 unsuccessful lysis	5.4	24.0
Weinstein et al (1983)	224	Ø	77 standard therapy	4.5	14.6
Kennedy et al (1983)	527	Ø	148 unsuccessful lysis	3.7	10.8

REFERENCES

1. Bleifeld W, Mathey D G, Hanrath P, Buss H, Effert S 1977 Infarct size estimated from serial creatine phosphokinase in relation to left ventricular hemodynamics. Circulation 55: 303–311
2. Braunwald W, Maroko P R 1974 The reduction of infarct size – an idea whose time (for testing) has come. Circulation 50: 206–208
3. Maroko P R, Kjekshus J K, Sobel B D et al 1971 Factors influencing infarct size following experimental coronary artery occlusion. Circulation 63: 67–82
4. Opie L H 1980 Myocardial infarct size. Part I Basic considerations. Am. Heart J. 100: 355–372
5. De Wood M A, Spores J, Notske R, Mouser L T, Vurroughs R, Golden M S, Lang H T 1980 Prevalence of total coronary occlusion during the early hours of transmural myocardial infarction. New Engl. J. Med. 303: 897
6. Kramer C, Gerhardt H J, Bleifeld W 1974 A model for closure of arterial vessels with special regard to the coronary arteries. Basic Res. in Cardiology 69: 585
7. Fletcher A P, Sherry S, Alkjaersig N, Smyrniotis F E, Jick S 1959 The maintenance of a sustained thrombolytic state in man II. Clinical observations on patients with myocardial infarction and other thromboembolic disorders. J. Clin. Invest. 38: 1111
8. Chazow E L, Matveeva L S, Mazaev A V, Sargin K E, Sadoskaya G V, Ruda M Y 1975 Intracoronary administration of fibrinolysin in acute myocardial infarction. Terapeuticheskii Arkhiv 8: 19
9. Houck E, Bolton M D, Fernando A, Tapia M D, Cabral H, Riera R, Mazel M S Chicago. Removal of acute coronary thrombus with fibrinolysin – In vivo experiment – A preliminary report on the use of fibrinolytic agents in the treatment of acute thrombosis – Vol. 175: No 4, p 307
10. Boucek R J, Murphy W P 1960 Segmental perfusion of the coronary arteries with fibrinolysis in man following a myocardial infarction. Am. J. Cardiol. 6: 525
11. Rentrop P, Blanke H, Wiegand V, Karsch K R 1979 Wiedereröffnung verschlossener Kranzgefäße im akuten Infarkt mit Hilfe von Kathetern (Transluminale Rekanalisation). Dt Med Wschr 104: 1401
12. Mathey D G, Kuck K H, Tilsner V, Krebber H J, Bleifeld W 1981 Nonsurgical coronary artery recanalization in acute transmural myocardial infarction. Circulation 63: 489–497
13. Ganz W, Buchbinder S, Marcus H, Mondkar A, Maddahi J, Charozi Y, O'Connor L, Shell W, Fishbein M, Kass R, Myamoto A, Swan H J C 1981 Intracoronary thrombolysis in evolving myocardial infarction. Am. Heart J. 101: 4–12
14. Schröder R 1983 Systemic versus intracoronary streptokinase infusion in the treatment of acute myocardial infarction: JACC 1: 1254

15. Mathey D G, Schofer J, Roewer N, Tilsner V, Becher H, Berkel H, Weidringer G 1984 Intravenöser Urokinase-Bolus im Frühstadium des akuten Myokard-infarktes. 90. Tagung der Deutschen Gesellschaft für Innere Medizin, Wiesbaden 29.04.-03.05.84
16. Van de Werf F, Ludbrook PH A, Bergmann St. R, Tiefenbrunn A J, Fox K A A, De Geest H, Verstraete M, Collen D, Sobel B 1984 Coronary thrombolysis with tissue-type plasminogen activator in patients with evolving myocardial infarction. New Engl. J. Med. 310: 609
17. Rogers W J, Mantle J A, Hood Jr W P, Baxley W A, Whitlow P L, Reeves R C, Soto B 1983 Prospective randomized trial of intravenous and intracoronary streptokinase in acute myocardial infarction. Circulation 68: 1051
18. Mathey D G, Schofer J, Krebber H J, Kuck K H, Tilsner V, Montz R, Bleifeld W, Rodewald W 1983 Use of streptokinase in coronary thrombosis. In: Hurst J W (ed) Clinical Essays on the heart, vol 1, McGraw Hill, New York
19. Rutsch W, Schartl M, Mathey D G, Kuck K H, Merx W, Dörr R, Rentrop R, Blanke H, Karsch K 1982 Perkutane transluminale, koronare Rekanalisation: Methodik, Ergebnisse und Komplikationen. Zschr. Kardiologie 71: 7-14
20. Merx W, Bethge Ch, Rentrop R, Blanke H, Karsch H R, Mathey D G, Kremer P, Rutsch W, Schmutzler H 1982 Selective Thrombolyse mit Streptokinase beim akuten Herzinfarkt. Stationärer Verlauf bei 204 Patienten. Zschr. Kardiol. 71: 14-21
21. Sobel B E, Bresnahan, Shell W E, Yoder R D 1972 Estimation of infarct size and its relation to prognosis. Circulation 46: 640
22. Baughmann K L, Maroko P R, Vatner S F 1981 Effects of coronary artery reperfusion on myocardial infarct size and survival in conscious dogs. Circulation 63: 317-323
23. Maddahi J, Grnz W, Ninomiya K, Hashiba J, Fishbein M C, Mondkar A, Buchbinder N, Marcus H, Geft J, Shah P K, Rozanski A, Swan H J C, Berman D S Myocardial salvage by intracoronary thrombolysis in evolving acute myocardial infarction: Evaluation using injection of thallium-201. Am. Heart J. 664-674
24. Schofer J, Mathey D G, Montz R, Kuck K H, Bleifeld W 1982 Nachweis akuter Tl-201 Aufnahme nach intrakoronarer Thrombolyse mittels sequentieller intrakoronarer Tl-201-Injektion Zschr. Kardiol. 71: 188
25. Sheehan F H, Mathey D G, Schofer J, Krebber H J, Dodge H T 1983 Effect of interventions in salvaging left ventricular function in acute myocardial infarction: A study of intracoronary streptokinase. Am. J. Cardiol. 52: 431
26. Mathey D, Schofer J, Stritzke P, Montz R, Krebber H J, Tilsner V, Bleifeld W 1983 Intrakoronare Thrombolyse-Therapie beim akuten Herzinfarkt Zeitschrift f. Klinik und Praxis, Heft 2: 3-15
27. Khaja F, Walton J A Jr, Brymer J F, Lo E, Osterberger L, O'Neill W W, Colfer H T, Weiss R, Tennyson L, Kurian T, Goldberg A D, Pitt B, Goldstein S. The New Engl. J. of Med., June 2
28. Anderson J L, Marshall H W, Bray B E, Lutz J R, Frederick P R, Yanowitz F G, Datz L F, Klausner St. C, Hagan A D 1983 A randomized trial of intracoronary streptokinase in the treatment of acute myocardial infarction. Engl. J. Med. 308: 1312
29. Rentrop P, Blanke H, Karsch K R, Rutsch W, Schartl M, Merx W, Dörr R, Mathey D G, Kuck K H 1981 Changes in left ventricular function after intracoronary streptokinase infusion in clinically evolving myocardial infarction. Am. Heart. J. 102
30. Smalling R W, Fuentes F, Matthews M W, Freund G C, Hicks Ch H, Reduto L A, Walker W E, Sterling R P, Gould K L 1983 Sustained improvement in left ventricular function and mortality by intra-coronary streptokinase administration during evolving myocardial infarction. Circulation 68: 131
31. Schwarz F, Schuler G, Katus H, Mehmel H C, Ohlshausen K, Hofmann M, Herrmann H J, Kübler W 1982 Intracoronary thrombolysis in acute myocardial infarction: Correlation among serum enzyme, scintigraphic and hemodynamic findings. The Am. Cardiol. 50: 32
32. Mathey D G, Kuck K H, Remmecke J, Tilsner V, Bleifeld W 1980 Transluminal recanalization of coronary artery thrombosis: a preliminary report of its application in cardiogenic shock. Eur. Heart J. 1: 207-212
33. Merx W, Dörr P, Rentrop P, Blanke H, Karsch K R, Mathey D G, Kremer P, Rutsch W, Schmutzler H 1981 Evaluation of the effectiveness of intracoronary streptokinase infusion in acute myocardial infarction: postprocedure management and hospital course on 204 patients. Am. Heart J. 102: 1181
34. Weinstein J 1983 The internation registry to support approval of intracoronary streptokinase thrombolysis in the treatment of myocardial infarction. Assessment of safety and efficacy. Circulation 68: Suppl. I: 1-61

35. Kennedy J W, Ritchie J L, Davis K B, Fritz J K 1983 Western Washington randomized trial of intracoronary streptokinase in acute myocardial infarction. N. Engl. J. Med. 309: 1477
36. Kennedy J W and the Registry Committee of the Society for Cardiac Angiography 1983 Intracoronary streptokinase in acute MI: Report from the Society for Cardiac Angiography Registry. Circulation 68, Suppl. III: 111-121, Abstract
37. Serruys P W, van den Brand M, Hooghoudt T E H et al 1982 Coronary recanalization in acute myocardial infarction: immediate results and potentials risks. Eur. Heart J. 3: 404
38. Kuck K H, Schofer J, Bleifeld W, Mathey D G 1984 Failure of lidocaine to prevent reperfusion arrhythmias J. Am. Coll. Cardiol. 3: 586

5. Thrombolytic effect of streptokinase on coronary artery occlusion in acute myocardial infarction by conventional intravenous administration over 24 hours

H. Straub, W. Jaedicke and M. Avramidis

The effectiveness of streptokinase (SK) in acute myocardial infarction (aMI) in lowering the mortality rate was examined in 12 controlled clinical studies published between 1966 and 1979 (4). The mechanism of action was assumed to be changes in the flow properties of the blood ('rheological fibrinolysis') (1). In the meantime early recanalization of the occluded coronary artery was detected for the intracoronary (2) and for the intravenous high-dosed short infusion (3) of SK. The object of this study was to determine whether coronary thrombolysis also occurs regularly and at an early stage with the dosage of SK used in the past.

METHOD

SK therapy was carried out in 26 men with an average age of 57.5 ± 6.4 years who had had an aMI and whose average duration of infarct at the start of therapy was 3.1 ± 1.3 hours. There were 14 infarctions of the anterior wall and 12 infarctions of the posterior wall of the heart. The dosage of SK with an initial dose of 250,000 U and a maintenance dose over 24 hours of 100,000 U/hour corresponds exactly to the dose used in the European Cooperative Study (5). The fibrinolytic efficacy of SK was monitored by determining the thrombin time and the fibrinogen before lysis and at 12-hour intervals for up to 48 hours after the beginning of lysis. The acute detection of early recanalization was carried out by means of the typical wash-out kinetics of the necrotic enzymes CK and CKMB (3) which were determined every 2 hours on the 1st day and at 4-hourly intervals on the 2nd day. 15 of the 26 patients (58%) were subjected to coronary angiography after an interval of on average 7.7 weeks. The time that had passed since aMI was 15.7 ± 5.1 weeks in the case of the first four patients, and 4.8 ± 0.9 weeks for the last 11 patients. Standardized ECG recordings were made before lysis, 6, 12, 24, 36, 48 hours after and 4 weeks after treatment. The extent of the initial ischaemia before lysis was quantified by means of the ECG leads with ST segment elevation and compared with the extent of the scar determined from the leads with a defined Q wave after 28 days. The evaluation of the laevocardiogram as the basis for assessment of a possible reduction in the infarcted zone was not possible with the small number of cases and without an acute laevocardiogram.

RESULTS

In accordance with a CK peak time of less than 16 hours the early recanalization rate is 61% and, if the cases that have probably been recanalized are included (CK peak 16th-19th hour), the recanalization rate is 81%. Angiography shows the infarct-related coronary vessel to be patent in the interval in 73% of cases. All the patent vessels show evidence of residual stenosis. When the sum of ECG leads with initial ST elevation was compared with the sum of the leads which demonstrate a Q wave after 28 days, the group of patients without early recanalization showed no significant change with -5.7%, whereas a reduction of 29.6% is detectable in the patients recanalized according to the CK curve. The expected changes in the coagulation tests occur with a fall in fibrinogen from 337 $\pm$ 61 to 85 $\pm$ 49 mg/dl and an increase in thrombin time from 17 $\pm$ 5.3 to 59 $\pm$ 4.9 sec.

DISCUSSION

According to the results of this study, it must be assumed that the conventional intravenous dosage of SK also gives rise to coronary thrombolysis, with the opening rate of the same order of magnitude as that of the other more recent forms of application of SK (2,3). The course of the ECG changes indicates that early recanalization of the coronary artery in aMI is associated with a reduction in the infarcted area. It can be concluded that the positive effect of SK on the mortality of aMI, which was detected in earlier studies (4), is based on the coronary thrombolytic effect of SK.

SUMMARY

The data presented show that with the conventional dosage of SK in aMI not only do rheological changes occur but recanalization of the occluded coronary artery with a reduction in the infarcted region takes place regularly and early on.

REFERENCES

1. Neuhof H, Hey D, Glaser E, Wolf H, Lasch H G 1975 Hemodynamic reaction induced by streptokinase therapy in patients with acute myocardial infarction. Europ. J. Intensive Care Medicine 1: 27
2. Rentrop P 1981 Lokale Anwendung der Streptokinase in stenosierten bzw. verschlossenen Koronargefäßen. Therapiewoche 31: 2581
3. Schröder R, Biamino G, v. Leitner E R, Linderer T, Heitz J, Vöhringer H F et al 1982 Systemische Thrombolyse mit Streptokinase-Kurzzeitinfusion bei akutem Myokardinfarkt. Z. Kardiol 71: 709
4. Straub H, Jaedicke W, Avramidis M 1983 Koronarthrombolytische Wirkung der Streptokinasetherapie beim akuten Myokardinfarkt unter Verwendung der her-kömmlichen intravenösen Standarddosierung. Herzmedizin 6: 65
5. Verstraete M, van de Loo J et al 1979 Streptokinase in acute myocardial infarction. N. Engl. J. Med. 301: 797

6. Systemic lytic effects and coagulation changes with intravenous thrombolytic therapy in evolving myocardial infarction

D.J. Doyle, A.G.G. Turpie, J.A. Cairns, D.A. Holder and M.P. McEwan

INTRODUCTION

Coronary thrombolysis has been demonstrated with intracoronary and intravenous thrombolytic therapy (Feldman et al, 1984; Ganz et al, 1984), but the intravenous dose and the optimal method of monitoring therapy have not been well established. Therefore, this study was carried out to monitor the coagulation and lytic effects of high-dose, short duration intravenous thrombolytic therapy in evolving myocardial infarction and to compare the effect of urokinase with streptokinase on these changes and to correlate them with peak creatine kinase washout (Cairns et al, 1978).

METHODS

Twenty patients with evolving myocardial infarctions were treated with high-dose intravenous urokinase (n = 11, mean dose 1.3×10^6U over 81 minutes) or streptokinase (n = 9, mean dose 1.0×10^6U over 81 minutes). Blood sampling was commenced prior to the initiation of thrombolytic therapy, at 30 and 60 minutes during infusion and 1 hour, 6 hours, 12–24 hours and 36–48 hours post-thrombolytic therapy. Continuous IV heparin was commenced 2 hours post-infusion of streptokinase or urokinase. The following coagulation tests were done: prothrombin time, partial thromboplastin time, 2 and 6 unit thrombin clotting time and reptilase clotting time. To test systemic lytic activity, euglobulin lysis time plasma plasminogen concentration, plasma fibrinogen concentration, fibrinogen fibrin degradation products were measured. Factors VIIIc and V were measured to determine the extent of their proteolysis by plasmin. The inhibitors, alpha$_2$-plasmin inhibitor and alpha$_2$-macroglobulin were also measured. Serial creatine kinase were drawn initially by half-hour intervals and two-hourly for 72 hours to determine the time of peak CK washout.

RESULTS

Table 6.1 shows the results of the tests obtained with urokinase and Table 6.2 shows the results obtained with streptokinase indicating rapid onset of a systemic lytic state with both drug infusions.

41

Table 6.1 Urokinase Results (n = 11, mean ± SD)

Test	Pre	During Infusion 30 min	60 min	1 hour	6 hours	Post Infusion 12-24 hours	36-48 hours
PT secs	12.1 ± 1.0	14.0 ± 2.9	16.8 ± 2.4	17.3 ± 3.2	17.8 ± 4.9	13.8 ± 1.9	12.5 ± 0.5
PTT secs	30.1 ± 2.8	34.4 ± 8.5	47.1 ± 18.3	48.0 ± 18.6	67.0 ± 32.0	48.9 ± 11.0	55.6 ± 12.1
TCT (IOU) secs	8.5 ± 1.8	15.2 ± 4.8	18.3 ± 7.9	22.0 ± 9.7	44.0 ± 15.0	28.3 ± 15.5	22.1 ± 25.0
TCT (2U) secs	24.0 ± 2.8	44.5 ± 12.1	45.7 ± 13.5	15.2	69.0 ± 12.5	63.9 ± 25.0	70.0 ± 24.0
Reptilase secs	26.0 ± 4.6	44.6 ± 13.4	49.8 ± 14.3	61.4 ± 20.0	66.9 ± 20.0	51.1 ± 27.7	29.0 ± 9.1
Euglobulin Activity 300/min	1.55 ± 1.2	124.0 ± 140.0	230.0 ± 48.0	128.0 ± 146.0	2.26 ± 0.63	1.29 ± 0.35	1.02 ± 0.19
Fibrinogen mg/100	342.0 ± 93.0	132.0 ± 76.0	110.0 ± 76.0	67.0 ± 49.0	53.0 ± 35.0	179.0 ± 63.0	376.0 ± 116.0
Plasminogen CTU/ml	3.4 ± 0.6	1.9 ± 0.7	1.4 ± 0.6	1.1 ± 0.3	1.5 ± 0.3	2.0 ± 0.4	2.5 ± 10.4
2 Plasmin Inhibitor %	96.7 ± 21.8	3.7 ± 9.8	9.6 ± 16.0	7.7 ± 12.0	27.8 ± 23.5	54.0 ± 24.0	114.0 ± 17.0
2 Macro-Globulin %	68.0 ± 18.0	71.0 ± 34.0	66.0 ± 35.0	63.0 ± 24.0	54.0 ± 17.0	61.0 ± 26.0	57.0 ± 30.0
Factor VIIIc %	176.0 ± 69.0	84.0 ± 61.0	59.0 ± 36.0	40.0 ± 31.0	60.0 ± 29.0	114.0 ± 47.0	174.0 ± 79.0
Factor V %	91.0 ± 27.0	51.0 ± 28.0	46.0 ± 22.0	37.0 ± 18.0	53.0 ± 9.0	81.0 ± 46.0	101.0 ± 54.0
Frag E μg/ml	0245 ± 206	13159 ± 22191	20913 ± 19930	10450 ± 9497	13132 ± 11359	7050 ± 7279	438 ± 575
FDP μg/ml	0.020 ± 0.016	0.450 ± 0.60	0.534 ± 0.695	0.854 ± 0.799	0.740 ± 0.799	0.265 ± 0.290	0.60 ± 0.046

Table 6.2 Streptokinase Results (n = 9, mean ± SD)

Test	Pre	30 min	60 min	150 min	6 hours	18 hours	42 hours
PT secs	12.2 ± 0.8	19.8 ± 5.5	25.3 ± 3.1	24.8 ± 3.3	21.4 ± 3.5	15.8 ± 1.6	13.2 ± 0.7
PTT secs	30.6 ± 1.9	48.4 ± 8.3	56.1 ± 15.4	49.8 ± 13.0	50.6 ± 18.3	54.3 ± 25.3	52.3 ± 15.6
TCT (1OU) secs	8.9 ± 1.1	33.9 ± 24.0	36.7 ± 23.6	36.6 ± 33.6	37.4 ± 14.2	35.7 ± 30.1	14.9 ± 5.8
TCT (2U) secs	23.7 ± 29	56.2 ± 17.2	64.0 ± 19.1	63.0 ± 18.7	54.5 ± 6.0	58.7 ± 23.8	53.2 ± 8.4
Reptilase secs	23.7 ± 3.8	74.8 ± 18.1	84.1 ± 16.0	90.2 ± 18.0	84.6 ± 22.6	49.6 ± 23.6	29.6 ± 6.5
Euglobulin Activity 300/min	1.24 ± 0.54	258 ± 102	225.7 ± 128	226 ± 128	6.1 ± 0.7	2.26 ± 1.65	1.19 ± 0.46
Fibrinogen	319 ± 60	<50mg	<50mg	<50mg	<50mg	68 ± 49	264 ± 118
Plasminogen CTU/ml	3.5 ± 0.40	0.6 ± 0.2	0.29 ± 0.04	0.18 ± 0.06	0.21 ± 0.44	1.1 ± 0.44	2.01 ± 0.28
2 Plasmin Inhibitor %	107 ± 17.5	<0.01	<0.01	<0.01	<0.01	30 ± 26	94.8 ± 16
2 Macro-Globulin %	81 ± 11	59 ± 10	59 ± 9.8	57 ± 8.8	49 ± 0.7	44 ± 9	48 ± 7.0
Factor VIIIc %	173 ± 96	33 ± 18	20 ± 8	32 ± 9	50 ± 14	79 ± 22	136 ± 36
Factor V %	89 ± 20.6	25 ± 15	25 ± 12.5	25 ± 14.9	33.2 ± 17.2	53.8 ± 14.9	76.4 ± 16.3
Frag E μg/ml	96 ± 32	18632 ± 12253	—	—	—	6874 ± 6182	1200 ± 1134
FDP μg/ml	0.012 ± 0.004	0.660 ± 0.578	0.965 ± 0.637	1.237 ± 0.955	0.768 ± 0.318	0.318 ± 0.240	0.054 ± 0.037

Figure 6.1 shows the time to peak CK concentration in the high and low dose urokinase or streptokinase regimens. There was a significant reduction in time to peak CK with both urokinase compared with low dose urokinase and there was a significant correlation between the dose ($r = -.55$ $p < 0.05$) of thrombolytic agent and time to peak CK.

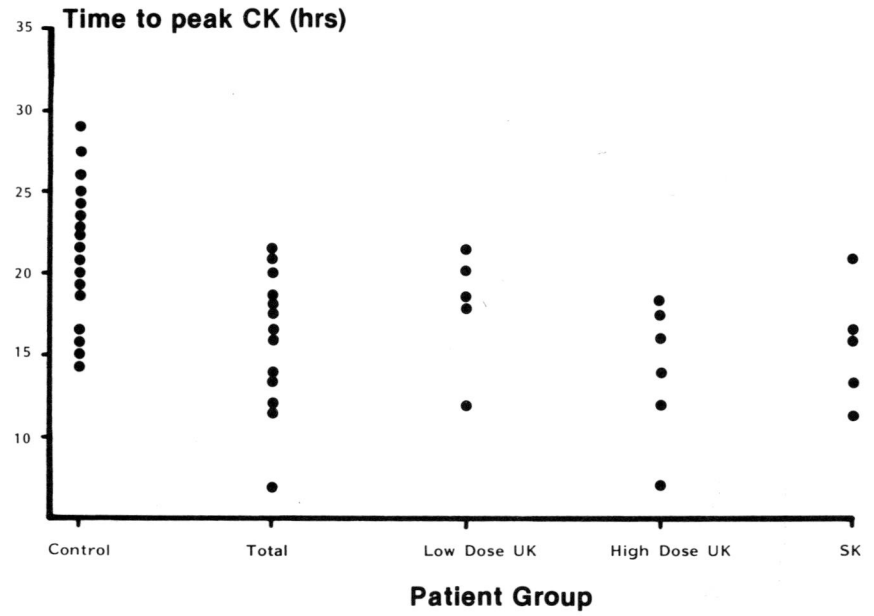

Fig. 6.1 Time to peak CK in controls and UK/SK regimens

DISCUSSION

The results of the study indicate that high-dose, short duration intravenous thrombolytic therapy with streptokinase or urokinase produces a brief intense systemic lytic effect followed by an anticoagulant effect. The results of this lytic activity can be detected by routine coagulation tests. The thrombolytic effect was detected at 30 minutes, was at maximum at the end of the infusion and reverted spontaneously by 3–6 hours.

The anticoagulant effect of the FDP's persisted for 12–24 hours. Urokinase produced a less marked plasmin generation than streptokinase and a smaller fall in fibrinogen, alpha$_2$-macroglobulin and alpha$_2$-antiplasmin. The study indicates that measurement of the prothrombin time, thrombin clotting time and reptilase time was sufficient for clinical monitoring of short duration thrombolytic therapy because these tests detected the onset of the lytic state, fibrinogen degradation produce clearance and the return of fibrinogen concentration to normal. The results of the tests also provided a guide to the time that anticoagulant therapy should be started.

REFERENCES

Cairns J A, Missirlis E, Fallen D L 1978 Myocardial infarction size from serial CPK: variability of CPK serum entry ratio with size and model of infarction. Circulation 58: 1143

Feldman R L, Hill J A, Conti C R, Pepine C J 1984 Intracoronary streptokinase in evolving acute myocardial infarction. American Heart Journal 107 (4): 823–825

Ganz W, Geft I, Shah P K, Lew A S, Rodriguez L, Weiss T et al 1984 Intravenous streptokinase in evolving acute myocardial infarction. The American Journal of Cardiology 53 (9): 1209–1216

7. Streptokinase (SK) bolus injection in acute myocardial infarction (AMI) — a prospective randomized trial

P. Hellstern, M. Köhler, C Özbek, P. Doenecke,
B. Reiter, C. Miyashita, R. Kiehl, L. Burger,
G. von Blohn, L. Bette and E. Wenzel

In addition to intracoronary thrombolysis the systemic application of SK is a well established method for the treatment of AMI. Because of the variety of treatment regimens we prospectively examined the effectiveness of a simple high dose intravenous SK-bolus injection. In addition to the evaluation of clinical success of this method we also investigated the intensity and duration of the hemostaseological alterations.

PATIENTS AND METHODS

Until the end of January, 1984, 31 out of 112 patients suffering from AMI randomly received 750,000 or 1.5 million U SK intravenously within 5 min. The remaining patients were not treated with SK due to contraindications or an infarct age greater than 6 hours. The mean age of AMI in the patients treated with SK was 3 hours, the average patient age was 59 years (min. 45 years, max. 79 years old). The following hemostaseological parameters were measured before, 15 min, 30 min, 1 h, 3 h, 6 h, and 12 h after SK: prothrombin time, aPTT, thrombin time, thrombincoagulase time, fibrinogen (Clauss' method and radial immunodiffusion), plasminogen concentration and activity (test-kit Behringwerke Marburg), alpha$_2$-antiplasmin concentration and activity (test-kit Boehringer Mannheim), and SK-plasminogen activator activity by means of S-2444 (Kabi Munich) and by fibrin plate method. The fibrin plate method was calibrated with SK and UK, and human fibrinogen was used.

ECG and CK-MB were closely monitored. Coronary angiography was performed in 14 patients. Heparin therapy was started as soon as aPTT returned to normal values.

CLINICAL RESULTS

Within 6 weeks after AMI one patient died of infarct complications, two additional patients died of surgical complications. Coronary arteries were patent in 9 out of 14 patients. No serious bleeding complications occurred. Bleeding from venous and arterial punctures were observed in some patients. In some cases blood pressure decreases of up to 70 mm Hg were observed and were easily and rapidly corrected by antihypotonic drugs. Severe anaphylactic reactions did not occur.

HEMOSTASEOLOGICAL RESULTS

A pronounced fibrinogenolysis could be demonstrated up to 12 h after SK administration. At that time, the mean fibrinogen level measured by the Clauss' method was 80 mg/100 ml. Plasminogen activity as well as alpha$_2$-antiplasmin activity decreased markedly and were significantly diminished 12 h after SK (Fig. 7.1). Fifteen min. after SK administration extremely high levels of activator

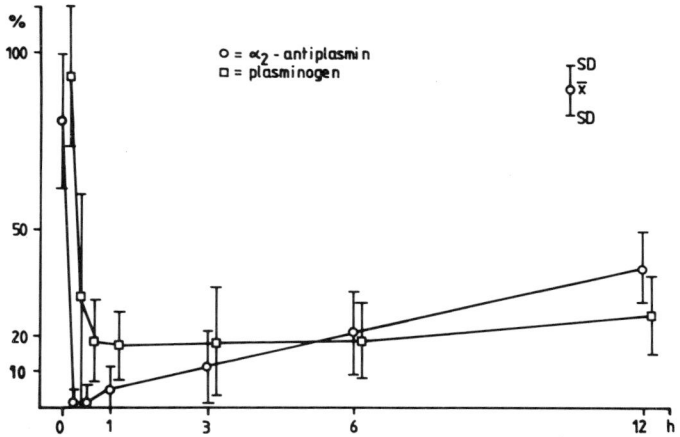

Fig. 7.1 Plasminogen and alpha$_2$-antiplasmin activity after bolus injection of 750 000 U SK (N = 12).

activity were measured with both methods, which decreased almost exponentially (Fig. 7.2). None of the parameters was influenced by the two above mentioned SK dosages to a significantly different degree.

The half-life of SK-plasminogen activator measured by S-2444 was 140 min and significantly longer than that measured by the fibrin plate method (60 min). The values of the 5 patients with occluded coronary arteries were not significantly different from those 9 with patent vessels. An insufficient anticoagulation with heparin was observed in 4 out of 5 patients with occluded coronary arteries.

CONCLUSIONS

1. Intravenous SK-bolus injection proved to be a simple and effective method of thrombolysis in AMI. The clinical efficacy is comparable to present therapeutic

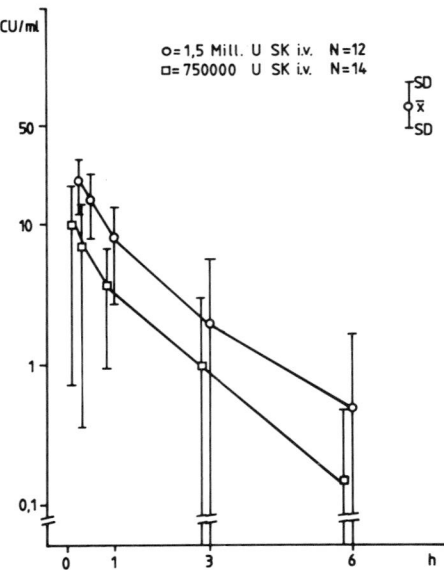

Fig. 7.2 Behaviour of SK-plasminogen activator activity after bolus injection of 750 000 U (N = 12) and 1.5 mill. U SK (N = 14), respectively. The fibrin plate method was calibrated using SK and urokinase.

regimens. Bleeding complications appear to be mild and comparatively less frequent.

2. The behaviour of hemostaseological parameters indicates that continuous SK infusions after a bolus injection are unnecessary or superfluous.

3. The variation of half-lives of activator activity measured by both methods may be the result of the inclusion of activator-inhibitor complexes by the S-2444 method.

4. An elevation of the dosage beyond 750.000 U exhibits no advantage.

5. An early and sufficient heparinization significantly influences the outcome.

8. Systemic fibrinolysis as an effect of intracoronary thrombolysis

M. Barthels, D. Gulba and M.J. Engel

Intracoronary thrombolysis is supposed to induce only a moderate systematic fibrinolysis with fibrinogen and plasminogen levels decreased only slightly or not at all (Köstering 1981, Rentrop 1981, Pickering et al. 1983). Assaying various parameters of the plasma fibrinolytic system we observed a marked systemic fibrinolysis in 6 patients who received selective intracoronary thrombolysis.

MATERIAL AND METHODS

Intracoronary thrombolysis

Acute angiography was performed by the Judkin's technique and was followed by intracoronary streptokinase infusion (80,000-400, 000 I.U. Streptase Behringwerke Marburg, FRG), at a constant flow rate over a period of 60 to 210 minutes. Prior to the coronary angiography 5000 I.U. heparin were administered intravenously to each patient. Further on heparinisation was performed.

Coagulation and fibrinolysis assays

Fibrinogen assay: Clauss' method (reagents Behringwerke Marburg, FRG). Fibrinogen degradation products (FDP): Laurell-technique using an antifibrinogen serum from rabbits (Behringwerke Marburg, FRG), after defibrination of the samples with thrombin in a dosage of 2 I.U./ml blood and aprotinin 80 K.I.U./ml blood.

Plasminogen (Plg) and alpha-2-antiplasmin (alpha-2-Ap): with chromogenic peptide substrate S-2251 (Deutsche KabiVitrum Munich, FRG).

Thrombincoagulase time (test kit Boehringer Mannheim GmbH, FRG).

RESULTS

Immediately after the start of the streptokinase infusion, systemic activation of the fibrinolytic system was observed. Thus, Plg-levels dropped to a minimum of $<25\%$, except in one patient where the Plg-concentration was reduced to 58%, and rapid normalization of all parameters was observed. In all 6 patients, however, alpha-2-Ap-levels were below 30%. FDP concentration rose to a maximum of 72 mg%. Only in one patient no FDP were detected after the onset of streptokinase infusion. Fibrinogen levels dropped to a minimum of less than 0.85 g/l in 5 of 6 patients, while in one case no change was observed. Thrombincoagulase time was prolonged to 40–150 s in all six cases. No bleeding complications occurred. Reopening of the occluded vessel was achieved in all cases. Fig. 1 exemplarily shows our data from one patient (pat. R.A.).

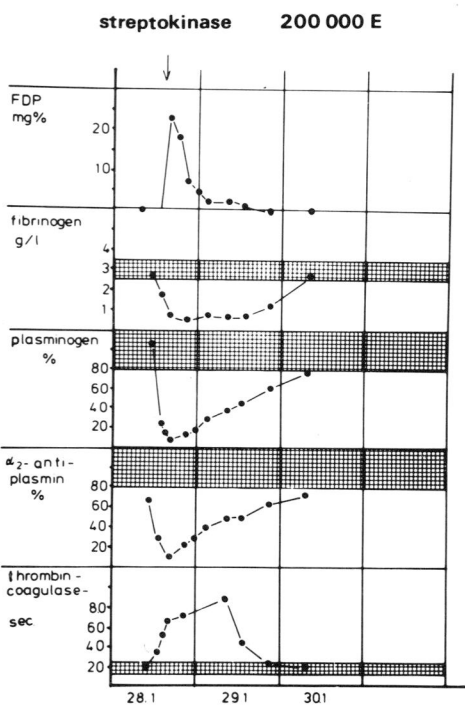

Fig. 8.1 Systemic fibrinolysis during intracoronary thrombolysis.

DISCUSSION

Our data show a marked systemic fibrinolysis during and after intracoronary infusion of streptokinase in all 6 cases, with rather persistent low concentrations of alpha-2-Antiplasmin, Plasminogen and fibrinogen as reported also by Huhmann et al (1981). In contrast, Rentrop and Köstering (Rentrop et al 1981, Köstering et al 1981) reported that in their studies the decrease in fibrinogen- and plasminogen-levels was only mild.

Probably, the full extend of the systemic fibrinolysis was not registered by the methods the authors used. Determination of fibrinogen by heat precipitation also includes FDP (Huseby & Bang 1971). Similarly plasminogen levels measured immunologically also include inactive alpha-2-antiplasmin-plasminogen complexes.

REFERENCES

Huhmann W, Allner R, Nieth 1981 Verhalten der Blutgerinnungswerte nach intracoronarer Streptokinase. Zeitschrift für Kardiologie 70: 323

Huseby R M, Bang N U 1971 Fibrinogen. In: Bang N U, Beller F K, Mammen E F (eds) Thrombosis and Bleeding Disorders. Georg Thieme, Stuttgart, p 242

Köstering H, Rentrop P, Blanke H, Tebbe U, Neuhaus K L, Kreuzer H 1981 Blutgerinnungsveränderungen bei Patienten mit akutem Myocardinfarkt unter einer intracoronaren und einer hochdosierten systemischen Streptokinasebehandlung. In: Blümel G, Haas S (eds) Mikrozirkulation und Prostaglandinstoffwechsel. F.K. Schattauer, Stuttgart. p 305

Pickering N J, Brody J J, Fink G B, Wolf N M, Meister S G 1983 In vivo determinants associated with successful streptokinase therapy myocardial infarction. Thrombosis and Haemostasis 50: 408

Rentrop P, Blanke H, Karsch K R, Kaiser H, Köstering H, Leitz K 1981 Selective intracoronary thrombolysis in acute myocardial infarction and unstable angina pectoris. Circulation 63: 307

9. Considerations on the biochemical effects of high dose streptokinase infusion

S.A. Cederholm-Williams

A high level of interest is currently being shown in the use of high dose streptokinase (SK) infusion for the treatment of recent myocardial infarction. The requirements of the cardiologist are different to those of the physician who treats deep vein thrombosis by continuous or intermittent infusion of SK. The cardiologist deals with a much higher risk of death and a much shorter history of painful symptoms. At the time of treatment it is rare to have definite evidence confirming the thrombotic nature of the coronary occlusion. The minor side effects of fever, occasional rigor and bruising at puncture sites are easily outweighed by the therapeutic objectives of restoring local perfusion and limiting irreversible muscle damage. These new objectives have fostered the development of the high dose streptokinase regime.

Verstraete et al (1) showed that a dose of 290,000 units (2.9 mg) SK was sufficient to neutralise the inhibitory antibodies present in 95% of a European population and continuous infusion of 100,000 units/h, induced substantial defibrination and plasminogen depletion. The high dose regime of $1.5-1.8 \times 10^6$ units infused over a period of 60 minutes (2) is aimed at producing an immediate short term effect. This approach has not yet been analysed in biochemical detail and it is of great interest to know what fibrinolytic responses are induced.

Certain predictions can be made from a theoretical basis. The formation of the 1:1 bimolecular SK-plasmin(ogen) activator complex is known to be one of the fastest protein-protein interactions described, with an association rate of $5.4 \times 10^7 \, M^{-1} S^{-1}$ (3). For practical purposes this reaction may be regarded as virtually instantaneous. The resulting complex is very tightly associated (Kd 5×10^{-11}M) and is not inhibited by the major plasma fibrinolytic inhibitor, α-2-antiplasmin (3). Thus, for as long as the SK-plasmin(ogen) complex remains in the circulatory system it remains an active plasminogen activator.

The normal plasma plsminogen concentration is 0.14g/L and, given an average plasma volume of 3L, represents 0.42g (4.7μMoles). Only 40% of the total body plasminogen is found in the blood, the remainder being in the extra-vascular compartment, with which the plasma plasminogen exchanges freely. The total body plasminogen normally turns over at a rate of 2.6 mg $Kg^{-1} day^{-1}$ giving a plasma half life of 50 hours (4). This normal plasminogen consumption is due to the action of the liver and/or the reticuloendothelial system. Plasminogen re-enters the circulation from the extravascular compartment at a rate of 0.94 mg Kg^{-1} day^{-1}.

The infusion of high dose streptokinase (16 mg, 0.33 μMoles) into an average plasma compartment of 3L represents a molar ratio of SK to plasminogen of 1:14. Since the bimolecular complex formation occurs instantaneously, the generation of plasminogen activator activity should be directly related to the infusion rate (minus the effect of neutralising antibodies, which should be small). The uncomplexed plasminogen (93%) is converted to plasmin in the circulation by the plasminogen activator complex. The speed of this reaction is broadly dependent upon the SK infusion rate, the faster the infusion the faster the plasmin generation. Plasmin action is rapidly and effectively limited by the inhibitor α-2-antiplasmin (5). Half (52%) the total body α-2-antiplasmin is present in the vascular compartment and the inhibitor re-enters the plasma from the extravascular compartment at a rate of 0.65 mg Kg^{-1} day^{-1} which, in molar terms, is virtually identical to the plasminogen re-entry rate (5). The total plasma α-2-antiplasmin is capable of inhibiting only 67% of the plasma plasmin(ogen), leaving 26% (33% $-$ 7% [plasmin-SK]) free plasmin. This plasmin is the thrombolytic agent that must clear any thrombotic occlusion.

In the absence of functional α-2-antiplasmin, free plasmin rapidly destroys fibrinogen and induces a state of defibrination in the plasma. Plasmin-α-2-antiplasmin complexes are cleared at a rate of 1.0 mg Kg^{-1} day^{-1} giving a plasma half life of 21 hours.

Preliminary studies (Cederholm-Williams, Alexopoulous and Sleight, unpublished) have indicated that the SK plasminogen-activator induced by infusion of 15 mg SK over 60 minutes is cleared from the circulation by a first order process with a half life of 60–90 minutes. This means that the effective fibrinolytic action lasts for only 7 hours after which the normal synthetic processes and re-equilibration with the extravascular components begins to replenish the plasma fibrinolytic proteins.

The infusion of high dose streptokinase induces a rapid response due to the generation of free plasmin which lasts only for a short period after the discontinuation of infusion.

REFERENCES

1. Verstraete M, Vermylen J, Amery A, Vermylen C 1966 Thrombolytic therapy with streptokinase using a standard dosage scheme. British Medical Journal 1: 454–456
2. Spann J F et al 1982 High dose, brief intravenous streptokinase early in acute myocardial infarction. American Heart Journal 104: 939–945
3. Cederholm-Williams S A, DeCock F, Lijnen H R, Collen D 1979 Kinetics of the reactions between streptokinase, plasmin and α-2-antiplasmin. European Journal of Biochemistry 100: 125–132
4. Cederholm-Williams S A, Dornan T L, Turner R C 1981 The metabolism of fibrinogen and plasminogen related to diabetic retinopathy in man. European Journal of Clinical Investigation 11: 133–138
5. Collen D, Wiman B 1979 Turnover of antiplasmin, the fast acting plasmin inhibitor of plasma. Blood 53: 313–324

10. Plasminogen? What are we measuring after I.V. streptokinase (SK) therapy?

L.L. Phillips, M.V. Sherrid, A.J. Peppe, S. Friedman and R. Kunis

In 1983, 20 patients with myocardial infarction were infused I.V. with 1 million units SK in one hour within four hours of onset of pain. Two died of cardiogenic shock (1 in 1 hr., 1 in 1 day, both were S/P CABG). Twelve (60%) had patent infarct arteries at catheterization 1–2 weeks later; 11 had CKMB peaks less than 12 hrs.; 4 had ventricular fibrillation (2 prior to SK). Two were converted by electro-shock and are alive, another re-occluded 3 hrs. after SK, fibrillated, was resuscitated and is alive. One died. Two patients had transient bradycardia. One had mild epistaxis — the only bleeding complication; no transfusions were needed. Five pts. had subsequent CABG and 1 angioplasty while 12 were treated medically with ASA, Persantin, nitrates, etc. All were given 1000 U heparin/hr starting 4–6 hrs after SK.

Prothrombin time (PT), activated partial thromboplastin time (APTT) and thrombin time (TT) were measured before, 1 and 4 hrs. after start of SK. Any of these can show activation of the fibrinolytic system. To indicate optimum time for institution of heparin APTT was most useful since 100% of this group

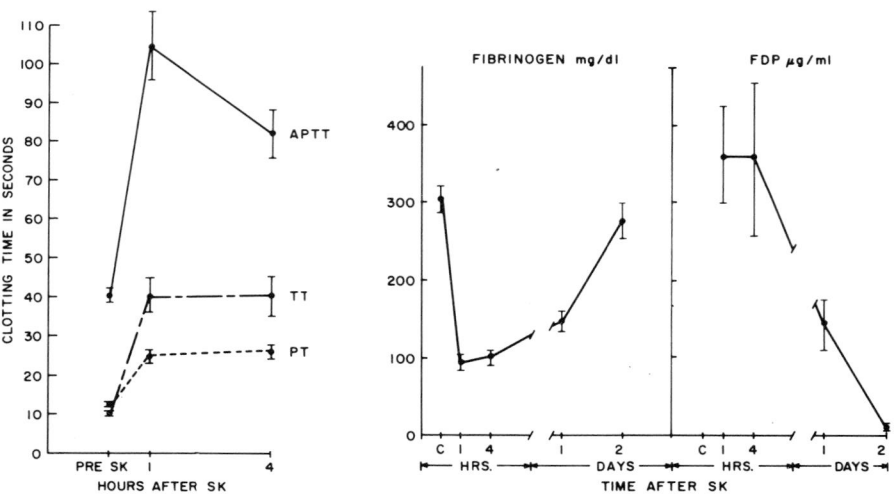

Fig. 10.1   Fig. 10.2

54

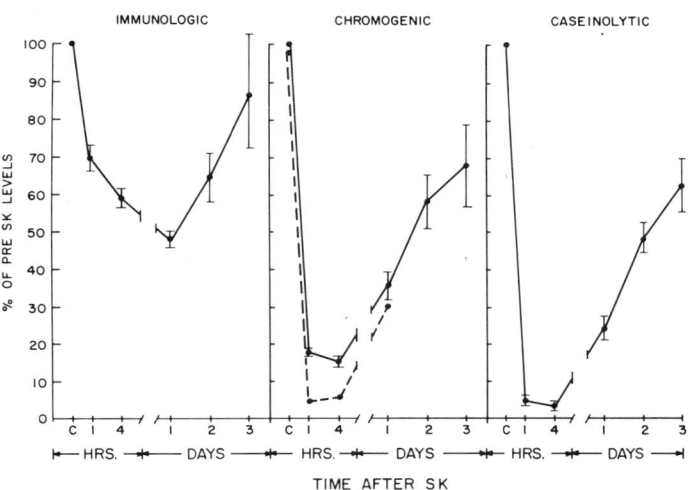

Fig. 10.3

showed shorter times at 4 hrs. than at 1 hr. PT was shorter in 22% and TT in 50%. (Fig. 10.1) A pt. on another protocol had PT, APTT and TT greater than 600 sec and fibrinogen less than 20 mg/dl for 6 hrs. Heparin in this case was witheld until 20 hrs. and there was no bleeding.

Fibrinogen (Ratnoff & Menzie, 1951), FDP, and plasminogen (PLG) levels were determined pre-SK, 1 and 4 hrs. and 1, 2, 3 days. Fibrinogen (FIB) was decreased and FDP elevated for the first 24 hours, but returned to normal by day 2 (Fig. 10.2).

Plasminogen was measured by immunologic (I), chromogenic (CHR) and caseinolytic (CAS methods (Fig. 10.3). For easy comparison results are reported in % pre-SK levels. Much higher results were obtained by I than by the other methods. Plasmin, inactivated plasmin, as well as PLG and PLG-SK complex are probably measured by I.

CHR method (solid line — center) appears to give 10–20% higher levels than CAS. However, if residual PLG-SK levels formed from in vivo infusion of SK are subtracted, the levels at 1 to 24 hrs (dotted line) are nearly the same as found in the CAS method. The in vivo levels are determined by measuring PLG-SK in the plasma without addition of SK to the reaction mixture used in the standard CHR determination.

CAS shows 0–10% pre-SK levels at 1 and 4 hrs. In this assay (Phillips & Skrodelis, 1958) PLG can be determined on whole plasma and on euglobulin precipitate (EP) from which non-specific inhibitors have been removed. The difference between EP and plasma determinations is a measure of inhibitors. The % pre-SK levels for all three parameters were the same at 1 to 24 hrs. Later, inhibitors rise rapidly and higher levels are found in the uninhibited EP than in the whole plasma. (Fig. 10.4).

55

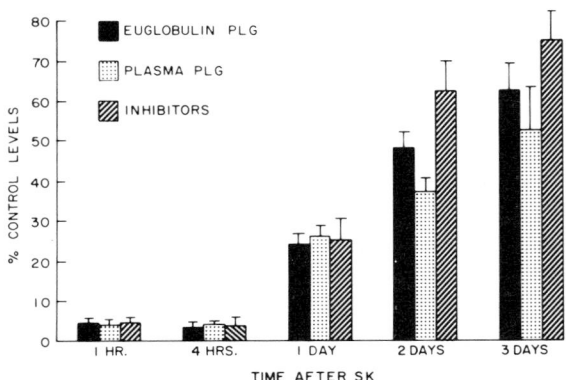

Fig. 10.4

There were no significant differences in any of the coagulation studies between those patients with open or occluded vessels at any time. Results obtained at 1 and 4 hours are shown in table 10.1.

Table 10.1 Mean Levels of Coagulation Studies ± Standard Error

	1 Hour		4 Hours	
	Patent	Occluded	Patent	Occluded
PT — sec.	24.1 ± 2.1	26.8 ± 3.3	24.0 ± 1.9	29.2 ± 3.4
APTT — sec.	96.2 ± 11.4	118.4 ± 15.7	76.0 ± 6.4	92.1 ± 11.5
TT — sec.	35.5 ± 5.2	47.6 ± 6.8	37.0 ± 5.8	48.6 ± 8.9
Fib. — mg/dl	102.9 ± 14.8	91.7 ± 12.3	108.6 ± 15.2	93.5 ± 10.7
FDP — ug/ml	326 ± 89	440 ± 120	360 ± 160	360 ± 123
Plasminogen % pre-				
SK Immunologic	66.1 ± 4.8	72.5 ± 4.4	57.6 ± 3.8	60.8 ± 3.7
Chromogenic	17.3 ± 1.9	17.5 ± 1.3	14.9 ± 2.2	14.7 ± 2.4
Caseinolytic	4.8 ± 1.2	5.5 ± 1.3	4.8 ± 1.2	2.0 ± 1.1

CONCLUSIONS

Immunologic methods for PLG give higher levels than either CHR or CAS and measures something other than activatable PLG. Chromogenic and caseinolytic methods give similar results provided the residual PLG-SK complex formed in vivo during SK therapy is subtracted from the standard CHR test. Inhibitors to the fibrinolytic system return toward normal before plasminogen does. Some form of monitoring, preferably APTT is advisable to indicate that activation of PLG has occurred, and later to indicate the best time to institute heparin.

REFERENCES

Phillips L L, Skrodelis V 1958 The fibrinolytic enzyme system in normal hemorrhagic, and disease states. Journal Clinical Investigation 37: 965–973
Ratnoff O D, Menzie C 1951 A new method for determination of fibrinogen in small samples of plasma. Journal Clinical & Laboratory Medicine 37: 316–320

11. Clinical results on acylated activator complexes

G. S. Harris

Acute coronary artery occlusion by fibrin based thrombi results in the rapid evolution of myocardial infarction. Fibrinolytics are therefore being evaluated as a means of coronary artery reperfusion.

Because myocardial salvage depends on early treatment and rapid reperfusion, there is a need for a therapeutic agent which can be given by a push injection and quickly lyses thrombi. Prolonged fibrinolytic activity to reduce the incidence of early coronary artery reocclusion is also required.

A streptokinase activator acylated with anisic acid BRL 26921 is currently being evaluated in acute coronary artery occlusion. This deacylates in vivo with a $T_{\frac{1}{2}}$ of 44 mins. The in vivo clearance of fibrinolytic activity occurs with mean $T_{\frac{1}{2}}$ of 60 mins. compared to 10 mins. with streptokinase. The pharmacokinetic profile of BRL 26921 is therefore consistent with the therapeutic aim of a push intravenous injection, rapid clot lysis and prolonged prophylactic activity against rethrombosis.

To establish the in vivo activity of BRL 26921, the compound was administered in multicentre dose ranging studies. Doses of 5–20mg have been administered by intracoronary artery catheter and the time of reperfusion recorded.

The results of intracoronary administered BRL 26921 are shown in Table 11.1.

Intracoronary dosing requires resources most centres cannot accommodate. The delay inherent in intracoronary administration and the risks also reduce the possible benefit of coronary artery reperfusion.

Intravenous dosing of BRL 26921 was undertaken as soon as possible and dose ranging studies have used 5–30 mg given over 1–2 minutes. To this time, 122 cases have been treated and reperfusion has been confirmed following intravenous

Table 11.1 Initially the lytic activity of BRL 26921 was assessed in AMI patients by administration via the intracoronary route

Dose BRL 26921 (mg)	Number of Cases treated	% Cases with Reperfusion
5	10	50
10	23	74
15	24	75
20	17	71

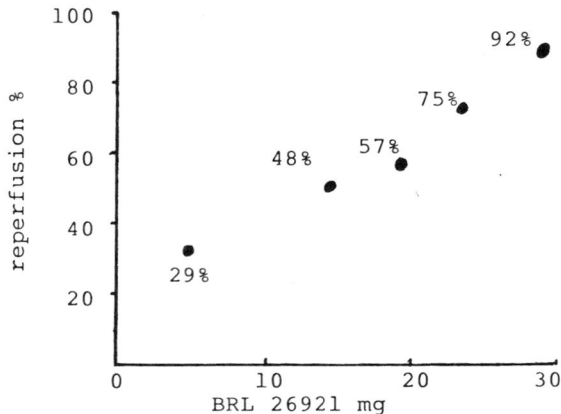

Fig. 11.1 Intravenous BRL 26921 dose response relationship

dosing by a coronary angiogram in more than half the cases. The frequency of reperfusion after intravenous administration of BRL 26921 is given in Figure 11.1.

The time of reperfusion has been estimated following intravenous dosing with 30mg of BRL 26921 to be 15–60 minutes after dosing.

An intravenous dose of 30mg of BRL 26921 has been chosen for further clinical evaluation. At this dose systemic changes such as a reduction in fibrinogen, plasminogen and α_2 antiplasmin occur but there appears to be a marked intersubject variation in the extent of the systemic responses.

The time of reperfusion has been estimated following intravenous dosing with 30mg of BRL 26921 to be 15–20 minutes after dosing.

An intravenous dose of 30mg of BRL 26921 has been chosen for further clinical evaluation. At this dose systemic changes such as a reduction in fibrinogen, plasminogen and α_2 antiplasmin occur but there appears to be a marked intersubject variation in the extent of the systemic responses.

Reported Events n = 523 at 30mg

Venepuncture site bleeding n = 1
Haematemesis   n = 1
Hypotension   n = 1
Fever   n = 1
Nausea   n = 1

At this time, studies are being undertaken to confirm patient benefit following a 30mg dose of BRL 26921 administered within three hours of the onset of ischaemic pain.

12. Fibrin-specific lysis of pulmonary emboli by pro-urokinase (pro-UK) in rabbits and dogs

V. Gurewich, R. Pannell, S. Louie and P. Kelley

A single-chain form of urokinase (UK) was originally identified in our laboratory by performing affinity chromatography on fibrin/celite (Husain et al 1981) to freshly voided human urine (Husain et al 1981). The single-chain UK bound to the fibrin/celite and was eluted with arginine (0.1M), whereas two-chain UK or LMW-UK did not bind under the conditions used (Husain et al 1983). Purification of the single-chain UK was achieved by gel filtration but only limited characterization was possible because urine proved to be an inadequate source of the activator.

A far more plentiful source of single-chain UK was found in a transformed human kidney cell line developed by Collaborative Research Inc. (CRI) of Lexington, MA. The single-chain UK which was purified from the spent culture medium appeared to be identical to that obtained from urine. Characterization of its properties revealed that it was a pro-enzyme (pro-UK) (Gurewich et al in press). Clot-lysis experiments in plasma indicated that pro-UK was fibrin-specific in its proteolytic effect and induced lysis at less than one fifth the concentration of UK. On the basis of these findings, in vivo studies were undertaken.

MATERIALS AND METHODS

Pro-urokinase was obtained from CRI. Two-chain, HMW-UK was obtained from Breon Laboratories (New York, NY) and from Serono Laboratories (Randolph, MA). Since pro-UK is a zymogen, the units of activity referred to in this study represent those obtained after full activation by plasmin. Low molecular weight UK was obtained from Abbott Laboratories (Chicago, IL). Standardized, 1 ml plasma (human) clots into which ^{125}I-fibrinogen was incorporated were made up the night before and used for in vitro studies or embolized into a peripheral vein in rabbits or dogs. Clot lysis was quantitated by measuring the radioactive fibrin degradation products released from the clot.

In vitro studies were performed in anesthetized animals. After embolization (1 clot in rabbits and 6 in dogs), the animals were infused with saline, UK or pro-UK. The rabbits weighed about 2 kg and the dogs 10–12 kg.

RESULTS AND DISCUSSION

A broad range of sensitivities to pro-UK and UK was found among in the animal plasmas tested reflecting the species specificity of UK. In each case, the sensitivity to pro-UK was 5–10 times greater than for UK (Table 12.1).

Table 12.1 Species Sensitivity Index

SPECIES	PRO-UK	UK
Man	3.1	0.33
Monkey	2.6	0.33
Dog	2.6	0.33
Rabbit	0.11	<0.05
Cat	<0.06	<0.02
Pig	<0.06	<0.02

In rabbit plasma, clot lysis without fibrinogenolysis was obtained with pro-UK at concentrations of 200, 100 and 50 IU/ml but only after 43, 50 and 64 hours respectively. The clots incubated in rabbit plasma were resistant to UK even at a concentration of 500 IU/ml. This experiment also demonstrates the stability of pro-UK in plasma by showing the persistence of fibrinolytic activity over many hours. By contrast, UK is rapidly inactivated and loses its fibrinolytic capacity quickly (Fig. 12.1).

This resistance of rabbits to pro-UK and UK was borne out by the in vivo findings. At 100,000 IU/hour, little lysis was achieved with either pro-UK or UK.

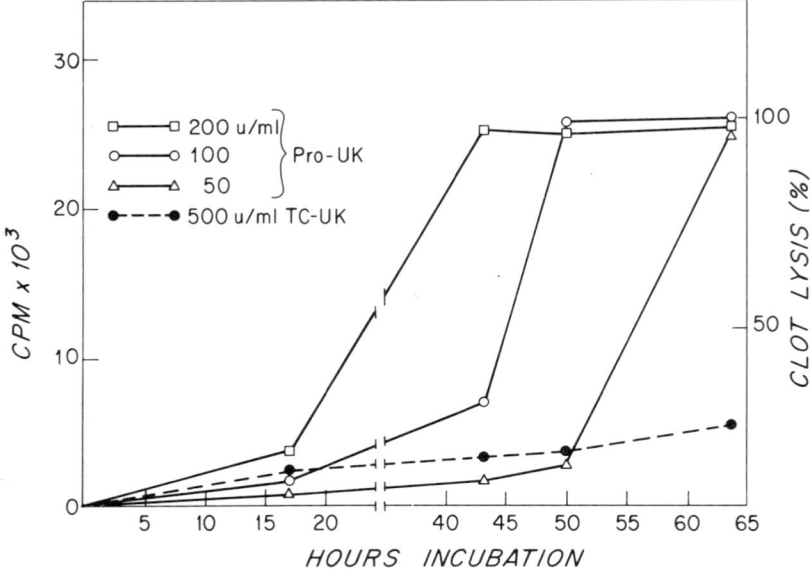

Fig. 12.1 ^{125}I-clot lysis in rabbit plasma after the addition of pro-UK (50, 100, 200 IU/ml) or UK two-chain (UK, 500 IU/ml.

When this infusion rate was doubled, clot lysis was achieved with pro-UK but little lysis occurred in the UK infused animals (p<0.001). Another difference found was that unlike UK, a loading dose was found not to be necessary for pro-UK (Fig. 12.2). The fibrinogen concentration at the end of the infusion, expressed as % baseline value was 70.4% (25–100) in the UK animals and 86.6% (72–96) in the pro-UK animals (not significant). Therefore although a highly significant difference in efficacy between pro-UK and UK was found, superior specificity was not established in this species in vivo.

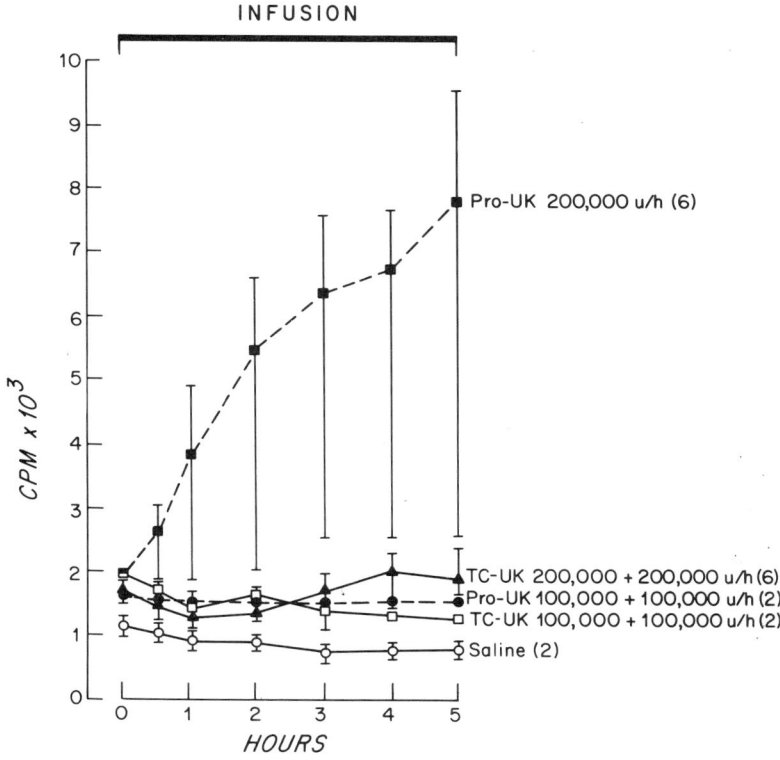

Fig. 12.2 ^{125}I-clot lysis in rabbits infused with saline, UK (two-chain UK) or pro-UK.

In dogs, complete lysis of the embolized clots occurred with pro-UK but not UK at an infusion rate of 75,000 IU/hour. When the UK infusion rate was increased to 100,000 IU/hour, equivalent clot lysis was also achieved (Fig. 12.3).

However, whereas in the pro-UK treated dogs, no degradation of fibrinogen was found, the animals infused with UK (100,000 IU/h) developed complete afibrinogenemia after 2 hours of infusion. Moreover, these dogs bled profusely and uncontrollably. The pro-UK dogs were found to have only mild, intermittent oozing from cut surfaces. Bolus infusions of up to a million units of pro-UK did not induce fibrinogen degradation.

In conclusion, pro-UK is a more effective thrombolytic agent than UK in rabbits and dogs and induces a proteolytic effect which appears to be fibrin-

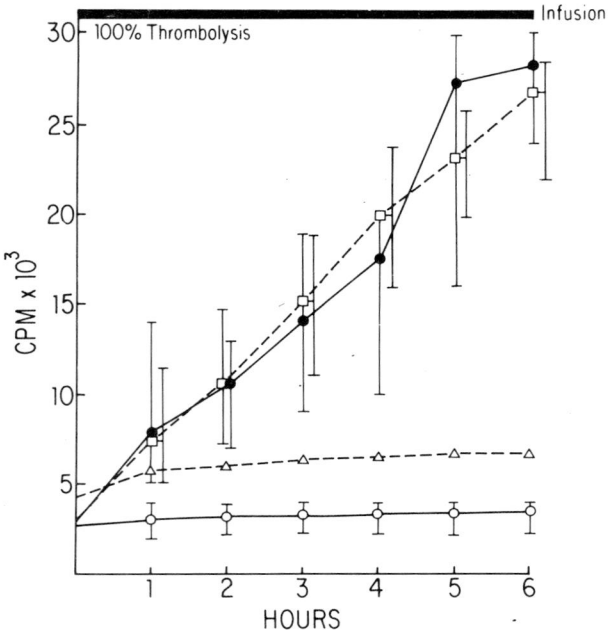

Fig. 12.3 ^{125}I-clot lysis in dogs infused with saline (O——O), UK [LMW-UK, 75,000 IU/h (Δ----Δ) or 100,000 IU/h (☐----☐)] or pro-UK 75,000 IU/h (●----●).

specific. These findings in animals are comparable to those observed when clot lysis was studied in human plasma in test tubes. Since UK is quite species specific, the prospects for obtaining equivalent or better results in man appear favourable.

REFERENCES

Husain S S, Lipinski B, Gurewich V 1981 Rapid purification of a high-affinity plasminogen activator from human blood plasma by specific adsorption on fibrin/celite. Proceedings of the National Academy of Sciences, USA 78: 4265–4269

Husain S S, Gurewich V, Lipinski B 1981 Purification of a new high molecular weight form of urokinase from urine. Thrombosis & Haemostasis 46: 11 (abstract 16)

Husain S S, Gurewich V, Lipinski B 1983 Purification and partial characterization of a single-chain, high molecular weight form of urokinase from human urine. Archives Biochemistry and Biophysics 220: 31–38

Gurewich V, Pannell R, Louie S, Kelley P, Suddith R L, Greenlee R 1984 Effective and fibrin-specific clot lysis by a zymogen precursor form of urokinase (pro-urokinase). Journal of Clinical Investigation: in press

13. Intra-arterial infusion of urokinase (UK)-lys-plasminogen (Plg) in arterial ischemia of lower limbs

J-N. Fiessinger, M. Roncato, J.C. Gaux,
J.F. Vitoux, M. Aiach and M-D. Vandenbroek

In arterial occlusions of lower limbs, the efficacy of urokinase administered intra-arterially in small doses is limited by the variability of blood plasmin levels (Fiessinger et al 1981). The administration in situ of Lys-plasminogen may allow the efficacy of urokinase to be increased.

PATIENTS AND METHODS

Seventeen patients — 10 males and 7 females — with a mean age of 69.5 years (range 52 to 84) were treated. All had atherosclerotic arterial disease and had presented with symptoms of an aggravation of ischemia for less than 30 days (mean 8.5 days). Three patients were treated for severe intermittent claudication, 8 of the patients had rest pain, the six remaining patients had critical ischemia.

The decision to administer thrombolytic treatment was based after angiography, on the severity of ischemia, the absence of surgical indication and the accessibility of the thrombus by catheterisation. The catheter was passed into contact with the thrombus by a homolateral route in 8 patients, controlaterally in 4 patients and by axillary route in 3 patients. Diagnostic angiographies were repeated using this catheter so that it might be moved in response to thrombolytic developments. Urokinase was administered by intra-arterial infusion using an electric pump at the rate of 1,000 units/kg/hour. This infusion was interrupted every half-hour for a bolus of one vial of lys-plasminogen. All patients received intravenous heparin concurrently in effective doses. Laboratory tests were carried out before the initiation of therapy and at 4-hour intervals thereafter. The tests included assays of fibrinogen, alpha 2 antiplasmin, plasminogen, fibrin degradation products (FDP) and heparin monitoring tests.

RESULTS AND DISCUSSION

The mean duration of the treatment was 9 hours. Treatment was suspended by the fouth hour in 4 patients, in 3 cases because of the mobilization of the catheter and in one case because of the efficacy of the treatment.

Twelve patients had acute arterial occlusions complicating occlusive arterial disease. The occlusion was located in the iliac region in 3 cases and in the femoropopliteal region in the other 9 cases. Thrombolysis was a success in 8 of these 12 patients (Table 13.1). In one patient the persistence of a superficial femoral stenosis was complicated by a recurrence or thrombosis on the fourth day. In another a femoral angioplasty was carried out immediately after the thrombolytic treatment. The 6 remaining patients remain patent after a mean follow-up period of one month. Five patients were treated for the occlusion of a

Table 13.1 Results of the intra-arterial of urokinase-lys-plasminogen

	N	Thrombolysis	Failure
Acute arterial occlusions	12	8	4
PTFE	5	3	2
	17	11 (64.5%)	6

polytetrafluoroethylene (PTFE) graft. Complete thrombolysis was achieved in 2 of the 3 patients with an aortofemoral graft, the third case was a failure in which the catheter was mobilized and treatment stopped early. A partial clearing of the occluded iliofemoral shunt by the thrombolytic treatment was completed by a thrombectomy. The femorotibial shunt was cleared but became occluded shortly after the treatment was stopped probably because of poor run-off. Finally thrombolysis was achieved (Table 13.1) in 11 of the 17 patients (64.5%). Of the 6 patients in whom thrombi were not lyzed, one had an amputation, 4 had by-pass surgery for limb salvage and 1 was treated medically. Although it is difficult to compare these results with those of other studies, it appeared that this treatment was more effective than intra-arterial urokinase in small doses (Fiessinger et al 1981). Its efficacy was comparable to that of intra-arterial streptokinase (Hargrove et al, Becker et al). The clinical efficacy of thrombolysis is supported in this study by the limited number of amputations; despite the initial severity of ischemia only one patient required amputation. Two patients died during treatment from complications of ischemic disease. These deaths were unrelated to the treatment and reflected the grave condition of the patients before the thrombolytic therapy. None of the 17 patients had systemic hemorrhagic or embolic complications. Two patients had distal emboli during thrombolytic treatment in a prothesis. In both cases the ischemia subsided after continued treatment. Another patient had a large hematoma in Scarpa's triangle after a successful femoral angioplasty.

The general complications of medical thrombolysis are related to increased plasmin concentrations, which are reflected in a decrease in fibrinogen levels. Intra-arterial streptokinase in doses of 5,000 units/hour rapidly induces systemic fibrinolysis which justifies laboratory monitoring of hemostasis (Becker et al 1983, Hargrove et al 1980, Fiessinger et al 1984). With the combination of Lys-plasminogen and urokinase, the circulating fibrinogenolysis remained moderate. After 8 hours of treatment the mean concentration of fibrinogen, plasminogen, alpha 2 antiplasmin were respectively 3.5 g/l, 77% and 39%. No patient had at any moment a fibrinogen concentration lower than 2 g/l. It therefore appears reasonable to attribute the low incidence of systemic complications with lys-plasminogen and urokinase to a limited proteolysis during the treatment.

REFERENCES

Becker G J, Rabe F E, Richmond B D, Holden R W, Yune H Y, Dilley R S, Bang N U, Glover J L, Klatte E C 1983 Low-dose fibrinolytic therapy. Radiology 148: 663–670
Fiessinger J-N, Aiach M, Capron L, Devanlay M, Vayssairat M, Juillet Y 1981 Effect of local urokinase on arterial occlusion of lower limbs. Thrombosis Haemostasis (Stuttgart) 45: 230–232
Fiessinger J-N, Aiach M, Roncato M, Debure C, Gaux J-C 1984 Critical ischemia during heparin-induced thrombocytopenia. Treatment by intra-arterial streptokinase. Thrombosis Research 33: 235–238
Hargrove W C, Barker C F, Berkowitz H D, Perloff L J, McLean G, Freiman D, Ring E J, Roberts B 1982 Treatment of acute peripheral arterial and graft thromboses with low-dose streptokinase. Surgery 92: 981–993

14. Thrombolysis with human tissue-type plasminogen activator

D. Collen and H. R. Lijnen

INTRODUCTION

During the last years significant progress has been made in our understanding of the molecular mechanisms involved in the regulation of the fibrinolytic enzyme system in vivo (Collen 1980). The present communication will mainly deal with our present knowledge on tissue-type plasminogen activator (t-PA) and its importance for physiological and therapeutic thrombolysis.

PHYSICOCHEMICAL PROPERTIES OF TISSUE-TYPE PLASMINOGEN ACTIVATOR

The first satisfactory purification of t-PA from human tissues has been obtained from human uterus (Rijken et al 1979). Tissue-type plasminogen activator, vascular plasminogen activator and blood plasminogen activator are immunologically identical, but different from urokinase (Rijken et al 1980). The mean level of t-PA antigen in human plasma at rest is 6.6 ± 2.9 ng/ml, of which only about one third represents active t-PA (Rijken et al 1983). t-PA has been purified from the culture fluid of a human melanoma cell line in sufficient amounts to study its biochemical and biological properties (Rijken & Collen 1981). Recently, the gene of human t-PA was cloned and expressed (Pennica et al 1983). Human t-PA, obtained by expression of recombinant DNA in eukaryotic cells, was shown to be indistinguishable from the natural activator isolated from human melanoma cell cultures, with respect to biochemical properties, turnover in vivo and specific thrombolytic effect (Collen et al 1984).

MECHANISM OF ACTION OF TISSUE-TYPE PLASMINOGEN ACTIVATOR

t-PA is a poor enzyme in the absence of fibrin, but the presence of fibrin strikingly enhances the activation rate of plasminogen. This has been explained by an increased affinity of fibrin-bound t-PA for plasminogen (Michaelis constant 65 μM in the absence and 0.16 μM in the presence of fibrin) without significantly influencing the catalytic efficiency of the enzyme (Hoylaerts et al 1982). The kinetic data of Hoylaerts et al (1982) support a mechanism in which t-PA and plasminogen adsorb to a fibrin clot in a sequential and ordered way yielding a ternary complex. Fibrin essentially increases the local plasminogen concentration by creating an additional interaction between t-PA and its substrate. The high affinity of t-PA for plasminogen in the presence of fibrin thus allows efficient activation on the fibrin clot, while no efficient plasminogen activation by t-PA occurs in plasma.

Plasmin formed on the fibrin surface has both its lysine-binding sites and active site occupied and is thus only slowly inactivated by α_2-antiplasmin (half-life of about 10–100 s compared to 100 ms for free plasmin) while free plasmin, if formed, is rapidly inhibited by α_2-antiplasmin (Collen 1980).

The fibrinolytic process thus seems to be triggered by and confined to fibrin.

STUDIES ON THE THROMBOLYTIC PROPERTIES OF t-PA

Efficient thrombolysis in vivo seems to be regulated via adsorption of t-PA and plasminogen on the fibrin surface and in loco generation of plasmin, out of reach of the fast-acting α_2-antiplasmin in the blood.

The most promising approach to obtain specific thrombolysis therefore seems to be the use of fibrin-specific agents. Indeed, streptokinase and urokinase which have no specific affinity for fibrin, activate circulating and fibrin-bound plasminogen relatively indiscriminately. Plasmin formed in the circulation is immediately neutralized by α_2-antiplasmin, and once the inhibitor is exhausted several plasma proteins are degraded by plasmin (fibrinogen, factor V, factor VIII, etc), causing a bleeding tendency. Therefore, fibrin-specific plasminogen activators such as t-PA and possibly pro-urokinase might constitute better thrombolytic agents.

Studies in animals

The thrombolytic effect of t-PA and urokinase was compared in rabbits with an experimental pulmonary embolus (Matsuo et al 1981). t-PA caused thrombolysis at lower doses than urokinase (on a molar basis); thrombolysis with t-PA was achieved without extensive plasminogen activation in the circulating blood and without hemostatic breakdown.

In dogs with an experimental thrombosis of the femoral vein, urokinase infusion at a rate of 2,500 IU per kg per hour for 4 hours did not induce significant lysis (Korninger et al 1982). With 25,000 IU of urokinase per kg per hour for 4 hours about 30 percent lysis was obtained, but this was associated with defibrinogenation. Infusion of 2,500 urokinase equivalent units of t-PA per kg per hour for 4 hours causing 20 to 45 percent lysis without causes any fibrinogen breakdown.

In a preliminary report, Sampol et al (1983) reported successful recanalization with porcine t-PA in dogs with femoral vein thrombosis. Carlin et al (1983) induced lysis of intravascular fibrin deposits in the lungs of rats following infusion of human t-PA.

In rabbits with experimental jugular vein thrombosis the extent of thrombolysis by t-PA is mainly determined by the dose of t-PA and its delivery in the vicinity of the thrombus and much less by the age of the thrombus or the molecular form of the activator (Collen et al 1983).

In dogs with 1–2 hours old left anterior descending coronary artery thrombus induced with a copper coil, thrombolysis was induced by intravenous infusion of human t-PA obtained from melanoma cell cultures (Bergmann et al 1983) or by recombinant DNA technology (Van de Werf et al 1984a). In addition to inducing clot lysis, infusion of t-PA also restored intermediary metabolism and nutritional blood flow, without causing systemic fibrinolytic activation.

Gold et al (1983) found a linear correlation between the rate of infusion of recombinant t-PA and the time to reperfusion in dogs with a 2 hours old coronary thrombus. Timely reperfusion was associated with substantial salvage of myocardial tissue and this was obtained in the absence of systemic fibrinogen breakdown.

Flameng et al (1984) produced a coronary thrombus in baboons, obtained reperfusion by intravenous administration of recombinant t-PA and found a linear correlation between the coronary occlusion time and the infarct size.

Buchanan et al (1984) used a quantitative bleeding model in rabbits to demonstrate that t-PA, in contrast to streptokinase, did not provoke hemorrhage at thrombolytic doses.

Studies in patients
The first patients were treated with t-PA in 1981. Intravenous administration of human t-PA (7.5 mg over 24 hours) induced complete lysis of a 6 weeks old renal and iliofemoral thrombosis in a renal allograft recipient (Weimar et al 1981). Thrombolysis was achieved without systemic fibrinolytic activation or hemostatic breakdown, and was not associated with bleeding. The second case was a 73-year-old man with the nephrotic syndrome, who developed an ascending thrombosis of the iliofemoral vein after removal of an infarcted femoral-popliteal graft and mid-thigh amputation of the right leg. Venography showed thrombotic masses in the vena cava, and selective venography revealed a thrombus of the right renal vein. t-PA, 5 mg, given intravenously over 24 hours, resulted in resolution of the thrombosis in the iliac vein, vena cava, and renal vein. No side effects were noted, and again this thrombolytic therapy was not associated with consumption of fibrinogen, plasminogen, α_2-antiplasmin or factor V (Weimar et al 1981).

In four patients with deep vein thrombosis over extended segments of the iliac and femoral veins, intravenous infusion of 5 to 15 mg of t-PA over 24 to 36 hours did however not result in thrombolysis (unpublished).

Coronary thrombolysis was induced within 19 to 50 minutes with intravenous or intracoronary infusion of t-PA in 6 of 7 patients with evolving myocardial infarction and confirmed angiographically in each case. Circulating fibrinogen, plasminogen and α_2-antiplasmin were not depleted. In the one patient in whom lysis was not inducible with t-PA, it was not inducible with streptokinase either (Van de Werf et al 1984b).

From all these studies it thus appears that specific thrombolysis without systemic activation of the fibrinolytic system can be achieved with t-PA. Limited experience in treatment of patients with myocardial infarction suggests that the potentially widely available recombinant t-PA offers a promising practical approach for coronary thrombolysis.

REFERENCES

Bergmann S R, Fox K A A, Ter-Pogossian M M, Sobel B E, Collen D 1983 Clot-selective coronary thrombolysis with tissue-type plasminogen activator. Science 220: 1181–1183
Buchanan M R, Boneu B, Agnelli G, Fernandez F, Hirsh J, Collen D 1984 Hemorrhage-free thrombolysis by tissue plasminogen activator in rabbits: A comparison with streptokinase. Blood (in press)
Carlin G, Einarsson M, Saldeen T 1983 Tissue plasminogen activator effectively lyses intravascular fibrin deposits in the rat lung. In: Davidson J F, Bachmann F, Bouvier C A, Kruithof E K O (eds) Progress in Fibrinolysis, vol 6. Churchill Livingstone, Edinburgh 471–474
Collen D 1980 On the regulation and control of fibrinolysis. Thrombosis and Haemostasis 43: 77–89
Collen D, Stassen J M, Verstraete M 1983 Thrombolysis with human extrinsic (tissue-type) plasminogen activator in rabbits with experimental jugular vein thrombosis. Effect of molecular form and dose of activator, age of the thrombus, and route of administration. Journal of Clinical Investigation 71: 368–376
Collen D, Stassen J M, Marafino B J, Builder S, De Cock F, Ogez J, Tajiri D, Pennica D, Bennett W F, Salwa J, Hoyng C F 1984 Biological properties of human tissue-type plasminogen activator obtained by expression of recombinant DNA in mammalian cells. Journal of Pharmacology and Experimental Therapeutics (in press)
Flameng W, Van de Werf F, Vanhaecke J, Verstraete M, Collen D 1984 Coronary thrombolysis and infarct size reduction following intravenous infusion of recombinant tissue-type plasminogen activator in non-human primates. Journal of Clinical Investigation (in press)
Gold H K, Fallon J T, Yasuda T, Khaw B A, Guerrero J L, Vislosky J M, Leinbach R C, Harper R, Hoyng C, Grossbard E, Collen D 1983 Coronary thrombolysis with recombinant human tissue plasminogen activator. Circulation 68: suppl III, 150 (abstract)
Hoylaerts M, Rijken D C, Lijnen H R, Collen D 1982 Kinetics of the activation of plasminogen by human tissue plasminogen activator. Role of fibrin. Journal of Biological Chemistry 257: 2912–2919
Korninger C, Matsuo O, Suy R, Stassen J M, Collen D 1982 Thrombolysis with human extrinsic (tissue-type) plasminogen activator in dogs with femoral vein thrombosis. Journal of Clinical Investigation 69: 573–580
Matsuo O, Rijken D C, Collen D 1981 Thrombolysis by human tissue plasminogen activator and urokinase in rabbits with experimental pulmonary embolus. Nature 291: 590–591
Pennica D, Holmes W E, Kohr W J, Harkins R N, Vehar G A, Ward C A, Bennett W F, Yelverton E, Seeburg P H, Heyneker H L, Goeddel D V, Collen D 1983 Cloning and expression of human tissue-type plasminogen activator cDNA in E. Coli. Nature 301: 214–221
Rijken D C, Collen D 1981 Purification and characterization of the plasminogen activator secreted by human melanoma cells in culture. Journal of Biological Chemistry 256: 7035–7041
Rijken D C, Wijngaards G, Welbergen J 1980 Relationship between tissue plasminogen activator and the activators in blood and vascular wall. Thrombosis Research 18: 815–830
Rijken D C, Juhan-Vague I, De Cock F, Collen D 1983 Measurement of human tissue-type plasminogen activator by a two-site immunoradiometric assay. Journal of Laboratory and Clinical Medicine 101: 274–284
Rijken D C, Wijngaards G, Zaal-de Jong M, Welbergen J 1979 Purification and partial characterization of plasminogen activator from human uterine tissse. Biochimica et Biophysica Acta 580: 140–153
Sampol J, Mercier C, Houel F, David G, Daver J 1983 Studies of the thrombolytic action of a tissue plasminogen activator in dogs. In: Davidson J F, Bachmann F, Bouvier C A, Kruithof

E K O (eds) Progress in Fibrinolysis, vol 6. Churchill Livingstone, Edinburgh 463–466

Van de Werf F, Bergmann S R, Fox K A A, De Geest H, Hoyng C F, Sobel B E, Collen D 1984a Coronary thrombolysis with intravenously administered human tissue-type plasminogen activator produced by recombinant DNA technology. Circulation 69: 605–610

Van de Werf F, Ludbrook P A, Bergmann S R, Tiefenbrunn A J, Fox K A A, De Geest H, Verstraete M, Collen D, Sobel B E 1984b Clot selective coronary thrombolysis with tissue-type plasminogen activator in patients with evolving myocardial infarction. New England Journal of Medicine 310: 609–613

Weimar W, Stibbe J, Van Seyen A J, Billiau A, De Somer P, Collen D 1981 Specific lysis of an iliofemoral thrombus by administration of extrinsic (tissue-type) plasminogen activator. Lancet ii: 1018–1020

Section 4
PHARMACOLOGICAL STIMULATION OF ENDOGENOUS FIBRINOLYSIS

15. The effects of the synthetic steroid Org OD14 on fibrinolysis in menopausal women

I. D. Walker, J.F. Davidson, A. Richards, R. Yates and H.P. McEwan

INTRODUCTION

In menopausal women the synthetic steroid Org OD14 prevents bone loss and suppresses climacteric symptoms without stimulating endometrial growth (Lindsay et al 1980; Kicovic et al 1982). Because of its pharmacologic and clinical properties we felt it important to seek information about its effect on various biochemical and haematological parameters.

MATERIALS AND METHODS

Twenty-seven women aged 38–67 years who had undergone either a natural or a surgical menopause were studied. Apart from climacteric symptoms, all were clinically well.

In a double blind group comparative study, the patients were allocated in a predetermined randomised order to treatment either with tablets containing Org OD14 2.5 mg daily or with an identical-looking placebo. Thirteen took Org OD14 and 14 took placebo. The study consisted of a 7-day pre-treatment period followed by 12 weeks on treatment and a 2-week post-treatment period. Fasting blood samples were collected one week pre-treatment (week -1), just prior to starting treatment (week 0), after 6 weeks and 12 weeks on-treatment (weeks 6 and 12) and 2 weeks after stopping treatment (week $+2$).

The following parameters were measured — full blood count and platelet count using a Coulter S Plus counter; total triglycerides, total cholesterol and very low density lipoprotein (VLDL), low density lipoprotein (LDL) and high density lipoprotein (HDL) cholesterols according to the manual of laboratory operations of the Lipid Research Clinical Programme of the National Institute of Health (NIH 75/268); plasma fibrinogen using the method described by Clauss (1957); α_2 antiplasmin (α_2 PI) and plasminogen using end point amidolytic assays using the synthetic substrate S2251 (Kabi AB) (Friberger 1982), antithrombin III (ATIII) using an end point amidolytic assay using S2238 (Kabi AB) (Abilgaard et al 1977) and plasma fibrinolytic activity by incubating drops of resuspended euglobulin precipitate (pH 5.9, dilution 1/10) on plasminogen rich bovine fibrin plates (Kluft et al 1976).

Statistical analysis was done by means of an analysis of co-variance, taking the pre-treatment value (week 0) as co-variable, and the value during treatment or the post-treatment value as response variable value.

RESULTS

Full blood and platelet counts
The mean values for full blood and platelet counts at each assessment point are shown in Table 15.1.

Table 15.1

Weeks	− 1	0	6	12	+ 2
Hb g/dl					
OD 14	13.4	13.0	13.6*	13.9**	13.8**
Placebo	13.4	13.2	13.2	13.3	13.5
Hct %					
OD14	41	40	42**	43**	42**
Placebo	41	40	40	40	40
WBCx10⁹/1					
OD14	5.4	5.1	5.9*	5.1	4.6
Placebo	5.0	4.9	4.8	4.8	5.4
Platesx10⁹/1					
OD14	270	266	319**	305**	266
Placebo	264	273	253	241	241

Mean values for haemoglobin (Hb), haematocrit (Hct), white cell count (WBC) and platelet count (plates) before, during and after treatment. Mean values in the OD14 group significantly different from corresponding mean values in the placebo group are highlighted — $2P < 0.05$*, $2P < 0.005$**.

Haemostasis and Fibrinolysis
The mean values for haemostasis and fibrinolysis parameters at each assessment point are shown in Table 15.2. Org OD14 induced a clear decrease in mean

Table 15.2

Weeks	− 1	0	6	12	+ 2
Fl g/l					
OD 14	2.7	2.7	2.3**	2.4**	2.6
Placebo	3.0	2.9	3.0	3.0	3.0
Plg %					
OD14	96	96	124**	125**	104
Placebo	102	101	99	105	109
a_2PI%					
OD14	103	102	101	107	106
Placebo	102	101	99	105	109
ATIII %					
OD14	102	101	109**	114**	106
Placebo	101	101	96	98	103
FP lysis mm					
OD14	12	12	14**	14**	13
Placebo	12	12	12	12	14

Mean values for fibrinogen (Fl), plasminogen (Plg), α_2 antiplasmin (α_5PI), antithrombin III (ATIII) and fibrinolytic activity (FP) before, during and after treatment. Mean values in the OD14 group significantly differ from corresponding mean values in the placebo group are highlighted — $2P < 0.05$*, $2P < 0.005$**.

fibrinogen levels and a clear increase in mean antithrombin III levels. Mean plasminogen levels and mean fibrinolytic activity on fibrin plates increased on Org OD14 at 6 and 12 weeks on treatment.

Biochemistry

The mean values for the lipid parameters at each assessment point are shown in Table 15.3. Org OD14 induced no significant changes in the mean values for total triglyceride, total cholesterol or VLDL cholesterol but the mean HDL cholesterol levels were statistically significantly lower in the Org OD14 group than in the placebo group at 6 and 12 weeks on treatment.

Table 15.3

Weeks	− 1	0	6	12	+ 2
Trig mmol/l					
OD 14	1.6	1.1	0.8	0.8	1.3
Placebo	1.3	1.2	1.0	1.0	1.1
VLDL mmol/l					
OD14	0.5	0.5	0.3	0.5	0.4
Placebo	0.6	0.6	0.4	0.4	0.6
LDL mmol/l					
OD14	3.8	3.6	4.5	4.8	4.2
Placebo	3.8	4.1	3.8	4.3	3.7
HDL mmol/l					
OD14	1.8	1.7	1.3**	1.2*	1.6
Placebo	1.6	1.6	1.7	1.6	1.7

Mean values for triglyceride (trig), very low density lipoprotein (VLDL), low density lipoprotein (LDL) and high density lipoprotein (HDL) cholesterols before, during and after treatment. Mean values in the OD14 group significantly different from corresponding mean values in the placebo group are highlighted — $2P < 0.05$*, $2P < 0.005$**.

DISCUSSION

Org OD14, a synthetic steroid with an unusual endocrine profile has been shown to be effective in relieving climacteric symptoms (Lindsay et al 1980, Kicovic et al 1982) and preventing bone loss in post-menopausal women without inducing appreciable endometrial hyperplasia. In view of the structure and pharmacological properties of Org OD14 it was decided to investigate its effect on various haematological and biochemical parameters. The observed increases in haemoglobin, haematocrit and platelet count in the Org OD14 group are considered to be related to the androgenic properties of the compound. In only one patient did the haematocrit exceed 50% on treatment. During Org OD14 treatment changes were observed in haemostatic and fibrinolytic parameters similar to those recorded in individuals taking anabolic steroids (Preston et al 1981). The lowering of fibrinogen levels along with the increases in AT III and fibrinolytic activity are viewed as potentially beneficial. The mechanisms responsible for these changes are unknown but it has been suggested that the apparent increase in fibrinolytic activity induced by anabolic steroids is the result of a decrease in the level of the fast acting inhibitor of plasminogen activator.

Like the anabolic steroids (Small et al 1982), Org OD14 induces a slight rise in

LDL cholesterol and a significant fall in HDL cholesterol. This effect is considered to be due to the intrinsic androgenic properties of the compound. The reduction in HDL cholesterol levels during Org OD14 may constitute a risk for arterial disease and would therefore have to be considered potentially disadvantageous.

The changes in haematological, fibrinolytic and lipid parameters associated with treatment with Org OD14 are similar to those observed during anabolic steroid therapy. The effects of Org OD14 on the fibrinolytic system would appear to be an added benefit but may be partially offset by the changes in the full blood count and plasma lipids.

REFERENCES

Abilgaard U, Lie M, Odegard O R 1977 Antithrombin (heparin co-factor) assay with new chromogenic substrates (S-2238 and Chromozym TH). Thrombosis Research 11: 549–553
Clauss A 1957 Gerinnungphysiologische Schnell methode zur Bistimmung des Fibrinogens. Acta Haematologica (Basel) 17: 237–246
Friberger P 1982 Chromogenic peptide substrates. Their use for assay of factors in the fibrinolytic and the plasma kallikrein-kinin systems. Scandinavian Journal of Clinical and Laboratory Investigation 42: Suppl 162, 41–54
Kicovic P M, Cortes-Prieto J, Luis M, Milojevic S, Franchi F 1982 Placebo controlled cross-over study of effects of Org OD14 in menopausal women. Reproduccion 6: 81–91
Kluft C, Brakman P, Veldhuyzen-Stolk E C 1976 Screening of fibrinoytic activity in plasma euglobulin fractions on the fibrin plate. In: Davidson J F, Samama M M, Desnoyers P C (eds) Progress in Chemical Fibrinolysis and Thrombolysis Vol 2. Raven Press, New York. p 67–65
Lindsay R, Hart D M, Kraszewski A 1980 Prospective double-blind trial of synthetic steroid (Org OD14) for preventing post-menopausal osteoporosis. British Medical Journal 1: 1207–1209
Preston F E, Burakowski B K, Porters N R, Malia R G 1981 The fibrinolytic response to stanozolol in normal subjects. Thrombosis Research 22: 543–551
Small M, McArdle B M, Lowe G D O, Forbes C D, Prentice C R M 1982 The effect of intramuscular stanozolol on fibrinolysis and blood lipids. Thrombosis Research 28: 27–36

16. The effect of pentosan polysulphate (SP54) on the fibrinolytic enzyme system. A proposal for the mode of action

N. A. Marsh and P. J. Gaffney

Heparinoids have been known to stimulate fibrinolysis for some time (Halse, 1962) and more recently there has been renewed interest in the use of pentosan polysulphate in preventing deep vein thrombosis (Bergqvist and Ljungner, 1981) and in the treatment of transient ischaemic attacks (Vinazzer, 1984). Heparinoids stimulate fibrinolysis probably by releasing plasminogen activator from the endothelium. This has been demonstrated in animal preparations (Klocking and Markwardt, 1984) and we have also shown a similar phenomenon in man after subcutaneous injection of SP54 (Fischer et al 1982) and after oral ingestion (Marsh and Gaffney, 1983). We here suggest a possible mode of action for pentosan polysulphate.

METHODS

Euglobulin clot lysis times were estimated using the method of Nilsson and Olow (1962) expressing activity in arbitrary units (Marsh, 1981).

Plasminogen activator activity was also estimated on fibrin plates using the modification of Marsh and Arocha-Pinango (1972).

Factor XIIa activity was measured using a prekallikrein-kallikrein conversion method (Vinazzer et al 1982).

Healthy male volunteers gave informed consent to the study.

Pentosan polysulphate (SP54) was provided by Benechemie.

RESULTS

In vivo studies

A single administration of SP54, either 50 mg subcutaneously or 500 mg by mouth, produced a significant increase in euglobulin clot lysis time activity (Fig. 16.1). The subcutaneous route produced an effect about twice that following oral ingestion. Fibrin plate lysis showed similar responses after SP54 but there was no change in parameters after placebo administration.

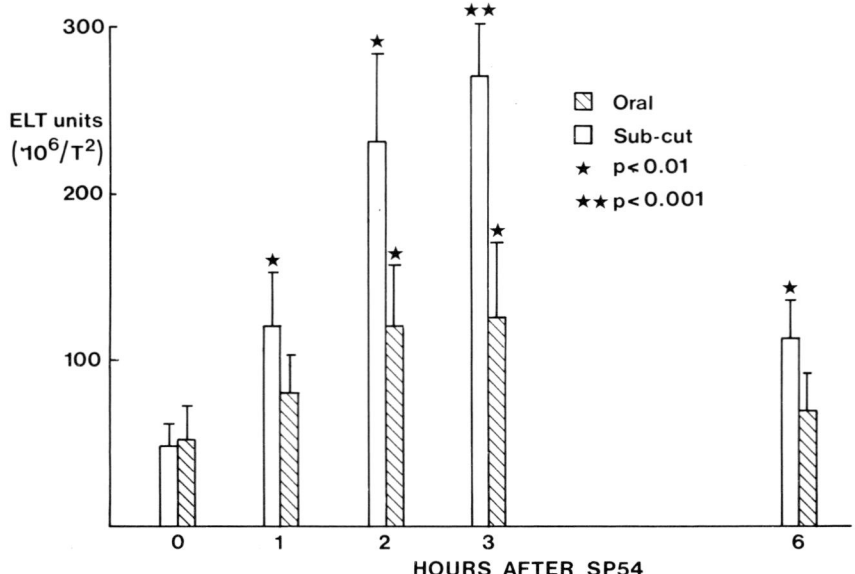

Fig. 16.1 The effect of pentosan polysulphate (SP54) on fibrinolytic activity in man. (Mean + SEM, N = 6).

Multiple doses of oral SP54 elicited comparable increases in ELT activity over the course of 5 days (Fig. 16.2).

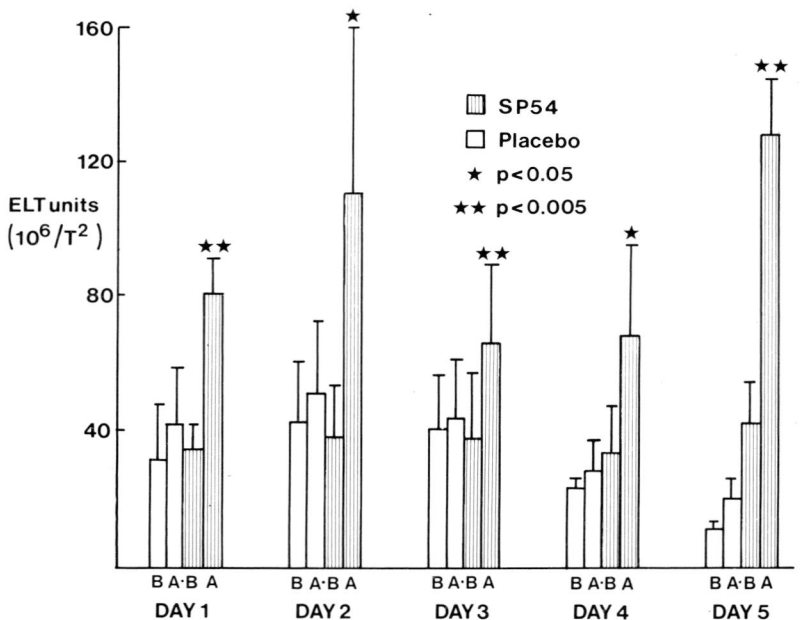

Fig. 16.2 The effect of multiple oral doses of SP54 (500 mg p.d.) on fibrinolytic activity in man (Mean + SEM, N = 6). B: Activity before SP54 or placebo, A: Activity 2 hours after SP54 or placebo.

In vitro studies

Pentosan polysulphate was added to normal pooled plasma in the concentration range 5 to 20 μg/ml and to the various tests carried out after 30 min. There was a dose-dependent increase in ELT activity, fibrin plate lysis and Factor XIIa generation. The increase in fibrin plate lysis produced by SP54 was compared with that following dextran sulphate and sodium flufenamate, known activators of 'intrinsic' fibrinolysis. The SP54-induced increase was about half that caused by dextran sulphate-flufenamate.

DISCUSSION

Our results with normal volunteers concord with those of several workers who have shown an increase in plasma plasminogen activator activity following pentosan polysulphate.

The *in vitro* data confirms the findings of Vinazzer et al (1982) in that SP54 can have a significant effect in *in vitro* test systems. It is a matter for conjecture however, as to the level of SP54 reached in the blood *in vivo* after subcutaneous injections or oral ingestion and whether or not this is sufficiently high to influence measurements *ex vivo*.

Activation of Factor XIIa suggests the involvement of 'intrinsic' fibrinolysis but again blood levels are not sufficiently high to cause activation *in vivo*.

Although we have yet to show conclusively that tPA is released from the vascular endothelium in man following SP54, we believe that the experiments with 'bloodless' animal preparations are strongly suggestive of this (Klocking and Markerardt, 1984).

We suggest therefore that the fibrinolytic state induced by SP54 is due to raised tPA activity in blood and that three mechanisms are involved:

1. Release of endothelial tPA into the bloodstream as a direct result of SP54 action.
2. Partial activation of Factor XII-dependent plasminogen activator activity.
3. Enhancement of euglobulin precipitate activity *in vitro*.

REFERENCES

Bergqvist D, Ljungner H A 1981 A comparative study of Dextran 70 and a sulphated polysaccharide in the prevention of post-operative thromboembolic complications. British Journal of Surgery 68: 449–451
Fischer A M, Merton R E, Marsh N A, Williams S, Gaffney P J, Barrowcliffe T W, Thomas D P 1982 A comparison of pentosan polysulphate and heparin II: Effects of subcutaneous injection. Thrombosis and Haemostasis 47: 109–113
Halse Th. 1962 Aktivierung der Fibrinolyse und Thrombolyse durch Polysaccharid-schwefelsäureester (Heparin, Herparinoide). Arzneim Forschung 12: 574–582
Klöcking H-P, Markwardt F 1984 Pentosan polysulphate-induced release of plasminogen activator. Haemostasis 14: 121
Marsh N A 1981 Fibrinolysis, John Wiley and Sons, Chichester
Marsh N A, Arocha-Pinango C L 1972 Evaluation of the fibrin plate method for estimating plasminogen activators. Thrombosis et diathesis haemorrhagica 28: 75–88

March N A, Gaffney P J 1983 The effect of pentosan polysulphate (SP54) on the fibrinolytic system of man. Thrombosis and Haemostasis 50: 83

Nilsson I M, Olow B 1962 Fibrinolysis induced by streptokinase in man. Acta Chirurgica Scandinavica 123: 247–266

Vinazzer H 1984 Clinical and experimental data on the fibrinolytic action of pentosan polysulphate. Haemostasis 14: 122

Vinazzer H, Stemberger A, Haas S, Blümel G 1982 Influence of heparin; of different heparin fractions and of a low molecular weight heparin-like substance on the mechanism of fibrinolysis. Thrombosis Research 27: 341–352

17. Defibrotide, an experimental antithrombotic agent

S. Coccheri, G. Prino, F. Grauso, C. Legnani, M. Mantovani and G. Biagi

INTRODUCTION

Defibrotide (D) is a natural extractive polydeoxyribonucleotide obtained from bovine lung (see U.S. and British patents). Its molecular weight is between 20,000 and 35,000 daltons. Adenine, thymine, guanine and cytidine are present in D as purinic and pyrimidinic bases. The molar ratio purines/pyrimidines is greater than 0.85 (unpublished data).

The pharmacologic properties of D do not change with m.w. within the said limits of 20,000 to 35,000. However, they disappear with advanced degradation to mono- or oligonucleotides. D has a defined electrophoretic mobility and a reversible hyperchromicity corresponding to 10–20% of native DNA (unpublished data). The extraction procedure has been defined by Crinos (Como, Italy) and standardization is performed biologically on the basis of the ability of the compound to stimulate fibrinolytic activity of euglobulins after injection 'in vivo' in the rabbit (Mantovani et al 1978).

ANTITHROMBOTIC ACTIVITY. EXPERIMENTAL DATA

Antithrombotic activity of D was studied in several models of experimental thrombogenesis. In collagen induced thrombosis the ED 50 is around 85.6 mg/Kg i.v. and 32.1 mg/Kg/os. In thrombosis due to electric stimulation ED 50 is 80.9 mg/Kg i.v. For prevention of the Schwartzmann reaction ED 50 is around 44.9 mg/Kg/os.

When infused intravenously into rabbits with 24 hrs old thrombi, D (20 to 50 mg/Kh/h for 6 hrs) also shows a dose-related thrombolytic activity (Niada et al 1982).

POSSIBLE MECHANISMS OF THE ANTITHROMBOTIC EFFECT

a) Fibrinolytic activity

D added *in vitro* to human plasma prior to euglobulin precipitation (100 μg/ml) or to blood prior to dilution (2.5 to 5 mg/ml) activated fibrinolysis respectively in the euglobulin clot lysis and in the dilute blood clot lysis times (Coccheri et al 1982).

In vivo, after intravenous injection in the rabbit, D enhances euglobulin fibrinolytic activity measured on standard fibrin plates and this effect is so reproducible that it is used for standardization purposes. Mussoni and Co. (1979) showed that D injected in rats (150 mg/Kg) induced significant increase of the fibrinolytic activity of euglobulins especially 30' and 60' after injection. In the same experiments D also increased the Tissue Plasminogen Activator stores in the lungs and in the main vessels of rats.

In humans, the fibrinolytic response of normal volunteers and of patients with vascular disease was studied by us (Coccheri et al 1982) after intravenous or intramuscular injection of 1.5 to 3 mg/Kg of the substance. The increased fibrinolytic activity of the euglobulin fraction after a single intravenous injection (3 mg/Kg), was significantly greater than that observed after placebo and occurred within 30' and 360' from injection. D was also effective after repeated daily administration for 10–15 days. Incidentally, this study also showed that coagulation parameters remained unchanged after D.

Tissue plasminogen activator (TPA) in blood was measured according to Wiman et al (1983) in 8 patients with third stage peripheral arterial disease, after daily i.v. infusion of D, 10 mg/Kg/die, or placebo, for 11 days (unpublished data). The results are shown in Table 17.1.

Table 17.1   TPA, percent changes in units (see text) during daily intravenous treatment with D or placebo in 8 patients with peripheral obliterative arterial disease in stage 3.

		Days of treatment		
	0	3	8	11
Defibrotide (n = 4)	=	+ 10.2%	+ 14.5%	+ 21.6%
Placebo (n = 4)	=	− 6.1%	− 6.5%	− 10.1%

A moderate and steady increase in TPA was observed throughout day 11. No data are as yet available on TPA inhibitor levels after D.

b) Activities related to platelets and prostanoid metabolism

In vitro platelet aggregation due to collagen (1 μg/ml) in human PRP is completely abolished by preincubating PRP with D, 4 mg/ml, and is strongly inhibited with 2 mg/ml (Fig. 17.1) (unpublished data). Similar results are obtained in platelet aggregation stimulated by collagen in whole blood (Fig. 17.2).

The effect increases by prolonging the incubation time of D in PRP. In comparison to ASA, D is much less active in terms of actual weight, but almost as active in terms of molar concentration, being a large molecule. Moreover, D preincubated in PRP significantly potentiates the inhibiting effect of PGI_2 on ADP aggregation (Table 17.2).

In animal experiments, Niada and Co. (1981) showed that the blood of hamsters treated with D induced increased generation of PGI_2 like material

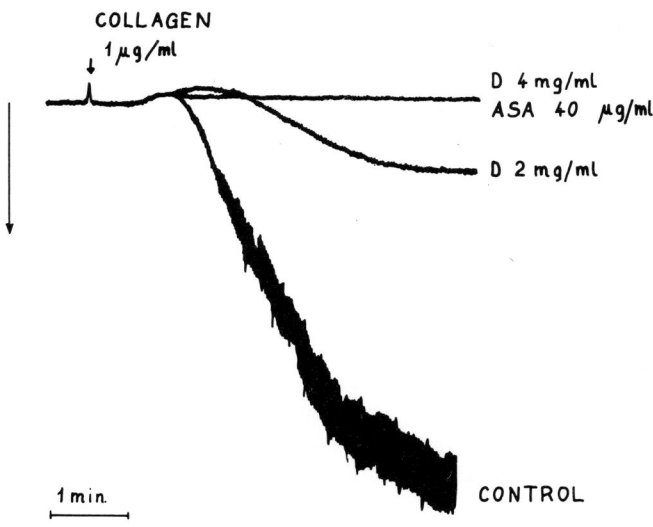

Fig. 17.1 In vitro effect of Defibrotide (D) and ASA on platelet aggregation in PRP induced by collagen (1 μg/ml).

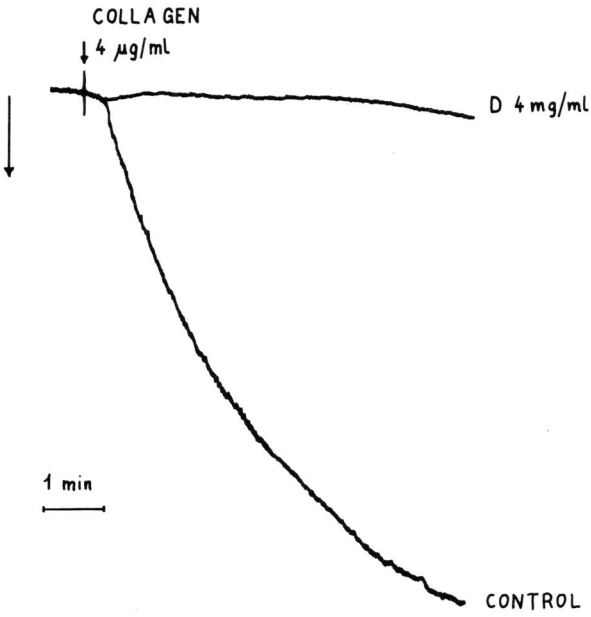

Fig. 17.2 In vitro effect of Defibrotide (D) on platelet aggregation induced in whole blood by collagen (4 μg/ml).

Table 17.2 Synergistic effect Defibrotide and PGI_2 in vitro on ADP induced platelet aggregation in human PRP (mean vales of 6 experiments)

PGI_2 ng/ml	Defibrotide mg/ml	% inhibition $(m \pm D.S)$	Significance
0.6	0	64 ± 10	
0.6	0.1	71 ± 7	
0.6	0.5	85 ± 6	$p < 0.015$
0.6	1.0	94 ± 5	$p < 0.05$
0.3	0	18 ± 7	
0.3	0.1	32 ± 10	
0.3	0.5	53 ± 9.5	$p < 0.01$
0.3	1.0	53 ± 11	$p < 0.01$

(bioassay), of 6 Keto PGF 1α from aortic rings (200 mg/Kg i.v. and 8 to 32 mg/Kg orally), and of a platelet deaggregating activity in blood (25–50 mg/Kg i.v.). In preliminary acute experiments in man we have measured various parameters after a single intravenous injection or perfusion of 400 and 800 mg (from 5 to 12 mg/Kg) both in volunteers and in patients with peripheral arterial disease (unpublished data). No consistent changes in platelet aggregation and in free and stimulated (Defreyn et al 1982) 6 Keto PGF 1α could be observed (Table 17.3). However, in 3 or the 6 patients a definite increase after 24 hrs in stimulated 6 Keto PGF 1α levels was seen. Although this effect was not consistent in all patients, it indicates a mechanism that should be furtherly investigated.

Table 17.3 Changes in free and stimulted 6 Keto PGF 1 α after single i.v. infusion of D, 10-12 mg/Kg, in 6 patients with peripheral arterial disease. No significances

	0	30′	2 h	4 h	24 h
Free 6 Keto PGF 1 α (pg/ml)	25 ± 4	46 ± 44	26 ± 11	24 ± 9	21 ± 5
Stimulated 6 Keto PGF 1 α (pg/ml)	216 ± 184	192 ± 53	186 ± 79	147 ± 98	273 ± 133

In another experiment, we treated with D, 800 mg daily (4 × 200), per os, for 45 days, a group of climbers participating in a high mountain expedition (1982 HME). Of 14 climbers, 7 were treated with D and 7 with placebo. Blood samples were taken before departure and immediately after return (45 days later). The results are presented in Table 17.4 and show that administration of D protected the platelets from activation due to heavy physical effort at high altitude, by inhibiting the increase in βTG (and, not significantly, of PF4), and reducing the amplitude and the slope of collagen aggregation in whole blood.

Free 6 Keto PGF 1α did not change in either group after return, while 'stimulated' PGF 1α increased in average in both groups, with a trend to a more pronounced increase in the D treated climbers.

CONCLUSION

Defibrotide (D), a polydeoxyribonucleotide extracted from mammalian lung, and biologically standardized according to its ability of stimulating fibrinolytic

Table 17.4 Parameters of platelet activation, whole blood aggregation (collagen), and free stimulated 6 Keto PGF 1 α in placebo or Defibrotide (800 mg/die orally) treated climbers before and after a high altitude expedition (see text). * = <0.05, ** = <0.01

	Placebo (n = 7)		Defibrotide (n = 7)	
	Departure	Return	Departure	Return
βTG (mg/ml)	39 ± 11	52 ± 21*	49 ± 21	43 ± 12
PF$_4$ (mg/ml)	5 ± 3	7 ± 4	8 ± 6	4 ± 2
Collagen amplitude (whole blood agg.)	48 ± 14	47 ± 9	52 ± 15	41 ± 7**
Collagen slope (whole blood agg.)	47 ± 8	39 ± 9*	47 ± 14	29 ± 12**
Free 6 Keto PGF 1 α (pg/ml)	19 ± 9	21 ± 9	24 ± 9	18 ± 6
Stimulated 6 Keto PGF 1 α (pg/ml)	42 ± 26	119 ± 134	43 ± 24	146 ± 118

activity of euglobulins after injection in the rabbit, has antithrombotic properties in a number of models of experimental thrombogenesis. Besides enhancing fibrinolytic activity, probably by inducing release of TPA, D stimulates release of prostacyclin-like materials in experimental models. In vitro, in high doses, it inhibits collagen aggregation and potentiates exogenous PGI$_2$.

In preliminary experiments in humans we could confirm that D has fibrinolysis enhancing activity, but we found no consistent activity on free 6 Keto PGF 1α levels. A delayed enhancement of stimulated 6 Keto PGF 1α levels was seen in a number of cases. After prolonged oral administration in subjects undergoing a process of platelet activation (physical stress at high altitude) Defibrotide was able to protect the platelets from becoming activated. The discrepancies between the limited effects observed in vivo and the evident activities in vitro and in animal experiments may be due to inadequacy of the doses used in vivo or to the existence of 'non responders'.

Defibrotide deserves further evaluation of its mechanism of action, and future work will decide whether its experimental antithrombotic effect may have clinical significance.

REFERENCES

British Patent No 1, 367, 655 (1975)
Coccheri S, De Rosa V, Dettori A G et al 1982 Effect on fibrinolysis of a new antithrombotic agent: Fraction P (Defibrotide). A multicentre trial. Int J Clin Pharmacol Res 2(3): 227–245
Defreyn G, Deckmyn H, Vermylen J 1982 A thromboxane synthetase inhibitor reorients endoperoxide metabolism in whole blood towards prostacyclin and prostaglandin E$_2$. Thrombosis Research 26: 389–400
Mantovani M, Prino G, Rescador R 1978 Activation of fibrinolytic processes by a substance of polydesoxynucleotidic nature (Fraction P). In: Strano, A (ed) 'Advances in coagulation, fibrinolysis, platelet aggregation and atherosclerosis'. C.E.P.I., Roma: 274–281
Mussoni I, Evolvi C, Donati M B 1979 Activation of plasma and vascular fibrinolytic activity by a polydeoxyribonucleotidic substance, Fraction P, in rats and rabbits (Abstract). Thrombos Haemostas 42: 388
Niada R, Mantovani M, Prino G et al 1981 Antithrombotic activity of a polydeoxyribonucleotidic substance extracted from mammalian organs: a possible link with prostacyclin. Thrombos Res 23: 233–246

Niada R, Mantovani M, Prino G et al 1982 PGI$_2$-generation and antithrombotic activity of orally administered Defibrotide. Pharmacol Res Commun 14: 949–957

U.S. Patent No 3, 770, 720 (1973)

No 3, 829, 567 (1974)

No 3, 899, 481 (1975)

Wiman B, Mellbring G, Rånby M 1983 Plasminogen activator release during venous stasis and exercise as determined by a new specific assay. Clin Chim Acta 127: 279–288

18. A new quantitative model of early venous thrombosis. Evaluation of a novel fibrinolytic compound CP2129AL in this model

T. R. F. Paes and V. V. Kakkar

In order to evaluate the potential of a fibrinolytic agent, a model of thrombosis is required that is reproducible and can be used in large numbers in a quantitative fashion. Henry (1971) and Klöcking (1978) have reviewed the literature but few models have attained a satisfactory degree of quantification. The model described here utilises a small electrical charge to initiate thrombosis in the rabbit vena cava. ^{125}I-labelling enables the model to be used quantitatively and the model has been applied to the assessment of a new fibrinolytic agent CP2129AL (Continental Pharma).

EXPERIMENTAL METHOD

New Zealand male white rabbits (3–5 kg) are anaesthetised and the infrarenal vena cava exposed through a midline laparotomy with an absolute minimum of handling of the vein. A suitable 2 cm segment of vena cava is cleared of attachments to allow placement behind it of two platinum electrodes mounted 1 cm apart on a perspex template. A pre-counted dose of ^{125}I-fibrinogen is now injected intravenously and after a 5 minute equilibration period blood is withdrawn for measurement of radioactive count per ml per minute, and for fibrinogen concentration. 5 ml of N-saline (control) or 5 ml of CP2129AL (treatment; 15 mg/kg) is then administered and a charge of 200 mCoulombs (20 mA over 10 seconds) passed between the electrodes. These are then removed and the abdomen closed for a period of one hour. The treatment segment of vena cava is then removed and counted in a 8 counter well.

TREATMENT OF RESULTS

The following parameters are obtained,
C_1 = Counts/minute/ml of blood
C_2 = Counts/minute of treated vena caval segment
[fib] = Fibrinogen concentration (mg/ml).

A simple calculation now enables the quantification of the exact weight of fibrinogen (M) incorporated in the thrombus formed in the cava.

$$M = \frac{C_2}{C_1} \times [fib]$$

The amount of thrombus formed is very small and not normally discernible to the naked eye, although it is easily visualised microscopically.

RESULTS

Controls

Rabbit Weight (kg)	C_1	C_2	[fib]	M
4.610	40006	12806	2.36	0.753
3.900	30069	8433	1.95	0.547
4.160	56910	18611	2.10	0.686
3.650	96858	23028	2.65	0.630
3.630	36080	12502	2.05	0.710

Treatment

Rabbit Weight (kg)	C_1	C_2	[fib]	M
4.330	174145	38350	1.83	0.403
4.050	80517	20028	1.99	0.495
3.880	65746	14519	2.40	0.530
3.810	133706	24316	2.15	0.391
3.750	85487	19450	2.10	0.480

Mean mass of deposited thrombus,
Control　　　　　　　　= 0.665 ± 0.036 mg
Treatment (CP2129AL) = 0.460 ± 0.027 mg
p = 0.01 (t test)

COMMENTS

This model produces a highly quantifiable means of assessing agents which modify the thrombotic process. Electron microscopic study shows that electric current produces a gradual development of thrombus with platelet deposition initially, a situation akin to that which occurs in physiological states, hence the results might be expected to bear a good relation to the outcome in clinical use. The fibrinolytic agent CP2129AL produced by Continental Pharma is shown in this model to inhibit thrombus formation by about 33%.

REFERENCES

Henry R L 1971 In: Thrombosis and bleeding disorders; Academic Press, London, p 498
Klöcking H P 1978 In: Markwardt F (ed) Fibrinolytics and Antifibrinolytics. Springer Verlag, Berlin, p 151

19. Fibrinolytic effects of Ciprofibrate in patients with hypercholesterolaemia

I. A. Simpson, A. R. Lorimer, I. D. Walker and J. F. Davidson

INTRODUCTION

Ciprofibrate, a phenoxyisobutyrate, is an orally effective hypolipidaemic agent (Illingworth et al 1982) related in structure to clofibrate. The fibrinolytic effects of clofibrate were described by Chakrabarti and Fearnley (1968), but have not previously been reported for ciprofibrate.

SUBJECTS

Six male patients with known hypercholesterolaemia, and with fasting serum cholesterol consistently > 7.8 mmol/l were given ciprofibrate 100 mg daily for 12 weeks following a 4 week placebo run-in phase. Ages ranged from 38–63 years with a mean of 48.4 years and all remained on a low cholesterol diet throughout with no other medical therapy.

Resting, fasting blood samples were taken following 4 weeks placebo and after 2, 6 and 12 weeks on active therapy, for lipid and fibrinolytic analysis, and for routine haematological and biochemical testing.

RESULTS

All patients tolerated the drug well.

Fibrinogen and fibrinolysis (see Table 19.1)
Platelet aggregation induced by ADP, adrenaline, collagen and arachidonic acid remained unchanged throughout.

Lipid analysis
By 6 weeks total cholesterol had fallen from a mean of 8.68 mmol/l (SD $\pm$ 0.68) at control to a mean of 7.54 mmol/l (50 $\pm$ 0.75) P < 0.05. This was mainly due to

Table 19.1 Fibrinolysis (using paired Wilcoxon analysis)

Patient	Fibrinogen (g/l)			Plasminogen %		
	Control	Wk 6	Wk 12	Control	Wk 6	Wk 12
1	2.40	1.90	2.15	97	100	107
2	2.90	1.80	1.80	116	114	117
3	2.33	1.45	1.63	100	99	111
4	2.60	2.50	2.65	124	129	130
5	3.10	2.60	2.65	82	87	91
6	2.60	2.40	2.00	94	112	92
Mean	2.66	2.11	2.17	102.17	106.8	108
s.d.	± 0.29	± 0.46	± 0.43	± 15.32	± 14.62	± 14.97
		$p < 0.05$	$p < 0.05$		NS	NS

Patient	Antiplasmin %			Fibrin Plate (mm)		
	Control	Wk 6	Wk 12	Control	Wk 6	Wk 12
1	87	90	100	15	16	15
2	113	118	123	11	13	15
3	96	96	101	11	14	15
4	102	112	101	16	17	17
5	96	91	98	15	16	16
6	98	100	112	15	14	16
Mean	98.67	101.17	105.83	13.83	15	15.66
s.d.	± 8.57	± 11.46	± 9.75	± 2.2	± 1.55	± 0.82
		NS	$p < 0.05$		NS	$p < 0.05$

a reduction in LDL cholesterol from a mean of 6.53 mmol/l (SD ± 1.07) to a mean of 5.64 mmol/l (SD ± 0.76) $P < 0.05$. Total triglyceride also fell significantly from a mean of 1.70 mmol/l (SD ± 0.93) at control to a mean of 1.23 mmol/l (SD ± 0.66) at 6 weeks. Though a slight fall in VLDL cholesterol was noted this did not reach statistical significance and HDL cholesterol remained unchanged.

Haematology and biochemistry
Alkaline phosphatase was significantly reduced from a mean of 192.2 u/l (s.d. ± 56.2) at control to a mean of 134.7 u/l (s.d. ± 39.6) and a mean of 123.3 u/l (s.d. ± 35.0) at weeks 6 and 12 respectively ($p < 0.001$). A small increase in platelet count was noted at week 12 (319×10^9/l (s.d. ± 71)) compared to control (267×10^9/l s.d. ± 45) ($p < 0.05$). There was no other change in routine haematology or biochemistry throughout the study.

COMMENT

This study has confirmed the significant hypolipidaemic effect of ciprofibrate in the treatment of patients with hypercholesterolaemia. The expected fall in alkaline phosphatase presumably due to liver enzyme induction was of a similar magnitude to that reported with clofibrate (Panchenko et al 1982).

Ciprofibrate caused a significant reduction in fibrinogen levels and a modest increase in fibrinolytic activity, potentially beneficial effects in this high risk group of patients.

90

REFERENCES

Chakrabarti R, Fearnley G R 1968 Effect of Clofibrate on Fibrinolysis, platelet stickiness, plasma fibrinogen and serum cholesterol. Lancet 2: 1007–09

Illingworth D R, Olsen G D, Cook S F, Sexton G J, Wendel H A 1982 Ciprofibrate in the therapy of Type II Hypercholesterolaemia. A double-blind trial. Atherosclerosis 44 (2): 211–221

Panchenko L F, Popova S V, Antonenkov V O 1982 Including effect of Clofibrate on alkaline phosphatase and histidine glyoxylate aminotransferase in rat liver. Experientia, 38 (4): 433–4

20. Danazol — effects on fibrinolysis

H. Hambley, A. Richards, J. F. Davidson,
I. D. Walker and H. P. MacEwan

INTRODUCTION

Danazol is a 17α alkylated anabolic steroid which has been in use for several years for a variety of conditions e.g. premenstrual tension, dysfunctional uterine bleeding, angioneurotic oedema and a number of other diverse conditions (1,2). Studies to date had indicated that danazol had no effect on fibrinolysis (1,3). However, closer examination of some studies (3) showed changes which, although not reaching statistical significance, would suggest that danazol could be capable of enhancing fibrinolysis in a way similar to other 17α alkylated steroids e.g. stanozolol (4,5). The occurrence of clinically significant hypofibrinogenaemia (0.8 G/litre) in a young woman taking danazol (6) prompted a further examination of the effect of danazol on fibrinolysis.

PATIENTS

Ten women (age range 20–30 years) were recruited from the gynaecology out patient clinic: patients were attending the clinic because of premenstrual tension or dysfunctional uterine bleeding. All patients gave informed consent. After two sets of baseline blood samples (sample 1 and 2), patients were started on danazol 200 mg daily within the first seven days of their next menstrual cycle.

Further samples were taken one month (sample 3) and two months (sample 4) after starting danazol. Danazol was discontinued after two months and a final sample (sample 5) was taken one month after stopping danazol. Three patients were excluded from the study because of non-compliance either with sampling requirements or with drug taking.

METHODS

Blood was obtained by clean venepuncture after an overnight fast and thirty minute rest and anticoagulated by adding to 0.13 M trisodium citrate in a ratio of 9:1. Fibrinogen was measured by the method of Clauss. Plasminogen and α_2

92

antiplasmin were assayed by an amidolytic technique using the chromogenic substrate S-2251 (Kabi, Sweden) and antithrombin III was also measured by an amidolytic technique (S-2238 Coatest, Kabi). Plasma plasminogen activator was measured by the diameter of lysis on a plasminogen rich fibrin plate produced by the euglobulin fraction. Statistical analysis (mean, standard deviation and paired Student's T Test) were done on an Apple 11e microcomputer using a commercial programme (Biostats III).

RESULTS

No difference between any values of sample 1 and 2 was found: all changes in the text subsequently refer to sample 1.

A significant fall in fibrinogen from 2.54 G/litre to 1.94 G/litre ($p < 0.05$) was associated with a rise in plasminogen, antithrombin III and plasma plasminogen activator (see Table 20.1). The level of α_2 antiplasmin remained unchanged throughout.

Table 20.1 Effect of Danazol on various fibrinolytic parameters (results expressed as mean ± standard deviation $* < 0.05$, $**p < 0.01$).

	Sample 1	Sample 2	Sample 3	Sample 4	Sample 5
Fibrinogen (g/l)	2.54 ± 0.4	2.2 ± 0.5	1.94 ± 0.5*	2.1 ± 0.3*	2.3 ± 0.3
Plasminogen (%)	89 ± 12	97 ± 27	112 ± 29**	111 ± 15**	106 ± 7*
α_2-Anti-plasmin	105 ± 6	105 ± 6	108 ± 7	109 ± 9	105 ± 13
Antithrombin III (%)	92 ± 11	99 ± 14.5	103 ± 14.5	109 ± 8.5**	102 ± 5
Fibrin plate lysis (mm)	11.9 ± 2.6	12.8 ± 2.7	14.3 ± 2.4*	14.4 ± 3.3	13.4 ± 3.8

DISCUSSION

This pattern of results i.e. fall in fibrinogen, rise in plasminogen, antithrombin III and plasminogen activator is similar to that seen with other anabolic steroids (e.g. stanozolol which are known to enhance fibrinolysis (4,5). Effects on plasminogen and antithrombin III had been noted earlier by immunological techniques (7) but this is the first report, we believe, of a significant fall in fibrinogen associated with a rise in plasminogen activator. It is concluded, therefore, that danazol is capable of enhancing fibrinolysis in vivo.

REFERENCES

1. Fraser I S 1979 Danazol — a steroid with a unique combination of actions. Scot Med J 24: 147–150
2. Gelfand J A 1983 Exploiting sex for therapeutic purposes. New Eng J Med 308: 1417–1419
3. Chuntra T H, Cope E, Anderson A B M, Bolton F G 1979 The effect of danazol on menorrhagia, coagulation mechanisms, haematological indices and body weight. Br J Obs Gyn 86: 46–50

4. Davidson J F, Lochead M, McDonald G A, McNicol G P 1972 Fibrinolytic enhancement by stanazolol: a double blind trial. Brit J Haem 22: 543-559
5. Small M, McArdle B M, Lowe G D D, Forbes C D, Prentice C R M 1982 The effect of intramuscular stanazolol on fibrinolysis and lipids. Thromb Res 28: 27-36
6. Mowat J M Personal communication
7. Laurell C B, Rennevik G A 1979 A comparison of plasma protein changes induced by danazol, pregnancy and estrogens. J Clin Endocrin Metab 49: 710-725

21. Phytosterol-stimulated production of plasminogen activator in cultured endothelial cells from bovine carotid artery

H. Hagiwara, M. Shimonaka and
Y. Inada

The endothelial cell is a rich source of plasminogen activator that is associated with fibrinolytic activity in blood vessels. In the present study, Hagiwara et al (1984) demonstrated a stimulative effect of sitosterol and fucosterol on the production of plasminogen activator in cultured endothelial cells from bovine carotid artery. Sitosterol and fucosterol are commonly found in leaves of higher plants and brown algae, respectively, and they are never found in animals (Fig. 21.1).

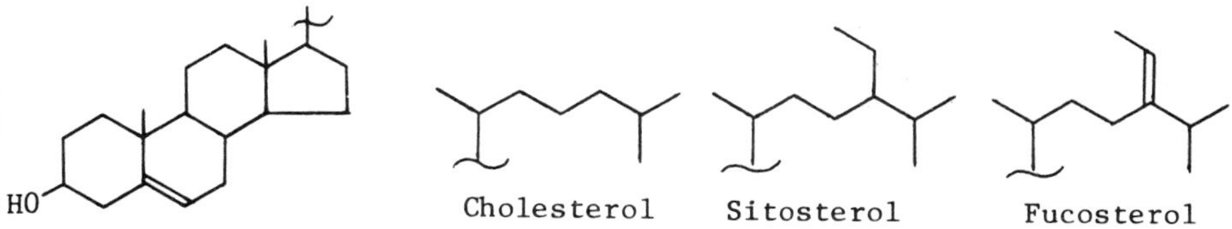

Fig. 21.1 The structure of sterols used in this study.

As shown in Table 21.1, addition of sitosterol or fucosterol to the culture medium of the cells gave rise to a marked increment of the activity of plasminogen activator in the culture medium and in the cells. Removal of these plant sterols from the culture medium resulted in a decrease of plasminogen

Table 21.1 Extracellular and intracellular activities of plasminogen activator in sitosterol- or fucosterol-treated endothelial cells

| Treatment | Plasminogen activator activity (urokinase units/10^7 cells) | | | |
| | Cellular Extracts After Incubation for | | Conditioned Media After Incubation for | |
	0 hr	8 hr	0 hr	8 hr
Control	0.08	0.08	0.00	0.32
+ Sitosterol	0.20	0.20	0.00	0.95
+ Fucosterol	0.40	0.58	0.00	2.11

Endothelial cell monolayers obtained in the medium with and without 25 μM sitosterol or fucosterol were washed and were cultured with a fresh serum-free medium. After incubation, conditioned media and cellular extracts were prepared and were assayed by the method of Saito et al (1983).

activator activity back to normal level. These phenomena were not observed for other steroids such as cholesterol, stigmasterol, isofucosterol, 5-androsten-3β-ol, 20(R)-propyl-5-pregnen-3β-ol and 20(R)-heptyl-5-pregnen-3β-ol.

Sitosterol or fucosterol itself had no fibrinolytic activity and did not directly stimulate the plasminogen activator activity.

To see whether sitosterol or fucosterol stimulates the synthesis of plasminogen activator in cells or not, an inhibitor of protein synthesis, cycloheximide, was introduced into the cell culture system free from serum. The synthesis of plasminogen activator in sitosterol- or fucosterol-treated cells was inhibited by cycloheximide.

From the results obtained above, it may be concluded that sitosterol or fucosterol enhances not only secretion of plasminogen activator from the cells but also synthesis of the activator in the interior of the cells, although its mechanism is unclear. This finding may lead these plant sterols to a novel agent for prevention and therapy of patients with thrombosis.

REFERENCES

Hagiwara H, Shimonaka M, Morisaki M, Ikekawa N, Inada Y 1984 Sitosterol-Stimulative Production of Plasminogen Activator in Cultured Endothelial Cells from Bovine Carotid Artery. Thrombosis Research 33: 363–370
Saito Y, Takabayashi K, Tsukada T, Inada Y 1983 Nephelometric Determination of Plasminogen and Plasma Inhibitors in Human Plasma Using Fibrin Suspension as a Substrate. Thrombosis Research 30: 47–53

22. Influence of stanozolol on euglobulin clot lysis

K. Winther, J. B. Knudsen and J. Gormsen

Following the discovery that stanozolol possesses marked fibrinolytic activity (2,3) and in view of the current lack of simple and effective treatment, it was decided to investigate, whether stanozolol could offer a clinically viable method to enhance fibrinolysis. The criteria of clinical viability in this study were achievement and long term maintenance of normalized euglobulin clot lysis time (E.C.L.T.) and acceptable patient tolerance of the medication.

MATERIAL AND METHODS

Patients were selected for treatment if they had 1) a diagnosis of a thromboembolic condition such as deep venous thrombosis (DVT), acute myocardial infarction (AMI), stroke or transient cerebral ischemic attack (TIA); 2) pathological E.C.L.T. value (>360 min. without and/or >120 min. with venous compression) and 3) absence of a contraindication against treatment with an anabolic steroid. E.C.L.T. was measured as described elsewhere (1). Venous compression at the mean of diastolic and systolic pressure was applied for five minutes. Fasting blood samples from a cubital vein before and at intervals during treatment were drawn between 8.30 and 10.30 a.m. The dose of stanozolol was usually 5 mg b.d. In a minority of patients the daily dose was decreased to 5 mg (n = 23) or temporarily increased to 15 mg (n = 10).

A total of 150 patients, 125 males and 25 females, were included. The diagnoses were DVT in 37, AMI in 7, stroke or TIA in 93, and axillary, mesenteric and retinal thrombosis, respectively, in 13 patients. Twelve males and three females had a history of two or more thromboembolic diagnoses. At the time of entrance, the mean age $\pm$ SD (range) of males was 51.4 ± 12.3 (21–81.5) years and of females 55.4 ± 13.7 (30–77.5) years. So far, 130 patients (86.7%) have been treated for >6 months, 91 (60.7%) >1 year, 23 (15.3%) > 2 years, and 6 patients in excess of five years, with a maximum of 9 years. Currently, the mean duration of treatment is 18.5 ± 1.4 (SEM) years corresponding to 231 patient treatment years. Adverse reactions were recorded as reported/observed. Additionally, during the compilation of our data, each patient was questioned actively, according to a check list, to enquire about possible adverse drug experiences that may have escaped previous records. Each type of reaction reported by an individual is recorded once. Thus, a single patient can account for several complaints but only once for each type.

RESULTS

The change in E.C.L.T. without venous compression during stanozolol treatment is shown in Figure 22.1.

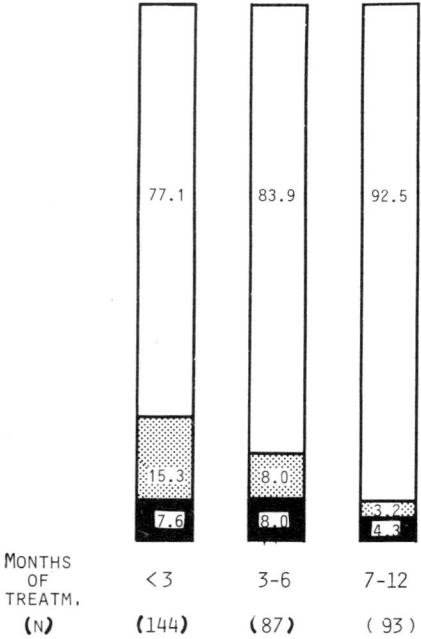

| MONTHS OF TREATM. | <3 | 3-6 | 7-12 |
| (N) | (144) | (87) | (93) |

Fig. 22.1 Percentage of patients with normalized (☐), improved but not normalized (▒), and unimproved (■) E.C.L.T. value during stanozolol treatment (5 mg b.d.). All patients had pathological E.C.L.T. values (>360 minutes) before treatment.
   The variation in total number of patients is accounted for as follows: E.C.L.T. values within the first three months of treatment are missing in 6 patients, who were not fasting or failed to come. Thereafter, control intervals were allowed to vary between 3–6–9 months in those patients, who had E.C.L.T. normalized within ≤3 months.

The proportion exhibiting complete normalization of E.C.L.T. during treatment is statistically highly significant (binomial distribution $P<0.001$ at <3, 3–6, and 7–12 months' samples, respectively). The improvement following venous compression was at least as marked: After <3, 3–6, and 7–12 months of treatment normal values were obtained in 78.7, 89.9 and 92.2% of patients respectively, improvement but not complete normalization was observed in a further 14.7, 6.0 and 7.0%, respectively, and apparently no improvement was seen in 6.6, 3.8, and 1.1% respectively.
   There was no sign of tachyphylaxis, as illustrated by two patients treated for 40

98

months (Fig. 22.2A) and 17 months (Fig. 22.2 B), respectively. The latter case
also illustrates, that E.C.L.T. returned to pathological values as soon as
treatment was stopped. Reinstituting treatment rapidly normalized E.C.L.T.

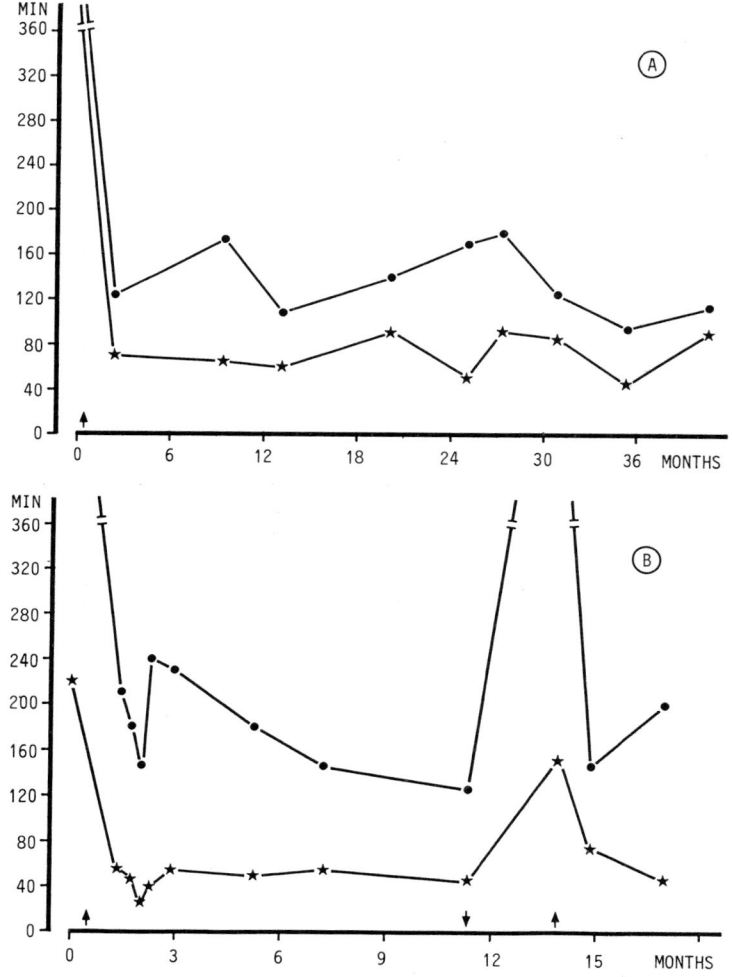

Fig. 22.2 E.C.L.T. without (● ——— ●) and with (* ——— *) venous compression before and
during stanozolol treatment 5 mg b.d. in two patients. A) a 38 year old man with two previous
venous thromboses and pre-treatment E.C.L.T. >21 h without, and >8 h with venous
compression. B) a 37.5 year old man with two previous attacks of TIA and pre-treatment
E.C.L.T. >8 h; stanozolol treatment started (↑) and stopped (↓), respectively.

Type and number of complaints reported are given in Table 22.1. It is evident
that complaints were much more frequent in females than in males. The 8 females
who stopped treatment on account of side effects did so after 10.1 ± 2.7 (SEM)
months (range 4–26 months). Their age at the time of starting medication was
54.8 ± 4.8 (SEM) years (range 32.5–71 years). For comparison, the 12 female
patients currently on medication have also been treated for 10.4 ± 1.7 (range
3–20) months so far, and their age at the time of starting was similar, i.e. 56.4 ±

Table 22.1 Complaints in 150 patients treated with stanozolol for 18.5 ± 1.4 (mean ± SEM) months

Type of complaint	Number of male patients reporting	Number of male patients stopping treatment	Number of female patients reporting	Number of female patients stopping treatment
Nausea/heartburn	5		2	
Headache/migraine	4	1	1	
Dizziness	4	1^+, 1^{++}	—	
Irritability	1	1*	—	
Fatigue/weakness	4	1^{++}	—	
Muscle cramps/restless legs	4	1*	2	
Sweating/flush	1		1	1^+
Pruritus	1	1^+	—	
Weight gain >2 kg	1		3	1°
Oedema	1	1	2	1°
Pathol. ASAT/ALAT	—		1	1
Miscellaneous	3			
Impotence	3	1*		
Acne			1	1^+
Increased facial hair			2	1^{++}, 1*
Hair loss			1	1^{++}
Slight voice change			3	1, 1, 1*
Amenorrhoea			1	1
Number of complaints	32	9	20	12
By number (%) of patients	24 (19)	5 (4)	14 (56)	8 (32)

*, $^+$, $^{++}$, $^\circ$, respectively, signify the various complaints by patients, who stopped treatment reporting more than one type of complaints.

4.6 (range 30–77.5) years. However, in six of them the dose was reduced to 5 mg of stanozolol a day after initial treatment with 10 mg a day for 1–14 months. This dose reduction was not primarily triggered by troublesome adverse reactions, but mainly serves the purpose of studying the proportion of patients in whom normal E.C.L.T. levels can be maintained at a lower dose of stanozolol. However, this group does include a 70 year old woman who stopped medication after four months' treatment with 10 mg a day due to increase in facial hair and beginning voice change. One year later, treatment was resumed with 5 mg a day and has, so far, been ongoing for five months without adverse effects. Side effects were found to be reversible after cessation of therapy. This was also true for androgenic side effects, including voice change, since it was a strict policy to stop treatment immediately following observation of suspect hoarseness.

In males, adverse reactions were usually mild and/or transient. In three cases the dose was reduced to 5 mg a day on account of side effects (headache in two cases disappeared, muscle cramps in the third case were reduced but not eliminated). The three cases of reported impotence are somewhat difficult to interpret. In two of the patients (57 and 59.5 years, respectively) treatment was started following a stroke, one of them had slight impotence even before. In the third patient the diagnosis was TIA at the age of 72 years, and he is receiving concomitant medication with a β-blocker.

Although, in the absence of a control group, no conclusions can be drawn as to whether stanozolol treatment was significantly effective in preventing recurrence of thromboembolic episodes, it appears encouraging that only 1/36 patients developed a single thrombus during therapy and only 2/93 patients with TIA had a further attack. No recurrences were seen in the remaining patients.

SUMMARY AND CONCLUSIONS

Stanozolol treatment appears to be a clinically viable treatment to enhance fibrinolysis. Complete normalization of E.C.L.T. was achieved in $>90\%$ of 150 patients treated for 18.5 ± 1.4 (mean $\pm$ SEM) months. In $>75\%$ of patients normalization of E.C.L.T. with and without venous comparison was observed within three months of stanozolol treatment, usually 5 mg b.d. Tachyphylaxis was not observed. Side effects were usually mild and not troublesome in males, but frequent and more disturbing in females. Although side effects were reversible following withdrawal of therapy, preliminary data suggest that it may be prudent to lower the dose in females to 5 mg a day and to increase it only, if the lower dose fails to normalize E.C.L.T.

REFERENCES

1. Austen D E G, Rhymes I L 1975 Laboratory Manual of Blood Coagulation. Blackwell Scientific Publications Ltd (ISBN 06-32-00781-8), Oxford, London, p 80
2. Preston F E, Burakowski B K, Porter N R 1981 The fibrinolytic response to stanozolol in normal subjects. Thrombosis Research 22: 543-551
3. Walker I D, Davidson J F 1978 Long term fibrinolytic enhancement with anabolic steroid therapy: A five year study. In: Progress in Chemical Fibrinolysis and Thrombolysis vol 3, Raven Press, New York, 3: 491-499

23. Decreased level of rapid tissue-type plasminogen activator inhibition by oral administration of stanozolol

J. H. Verheijen, D. C. Rijken, G. T. G. Chang, F. E. Preston and C. Kluft

INTRODUCTION

Drugs that cause an increase in t-PA activity levels in plasma are of considerable interest as potential therapeutics for prevention or treatment of thrombosis. Some drugs such as DDAVP (1-des-amino-8-D-arginine vasopressin) induce a rapid and substantial increase in t-PA activity in plasma, which is however of short duration (Gader et al 1973; Brommer et al 1982).

Already it has been known for some years that anabolic steroids, such as stanozolol, significantly increase plasma fibrinolytic activity (Davidson et al 1972). Recently, it has been shown that this increase in activity could completely be ascribed to tissue-type plasminogen activator (t-PA) (Kluft et al 1984). It is generally assumed that a higher t-PA activity is caused by an increased synthesis or release of t-PA.

In this report it will be shown that this is not the case, but that changes in the level of a recently discovered rapid t-PA inhibitor modulate the t-PA activity.

MATERIALS

Stanozolol (Stromba®).17-β-hydroxy-17-α-methyl androstano 3,2-c pyrazole was obtained from Sterling Winthrop U.K. To nine healthy volunteers the drug was administered orally in two 5 mg doses per day for a period of six weeks. Blood collection was performed in the morning at rest, plasma was prepared immediately, snap-frozen and stored at $-70°C$. T-PA antigen was determined with an enzyme immunoassay (Rijken et al 1984), t-PA activity in plasma euglobulin fractions with an indirect spectrophotometric assay (Verheijen et al 1982). Inhibition of t-PA was determined with a titration assay (Verheijen et al 1983; 1984). Known amounts of t-PA were added to 25 mićroliter of plasma and the resulting activity was measured with the indirect spectrophotometric assay.

RESULTS AND DISCUSSION

Oral administration of stanozolol markedly increases t-PA activity, the t-PA antigen level was not increased but slightly decreased (Fig. 23.2). Measurement of the rapid t-PA inhibition as illustrated in Figure 23.1 revealed a clear decrease (Fig. 23.1).

102

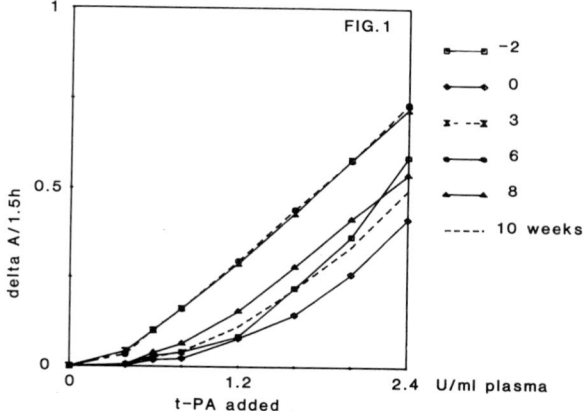

Fig. 23.1 Inhibition measurements in plasma of an individual before, during and after stanozolol use. Stanozolol was used from week 0 to week 6. Twenty-five microliter of plasma was titrated with t-PA and the resulting activity was measured.

The absolute decrease in inhibition level is apparently large enough to cause an increased activity in spite of a decreased t-PA antigen level. These results indicate that the rapid t-PA inhibition can be lowered by use of stanozolol which results in increased fibrinolytic activity. Changes in fibrinolytic activity can apparently be caused either by changes in t-PA release or synthesis, or by changes in inhibition level.

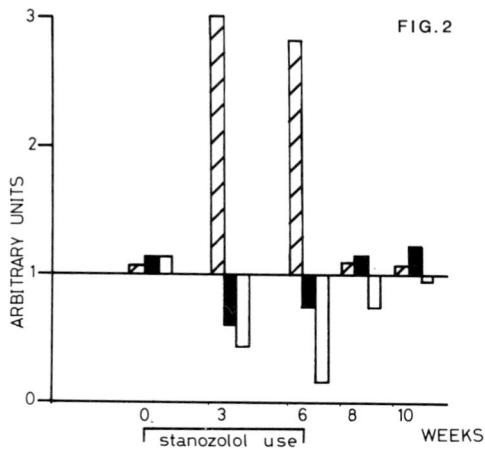

Fig. 23.2 Levels of t-PA activity, antigen and inhibition before, during and after stanozolol use. Results are the mean from nine individuals. Stanozolol was used where indicated, the level at two weeks before stanozolol use was arbitrarily assigned a value of 1 for all parameters. White bar — inhibition; black bar — antigen; striped bar — activity.

REFERENCES

Brommer E J P, Barrett-Bergshoeff M M, Allen R A, Schicht I, Bertina R M, Schalekamp
  M A D H 1982 The use of desmopressin acetate (DDAVP) as a test of the fibrinolytic capacity
  of patients. Analysis of responders and non-responders. Thrombosis & Haemostasis 48:
  156–161
Davidson J F, Lockhead M, McDonald G A, McNicol G P 1972 Fibrinolytic enhancement by
  stanozolol: a double blind trial. British Journal of Haematology 22: 543
Gader A M A, DaCosta J, Cash J G 1973 A new vasopressin analogue and fibrinolysis. Lancet 2:
  1417–1418
Kluft C, Preston F E, Malia R G, Bertina R M, Wijngaards G, Greaves M, Verheijen J H,
  Dooijewaard G 1984 Stanozolol induced changes in fibrinolysis and coagulation in healthy
  adults. Thrombosis & Haemostasis (in press)
Rijken D C, Van Hinsbergh V W M, Sens E H C 1984 Quantitation of tissue-type plasminogen
  activator in human endothelial cell cultures by use of an enzyme immunoassay. Thrombosis
  Research 33: 145–154
Verheijen J H, Mullaart E, Chang G T G, Kluft C, Wijngaards G 1982 A simple, sensitive assay
  for extrinsic (tissue-type plasminogen activator applicable to measurements in plasma.
  Thrombosis & Haemostasis 48: 266–269
Verheijen J H, Rijken D C, Brommer E J P, Chang G T G 1983 Measurement of tissue-type
  plasminogen activator activity, antigen and inhibition in plasma. In: Jespersen J, Kluft C,
  Korsgaard O (eds) Clinical Aspects of Fibrinolysis and Thrombolysis, South Jutland University
  Press, Esbjerg, Denmark p 121–131
Verheijen J H, Sprengers E D, Emeis J J, Van Hinsbergh V W M, Chang G T G, Kluft C 1984
  Fast-acting tissue-type plasminogen activator inhibition by endothelial cell conditioned medium
  and plasma (this book)

24. A comparative study of the influence of intramuscular stanozolol and subcutaneous heparin on coagulation and fibrinolysis following abdominal surgery

M. Greaves, F. E. Preston, C. Kluft,
R. M. Bertina, R. G. Malia and M. Simms

INTRODUCTION

The marked reduction in the fibrinolytic activity of blood after surgery may be a factor in the pathogenesis of post-operative deep vein thrombosis (Mansfield, 1972; Blamey et al 1983). Stanozolol, an anabolic steroid, has a potent stimulating effect on the fibrinolytic system (Kluft et al 1984). We have therefore studied the effects of stanozolol on coagulation and fibrinolysis in subjects undergoing elective abdominal surgery and compared the results with those in similar patients receiving perioperative subcutaneous heparin and with a group receiving no prophylactic agent.

PATIENTS AND METHODS

Four groups, each of 10 patients, were studied. Two groups received stanozolol, one subcutaneous heparin and one no prophylaxis. The regimes were: stanozolol 75 mg by intramuscular injection two days prior to surgery; stanozolol 75 mg intramuscularly one day before surgery; and subcutaneous heparin 5000 units two hours before surgery, then twelve-hourly for five days.

Blood was sampled, as previously described (Kluft et al 1984), on two occasions pre-operatively and on days 1, 3, 5 and 7; (day of surgery = day 0). On each occasion the following laboratory investigations were performed: Euglobulin clot lysis time (ECLT), tissue-type plasminogen activator activity (t-PA), plasma plasminogen, histidine-rich glycoprotein (HRG), protein C, antithrombin III (ATIII), and fibrinogen concentrations. All methods have been described previously (Kluft et al 1984). The concentration of 'free' plasminogen was calculated from:

Plasminogen + HRG $\rightleftarrows$ Plasminogen. HRG (Jespersen & Kluft, 1982).

RESULTS

In the group receiving no prophylaxis, abdominal surgery was associated with a post-operative increase in plasma fibrinogen concentration and lengthening of the ECLT, with a reduction in t-PA (Table 24.1). Plasma plasminogen and protein C concentrations were reduced on day 1, following which protein C rose gradually to baseline concentrations.

Table 24.1 Effect of stanozolol and heparin on ECLT, t-PA and protein C concentration peri-operatively

				Days		
	Pre-op.	0	1	3	5	7
ECLT (minutes) $\times$ 10 000						
SZ2	71	98**	52	55	59	53
SZ1	54	73	53	44	54	59
Heparin	60	78**	43	48	58	52
NP	51	65	37*	48	46	58
t-PA mu/ml: median values						
SZ2	29	99**	11	52	25	32
SZ1	6	25**	3	30	25	28
Heparin	13	34	·5	15	18	12
NP	5	15	4	9	4	6
Protein C (% change from baseline)						
SZ2	100	117**	96	125***	131***	129***
SZ1	100	136	111	147	166	169
Heparin	100	107	77***	87*	99	110*
NP	100	109	82*	95	106	116

* $p < 0.05$
** $p < 0.02$ relative to pre-operative values
*** $p < 0.01$

SZ2 = Stanozolol 2 days pre-operatively, SZ1 = Stanozolol 1 day pre-operatively, NP = No prophylaxis

Patients receiving the stanozolol regimes gave different results. No post-operative reduction in protein C concentration occurred (Table 24.1), a significant increase being noted immediately pre-operatively. HRG concentration fell after surgery with an increase in 'free' plasminogen. t-PA was significantly elevated at day 0, and, after a fall on day 1, an increase in t-PA was seen from day 3. Changes in ECLT mirrored those in t-PA until day 1 only (Table 24.1). Fibrinogen concentration increased post-operatively.

Patients receiving heparin again behaved differently. Both plasma plasminogen and HRG fell post-operatively, resulting in a significant increase in 'free' plasminogen. Again, t-PA was increased on day 0 (before the first injection) but no secondary increase was observed post-operatively (Table 24.1). Fibrinogen concentration increased post-operatively and, as in the no treatment group, protein C concentrations fell significantly post-operatively.

Throughout the study no change in the concentration of ATIII was noted.

DISCUSSION

Reduced fibrinolytic activity after surgery was confirmed, as demonstrated by prolongation of ECLT and reductions in t-PA, protein C and plasminogen.

Subcutaneous heparin had no measurable effect other than that of inducing some increase in 'free' plasminogen post-operatively. Indeed, the percentage reduction in protein C was greater and persisted for longer than in the untreated group.

We have previously demonstrated the potent stimulatory effect of stanozolol on fibrinolysis in normal subjects. In the present study intramuscular stanozolol induced a pre-operative increase in t-PA, but did not prevent the immediate post-operative reduction in activity. However, after day 3, a significant increase in t-PA was noted only in the stanozolol group. In addition, stanozolol prevented the post-operative reduction in protein C and, like heparin, was associated with an increase in 'free' plasminogen. Although it has been reported that stanozolol has a modifying effect on the increase in plasma fibrinogen concentration following surgery (Blamey et al 1983), we could not confirm this.

We conclude that although stanozolol failed to prevent the immediate post-operative depression of fibrinolysis after surgery, it reversed many of the changes in the fibrinolytic system in a way which is of potential clinical benefit. Further clinical studies are therefore indicated.

REFERENCES

Blamey S L, McArdle B M, Burns O, Lowe G D O, Forbes C D, Carter D C, Prentice C R M 1983 Prevention of fibrinolytic shutdown after major surgery by intramuscular stanozolol. Thrombosis Research 31: 451–459

Jespersen J, Kluft C 1982 Decreased levels of histidine-rich glycoprotein (HRG) and increased levels of free plasminogen in women on oral contraceptives low in estrogen. Thrombosis and Haemostasis 48: 283–285

Kluft C, Preston F E, Malia R G, Bertina R M, Wyngaards G, Greaves M, Verheijen J H, Dooijewaard G 1984 Stanozolol-induced changes in fibrinolysis and coagulation in healthy adults. Thrombosis and Haemostasis 51: 157–165

Mansfield A O 1972 Alteration in fibrinolysis associated with surgery and venous thrombosis. Br J Surg 59: 754–757

25. Changes in fibrinolytic activity in patients receiving prophylaxis with stanozolol for the prevention of post-operative deep vein thrombosis

H. M. Sue-Ling, J. A. Davies, C. R. M. Prentice, R. M. Bertina, J. H. Verheijen and C. Kluft

INTRODUCTION

There is a significantly greater decline in fibrinolytic activity after operation in patients who develop deep venous thrombosis (DVT), as compared with those who do not (Mansfield, 1972; Gordon-Smith et al 1974). The prevention of post-operative 'fibrinolytic shutdown' by enhancing fibrinolysis significantly reduces the incidence of post-operative DVT (Knight and Dawson, 1976). We report the changes in fibrinolytic activity occurring before and after operation in patients receiving prophylaxis with stanozolol as part of a continuing, randomised, controlled trial in the prevention of post-operative DVT.

MATERIALS AND METHODS

Euglobulin lysis time (units, $10^6/ELT^2$), At III, plasminogen, fibrinogen, protein C, tPA and fast-acting tPA-inhibitor, were measured in 20 patients randomly allotted to prophylaxis with stanozolol or sub-cutaneous heparin. Stanozolol, 10 mg orally per day, was administered for 14 days before, and 7 days after operation; heparin (5 000 IU, sc) 2 hours before operation and 8 hourly thereafter for 7 days. Samples of blood were obtained in the morning from patients who were resting after an overnight fast, and plasma was prepared immediately. Blood was collected on pre-op day -14, pre-op day -1, and on the 1st, 3rd, 5th and 7th days post-op. The Mann-Whitney 'U' test was used for analysis of results.

RESULTS

Stanozolol prophylaxis resulted in a significant increase between the 14th and 1st pre-operative days in the levels of protein C (116% to 161%; $p < 0.01$), At III (107% to 132%; $p < 0.002$), plasminogen (3.4 to 4.9 Cu/ml; $p < 0.001$), and ELT (25 to 177 units; $p < 0.002$); concentration of tPA rose (6.0 to 16.0 mU/ml,

$p > 0.1$). There was a significant reduction in tPA inhibitor (132% to 75%; $p < 0.02$) and fibrinogen (2.4 to 1.8 g/l; $p < 0.02$).

Surgery had a marked effect on fibrinolytic activity. In the stanozolol treated patients, there was a significant decline in tPA (16.0 to 3.2 mU/ml; $p < 0.01$) and ELT (177 to 16 units; $p < 0.01$); fast-acting tPA inhibitor increased (75% to 164%; $p < 0.01$). Similar changes were seen in the heparin treated patients (Fig. 25.1).

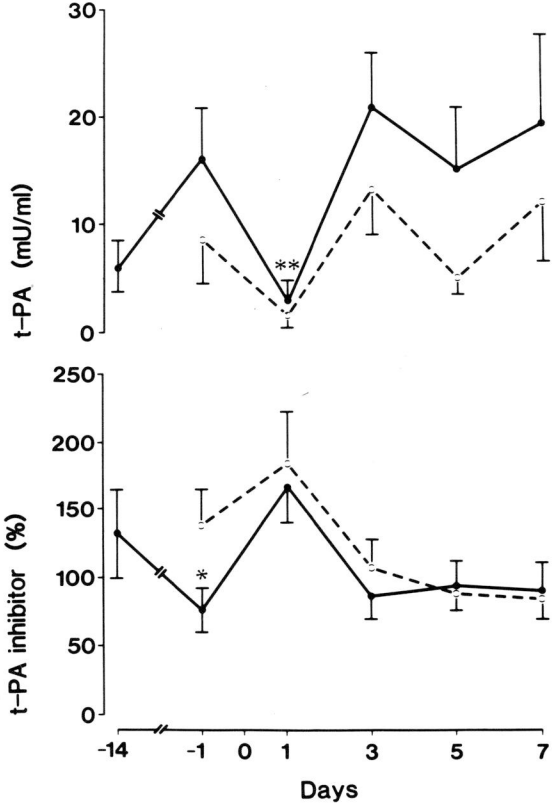

Fig. 25.1 Changes in the concentrations of tPA and fast-acting tPA inhibitor before and after operation. Patients received heparin, 5,000 IU SC, three times daily (dotted lines) or stanozolol, 10 mg/day, for 14 days pre-op (solid lines). * $p < 0.02$; ** $p < 0.01$.

Protein C, At III and plasminogen also fell sharply but levels did not fall below pre-treatment, and remained significantly ($p < 0.01$) higher than in the heparin group on post-op day 1.

CONCLUSIONS

These results indicate that treatment with stanozolol, 10 mg orally per day for two weeks pre-op, significantly enhanced fibrinolytic activity before operation, but did not prevent the decline in fibrinolytic activity which occurs after operation.

REFERENCES

Gordon-Smith I C, Hickman J A, Le Quesne L P 1974 Post-operative fibrinolytic activity and deep vein thrombosis. Br J Surg 61: 213–218

Knight M T N, Dawson R 1976 Effect of intermittent compression of the arm on deep vein thrombosis in the legs. Lancet 2: 1265–1268

Mansfield A O 1972 Alternations in fibrinolysis associated with surgery and venous thrombosis. Br J Surg 59 (10): 754–757

26. A study of stanozolol therapy for systemic sclerosis and Raynaud's phenomenon

M. I. V. Jayson, A. L. Keegan, C. D. Holland, J. Longstaff, L. Taylor and R. Gush

INTRODUCTION

Hyperfibrinogenaemia, impaired fibrinolysis and arterial endothelial fibrin deposition have been confirmed as having a potentially important role in systemic sclerosis (SS) and its associated Raynaud's phenomenon (RP), (Norton, 1970; Jarrett et al 1978; Holland and Jayson, 1983). Previously reported studies suggest that the administration of drugs that enhance fibrinolysis, in particular stanozolol, may be of value in improving not only the fibrinolytic parameters but also the peripheral blood flow (Jarrett et al 1978).

We present results from a long-term study of stanozolol therapy on SS and RP.

METHODS

Four methods of assessment have been used:—

(i) Subjective assessment of the frequency, duration and severity of Raynaud's attacks.

(ii) Objective assessment of digital ulceration and scleroderma.

(iii) Blood flow assessments using laser doppler, ultrasonic doppler, finger temperatures and Xenon clearance.

(iv) Fibrinolytic assessments by euglobulin clot lysis time (ELT), fibrin plate lysis area (FPLA), Fibrinogen, plasminogen, $\alpha 2$ antiplasmin and $\alpha 2$ macroglobulin measurements.

RESULTS AND CONCLUSIONS

Fourteen patients have completed the double-blind cross-over trial and significant (Wilcoxon Analysis) improvements in blood flow measurements and fibrinolytic measurements have been found. Furthermore, the majority of patients claimed some clinical benefit having recorded a decreased frequency, duration and severity of their Raynaud's attacks.

111

The results indicate that stanozolol may be of therapeutic value to some patients suffering from SS and its associated RP.

ACKNOWLEDGEMENT

The authors would like to thank Sterling-Winthrop for supporting this study.

REFERENCES

Norton W L 1970 Comparison of Microangiopathy of Systemic Lupus Erythematosis, Dermatomyositis, Scleroderma and Diabetes Mellitus. Laboratory Investigation 22: 301–308
Jarrett P E M, Morland M, Browse N L 1978 Treatment of Raynaud's Phenomenon by Fibrinolytic Enhancements. British Medical Journal 2: 523–525
Holland C D, Jayson M I V 1983 Venous Blood Fibrinolysis and Fibrinolytic Potential in Primary Raynaud's Phenomenon and Systemic Sclerosis Associated with Raynaud's Phenomenon. Arthritis and Rheumatism (in press)

Section 5
INHIBITORS OF PLASMINOGEN ACTIVATORS

27. Determination of tissue plasminogen activator and its inhibitor in plasma samples

J. Chmielewska, G. Urdén and B. Wiman

Different methods to measure the fibrinolytic potential in plasma have been compared. Samples from twenty healthy persons and 24 patients with deep venous thrombosis were analysed for tissue plasminogen activator (t-PA) activity or antigen concentrations, fibrin plate lytic capacity and the novel fast t-PA inhibitor. For t-PA assays two samples of blood were taken — at rest and after 10 min venous occlusion. For the t-PA inhibitor assay blood was taken from resting subjects. For the spectrophotometric t-PA assay *blood* was immediately acidified to pH = 4.0 in order to destroy inhibitors (Chmielewska et al 1983). After dilution of plasma at pH = 8.8 the t-PA assay was performed according to Chmielewska et al (1983) and Wiman et al (1983). Results of this assay were compared with the results obtained from parallelly prepared euglobulin fractions assayed on fibrin plates according to Norén et al (1975). t-PA antigen was also assayed using a solid phase double antibody radioimmunoassay (Urdén, Blombäck, 1984). For the t-PA inhibitor assay (Chmielewska et al 1983), 2 IU/ml t-PA were added to diluted plasma; after 20 min incubation plasma was acidified to pH = 4.0. The inhibitor concentration was calculated from the residual t-PA activity.

When the results of the spectrophotometric t-PA assay were compared with the results of the fibrin plate lysis (Fig. 27.1) a correlation coefficient of 0.71 was found. In some subjects overestimation of the t-PA level was obtained on the fibrin plates, which may be due to non t-PA mediated fibrinolysis. On the other hand, an underestimation of t-PA activity with the fibrin plate method was more common, particularly among the patients. Most likely this is due to the effect of the fast-acting t-PA inhibitor. Indeed, subjects with low t-PA level when assayed on fibrin plates but high t-PA activity when determined with the new assay had increased level of the fast t-PA inhibitor. Therefore, underestimation of t-PA level in euglobulin precipitates is likely to occur in all subjects with increased level of the fast t-PA inhibitor, taking into account that about 20 minutes normally elapse between blood sampling and euglobulin precipitation.

With the new assay, t-PA level in 20 normal subjects was determined as 0.04 ± 0.03 IU/ml (mean $\pm$ SD, range < 0.01–0.13 IU/ml) in plasma taken at rest and 2.0 ± 1.5 IU/ml (mean $\pm$ SD, range 0.6–5.4 IU/ml) after venous occlusion. In the same subjects t-PA antigen level was 4.4 ± 1.3 ug/l (mean $\pm$ SD, range 2.1–7.3 ug/l) in resting subjects and 13.9 ± 6.2 ug/l (mean $\pm$ SD, range 7.6–31.2

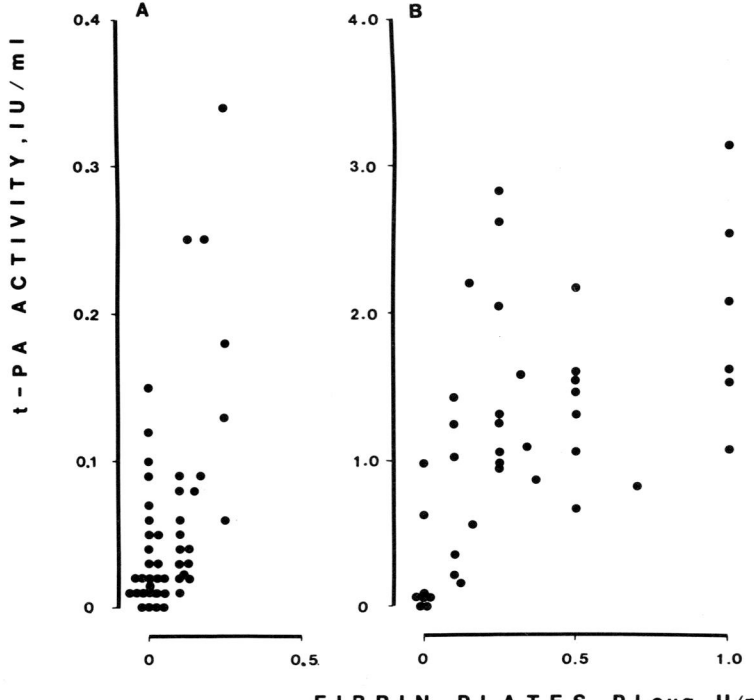

Fig. 27.1 t-PA level after venous occlusion — correlation with fibrin plates (a — preocclusion samples, b — post-occlusion samples).

ug/l) after venous occlusion (one 1 IU corresponds to about 4.6 ng/ml). On comparison of t-PA activity and antigen in the samples, it is evident that in plasma taken at rest as much as about 95% of the t-PA antigen is in an inactive form, probably in complex with the fast t-PA inhibitor. A high correlation (r = 0.91) was found between t-PA activity release and t-PA antigen released on venous occlusion in normal subjects.

t-PA inhibitor concentration in these subjects was estimated as 0.7 ± 20.7 U/ml (mean $\pm$ SD, range 0–2.4 U/ml). A weak inverse correlation with t-PA activity measured at rest was found (r = -0.40), but no correlation was found with t-PA values in the post-occlusion plasma.

REFERENCES

1. Chmielewska J, Rånby M, Wiman B 1983 Evidence for a rapid inhibitor to tissue plasminogen activator in plasma. Thrombosis Research, 31: 427–436
2. Norén I, Ramström G, Wallén P 1975 Fibrin plate method with reagents purified by affinity chromatography and its use for determination of fibrinolytic and other proteolytic activity in saliva, bile and plasma. Haemostasis 4: 110–124
3. Urdén G, Blombäck M 1984 Determination of tissue plasminogen activator in plasma samples by means of a radioimmunoassay. Scandinavian Journal of Clinical and Laboratory Investigation (in press)
4. Wiman B, Mellbring G, Rånby M 1983 Plasminogen activator release during venous stasis and exercise as determined by a new specific assay. Clinica Chimica Acta, 127: 279–288

28. Diurnal fluctuations in the activity of the fast-acting t-PA inhibitor

C. Kluft, J. H. Verheijen, D. C. Rijken,
G. T. G. Chang, A. F. H. Jie and C. Onkelinx

INTRODUCTION

Diurnal fluctuations in blood fibrinolytic activity have been observed since the onset of studies on blood fibrinolysis. The absence of a normal rhythm has been found to occur in patients with type IV hyperlipoproteinemia, in many subjects with coronary artery disease and in a high percentage of older subjects (Rosing et al 1973). It has been demonstrated that the diurnal fluctuations involve blood activity of tissue-type plasminogen activator (t-PA) (Kluft 1978; Kluft et al 1983).

It has been suggested that an abnormal diurnal rhythm in blood fibrinolytic activity reflects an abnormal physiological regulation of fibrinolysis and might be related to the development of coronary artery disease (Brakman, 1974).

The recent discovery of a specific, fast-acting t-PA inhibitor in blood (Kruithof et al 1982; Verheijen et al, 1983; Chmielewska et al 1983) necessitates reevaluation of fluctuations in t-PA activity. As shown schematically in Figure 28.1, the unique release of both active enzyme and its inhibitor in blood, besides individually clearing of these components, also results in rapid complex formation. In this situation t-PA activity may in principle vary by both changes in its release (VI) and changes in its removal via inhibitor reactions, e.g. by alterations in inhibitor release (V2).

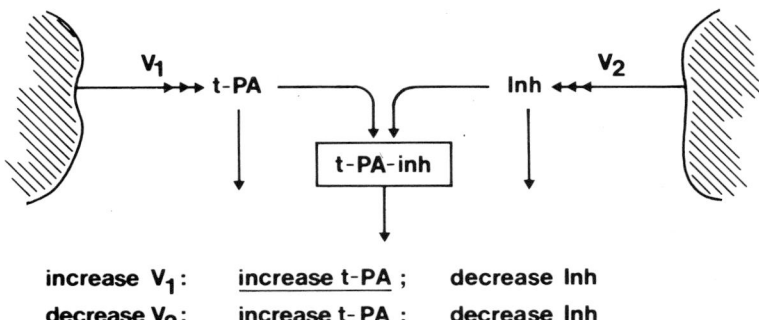

Fig. 28.1 Schematic presentation of the release and clearance of t-PA and its fast-acting inhibitor in blood and their mutual relationship. t-PA-inh = t-PA inhibitor-complex. Two hypothetical possibilities for increasing t-PA activity are given.

In the present study we have reevaluated the variation in t-PA activity during the period 09.00 a.m. to 03.00 p.m. in a group of ten apparently healthy male volunteers (age 22–34 years). We determined t-PA activity by the parabolic rate assay using synthetic substrate as described by Verheijen et al (1982). t-PA antigen was determined by enzyme immunoassay as described by Rijken et al (1984). Fast-acting t-PA inhibitor activity was determined by the method of Verheijen et al (1983) and values expressed in mU/ml of neutralized t-PA activity.

RESULTS AND DISCUSSION

As shown in Table 28.1, from 09.00 a.m. to 03.00 p.m. the activity of t-PA increased by about a factor of three, in accordance with its known diurnal behaviour during this period of the day. Interestingly, t-PA inhibitor activity showed a complementary pattern, being high in the morning and low (ca. 50%) in the afternoon. Also the t-PA antigen levels which represent both t-PA and t-PA-inhibitor complexes showed a significant fluctuation during daytime, being ca. 20% lower in the afternoon (Table 28.1).

Table 28.1 Diurnal variations in plasma parameters of in the extrinsic system of fibrinolysis*

	09.00 a.m.	03.00 p.m.	p**
t-PA activity (mU/ml)	9.9 ± 9.1	30.3 ± 17.5	<0.01
t-PA antigen (ng/ml)	13.5 ± 3.6	10.3 ± 3.0	<0.01
t-PA inhibitor (mU/ml)	744.0 ± 492.0	354.0 ± 228.0	<0.01

* Mean of 10 volunteers ± SD: ** Wilcoxon signed rank test.

Our conclusion is that the blood levels of all three parameters tested showed a significant diurnal fluctuation.

It should be noted that a similar pattern (increase in t-PA activity, decrease in t-PA antigen and decrease in t-PA inhibitor activity) as observed here (in the afternoon) is also observed as the result of stanozolol treatment (Verheijen et al 1984). It is suggested by them that stanozolol primarily induces a reduction in inhibitor synthesis or release, resulting in increased t-PA activity. Also for the diurnal fluctuations, t-PA inhibitor variability alone would be sufficient to explain the effects. It can at least be concluded that there is a primary diurnal fluctuation in t-PA inhibitor activity in blood; since the reduction in its activity cannot be attributed to the t-PA which showed no enhancement but a reduced level (antigen) in the afternoon. In view of the connection between t-PA and its inhibitor as schematically illustrated in Figure 28.1, it cannot be decided from the present results whether t-PA fluctuations are also primary or only a reflection of inhibitor fluctuations. The issue is further complicated by the possibility that fluctuations in blood levels may be caused by either release variations (V1, V2) or clearance variations (or both).

A practical consequence of the present findings is that studies on all three parameters discussed need to be standardized with regard to the time of blood sampling.

The present results identify the t-PA inhibitor metabolism as fluctuating rapidly and suggest a metabolic half-life for the t-PA inhibitor of clearly below 6 hours.

Furthermore, it suggests focussing attention on deviations in t-PA inhibitor regulation in the cases with an impaired diurnal rhythm in blood fibrinolytic activity mentioned in the introduction. This strengthens the case for concentrating attention on the t-PA inhibitor, rather than on t-PA itself in relation to thrombosis and coronary artery disease since recently, in such conditions, reduced t-PA activity (especially after venous occlusion and DDAVP administration) has also been found to be caused by elevated t-PA inhibitor levels in a majority of cases (Nilsson & Tengborn, 1983; Brommer et al 1984).

REFERENCES

Brakman P 1974 Regulation and control of fibrinolysis. In: Maas J (ed) Proceedings 4th International Symposium on Medicinal Chemistry. Noordwijkerhout, the Netherlands. Elsevier Scientific Publishing Company, Amsterdam. pp 209–225

Brommer E J P, Verheijen J H, Rijken D C 1984 Masking of fibrinolytic response to DDAVP, venous occlusion and exercise by high levels of fast acting inhibitors of tissue plasminogen activators. Haemostasis 14: 102 (abstr.)

Chmielewska J, Ranby M, Wiman B 1983 Evidence for a rapid inhibitor to tissue plasminogen activator in plasma. Thrombosis Research 13: 427–436

Kluft C 1978 C1-inactivator-resistant fibrinolytic activity in plasma euglobulin fractions: Its relation to vascular activator in blood and its role in euglobulin fibrinolysis. Thrombosis Research 13: 135–151

Kluft C, Jie A F H, Allen R A 1983 Behaviour and quantitation of extrinsic (tissue-type) plasminogen activator in human blood. Thrombosis and Haemostasis 50: 518–523

Kruithof E K O, Ransijn A, Bachmann F 1982 Inhibition of tissue plasminogen activator (TA) by human plasma. Haemostasis 11: 60 (abstr.)

Nilsson I M, Tenborn L 1983 Impaired fibrinolysis. New evidence in relation to thrombosis. In: Jespersen J, Kluft C, Korsgaard O (eds) Clinical Aspects of Fibrinolysis and Thrombolysis, South Jutland University Press, Esbjerg, Denmark. pp 273–291

Rosing D R, Redwood D R, Brakman P, Astrup T, Epstein S E 1973 Impairment of the diurnal fibrinolytic response in man. Effects of aging, type IV hyperlipoproteinaemia, and coronary artery disease. Circulation Research 32: 752–758

Rijken D C, Van Hinsbergh V W M, Sens E H C 1984 Quantitation of tissue-type plasminogen activator in human endothelial cell cultures by use of an enzyme immunoassay. Thrombosis Research 33: 145–153

Verheijen J H, Mullaart E, Chang G T G, Kluft C, Wijngaards G 1982 A simple, sensitive spectrophotometric assay for extrinsic (tissue-type) plasminogen activator applicable to measurements in plasma. Thrombosis and Haemostasis 48: 266–269

Verheijen J H, Rijken D C, Brommer E J P, Chang G T G 1983 Measurement of tissue-type plasminogen activator activity, antigen and inhibition in plasma. In: Jespersen J, Kluft C, Korsgaard (eds) Clinical Aspects of Fibrinolysis and Thrombolysis, South Jutland University Press, Esbjerg, Denmark, pp 121–131

Verheijen J H, Rijken D C, Chang G T G, Preston F E, Kluft C 1984 The level of rapid tissue-type plasminogen activator inhibition in plasma is decreased by oral administration of stanozolol. Haemostasis 14: 31 (abstr 51)

29. The novel fast tissue plasminogen activator inhibitor in pregnancy

B. Wiman, G. Csemiczky and L. Marsk

For a long time it has been known that the fibrinolytic potential is decreased in the late phase of normal pregnancy and that this phenomenon is normalized shortly after delivery (Åstedt et al 1970). The reason for this has not been understood at all.

Recently we were able to demonstrate the presence of a fast inhibitor towards tissue plasminogen activator in plasma samples (Chmielewska et al 1983). This inhibitor rapidly forms an enzymatically inactive complex with t-PA, with a molecular weight of about 120,000 (Wiman et al 1984a). The concentration of the inhibitor could be determined by adding a small specific amount of t-PA to properly diluted plasma. After incubation at room temperature for 20 min the residual t-PA activity was determined and used for calculation of the inhibitor concentration. The fast t-PA inhibitor concentration was found to be increased in plasma from many patients with thromboembolic disease (Wiman et al this volume). Moreover, increased levels in plasma were also found during pregnancy (Wiman et al 1984b).

The results obtained on healthy pregnant women at different stages of pregnancy is summarized in Table 29.1.

Table 29.1 Concentration of the novel fast t-PA inhibitor in plasma from healthy pregnant women as compared to samples from healthy non-pregnant women and to samples taken at the fifth day post partum

Stage of pregnancy	Number	Median	Range
Non-pregnant	20	0.4	0.0–3.1
First trimester	12	0.8	0.0–2.6
Second trimester	21	2.0	0.7–4.2
Third trimester	15	5.0	4.0–6.6
Post partum	17	1.0	0.2–2.5

The about ten-fold increase of t-PA inhibitor concentration found in the last trimester is most likely the sole explanation for the decreased fibrinolytic potential reported during late phase pregnancy. In risk pregnancies more variable results were obtained in the last trimester. Thus, in preeclampsia the concentration was determined as 5.8 ± 4.4 (SD) U/ml (median 5.0, range

0.5–25.0, n = 71) and in suspected fetal growth retardation the concentration was 5.7 ± 6.3 (SD) U/ml (median 4.0, range 0–24.0, n = 16). In patients with diabetes the t-PA inhibitor concentration was found to be 5.2 ± 1.3 (SD) U/ml (median 5.5, range 1.0–6.0, n = 11).

Thus, many patients with risk pregnancies have highly increased levels of the novel fibrinolytic inhibitor, but many seem to have decreased levels. The pathophysiological significance of these findings is at present unclear.

ACKNOWLEDGEMENTS

Financial support has been obtained from the Swedish Medical Research Council (project no 05193), KabiVitrum AB and Karolinska Institute.

REFERENCES

Åstedt B, Isacson S, Nilsson I M 1970 Fibrinolytic activity of veins during pregnancy. Acta Obstetrica Gynecologica Scandinavia 49: 171–173

Chmielewska J, Rånby M, Wiman B 1983 Evidence for a rapid inhibitor to tissue plasminogen activator in plasma. Thrombosis Research 31: 427–436

Wiman B, Chmielewska J, Rånby M 1984a Inactivation of tissue plasminogen activator in plasma: Demonstration of a complex with a new rapid inhibitor. Journal of Biological Chemistry 259: 3644–3647

Wiman B, Csemiczky G, Marsk L, Robbe H 1984b The fast inhibitor of tissue plasminogen activator in plasma during pregnancy. Thrombosis and Haemostasis. In press

Wiman B, Chmielewska J, Rånby M A novel fast inhibitor of tissue plasminogen activator in plasma. Progress in Fibrinolysis, vol 7. Churchill Livingstone, Edinburgh. In press

30. An inhibitor of plasminogen activator in pregnancy plasma

B. Astedt, L. Holmberg and I -M. Nilsson

During pregnancy the fibrinolytic activity in blood successively decreases and is hardly detectable at term, even after stimulation by venous occlusion (Åstedt et al 1970). It rapidly returns to non-pregnant levels after separation of placenta (Åstedt 1972). The low fibrinolytic activity could be due to either impaired synthesis or release of plasminogen activator of the tissue-type (t-PA) from vessel wall or binding of t-PA to a specific inhibitor.

We studied the concentration of t-PA in plasma, the t-PA inhibitory capacity of plasma and formation of t-PA/inhibitor complex during pregnancy and after delivery.

MATERIALS AND METHODS

Plasma samples were obtained from 57 normals and in 51 women during pregnancy and 1–2 days after delivery, distributed according to Fig. 30.1.

t-PA was determined by an immunoradiometric method (Holmberg et al 1982). The method is based on ^{125}I-labelled antibodies against t-PA from Bowes melanoma cell line. It detects t-PA in a concentration of 1 μg/l or even less.

Inhibitor of t-PA (t-PAI) was determined by addition of 10 ng purified t-PA from Bowes melanoma cell line to 1 ml of various plasma dilutions. After incubation at 37°C for 15 minutes (pH 7.4) residual t-PA activity was assayed using S-2251 (Gyzander et al 1983). t-PA was expressed in arbitrary units, one inhibitor unit defined as the amount neutralizing 1 ng t-PA.

Formation of t-PA/inhibitor complex was studied by zymographic fibrin overlayer technique (Granelli-Piperno & Reich, 1978). Plasma in dilutions 1:10-1:100 were incubated with melanoma cell derived t-PA for 1 h at 37°C. To each plasma dilution (70 μl) was added 0.2 ng melanoma cell derived t-PA. The method depends on the fact that complexes retain some lytic activity.

RESULTS

The concentration of t-PA at the end of pregnancy as determined immunologically was the same as in non-pregnant women (Fig. 30.1). The

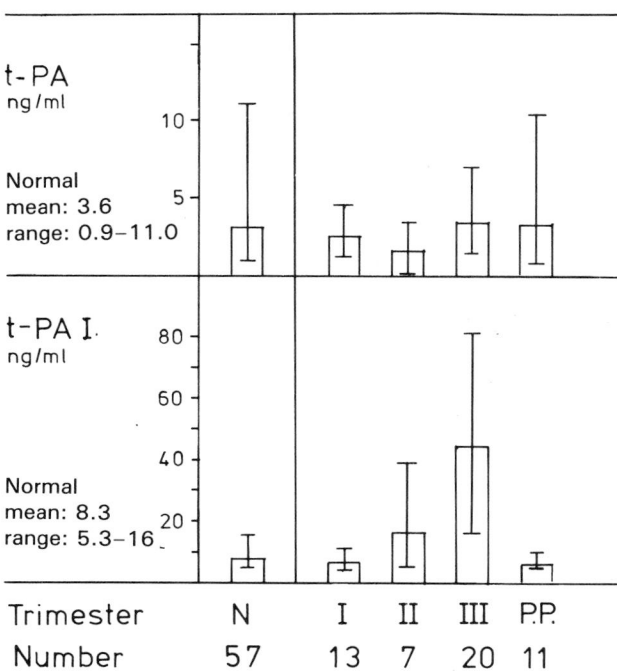

Fig. 30.1 Concentration of t-PA antigen and t-PAI in normals, pregnant women and women 1-2 days after delivery.

capacity of 3rd trimester pregnancy plasma to inhibit the amidolytic t-PA activity was 4–5 times higher than that of non-pregnancy plasma (Fig. 30.1). Increased inhibitory capacity of plasma during pregnancy was also illustrated by increased complex formation in the third trimester (Fig. 30.2). The fibrin overlayer technique also demonstrated that the inhibitor had a molecular weight of about 45 000 daltons.

DISCUSSION

The results thus show that in contrast to the well-known depressed fibrinolytic activity at term, the concentration of t-PA immunologically determined, is the same as in non-pregnant women. An inhibitor of 45 000 daltons forms a complex with t-PA and is present in increasing amounts during pregnancy and decreases after delivery. It was earlier believed that the low fibrinolytic activity during pregnancy was due to impaired release of t-PA from the vessel walls. Our findings clearly show that the decreased fibrinolytic activity instead is due to inactivation of t-PA by an inhibitor.

It is known that the fibrinolytic activity at term is low even when stimulated by venous occlusion (Åstedt et al 1970). Our results indicate that the inhibitory capacity of plasma at term is large enough to inhibit also the t-PA released from the vessel wall at venous occlusion. Alternatively, an additional release of t-PAI may also occur during venous occlusion.

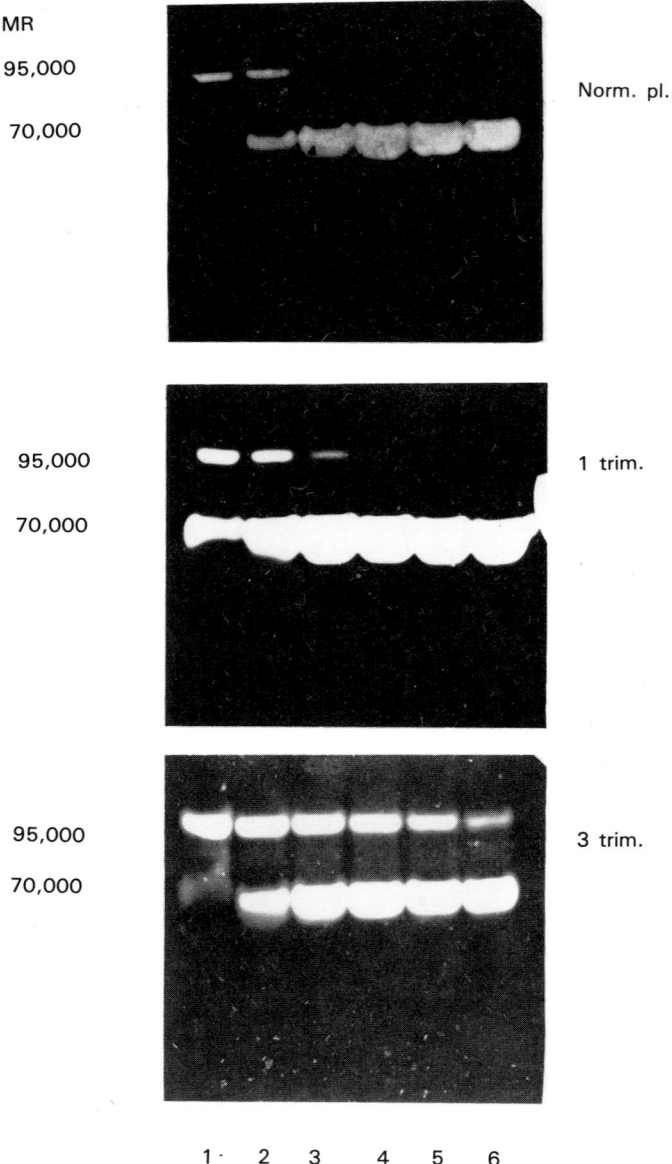

Fig. 30.2 t-PA-inhibitory capacity of normal plasma and plasma from pregnant women in the first and third trimester as demonstrated by fibrin overlayer technique. Lanes 1–6 are run with plasma in dilutions 1:10, 1:20, 1:50, 1:100, 1:200, 1:500 each dilution incubated with t-PA for 1 h at 37°C. To each plasma dilution (70 μl) was added 0.2 ng melanoma cell derived t-PA. t-PA of the molecular weight of 70 000 migrates after complex formation to a position of 95 000 MW. Third trimester plasma is capable of forming complex even in its highest dilution.

Placenta contains a specific plasminogen activator inhibitor which inhibits urokinase and t-PA but not plasmin (Kawano et al 1968; Holmberg et al 1978). This inhibitor is also released in placental tissue culture (Åstedt et al 1972). After separation of placenta the fibrinolytic activity rapidly returns to non-pregnant levels (Åstedt, 1972). This observation and the present results suggest similarity between the placental plasminogen activator inhibitor and the plasminogen activator inhibitor present in pregnancy plasma.

ACKNOWLEDGEMENTS

The investigation was supported by grants from the Swedish Medical Research Council (17X-04523; 19X-00087; 19X-04997).

REFERENCES

Åstedt B 1972 Demonstration of significance of placenta in depression of fibrinolytic activity during pregnancy. The Journal of Obstetrics and Gynaecology of the British Commonwealth 79: 205–206

Åstedt B, Isacson S, Nilsson I M, Pandolfi M 1970 Fibrinolytic activity of veins during pregnancy. Acta Obstetricia et Gynecologica Scandinavica 48: 171–173

Åstedt B, Pandolfi M, Nilsson I M 1972 Inhibitory effect of placenta on plasminogen activation in human organ culture. Proceedings of the Society for Experimental Biology and Medicine 139: 1421–1424

Granelli-Piperno A, Reich E 1978 A study of proteases and protease-inhibitor complexes in biological fluids. Journal of Experimental Medicine 148: 223–234

Gyzander E, Eriksson E, Teger-Nilsson A C 1983 Determination of tissue plasminogen activator in plasma after adsorption on lysine-Sepharose. In: Davidson J F, Bachman F, Bouvier C A, Kruithof E K O (eds) Progress in fibrinolysis. Churchill Livingstone, Edinburgh, vol 6, 425–428

Holmberg L, Kristoffersson A C, Lecander I, Wallén P, Åstedt B 1982 Immunoradiometric quantification of tissue plasminogen activator secreted by fetal organs. Comparison with urokinase. Scandinavian Journal of Clinical and Laboratory Investigation 42: 347–354

Holmberg L, Lecander O, Persson B, Åstedt B 1978 An inhibitor from placenta specifically binds urokinase and inhibits plasminogen activator released from ovarian carcinoma in tissue culture. Biochemica et Biophysica Acta 544: 128–137

Kawano T, Morimoto K, Uemura Y 1968 Urokinase inhibitor in human placenta. Nature 217: 253–254

31. Masking of the response to DDAVP, venous occlusion and exercise by high levels of the fast acting inhibitor of tissue plasminogen activator

E. J. P. Brommer, A. L. Boks, J. H. Verheijen and D. C. Rijken

In a normal person the fibrinolytic activity of the blood varies considerably, depending on the time of the day and on his physical and mental activity. Several stimuli, e.g. intravenous injection of nicotinic acid or DDAVP enhance the fibrinolytic activity of the blood, and venous occlusion causes a rise in the fibrinolytic activity in the occluded vessels. The increase in activity can safely be attributed to the release of tissue-type plasminogen activator (t-PA).

We observed a spontaneous rise in fibrinolytic activity, measured in euglobulin fractions on fibrin plates (Kluft et al, 1976), in a patient admitted with acute liver failure (Fig. 31.1). Within 24 hours after admission the fibrinolytic activity increased from zero to a higher than normal level (94 ± 41 mm^2). Since the t-PA-antigen (enzyme-immunoassay, Rijken et al, 1984) remained approximately at the same level, a spontaneous change in the newly discovered t-PA-inhibitor (Verheijen et al, 1983) was suggested. Indeed, measurement of the free fast-acting t-PA-inhibitor by titration of diluted plasma with purified t-PA (Verheijen et al, 1984) showed a drop in the inhibitor level which apparently occurred independently of treatment with haemodialysis.

Two tentative conclusions were drawn. First of all, contrary to former belief, some inhibitors, i.e. the t-PA-inhibitor in plasma, seem to influence the fibrinolytic activity of euglobulins. Secondly, if they do, an increase in t-PA may occur unnoticed after stimulation when only euglobulin fibrinolytic activity is followed. So, an inability to respond to stimulation with a rise in (euglobulin) fibrinolytic activity might be due, not to an impairment of t-PA-release (Brommer et al, 1982) but to a high level of the t-PA-inhibitor.

An inverse correlation between t-PA-activity, measured in euglobulins, and free t-PA-inhibitor was found in several groups of patients (Brommer et al, 1984a, 1984b). This is an argument in favour of the first conclusion.

Most poor responders to DDAVP, described before (Brommer et al, 1982), appeared on re-analysis to have a very high level of free t-PA-inhibitor. After stimulation with DDAVP this level only diminished, but it did not disappear as it does in normal responders. A similar phenomenon was found in poor responders to venous occlusion, encountered among hypercholesterolaemic patients and in patients with spontaneous recurrent thrombosis. In an apparently healthy

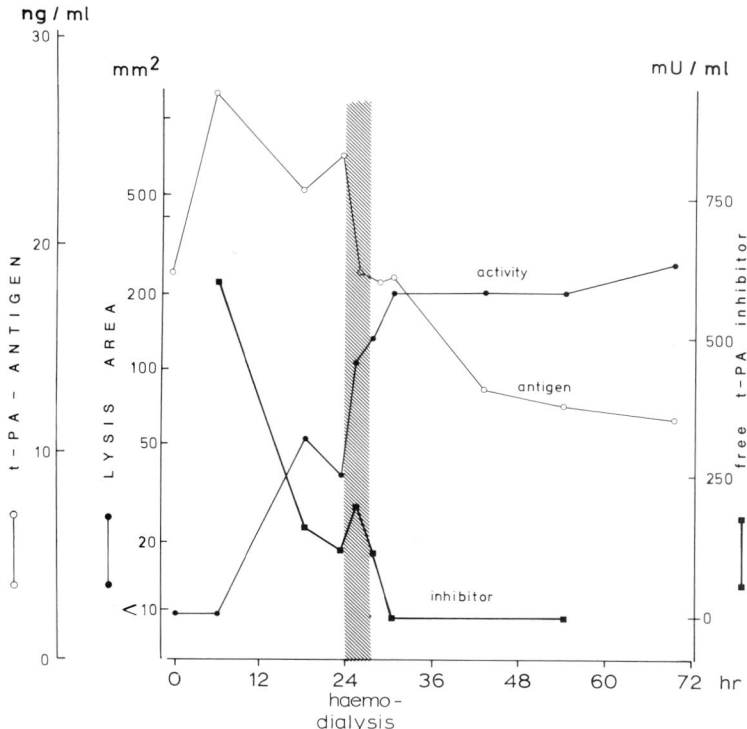

Fig. 31.1 t-PA activity (euglobulins on fibrin plates), t-PA antigen (enzyme immunoassay in plasma) and free t-PA inhibitor (titration method with purified t-PA in diluted plasma) of a patient admitted with acute liver failure.

volunteer whose fibrinolytic activity did not rise after exhaustive exercise also a higher than normal level of the inhibitor was found. The level of t-PA-antigen rose normally after the stimulus in each case.

A notable exception was a group of poor responders among uraemic patients on chronic haemodialysis. They proved to have a normal level of free t-PA-inhibitor which diminished after DDAVP-infusion but often not to zero, like it did in good responders. Furthermore, they showed only a minimal rise of the t-PA-antigen. We suggest that in these patients a true impairment of response exists. This is in agreement with the small change in factor VIII-antigen level after the same stimulus in the same patients (Brommer et al, 1982).

These observations are of importance for the interpretation of fibrinolytic activity of euglobulin fractions. Obviously, at a certain moment either free t-PA-inhibitor is present in the plasma (explaining the absence of fibrinolytic activity of whole blood and plasma, withdrawn in a resting state) or there is freely circulating t-PA (after stimulation, when all inhibitor is neutralized). The demonstration of activity (after precipitation and redissolution of euglobulins) when in fact there is still free inhibitor present in plasma, is unexplained and perhaps misleading. Probably, part of t-PA and inhibitor circulate in a reversible complex that dissociates during euglobulin preparation. The paradox is represented graphically in figure 2: despite high plasma levels of t-PA-inhibitor

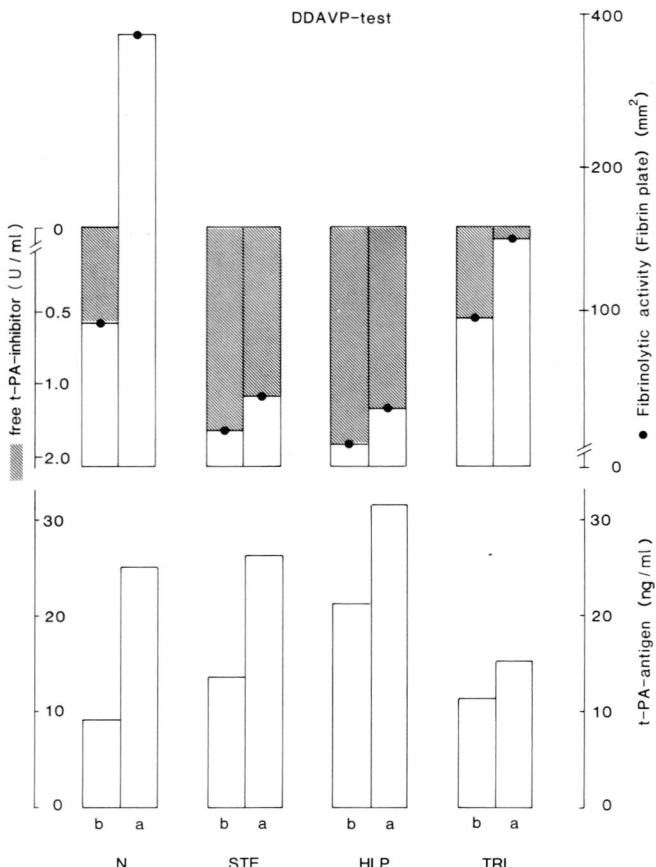

Fig. 31.2 Lower panel: t-PA-antigen in normal responders and in so-called poor responders, showing a rise after DDAVP, except in uraemic patients on chronic haemodialysis. Upper panel: tentative graphical representation of the apparent paradox of the simultaneous occurrence of fibrinolytic activity in euglobulins and free t-PA-inhibitor in plasma, showing their inverse correlation. Note the steep rise in fibrinolytic activity in normal responders as soon as the t-PA-inhibitor is completely neutralized. b = before; a = after DDAVP; N = Healthy volunteers; STE = spontaneous thromboembolism; HLP = hyperlipoproteinaemia; TRI = terminal renal failure.

some fibrinolytic activity is found in euglobulins, but a high activity occurs only in the absence of inhibitor. The breaking point appears to be in the neighbourhood of 150 mm². For the interpretation of the fibrinolytic activity measured in euglobulin fractions the assay of free t-PA-inhibitor is necessary, especially when the reaction to stimulation is tested.

REFERENCES

Brommer E J P, Barrett-Bergshoeff M M, Allen R A, Schicht I, Bertina R M, Schalekamp M A D H 1982 The use of desmopressin acetate (DDAVP) as a test of the fibrinolytic capacity of patients. Analysis of responders and non-responders. Thrombosis and Haemostasis 48: 156–161

Brommer E J P, Boks A L, Rijken D C, Verheijen J H 1984 Fast inhibitor of plasminogen activator in severe liver disease. Haemostasis 14: 111 (abstract)

Brommer E J P, Wijngaards G, Verheijen J H, Rijken D C 1984 Fibrinolytic activators and inhibitors in terminal renal insufficiency. Haemostasis 14: 116 (abstract)

Kluft C, Brakman P, Veldhuyzen-Stolk E C 1976 Screening of fibrinolytic activity in plasma euglobulin fractions on the fibrin plate. In: Davidson J F, Samama M M, Desnoyers P C (eds) Progress in Chemical Fibrinolysis and thrombolysis Vol. 2. Raven Press, New York, p 57–65

Rijken D C, Van Hinsbergh V W M, Sens E H C 1984 Quantitation of tissue-type plasminogen activator in human endothelial cell cultures by use of an enzyme immunoassay. Thrombosis Research 33: 145–153

Verheijen J H, Rijken D C, Brommer E J P 1983 Measurement of tissue-type plasminogen activator activity, antigen and inhibition in plasma. In: Jespersen J, Kluft C, Korsgaard O (eds) Clinical Aspects of Fibrinolysis and Thrombolysis. South Jutland University Press, Esbjerg, p 121–131

Verheijen J H, Chang G T G, Kluft C 1984 Evidence for the occurrence of a fast-acting inhibitor for tissue-type plasminogen activator in human plasma. Thrombosis and Haemostasis (in press)

32. Antiactivator levels in various disease states

E. K. O. Kruithof, A-L. Gudinchet, C. Tran-Thang, A. Ransijn and F. Bachmann

Recently a fast-acting inhibitor of tissue-type plasminogen activator (t-PA) has been demonstrated in human plasma (Kruithof et al, 1983; Kruithof et al, 1984; Chmielewska et al, 1983; Juhan-Vague et al, 1984; Verheijen et al, 1983). It forms at a fast rate (second order rate constant in the order of $10^7 M^{-1} s^{-1}$) complexes of a M_r of 110'000 with t-PA (Kruithof et al, 1984; Chmielewska wt al, 1983). Preliminary results suggest that it is also the primary inhibitor of urokinase in plasma (Kruithof et al, 1984; Juhan-Vague et al, 1984). Thus, we have proposed the name antiactivator to designate the primary inhibitor of t-PA and urokinase in plasma. Its pathophysiological role is still unclear. In the present study we have determined the concentration of antiactivator in apparently healthy subjects and in hospitalized patients.

MATERIALS AND METHODS

Subjects

Blood was obtained from apparently healthy laboratory workers, blood donors and from various groups of patients as indicated on Table 32.1.

Table 32.1 Antiactivator levels in healthy persons and hospitalized patients

	n	mean ± SD	median	observed range	p†
healthy controls	51	1.5 ± 6.9	0.7	0 – 13.8	—
intensive care	7	2.4 ± 1.6	2.6	0.6 – 5.1	0.02
infectious disease	15	1.6 ± 3.1	1.1	0.5 – 7.6	0.05
lung disease	12	1.3 ± 0.6	1.0	0.7 – 2.6	0.05
thromboembolic disease	21	3.5 ± 5.0	2.1	0 – 20.0	0.005
fractures	30	1.6 ± 1.8	1.2	0.3 – 10.0	0.01
extracorporeal circulation	10	8.4 ± 8.7	4.4	0.4 – 20,0	0.005
tumours	35	2.6 ± 2.5	1.7	0.4 – 10.3	0.002
postoperative	15	2.0 ± 2.0	1.2	0.2 – 8.0	0.05
liver disease	5	5.3 ± 5.0	3.3	2.5 – 14.2	0.002
coronary disease	18	4.0 ± 5.6	1.2	0.2 – 17.5	0.02
essential hypertension	6	2.8 ± 2.9	1.5	0.5 – 7.6	0.1

†p smaller than, as determined with the Mann-Whitney test

Plasma

Nine parts of blood were mixed with one part of 100mM citrate, pH 4.5, centrifuged for 15 min at 3600 g and 4°C and snap frozen at − 70°C. Prior to assay the frozen plasma was thawed for 10 min in a 37°C water bath.

t-PA

t-PA was purified to apparent homogeneity from the conditioned medium of human Bowes melanoma cells (Kruithof et al, manuscript submitted). 1 U of t-PA corresponds to 10 ng of pure t-PA.

Antiactivator assay

Antiactivator levels in plasma were determined as previously described (Kruithof et al, 1984). In short: t-PA was added to plasma at final concentrations of 2.5, 5, 10 and 20 U/ml. After 10 min incubation at 37°C, the plasma was clotted by the addition of thrombin (Topostasin[R], Roche, Basel, 10 U/ml final concentration), EDTA (10 mM) and aprotinin (Trasylol[R], Bayer, Leverkusen, 100 U/ml). After incubation for a further 10 min clots were isolated, depolymerized, and clot-bound t-PA measured on fibrin plates. The level of antiactivator was estimated from the decrease in t-PA activity (1 U is the amount of antiactivator which inhibits 1 U of t-PA).

RESULTS AND DISCUSSION

Plasma levels of antiactivator in hospitalized patients and healthy controls were extremely variable. They varied between 0 and 13.8 U/ml in healthy controls and between 0 and 20 U/ml in patients. The distribution of values was nongaussian. In the control group the concentration of antiactivator was 1.5 ± 6.9 U/ml (mean $\pm$ SD, median 0.7 U/ml). In 6% of the control group, antiactivator levels were above 10 U/ml. At present it is not known if these high levels are still within the normal range or are due to as yet unrecognized underlying disease states. In all subgroups of patients the level of antiactivator was significantly higher than in the healthy subjects (Table 32.1). Median antiactivator levels were over three times increased in intensive care patients, in thromboembolic disease, after extracorporeal circulation and in liver disease. The distribution of values after extracorporeal circulation indicated two groups of patients, one with a low antiactivator level (range: 0.4 to 1.6 U/ml, n = 5), another with a high level (range: 7.3 to over 20 U/ml, n = 5). Analysis of the time at which the plasmas had been collected indicated that antiactivator levels are greatly increased just after the operation and return to normal within a few days. The cause of this increase is not yet known. Is the antiactivator, like α_1-protease inhibitor an acute phase reacting protein or is it released from activated platelets? In view of its plasma concentration, which is in the same order of magnitude as that of t-PA released after physiological stimuli, e.g. venous stasis or exercise, and its fast rate of inhibition of t-PA, the antiactivator very likely plays an important role in the regulation of t-PA activity in plasma.

At present it appears as if high levels of antiactivator might predispose to thrombotic complications. We observed a high level of antiactivator in patients suffering from thromboembolic disease. However another possible explanation for these high levels would be a decreased turnover of antiactivator due to deficient release of t-PA.

This work was supported by the Swiss National Fund (grant no. 3.461.0.83).

REFERENCES

Chmielewska J, Rånby M, Wiman B 1983 Evidence for a rapid inhibitor to tissue plasminogen activator in plasma. Thrombosis Research 31: 427–436

Juhan-Vague I, Moerman B, De Cock F, Aillaud M F, Collen D 1984 Plasma levels of a specific inhibitor of tissue-type plasminogen activator (and urokinase) in normal and pathological conditions. Thrombosis Research 33: 523–530

Kruithof E K O, Ransijn A, Bachmann F 1983 Inhibition of tissue plasminogen activator by human plasma. In: Davidson J F, Bachmann F, Bouvier C A, Kruithof E K O (eds) Progress in Fibrinolysis Vol VI Churchill Livingstone Edinburgh p 365–369

Kruithof E K O, Tran-Thang C, Ransijn A, Bachmann F 1984 Demonstration of a fast-acting inhibitor of plasminogen activators in human plasma. Blood (in press)

Verheijen J H, Chang G T G, Mullaart E 1983 Inhibition of extrinsic (tissue-type) plasminogen activator by human plasma: evidence for the occurrence of a fast-acting inhibitor. Thrombosis and Haemostasis 50: 295 (abstract)

33. A novel fast inhibitor of tissue plasminogen activator in plasma

B. Wiman, J. Chmielewska and M. Ranby

The existence of inhibitors towards plasminogen activators has been a matter of controversy during the last decade. Several investigators (Gallimore, 1979; Hedner, 1981) have suggested that such inhibitors exist in plasma, but they have failed in providing reliable experimental data to confirm this hypothesis. Furthermore, quite recently Koringer and Collen (1981) claimed that alpha$_2$-antiplasmin was the major inhibitor of tissue plasminogen activator in human plasma and that no specific inhibitors existed. Recently we developed a specific and very sensitive method to determine tissue plasminogen activator in plasma samples (Wiman et al, 1983). With this method we could accurately determine residual t-PA activity after addition of small amounts of t-PA to plasma samples from different individuals. The ability of these samples to rapidly inactivate t-PA was highly variable, ranging from less than 0.1 IU/ml to about 50 IU/ml. Especially plasma from patients with thromboembolic disease and from women in late pregnancy was remarkably potent in this respect. The capacity to inactivate t-PA rapidly could be titrated in these samples and in spite of low concentrations of reactants an almost straight line was obtained. This suggested a high affinity between the enzyme and the novel inhibitor and from the initial decline in t-PA activity and assuming the formation of a stoichiometric 1:1 complex, a second order rate constant of $10^7 M^{-1}.s^{-1}$ was estimated (Chmielewska et al, 1983).

On gel-filtration (Sepacryl S-300) of plasma from patients with thromboembolic disease or with hemostatic disturbances in late pregnancy a symmetrical peak of fast t-PA inhibitory activity was obtained at an apparent molecular weight of about 210,000. Addition of an equimolar amount of radiolabelled one-chain t-PA prior to the gel-filtration step caused this peak to disappear. The radioactivity eluted as a symmetrical peak with an apparent molecular weight of about 120,000. In contrast, if radiolabelled t-PA was added to plasma low in the fast t-PA inhibitor and subsequently gel-filtered the radioactivity eluted at an apparent molecular weight of about 65 000 (Wiman et al, 1984a). This value is in agreement with the previously reported molecular weight for t-PA (Wallén et al, 1983).

Thus, the inhibitor moiety in the complex seems to have a molecular weight of about 50–55 000 as compared to 210 000 obtained from gel-filtration data. This discrepancy may be explained in different ways: the inhibitor may circulate as a

133

tetrameric structure or it may be associated to another plasma protein in plasma. Another possible explanation is that complex formation involves proteolytic cleavage and subsequent removal of a significant part of the inhibitor.

Attempts to purify the complex from plasma has been initiated. For this purpose radiolabelled t-PA (^{35}-S-Met-internally labelled or ^{125}I externally labelled) have been added to plasma or serum rich in the inhibitor in approximately equimolar amounts. The t-PA antigen (mostly the complex) was thereafter adsorbed onto insolubilized antibodies produced against porcine t-PA. After washing with a buffer of high ionic strength the t-PA antigen was eluted with 3M KSCN. The t-PA inhibitor complex was purified 2–4000 fold in this way (Wiman et al, 1984a). The material was dialyzed against a phosphate buffer containing tween 80 and thereafter adsorbed onto insolubilized monoclonal antibodies against human melanoma cell t-PA (kindly obtained from KabiVitrum AB, courtesy of Drs L O Andersson and J Brandt). About 75% of the radioactivity was adsorbed to the column, but the major portion of the protein passed unadsorbed. Elution was again performed with 3 M KSCN. A further 10–15 fold purification was obtained in this step. Thus a total purification factor of about 30 000 has been obtained so far. Examination of this material on dodecylsulphate polyacrylamide gel electrophoresis after staining with Comassie brilliant blue displayed four about equally strong bands, one of which was radioactive. This band has a molecular weight of about 120,000. After reduction, the radioactivity migrated as a rather broad band with an apparent molecular weight of about 40 000. The reason for this is at present not known, but the data suggests that a proteolytic degradation at least of the t-PA moiety in the complex has occurred.

In order to establish the pathophysiological role of this novel fibrinolytic inhibitor, its concentration has been determined in plasma samples from a number of healthy individuals and different kinds of patients. Among the healthy individuals the concentration was determined as 0.7 ± 0.7 U/ml (median 0.4, range 0–2.4 U/ml, n = 20). One unit of the inhibitor is defined as the amount which in properly diluted plasma inhibits 1 IU of t-PA (the specific activity of t-PA is about 200 000 IU/mg) in 20 min at room temperature. Increased levels of the inhibitor were found in a group of patients with a recent incident (2 months after the incident) of deep vein thrombosis. In this group 13 out of 37 (35%) of the patients displayed low t-PA activity in blood samples taken after venous occlusion although the release of t-PA antigen mostly were within normal limits. In these thirteen patients, the inhibitor level was determined as 6.4 ± 4.0 U/ml (range 2.1–15.0 U/ml, median 4.0). Thus, the decreased fibrinolytic activity found in about 35% of patients with a recent incident of deep venous thrombosis seems to a large extent depend on increased plasma levels of the novel inhibitor towards t-PA (Wiman et al, 1984c).

About 30% of patients with severe coronary heart disease was found to have increased levels (above 3 U/ml) of the fast t-PA inhibitor in plasma samples taken prior to coronary by-pass operations (Wiman B, unpublished results). In surgical patients the t-PA inhibitor is transiently increased about 2–3 fold with a maximum about 3 h–1 day postoperatively (Mellbring et al, 1984). This is most likely the explanation for the decreased fibrinolytic activity normally found in the immediate postoperative period.

134

During normal pregnancy the fast t-PA inhibitor level is steadily increased from week 10 to the time at about term, reaching levels of about 5–6 U/ml (Wiman et al, 1984b). It seems plausible that the increased levels of the fast t-PA inhibitor in the late phase of pregnancy is the explanation for the decreased fibrinolytic activity previously reported. In risk pregnancies including patients with preeclampsia, suspected fetal growth retardation, diabetes, thrombosis or a previous history of thrombosis a considerably higher variation was found in late pregnancy (range in last trimester 0–24 U/ml, n = 137). The concentration was found to be higher than expected in about 15% of the samples and lower than expected in about 30%. The pathophysiologic significance of this finding is still unclear.

The role of oestrogens in regulating the plasma levels of the fast t-PA inhibitor was studied in ten young girls on treatment with high doses of ethinyloestradiol because of expected tallness. Before treatment the inhibitor concentration was determined as 1.0 ± 0.7 U/ml as compared to 0.5 ± 0.4 U/ml and 0.8 ± 0.6 U/ml during and after the treatment, respectively (B Wiman and M Blombäck, unpublished results). Quite contrary to what was expected oestrogens seems to cause a decrease in plasma t-PA inhibitor levels. Thus, the reason for the increased levels found during pregnancy is still obscure.

In conclusion plasma samples contain varying amounts of a novel fast inhibitor of t-PA. Its molecular weight as evidenced by gel-filtration of unfractionated plasma is about 200 000. It forms rapidly a complex with t-PA with a molecular weight of about 120 000. This complex has been partially purified about 30 000 times from plasma rich in the inhibitor and after addition of an equivalent amount of radiolabelled t-PA. Increased levels of the t-PA inhibitor is frequently found in plasma samples from patients with thromboembolic disease, but also in normal pregnancy.

ACKNOWLEDGEMENTS
Financial support has been obtained from the Swedish Medical Research Council (project no 05193), KabiVitrum A B and Karolinska Institute.

REFERENCES

Chmielewska J, Ranby M, Wiman B 1983 Evidence for a rapid inhibitor to tissue plasminogen activator in plasma. Thrombosis Research, 31: 427–436

Gallimore M J 1979 Inhibitors of plasminogen activation present in human plasma. In: Collen D, Wiman B, Verstraete M (eds). The Physiological Inhibitors of coagulation and fibrinolysis, Elsevier/North Holland, Amsterdam, 199–217

Hedner U 1981 A human inhibitor of activated Hageman factor (F XIIa) In: Davidson J F, Nilsson I M, Åstedt B (eds) Progress in Fibrinolysis, vol 5, Churchill Livingstone, Edinburgh 152–156

Koringer C, Collen D 1981 Neutralization of human extrinsic (tissue-type) plasminogen activator in human plasma: No evidence for a specific inhibitor. Thrombosis Haemostasis 46: 662–665

Mellbring G, Dahlgren S, Wiman B 1984 Plasma fibrinolytic activity in patients subjected to abdominal surgery. Acta Chirurgica Scandinavica. Submitted

Wallén P. Pohl G, Bergsdorf N, Rånby M, Ny T, Jörnvall H 1983 Purification and structural characterization of a melanoma cell plasminogen activator. European Journal of Biochemistry 132: 681–686

Wiman B, Mellbring G, Rånby M 1983 Plasminogen activator release during venous stasis and exercise as determined by a new specific assay. Clinica Chimica Acta, 127: 279-288

Wiman B, Chmielewska J, Rånby M 1984a Inactivation of tissue plasminogen activator in plasma: Demonstration of a complex with a new rapid inhibitor. Journal of Biological Chemistry 259: 3644-3647

Wiman B, Csemiczky G, Marsk L, Robbe H 1984b The fast inhibitor of tissue plasminogen activator in plasma during pregnancy. Thrombosis and Haemostasis. In press

Wiman B, Ljungberg B, Chmielewska J, Urdén G, Blombäck M 1984c On the role of the fibrinolytic system in deep venous thrombosis. The Journal of Laboratory and Clinical Medicine. Submitted

34. An inhibitor of tissue-type plasminogen activator in human platelets, serum, and plasma

L. A. Erickson, M. H. Ginsberg and D.J. Loskutoff

We have shown previously that bovine serum contains several fibrinolytic inhibitors detectable by reverse fibrin autography (RFA) (Erickson et al, 1984). Here we review our findings that one such inhibitor, present in serum derived from human platelet-rich plasma (PRP) but not from platelet-poor plasma (PPP), is an anti-plasminogen activator (anti-PA) contained in and released from platelets. In addition, we demonstrate that this same anti-PA is present in plasma obtained from patients with suspected disturbance of the hemostatic system but not in plasma from healthy individuals.

MATERIALS AND METHODS

Preparation of plasma samples

Plasma from healthy individuals and patients was obtained as described (Chmielewska et al, 1983), and was kindly provided by Dr. Björn Wiman (Stockholm, Sweden).

Plasma antifibrinolytic activity

Plasma samples (20 μl) were analyzed for inhibitor activity either by RFA (Erickson et al, 1984) or by the ^{125}I-fibrin plate assay (Loskutoff & Edgington, 1977). In the latter case, plasma (4 μl) was pre-incubated for various times with tissue-type PA (t-PA, 0.0025 U) in 100 μl of buffer (0.1 M Tris-OH, pH 8.1, 0.1% gelatin). At the end of the pre-incubation period, the residual PA activity in each sample was determined.

Miscellaneous

Antiserum against an anti-PA purified from bovine aortic endothelial cells (BAEs) was used to immunoprecipitate inhibitor activity from patient plasma (25 μl) according to the procedure described by van Mourik et al (submitted). Fibrinogen (bovine; plasminogen- and thrombin-free), human plasminogen, human α-thrombin, and human t-PA were prepared or purchased as described (Erickson et al, 1984).

RESULTS

Detection and partial characterization of the inhibitor activity in serum and platelets

Serum obtained from human PRP contains one fibrinolytic inhibitor that is not detectable in serum from PPP, suggesting that it originates in the platelets (Erickson et al, in press). Indeed, both Triton X-100 platelet extracts and releasates prepared from thrombin-treated, gel-filtered platelets contain this 50,000 M_r inhibitor. The release of inhibitor from the platelets occurred in parallel with the release of platelet factor 4 and was blocked by pre-treating the platelets with PGE_1 and theophylline. Antiserum against the BAE inhibitor recognized a single protein of M_r 50,000 in platelet releasates, and removed both the inhibitor detected by RFA as well as the total anti-t-PA activity associated with the releasates. Thus, the activity responsible for the lysis-resistant zone and the anti-t-PA activity of platelets, reside in the same molecule.

Detection of the inhibitor in plasma

Consistent with these results with platelets and serum, inhibitor activity was not detectable in PPP obtained from healthy individuals (Fig. 34.1, left panel, lane 1). However, it was quite evident in the plasma obtained from patients with

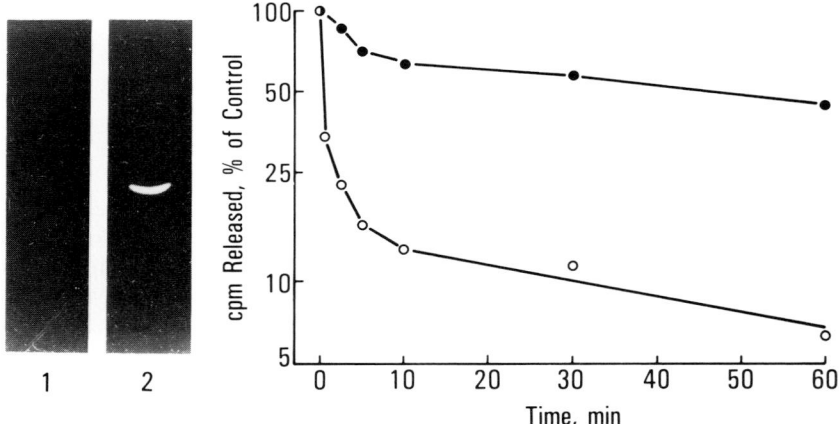

Fig. 34.1 Detection of inhibitor activity in human plasma. Plasma obtained from healthy individuals (lane 1) or patients (lane 2) was analyzed by RFA (left panel). These same samples also were analyzed in the ^{125}I-fibrin plate assay (right panel; normal, •; and patient, 0). In this case, residual fibrinolytic activity in the treated samples was expressed as a percentage of the activity present in samples pre-incubated with buffer only.

suspected disturbance of the hemostatic system (lane 2). In addition, the patient plasma rapidly neutralized t-PA activity, but the normal plasma did not (Fig. 34.1, right panel). It should be noted that the electrophoretic mobility of the inhibitor in plasma was altered by the large amount of albumin present (Erickson et al, in press). When the albumin was removed, the plasma inhibitor also had a M_r of about 50,000 (data not shown).

As in the case of the platelet inhibitor, the antiserum to the BAE inhibitor

138

immunoprecipitated the inhibitor detected in patient plasma (Fig. 34.2, lanes 1–3), whereas nonimmune serum did not precipitate any detectable inhibitor activity (lanes 4 and 5). Preliminary analysis (data not shown) of the 'inhibitor-depleted' plasma (Fig. 34.2, lane 2) suggests that the inhibitor detected by RFA is responsible for the fast-acting anti-t-PA activity depicted in Figure 34.1.

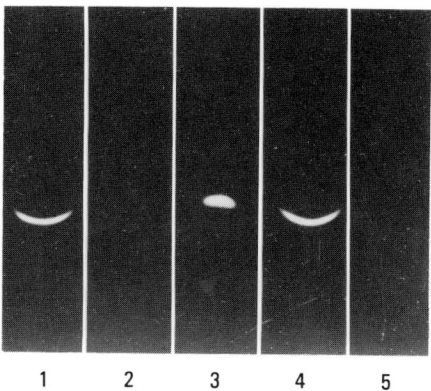

Fig. 34.2 Immunoprecipitation of inhibitor activity from patient plasma. Plasma was incubated with either the antiserum to the BAE inhibitor (lanes 2 and 3) or nonimmune serum (lanes 4 and 5). The starting plasma (20 μl, lane 1) and the respective immunosupernatants (20μl, lanes 2 and 4) and immunoprecipitates (20 μl, lanes 3 and 5) were analyzed by RFA.

DISCUSSION

A number of investigators have detected both anti-plasmin and anti-PA activities in plasma (Hedner, 1979). Although the plasma component responsible for the physiologic inhibition of plasmin, α_2-antiplasmin, has been purified and characterized (Wiman & Collen, 1977), the physiologic inhibitor of t-PA has not been identified as yet. Indeed, Korninger & Collen (1981) previously demonstrated that normal human plasma does not contain a physiologic inhibitor of t-PA. However, more recent studies have suggested the existence of a fast-acting anti-t-PA activity in certain samples of plasma obtained from patients with various hemostatic difficulties (Chmielewska et al, 1983; Kruithof et al, 1983). The experiments outlined in this report were designed to elucidate possible sources of this elevated anti-t-PA activity.

Our findings indicate that the inhibitor activity detected by RFA in serum from PRP originates in platelets. The removal of both this inhibitor activity and the anti-t-PA activity present in platelet releasates by antiserum to the BAE inhibitor, suggests that both activities reside in the same molecule. The finding that the inhibitor detected in patient plasma is related immunologically to both the platelet and BAE inhibitors, suggests that the anti-t-PA activity in the patient plasma may originate in platelets and/or endothelial cells. Our preliminary results suggesting that this inhibitor is at least partially responsible for the fast-acting anti-t-PA activity present in the plasma support this idea. Thus, the 50,000 M_r inhibitor described in this report may be the physiologic inhibitor of vascular PA. However, studies examining its overall specificity, mechanism of action, and localization await its purification from sources of human material. Conceptually, such an anti-PA may serve to prevent the premature degradation of a forming thrombus, and, as suggested by its presence in the patient plasma, may contribute to the development of thrombotic disease.

Acknowledgments
The authors thank Dr. Björn Wiman for the patient plasma samples, acknowledge the excellent technical assistance of Karen Roegner and Doug Dixon, and thank Gerry Josephs for typing the manuscript. This is Publication No. 3425-IMM from the Scripps Clinic and Research Foundation. This work was supported in part by a grant from Eli Lilly and Co. and by National Institutes of Health Grants HL22289 and HL16411 to D.J.L., by AM27214 to M.H.G., and by a fellowship to L.A.E. from the California Chapter of the American Heart Association.

REFERENCES

Chmielewska J, Rånby M, Wiman B 1983 Evidence for a rapid inhibitor to tissue plasminogen activator in plasma. Thrombosis Research 31: 427–436
Erickson L A, Ginsberg M H, Loskutoff D J Detection and partial characterization of an inhibitor of plasminogen activator in human platelets. The Journal of Clinical Investigation (in press)
Erickson L A, Lawrence D A, Loskutoff D J 1984 Reverse fibrin autography: a method to detect and partially characterize protease inhibitors after sodium dodecyl sulfate-polyacrylamide gel electrophoresis. Analytical Biochemistry 137: 454–463
Hedner U 1979 Inhibitor(s) of plasminogen activation distinct from the other plasma protease inhibitors — a review. In: Collen D, Wiman B, Verstraete M (eds) The Physiological Inhibitors of Coagulation and Fibrinolysis, Elsevier/North Holland, Amsterdam. p 189
Korninger C, Collen D 1981 Neutralization of human extrinsic (tissue-type) plasminogen activator in human plasma: no evidence for a specific inhibitor. Thrombosis and Haemostasis 46: 662–665
Kruithof E K O, Ransijn A, Bachmann F 1983 Inhibition of tissue plasminogen activator by human plasma. In: Davidson J F, Bachmann F, Bouvier C A, Druithof E K O (eds) Progress in Fibrinolysis, vol 6, Churchill Livingstone, Edinburgh. ch 79, p 365
Loskutoff D J, Edgington T S 1977 Synthesis of a fibrinolytic activator and inhibitor by endothelial cells. Proceedings of the National Academy of Science USA 74: 3903–3907
van Mourik J A, Lawrence D A, Loskutoff D J Purification of an anti-plasminogen activator synthesized by endothelial cells. (submitted)
Wiman B, Collen D 1977 Purification and characterization of human antiplasmin, the fast-acting plasmin inhibitor in plasma. European Journal of Biochemistry 78: 19–26

35. Tissue-plasminogen activator inhibition by human endothelial cell conditioned medium and plasma

J. H. Verheijen, E. D. Sprengers, J. J. Emeis,
V. W. M. van Hinsbergh, G. T. G. Chang and
C. Kluft

INTRODUCTION

Inhibition of tissue-type plasminogen activator (t-PA) by plasma has been discovered years ago (1,2). These studies were hampered by lack of purified t-PA and poor methodology and consequently little progress was made. Very recently a number of groups (3–10) have published about inhibition of t-PA by plasma or endothelial cell conditioned medium (ECCM), new methods have been developed and purified t-PA is present in sufficient quantities in a number of places. In a very short time the study of inhibition of t-PA has become a rapidly evolving field of research.

In this contribution we will focus on two interesting points: a. is only one inhibitor involved or are more different inhibitors involved and b. what is the mechanism of the inhibition.

MATERIALS AND METHODS

— t-PA activity was measured by a parabolic rate assay as described previously (11).
— t-PA inhibition was measured by a titration assay based on the parabolic rate assay (7) see text.
— gelelectrophoresis was performed according to Laemlli (12).
— fibrin autography (13) and reverse fibrin autography (9) were performed according to published procedures.
— two chain melanoma t-PA was purified by the method of Kluft et al (1).
— anti-t-PA Sepharose was prepared by coupling affinospecific goat anti-t-PA IgG to CNBr-activated Sepharose 4B according to the manufacturer's instructions.
— endothelial cells from human umbilical cord were isolated and cultured as previously described (15).
Serum-free medium was conditioned on these cells for 18 h (8).

RESULTS AND DISCUSSION

Assay of inhibitor

A quantitative assay for t-PA inhibition has been devised based on the following principle. To a fixed amount of endothelial cell conditioned medium (ECCM) or plasma increasing amounts of t-PA are added and the resulting activity measured (Fig. 35.1). The amount of inhibition present in the sample is obtained by extrapolating to the X-axis as shown in Figure 35.1.

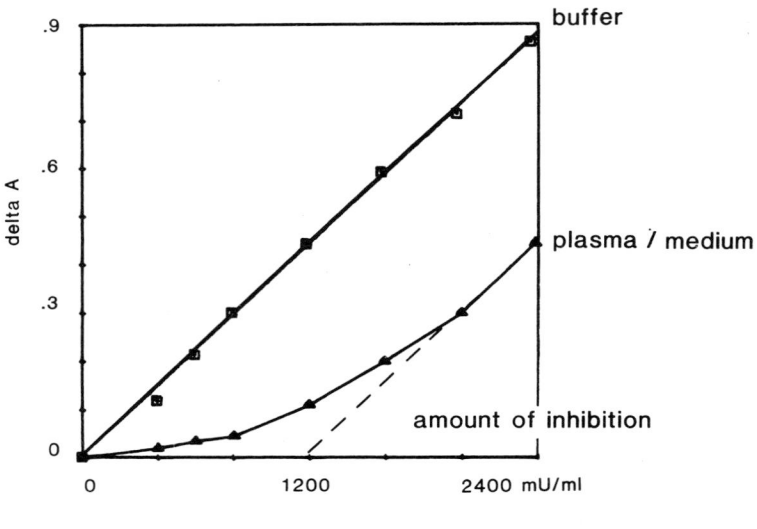

Fig. 35.1 Determination of inhibitor. To 25 μl of plasma increasing amounts of t-PA were added and the resulting activity measured after 2 h incubation. In a control experiment the same amounts of t-PA were added to buffer.

Characterization of inhibition

Using specific antibodies it was found that inhibition as measured in this assay was not caused by α_2-antiplasmin, α_2-macroglobulin or the placenta inhibitor (antibody kindly supplied by Professor Heimburger from Marburg, FRG) (results not shown).

To compare inhibition measured in the spectrophotometric assay with inhibition detected by reverse fibrin autography (9) the following experiment was designed (Table 35.1). In ECCM containing 3.3 U/ml of inhibition (titration assay), a 52 kDA lysis-resistant band was observed on reverse fibrin autography.

To this medium a 10-fold excess of t-PA was added and the medium was brought on an anti-t-PA column to remove the inhibitor-t-PA-complexes formed as well as the excess of free t-PA. In medium thus treated no inhibitory activity could be found using the spectrophotometric assay. On reverse fibrin autography, however, a 52 kDa lysis resistant band could still be observed, having the same intensity.

Table 35.1 Comparison of rapid t-PA inhibition measured spectrophotometrically and occurrence of 52 kDa lysis resistant band on reverse fibrin autography

	U/ml inhibition	52 k lysis resistance	direct lysis resistance
A ECCM	3.3	+	+
B after anti-t-PA column	2.7	+	+
C plus excess t-PA after anti t-PA column	0.0	+	−
D after heat treatment	0.0	+	−

In another experiment ECCM was heated at 70°C for 15 min, spectrophotometrically no inhibition could be observed but again the 52 kDa lysis resistant band on reverse fibrin autography was not changed. Furthermore, at least one additional lysis resistant band could be seen.

These same samples were also applied directly to reverse autography fibrin films without electrophoresis or SDS treatment. In this case the results are in agreement with those of the spectrophotometric assay (Table 35.1 last column), indicating that the inhibition which causes the lysis resistant band of 52 kDa is generated during SDS gelelectrophoresis.

We conclude from these results that t-PA inhibition in ECCM occurs in two forms, an active, heat-labile, form and an inactive, heat-stable, form. The latter form can be converted to an active inhibitor by SDS electrophoresis. A possible explanation might be that an inhibitor is complexed with another molecule (not t-PA or UK). SDS treatment dissociates this complex, liberating an active inhibitor. Whether any relation exists between the two forms of inhibitor found in ECCM is not yet clear.

Mechanism of inhibition

Our working hypothesis for t-PA inhibition is illustrated in Figure 35.2. We assume that the second irreversible complex has an only negligable contribution to the inhibition under the conditions of measurement, and that endogenous t-PA present in ECCM or plasma is present almost entirely in the irreversibly complexed form.

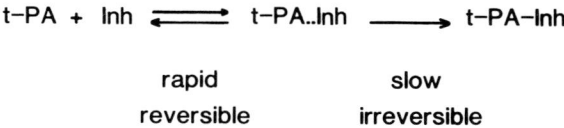

Fig. 35.2 Simple model for rapid-t-PA inhibition.

With these assumptions in mind we can interpret the titration curve of Figure 35.3a as follows: Each amount of total added t-PA can be divided in free t-PA contributing to the measured activity and t-PA which does not contribute to the activity because it is reversibly bound to the inhibitor (Fig. 35.3a). By replotting these data in a double reciprocal way (Fig. 35.3b) a graph is obtained which on extrapolation yields not only the total amount of inhibitor present but also the apparent inhibition constant K_i^{app} of the inhibitor for t-PA under these conditions.

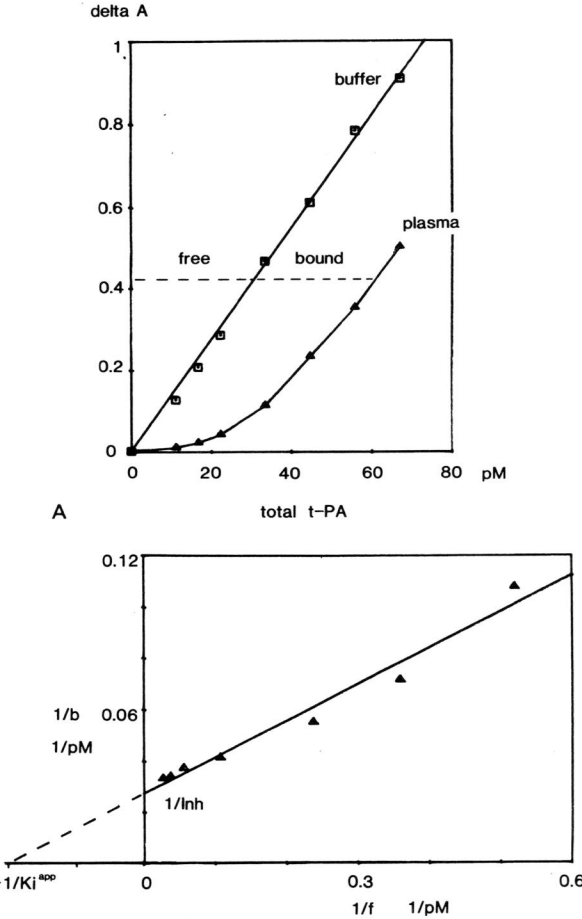

Fig. 35.3 Determination of affinity of inhibitor for t-PA. a. 25 μl of plasma was titrated as described in the text. b. From fig. 3[a] the free t-PA and bound t-PA were determined for each total amount of t-PA used. A plot was made of 1/bound (l/b) against 1/free (l/f).

Using this method a K_i^{app} of about 5.10^{-12} mol.l^{-1} has been found for inhibition of t-PA by ECCM or plasma, indicating a very high affinity. The excellent fit of the data with the model suggests that the assumptions are not unreasonable.

Concluding remarks
A fast-acting high affinity of t-PA occurs in ECCM and plasma. The low concentration, the high rate and high affinity of this inhibition makes a physiological role very well possible.

REFERENCES

Brakman P, Mohler E R, Astrup T 1966 A group of patients with an impaired plasma fibrinolytic system and selective inhibition of tissue activator-induced fibrinolysis. Scandinavian Journal of Haematology 3: 389

Chmielewska J, Ranby M, Wiman B 1983 Determination of tissue plasminogen activator in plasma. Evidence for a rapid inhibitor. Thrombosis and Haemostasis 50: 193 abstr.

Emeis J J, van Hinsbergh V W M, Verheijen J H, Wijngaards G 1983 Inhibition of tissue type plasminogen activator by conditioned medium from cultured human and porcine vascular endothelial cells. Biochemical and Biophysical Research Communications 110: 392–398

Granelli-Piperno A, Reich E 1978 A study of protease-inhibitor complexes in biological fluids. Journal of Experimental Medicine 148: 223–234

Hinsbergh V W M van, Havekes L, Emeis J J, Corven E van, Scheffer M 1983 Low density lipoprotein metabolism by endothelial cells from human umbilical cord arteries and veins. Arteriosclerosis 3: 547–559

Kluft C, van Wezel A L, van der Velden C A M, Emeis J J, Verheijen J H, Wijngaards G 1983 Large scale production of extrinsic (tissue-type) plasminogen activator from human melanoma cells. In: Mizrahi A, van Wezel A L (eds) Advances in biotechnological processes. A R Liss Inc, New York, vol 2, p 97–110

Kruithof E K O, Ransijn A, Bachmann F 1983 Inhibition of tissue plasminogen activator (TA) by human plasma. In: Davidson J F, Bachmann F, Bouvier C A, Kruithof E K O (eds) Progress in fibrinolysis. Churchill Livingstone, Edinburgh, vol 6, p 365–369

Kruithof E K O, Ransijn A, Tran-Thang C, Bachmann F 1983 Characteristics of a fast acting inhibitor of plasminogen activator in human plasma Thrombosis and Haemostasis 50: 193 abstr.

Laemlli U K 1970 Cleavage of structural proteins during the assembly of the head of bacteriophage T4. Nature 227: 680–685

Levin E G 1983 Latent tissue plasminogen activator produced by human endothelial cells in culture: Evidence for an enzyme-inhibitor complex. Proceedings of the National Academy of Science 80: 6804–6808

Loskutoff D J, van Mourik J A, Erickson L A, Lawrence D 1983 Detection of an unusually stable fibrinolytic inhibitor produced by bovine endothelial cells. Proceedings of the National Academy of Science 80: 2956–2960

Philips M, Thorsen S 1983 Binding of plasminogen activator (PA) to a component (X) of endothelial cells (EC) may explain the 95,000-Mr PA in human plasma. Thrombosis and Haemostasis 50: 193 abstr.

Verheijen J H, Mullaart E, Chang G T G, Kluft C, Wijngaards G 1982 A simple, sensitive spectrophotometric assay for extrinsic (tissue-type) plasminogen activator applicable to measurements in plasma. Thrombosis and Haemostasis 48: 266–269

Verheijen J H, Chang G T G, Mullaart E 1983 Inhibition of extrinsic (tissue-type) plasminogen activator by human plasma: Evidence for the occurence of a fast-acting inhibitor. Thrombosis and Haemostasis 50: 294 abstr.

Wijngaards G, Groeneveld E 1981 Inhibition of fibrinolytic enzymes by patient plasmas tested by different methods. In: Davidson J F, Nilsson I M, Astedt B (eds) Progress in fibrinolysis. Churchill Livingstone, Edinburgh, vol 5, p 328–331

36. The fast-acting inhibitor of tissue-type plasminogen activator is an acute phase reactant protein

I. Juhan-Vague, M. F. Aillaud, F. De Cock,
C. Philip-Joet, C. Arnaud, A. Serradimigni
and D. Collen

By means of the immuno-radiometric assay for tissue-type plasminogen activator (t-PA) described by Rijken et al (1983), we found (Juhan-Vague, 1983) markedly increased levels of t-PA related antigen in plasma of patients with several clinical conditions; there was, however, no correlation between immuno-assay and euglobulin fibrinolytic activity. Most of this immuno-reactive t-PA occurred as inactive high molecular weight forms which could not be identified as complexes of t-PA with known plasma protease inhibitors and which therefore were suggestive of complex formation with a specific inhibitor. These observations prompted us to investigate this phenomenon further.

A t-PA inhibitor assay was developed (Juhan-Vague et al, 1984) in which purified t-PA was added to plasma and residual activator measured in the euglobulin fraction after 5 min. incubation at 37°C. An increased level of this inhibitor was found in severely ill patients and also after major surgery. In the latter the raised titre of inhibitor found on the first post-operative day disappeared by the fifth post-operative day. The present study was carried out to determine if the inhibitor of t-PA is an acute phase reactant protein.

METHODS

— Blood was collected into citrate (final concentration 0.011 m) and immediately cooled on ice. Platelet poor plasma obtained by centrifugation at 4°C for 15 minutes at 3000 g was shell frozen in aliquots and stored at −70°C until used.
— t-PA related antigen (t-PA R:Ag) was measured using a two-site immuno-radiometric assay described by Rijken (1983) using a rabbit antiserum raised against purified t-PA obtained from melanoma cell culture fluid.
— Euglobulin fibrinolytic activity (EFA) was measured on bovine fibrin plates as described by Kluft (1976). Results are expressed as the mean of 2 diameters of the lysis area.
— t-PA inhibitor assay: purified t-PA was added to citrated plasma to a concentration of 5 IU (50 ng) per ml (or up to 30 IU per ml in inhibitor rich plasma), and the mixture was incubated at 37°C for 5 minutes; euglobulins were

then precipitated and their fibrinolytic activity was measured on fibrin plates, and expressed in IU by comparison with calibration curves constructed with purified t-PA. One unit of inhibitor is defined as the amount that neutralised one unit (10 ng) of t-PA.

— The acute phase reactant proteins C reactive protein (CRP), orosomucoid, fibrinogen, α_1 antitrypsin, haptoglobin, ceruloplasmin and C_3 were measured by nephelometric methods. Factor VIII related antigen (F VIII R:Ag) was measured by immunoelectrodiffusion according to Laurell.

— For statistical analysis, non parametric Spearman's test was used.

RESULTS

1. t-PA R:Ag, EFA and inhibitor level were assayed in 52 controls and 105 hospitalised patients (deep venous thrombosis 19; myocardial infarction 23, abdominal surgery 31; liver cirrhosis 12; malignant disease 20). We found a significant correlation (p < 0.01) between t-PA R:Ag and t-PA-inhibitor level (r = 0.35), but this weak correlation between the two determinations shows that the mechanisms which regulate the synthesis and the turnover of the two substances are different. There was also a significant negative correlation (p < 0.01) between inhibitor level and EFA (r = 0.23).

2. As in our previous study (Juhan-Vague, 1984), we found higher level of t-PA inhibitor in hospitalised patients (38%) than in controls (7%). In patients with deep venous thrombosis or myocardial infarction, blood samples were taken during the first seven days after admission. The mean inhibitor titre (Table 36.1) in the patients was greater than that in the controls and 25% of patients had a high titre of inhibitor. There was no variation in the level of inhibitor over the 7 days.

After major abdominal surgery, blood samples were taken during the first 3 days. The mean inhibitor titre (Table 36.1) was markedly elevated and more than 50% of patients had a high titre of inhibitor.

Table 36.1 t-PA inhibitor level in controls and in patients with acute clinical conditions.

	Inhibitor level IU/ml Mean ± SD	Number with >4 IU	% Patients >4 IU
Controls	1.27 ± 1.56	4/52	7%
Deep venous thrombosis	2.34 ± 1.80	5/19	22%
Myocardial infarction	2.30 ± 1.52	5/23	26%
Abdominal surgery	4.61 ± 3.76	21/31	66%

3. We studied the correlation between inhibitor level and acute phase reactant protein level in 18 controls and 73 patients with acute clinical conditions (deep venous thrombosis, myocardial infarction, abdominal surgery). The results are shown in Table 36.2. The acute phase reactant proteins are given in order of their rapidity of evolution as described by Colley et al (1983). C reactive protein (CRP)

Table 36.2 Correlation between t-PA inhibitor level and acute phase reactant protein levels.

r	CRP	Oroso-mucoid	Fibrin-ogen	α_1-Anti trypsin	VIII Ag	Hapto-globin	Cerulo plasmin	C_3
Inhibitor level	0.54**	0.40**	0.37**	0.22**	NS	NS	NS	NS

n = 91; ** p<0.01; * p<0.05

is the protein which increases fastest after surgery; it rises in the first few hours, and decreases rapidly over the subsequent 4 or 5 days. Orosomucoid, fibrinogen, and α_1 antitrypsin increase more slowly and also disappear slowly; the other proteins have even slower kinetics. The t-PA inhibitor level was very strongly correlated with CRP and less with orosomucoid, fibrinogen or α_1 antitrypsin but it did not correlate with the other acute phase reactant proteins. Therefore the evolution of the inhibitor seems to be very comparable with that of CRP. This is well illustrated by Figure 36.1.

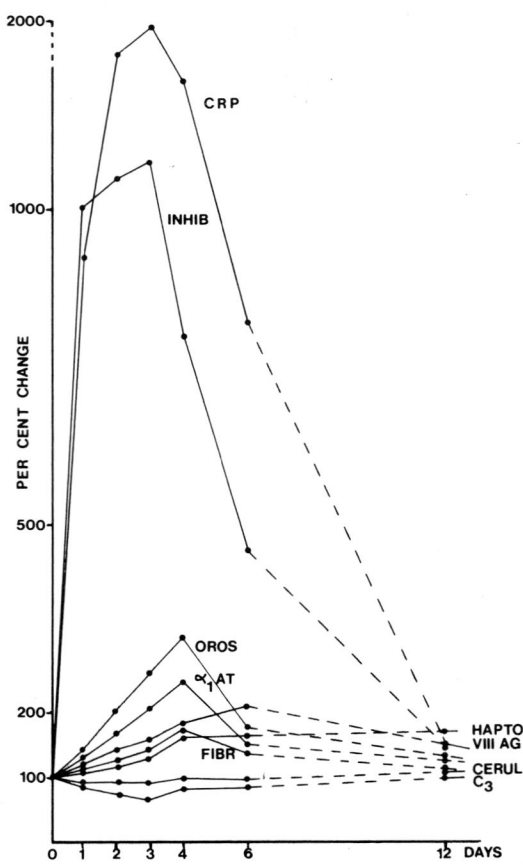

Fig. 36.1 Evolution of fast-acting t-PA inhibitor level (INHIB) and acute phase reactant protein levels in one patient after major abdominal surgery. OROS = orosomucoid – α_1 AT = α_1 antitrypsin – FIBR = fibrinogen – HAPTO = haptoglobin – CERULO = ceruloplasmin.

148

COMMENTS

Independent of our own studies, several laboratories have recently obtained evidence for the existence of a high level of t-PA-inhibitor in plasma samples from patients with severe clinical conditions (Wijngaards and Groeneveld, 1982) such as deep venous thrombosis (Chmielewska et al, 1983; Brommer et al, 1984; Haglund et al, 1984; Kruithof et al, 1984) and in post-operative period (Kruithof et al, 1984).

The physiopathological role of this inhibitor of t-PA is at present unknown. But the frequent occurrence of high levels of this inhibitor in high risk thrombotic patients, as in post-operative cases, merits further study. The evaluation of new preventive antithrombotic therapy directed against this inhibitor, which is an acute phase reactant protein, is also important to consider.

REFERENCES

Brommer E J P, Verheijen J H, Rijken D C 1984 Masking of fibrinolytic response to DDAVP, venous occlusion and exercise by high levels of fast acting inhibitors of tissue plasminogen activator. Haemostasis 14: 102 (abstract no 185)

Chmielewska J, Ranby M, Wiman B 1983 Evidence for a rapid inhibitor to tissue plasminogen activator in plasma. Thrombosis Research 31: 427– 436

Colley C M, Fleck A, Goode A W, Muller B R, Myers M A 1983 Early time course of the acute phase protein response in man. Journal of Clinical Pathology 36: 203–207

Haglund O, Wibell L, Saldeen T 1984 Plasminogen activators and inhibitors of plasminogen activator after venous occlusion in patients with deep venous thrombosis. Haemostasis 14: 102 (abstract no 186)

Juhan-Vague I, Rijken D C, De Cock F, Mendez C, Collen D 1983 Extrinsic plasminogen activator levels in clinical plasma samples. In: Davidson J F, Bachmann F, Bouvier C A, Kruithof E K D (eds) Progress in Fibrinolysis. Vol VI, Churchill Livingstone, Edinburgh, London, Melbourne and New York, pp 65–69

Juhan-Vague I, Moerman B, De Cock F, Aillaud M F, Collen D 1984 Plasma levels of a specific inhibitor of tissue-type plasminogen activator (and urokinase) in normal and pathological conditions. Thrombosis Research 33: 523–530

Kluft C, Brakman P, Veldhuyzen-Stolk E C 1976 Screening of fibrinolytic activity in plasma euglobulin fraction on the fibrin plate. In: Davidson J F, Samama M M, Desnoyers P C (eds) Progress in chemical fibrinolysis and thrombolysis. Vol II, Raven Press, New York, pp 57–65

Kruithof E K O, Ransijn A, Gudinchet A, Tran Thang C, Bachmann F 1984 Studies on the fast acting inhibitor of tissue-type plasminogen activator (t-PA) and urokinase (UK) in human plasma. Haemostasis 14: 38 (abstract no 63)

Rijken D C, Juhan-Vague I, De Cock F, Collen D 1983 Measurement of human extrinsic plasminogen activator by a two-site immuno-radiometric assay. Journal of Laboratory and Clinical Medicine 101: 274–284

Verheijen J H, Chang G I C, Mullaart E 1983 Inhibition of extrinsic (tissue-type) plasminogen activator by human plasma: evidence for the occurrence of a fast acting plasminogen activator inhibitor. Thrombosis and Haemostasis 50: 294 (abstract no 930)

Wijngaards G and Groeneveld E 1982 Temporarily increased inhibition by plasma of plasminogen activator activity in severely ill patients. Haemostasis 12: 106 (abstract no 188)

37. Human vascular smooth muscle cells produce in vitro inhibitors of plasminogen activators

C. Cheng and W. E. Laug

INTRODUCTION

Bovine vascular smooth muscle cells (VSMC) previously were shown to elaborate inhibitors of plasminogen activators (PA) (Laug, 1983). These inhibitors neutralized both urokinase-like (u-PA) and tissue type plasminogen activators (t-PA). In the present study human VSMC were shown to produce *in vitro* similar PA inhibitors. One of the PA inhibitors with an apparent Mr of 50 000 and reacting with both t-PA and u-PA, has been isolated and partially purified.

MATERIAL AND METHODS

Human VSMC were derived at autopsy from the aorta of a 13 year old patient. The cells, isolated and cloned as previously described for bovine VSMC (Laug et al, 1980), were grown in RPMI medium containing 20% fetal calf serum. The PA inhibitory activities of serum free conditioned medium and of the partially purified PA inhibitor were determined by mixing the samples with known amounts of either u-PA (Abbott Lab., Chicago, IL) or t-PA (kindly provided by Dr. D. Collen, Leuven, Belgium) followed by incubation on ^{125}I fibrin plates in the presence of human plasminogen (Laug, 1981). The PA inhibitory activities were expressed in a percentage of untreated PA samples.

RESULTS

Serum free medium from confluent cultures of human VSMC was found to contain PA inhibitory activities similar to those detected in the medium conditioned by bovine VSMC (data not shown). Reverse fibrin autography of the medium (Loskutoff et al, 1983) revealed the presence of a PA inhibitor with an apparent Mr of 50 000 which neutralized the activities of both u-PA and t-PA. This inhibitor was partially purified from serum free medium conditioned for 48 hours by confluent human VSMC cultures. The medium was pooled centrifuged to remove cell debris (2 000 rpm, 15 min, 4°C and concentrated tenfold by ultrafiltration using a Diaflow membrane YM-10. The proteins were precipitated by the addition of ammonium sulfate (75% W/V), centrifuged (10 000 rpm, 15 min., 4°C) and the pellet dissolved in 0.1M Tris HCl buffer pH 8.1. The material was applied to a DEAE cellulose column and eluted with a sodium chloride gradient (Fig. 37.1).

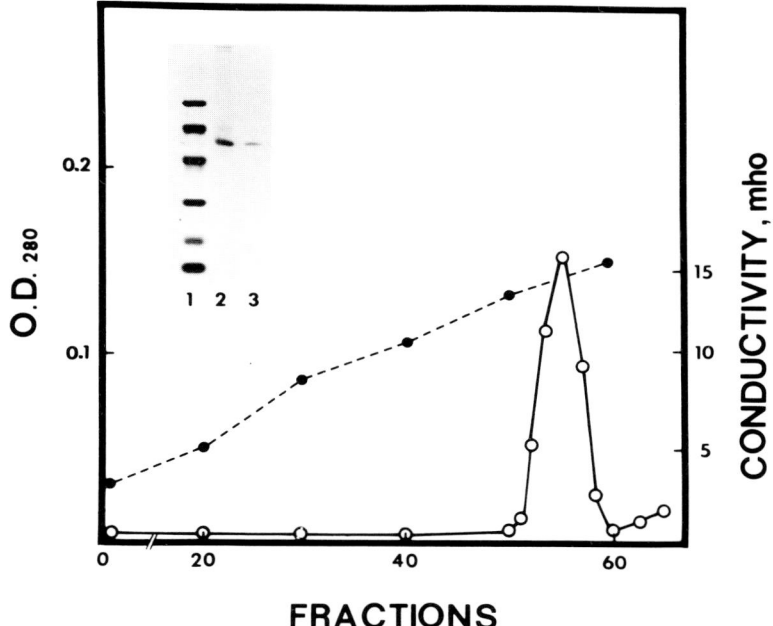

FRACTIONS

Fig. 37.1 Elution of PA Inhibitor from DEAE cellulose and gel electrophoresis of partially purified PA inhibitor (Insert). O.D. 280 (o———o) and conductivity (●— — —●). Insert, lane 1: Mr standards (from top 94K, 67K, 43K, 20,1K, 14.4K), lane 2: Medium conditioned by VSMC (tenfold concentrated) and lane 3: Partially purified PA Inhibitor.

The fractions 50 to 56 were combined and concentrated by ultrafiltration and tested for PA inhibitory activity. Gel electrophoretic analysis of this material on 10% SDS polyacrilamide slab gels followed by reverse fibrin autography demonstrated only one band of inhibition of fibrinolysis corresponding to a Mr of approximately 50 000. Staining of the gel revealed the presence of a major protein band with a Mr of 50 000 and some minor bands in the molecular weight range at 100 000 to 2000 000. Incubation of a constant amount (0.1 CTA units) of either u-PA or t-PA with increasing amounts of this partially purified material resulted in a progressive inhibition of u-PA and t-PA activity (Fig. 37.2).

The rate and degree of t-PA inhibition was significantly more pronounced than that of u-PA suggesting higher affinity of this inhibitor to t-PA than to u-PA.

DISCUSSION

A PA inhibitor with an apparent Mr of 50 000 was found to be secreted by human VSMC grown *in vitro*. This inhibitor was partially purified and found to inhibit both u-PA and t-PA. The rate and degree of t-PA inhibition was more

151

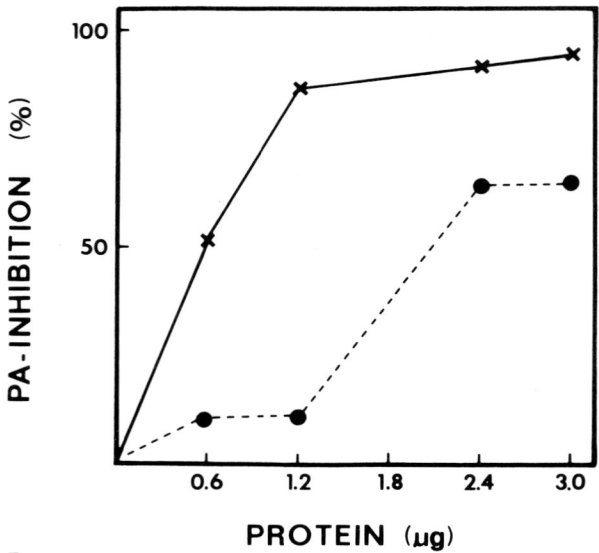

Fig. 37.2 Inhibition of 0.1 CTA units/ml of u-PA (● — — — ●) and t-PA (x———x) by increasing concentrations of partially purified PA Inhibitor.

pronounced than that of u-PA. A similar PA inhibitor was recently detected in bovine endothelial cells (Loskutoff et al, 1983) and several authors have described the presence of a PA inhibitor in human plasma with an approximate Mr of 50 000 (Chmielewska et al, 1983; Juhan-Vague et al, 1984). At the present time it is unknown whether these inhibitors are identical. In addition, comparison of these inhibitors with protease-nexin, a PA inhibitor secreted by fibroblasts (Baker et al, 1980) is indicated. The biological significance of the PA inhibitor secreted by VSMC is unknown but it may be of importance in arteriosclerotic lesions where VSMC proliferate in close vicinity of endothelial cells.

REFERENCES

Baker J B, Low D A, Simmer R L, Cunningham D D 1980 Protease-nexin: A cellular component that links thrombin and plasminogen activator and mediates their binding to cells. Cell 21: 37–45
Chmielewska J, Ranby M, Wiman B 1983 Evidence for a rapid inhibitor to tissue plasminogen activator in plasma. Thrombosis Research 31: 417–435
Juhan-Vague I, Moreman B, DeCock F, Aillaud M F, Collen D 1984 Plasma levels of a specific inhibitor of tissue-type plasminogen activator (and urokinase) in normal and pathological conditions. Thrombosis Research 33: 523–530
Laug W E 1981 Secretion of plasminogen activator by cultured bovine endothelial cells. Partial purification, characterization and evidence for multiple forms. Thrombosis and Haemostasis 45: 219–224
Laug W E 1983 Vascular smooth muscle cells inhibit plasminogen activators secreted by endothelial cells In: Davidson J F, Bachman F, Bouvier C A, Kruithof E R O (eds) Progress in Fibrinolysis, Volume VI, Churchill Livingstone Edinburgh, Ch 14, p 374
Laug W E, Tokes Z A, Benedict W F, Sorgente N 1980 Anchorage independent growth and plasminogen activator production by bovine endothelial cells. Journal Cell Biology 84: 281–293
Loskutoff D J, Van Mourik J A, Erickson L A, Lawrence D 1983 Detection of an unusually stable fibrinolytic inhibitor produced by bovine endothelial cells. Proceedings of the National Academy of Sciences (USA) 80: 2956–2960

Section 6
ACTIVATION AND INHIBITION OF FIBRINOLYSIS: METHODS OF STUDY

38. The influence of a preactivation phase on euglobulin fibrinolytic activity measured by the fibrin plate method

J. Gram, J. Jespersen and T. Astrup

The accurate assessment of euglobulin fibrinolytic activity continues to pose problems despite the efforts of many investigators to establish the conditions needed for the highest degree of reproducibility and precision. The acidity (pH) and the dilution, at which the active euglobulin fraction should be precipitated and separated, have been determined (Astrup & Rasmussen, 1958; Brakman et al, 1966). The presence of C_1-inactivator in euglobulins precipitated at pH 5.3, as used by a majority of investigators, was found to decrease the recovered activity in comparison with that obtained at pH 5.9 (Kluft, 1976). Problems related to the instability of the lytic activity in plasma (Fearnley, 1965) have been overcome by a strict standardization of the collection and handling of the samples with ice-cold utensils of siliconized glass or plastic materials or in evacuated glass tubes (Jespersen et al, 1982). We have now traced another source, which might influence the assay. Blood samples from patients may contain varying amounts of cryoglobulin, and Pepper et al (1978) have reported that cryoglobulin adsorbs plasminogen activator from plasma. We have therefore studied the influence of cryoglobulins on the separation and assay of fibrinolytically active euglobulins in normal plasma and in plasma rich in cryoglobulins.

MATERIALS

Plasma sampling
Pools of plasma were collected from normal women and from women using oral contraceptives low in oestrogen (P-plasma). Collection and handling of the blood samples was as described (Jespersen et al, 1982).

Assay procedure
Fibrin plates were prepared as described in detail elsewhere (Jespersen & Astrup, 1983).

The normal euglobulin fraction (NEF) was obtained from both pools of plasma by dilution of 0.5 ml plasma with 4.5 ml of ice-cold, distilled water and adjustment to pH 5.9 with 0.25% (v/v) acetic acid using an automatic titrator (Radiometer, Copenhagen).

The dextran sulphate euglobulin fraction (DEF) was prepared by dilution of

155

0.5 ml plasma with 4.0 ml ice-cold, distilled water followed by addition of 0.5 ml solution of dextran sulphate (100 mg 1^{-1}m M_{-r} 500.000, Pharmacia, Uppsala) in distilled water and adjusting pH to 5.9. The euglobulin precipitates (NEF or DEF) were collected by centrifugation in the cold and dissolved in 0.5 ml of DTA-barbital buffer (0.05 M sodium diethyl barbiturate; 0.10 M NaCl; 0.25% (w/v) gelatine, 2.7 mM EDTA pH 7.75; ionic strength 0.25). Thirty μl of the solutions were then placed in triplicate on the fibrin plates. After incubation for 17 hrs at 37°C on a level glass plate in a moist incubator the fibrinolytic activity was determined by the product (mm^2) of two perpendicular diameters. Recorded were also the activities after elimination of inhibitors by addition to each applied sample of 5 μl of 14 mM flufenamic acid.

EXPERIMENTS

When euglobulin solutions prepared from P-plasma were kept at 0°C until application on the fibrin plates visible cryoglobulins were formed. In the beginning of the preincubation period an increase in the recorded activities of NEF and DEF was obtained with the most marked increase occurring in the NEF solution. During this phase the recorded activities showed slight, irregular variations related to the amounts of cryoglobulin visible in the solution applied to the fibrin plate (Fig. 38.1).

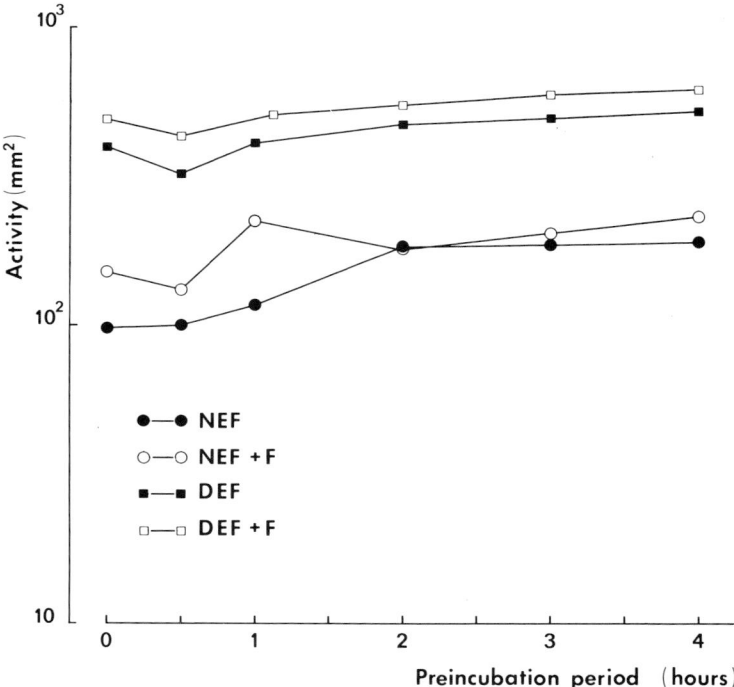

Fig. 38.1 Fibrinolytic activities (mm^2) recorded in euglobulins prepared from plasma rich in euglobulins and preincubated at various periods at 0°C without preheating prior to application on the fibrin plates. Ordinate: fibrinolytic activity (logarithmic scale).

When in a similar experiment the euglobulin solutions were preheated for 2 minutes at 37°C prior to the application on the fibrin plates, no visible cryoglobulins were left, but an increase in the activities in the beginning of the preincubation period was still observed (Fig. 38.2).

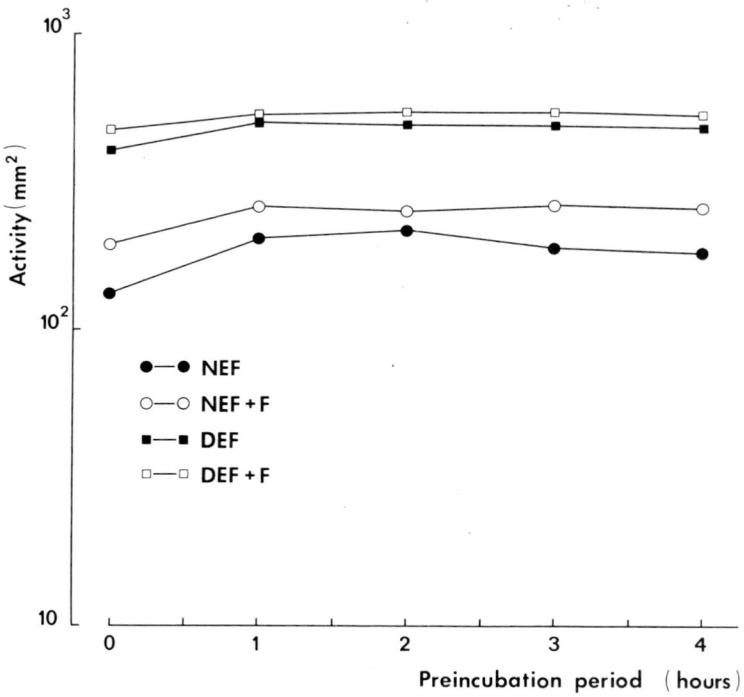

Fig. 38.2 Fibrinolytic activities (mm²) recorded in euglobulins prepared from plasma rich in euglobulins and preincubated at various periods at 0°C and preheated at 37°C for 2 min prior to application on the fibrin plates. Ordinate: fibrinolytic activity (logarithmic scale).

Next, the activities were recorded at briefer intervals during the first hour of preincubation at 0°C followed by preheating for 2 minutes prior to the application (Fig. 38.3A). For comparison the same experiment was made on plasma from normal women without detectable cryoglobulins (Fig. 38.3B). A plateau of activity was reached after 30 minutes at 0°C in euglobulins prepared from plasma rich in cryoglobulins, whereas in the euglobulins prepared from the normal plasma the plateau was reached without preincubation.

There were no visible cryoglobulins in the supernatant separated from the euglobulin in the P-plasma (NEF). The activities obtained in the precipitate separated after addition of 0.5 ml dextran sulphate solution (25 mg 1^{-1}) to the NEF supernatant gave no indication of a preactivation phase even if preheating at 37°C for 2 minutes was omitted (not shown).

If the euglobulins separated from plasma rich in cryoglobulins were kept at 0°C for at least 30 minutes and preheated to 37°C for 2 minutes prior to application, the recorded activities were stable as seen in Figure 38.4.

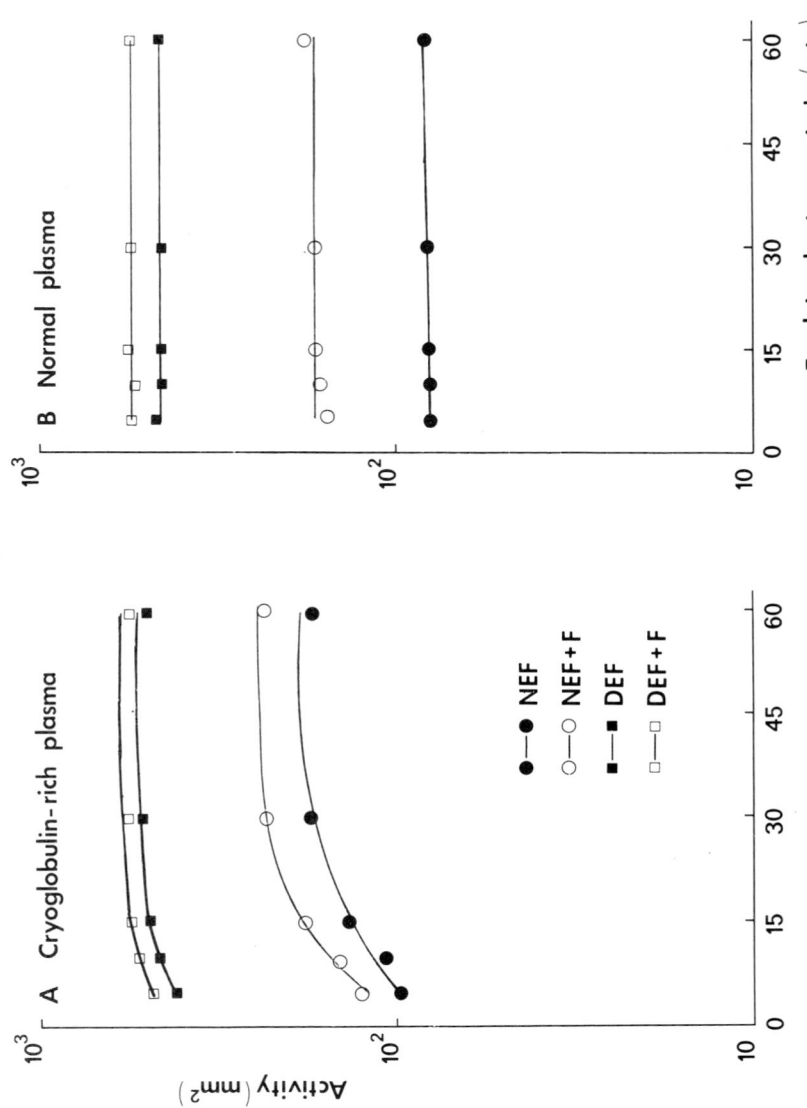

Fig. 38.3 Fibrinolytic activities (mm²) recorded in euglobulins at brief intervals in cryoglobulin-rich and normal plasma after preincubation for various periods at 0°C and preheated at 37°C for 2 min prior to application on the fibrin plates. Ordinate: fibrinolytic activity (logarithmic scale).

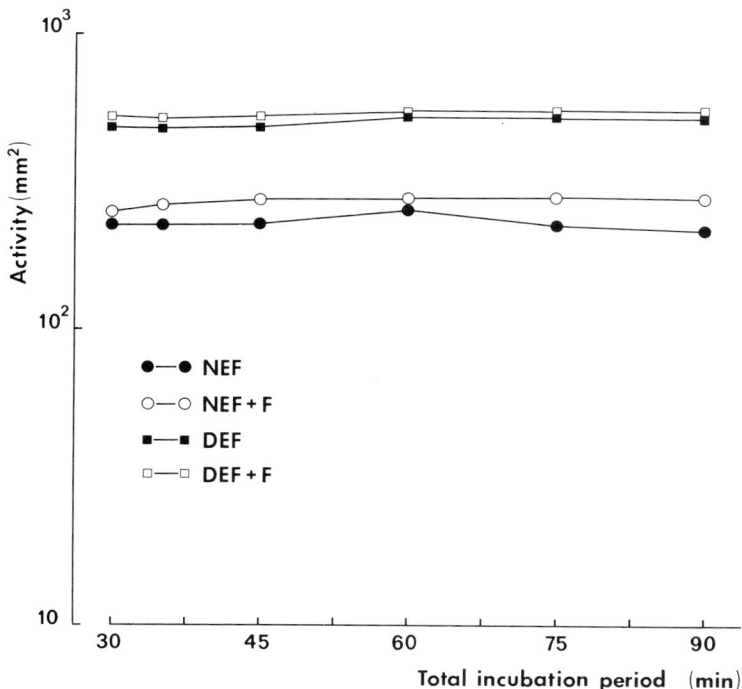

Fig. 38.4 Fibrinolytic activities (mm²) recorded in euglobulins after a preincubation period ⩾ 30 min at 0°C and preheated at 37°C for 2 min prior to application on the fibrin plates. Ordinate: fibrinolytic activity (logarithmic scale).

CONCLUDING REMARKS

An obvious result of these findings is that assays of euglobulin fibrinolytic activity in samples of plasma from patients may deviate because of the presence of cryoglobulins. This source of error is overcome by keeping the euglobulin suspension for at least 2 minutes at 37°C — enough to bring the cryoglobulins into solution. Thus the results explain why it was found necessary to adhere to such a procedure to obtain constant and reproducible determinations of euglobulin activities (Jespersen, 1983).

Another finding was that an increase in activity occurred after prolonged exposure of the euglobulins to the cold. The preactivation was amplified in plasma rich in cryoglobulins (Fig. 38.2). It might be related to the F-XII dependent pathway through a cold-promoted activation of prekallikrein (Kluft, 1978).

The overall results of the present study emphasize the necessity of a standardized handling of the euglobulins prior to application on the fibrin plates in order to obtain reproducible results. The euglobulins should be kept for at least 30 minutes at 0°C followed by at least 2 minutes at 37°C. It appears to be important to adhere to this procedure in all assays relying on euglobulin methods.

REFERENCES

Astrup T, Rasmussen J 1958 Estimation of fibrinolytic activity in blood In: Proceedings of the
   VIIth International Society of Hematology. Rome p 164–169
Brakman P, Albrechtsen O K, Astrup T 1966 A comparative study of coagulation and fibrinolysis
   in blood from normal men and women. British Journal of Haematology 12: 74–85
Fearnley G R 1965 Fibrinolysis Arnold, London 28–29
Jespersen J 1983 Sequential study of plasma euglobulin fibrinolytic activity during the normal
   menstrual cycle and in women on oral contraceptives low in oestrogen. Gynecologic and
   Obstetric Investigation 15: 266–274
Jespersen J, Astrup T 1983 A study of the fibrin plate assay of fibrinolytic agents optimal
   conditions, reproducibility and precision. Haemostasis 13: 301–315
Jespersen J, Knudsen L H, Sidelmann J 1982 The use of evacuated glass tubes for collection of
   blood samples for fibrinolytic assays. Thrombosis Research 25: 173–176
Kluft C 1976 Occurrence of C_1-inactivator and other proteinase inhibitors in euglobulin fractions
   and their influence on fibrinolytic activity. Haemostasis 5: 136–146
Kluft C 1978 Determination of prekallikrein in human plasma: Optimal conditions for activating
   prekallikrein. Journal of Laboratory and Clinical Medicine 91: 83–95
Pepper D S, Innes A, Chirnside A, Prowse C 1978 Vascular plasminogen activator,
   cryoprecipitation and the decay of Factor-VIII coagulant activity. British Journal of
   Haematology 39: 147

39. The determination of tissue plasminogen activator in the euglobulin fraction of the mouse with a chromogenic substrate

J, W. C. M. Jansen, H. van den Brink,
J. H. Verheijen and C. Kluft

INTRODUCTION

Recently Verheijen et al (1982) developed an assay for the direct determination of the tissue-type plasminogen activator (t-PA) in plasma. The assay is based on the presence of CNBr-fragments of fibrinogen (stimulator) which stimulate specific plasminogen activation by t-PA. In contrast with fibrin the stimulator is soluble. The active stimulator fragment is fragment FCB-2 (Nieuwenhuizen et al, 1983).

So far the method has been developed only for human material. We adapted the method for mouse plasma.

MATERIALS AND METHODS

Materials

PAF (platelet activating factor) was obtained from Bachem, Bubendorf, Switzerland; plasminogen, stimulator and the chromogenic substrate S-2251 were obtained from KABI, Stockholm, Sweden. Anti-t-PA-IgG (rabbit anti human) was prepared as described by Rijken et al (1980).

Animal experimentation

Male DAP mice (20–25 g) were anaesthetized with Nembutal (75 mg/kg ip), 20 min before iv administration of PAF (10 μg/kg) or placebo (Emeis and Kluft, 1984). After drug administration, the abdomen was opened and blood was taken from the abdominal vena cava, within 2 min of iv administration. Blood was collected in tubes containing citrate as anticoagulant and plasma prepared.

Euglobulin preparation

During the starting procedure the euglobulin fraction was prepared essentially as described by Verheijen et al (1982). After precipitation the euglobulins were dissolved in an equal volume of Tris-Tween buffer (0.1 M Tris Hcl pH 7.5; 0.1% v/v Tween 80).

161

t-PA assay
The euglobulin fractions of 3 mice were pooled and used for the chromogenic assay (S-2251) as described by Verheijen et al (1982). When anti-t-PA-IgG was used, an incubation period of 15 min together with stimulator and the euglobulin fraction was applied, before starting the assay. The linear increase in extinction per time^2 is indicative for the enzyme activation process.

RESULTS AND COMMENTS

Using the conditions of Verheijen et al (1982) on the euglobulin fraction of control mice, a high enzyme activity was obtained. Omitting the stimulator, leaving the stimulator independent activity (SI-activity), resulted in only slightly lower values. In preparing the mouse euglobulin fraction optimal conditions for decreasing the SI-activity were aimed at. As in the control situation very low levels of t-PA are expected, we continuously compared the euglobulin fractions of control mice with those of PAF stimulated mice.

Euglobulin precipitation
After varying several preparation parameters (data not shown), it appeared that optimal conditions were obtained when: 1) the plasma was diluted 15 times with pure aqua dest, 2) precipitation occurred at pH 5.9.

Addition of antibodies
In order to study the contribution of t-PA to the total enzyme activity, anti-t-PA-IgG was added to the assay mixture. Addition of anti-t-PA-IgG to the euglobulin fraction of control and PAF stimulated mice resulted in a roughly 20% and 65% lower activity, respectively. The neutralizing activity is IgG-concentration dependent (Fig. 39.1).

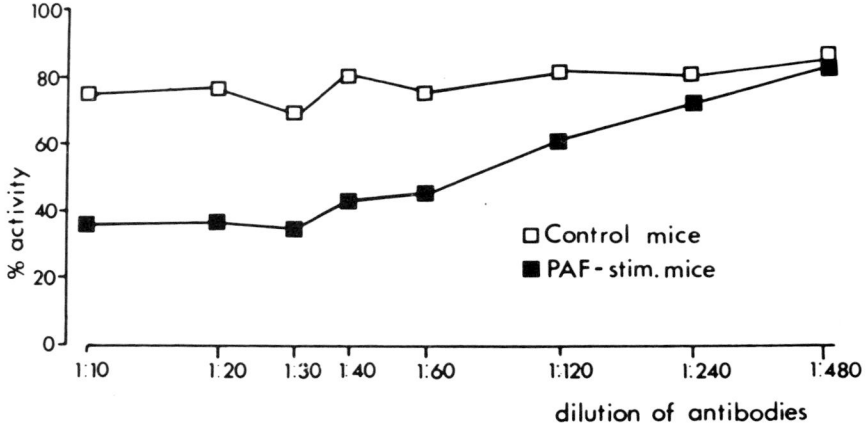

Fig. 39.1 Effect of addition of anti-t-PA-IgG on measured activity. The activity without anti-t-PA-IgG is set at 100%.

Background activity

Despite the presence of anti-t-PA-IgG a background activity still remained (non-t-PA-activity). To compare this activity with the SI-activity both these activities of control and PAF stimulated mice respectively, are calculated and summarized in Table 39.1.

Table 39.1 Composition of measured activity (activities expressed relative to the total activity of control mice = 100%)

	activity ± SEM	n
control mice		
total activity	100	
SI-activity°	61.3 ± 6.2	11
Non-t-PA-activity*	78.6 ± 3.7	10
PAF stimulated mice		
total activity	211.5 ± 15.1	7
SI-activity°	64.2 ± 7.8	7
Non-t-PA-activity*	73.2 ± 5.0	7

°ommitting stimulator from assay; *addition of anti-t-PA-IgG to assay

It appears from Table 39.1 that PAF stimulates the t-PA release but does not influence the background activity: the SI-activity and non-t-PA-activity respectively of control and PAF-stimulated mice are similar. Between both correction methods remains a difference: the addition of anti-t-PA-IgG results in a higher background activity (78.6 and 73.2%) than in the case that the stimulator is omitted (61.3 and 64.2%). Because it is certain that with anti-t-PA-IgG addition t-PA is neutralized, the use of these antibodies is recommended for background correction. The nature of the SI- and non-t-PA-activity is not yet established.

It can be concluded that the method of Veheijen et al (1982) with slight modifications is applicable to mouse plasma, but that, in contrast to human material, a correction for non-t-PA activity is essential. This is best achieved with anti-t-PA-IgG.

REFERENCES

Emeis J J, Kluft C 1984 PAF-acether induced release of tissue-type plasminogen activator from vessel walls. Involvement of a lipoxygenase pathway. Haemostasis 14: 92
Nieuwenhuizen W, Verheijen J H, Vermond A, Chang G T G 1983 Plasminogen activation by tissue activator is accelerated in the presence of fibrin(ogen) cyanogen bromide fragment FCB-2. Biochimica et Biophysica acta 755: 531–533
Rijken D C, Wijngaards G, Welbergen J 1980 Relationship between tissue plasminogen activator and the activators in blood and vascular wall. Thrombosis Research 18: 815–830
Verheijen J H, Mullaart E, Chang G T G, Kluft C, Wijngaards G 1982 A simple, sensitive spectrophotometric assay for extrinsic (tissue-type) plasminogen activator applicable to measurements in plasma. Thrombosis and Haemostasis 48: 266–269

40. The influence of several anaesthetics on the diluted blood clot lysis test of the rat

J. W. C. M. Jansen and H. H. Olieberg

INTRODUCTION

The fibrinolytic activity is increased during several types of anaesthesia in human surgery (Oyama et al, 1975; Simpson et al, 1982). In animal laboratory studies anaesthetics are used during animal surgery but also sometimes during blood sampling to avoid stress effects owing to the degree of desanguination. In order to minimalize the effect of anaesthesia on measured fibrinolytic activity several commonly used anaesthetics were studied. The lysis of blood clots of anaesthetized animals was compared with the lysis of blood clots from conscious rats with chronically implanted carotid cannulas.

MATERIALS AND METHODS

Materials
Nembutal was obtained from Sanofi, Paris (France), Hypnorm from Duphar, Amsterdam (The Netherlands), Ketaset from Bristol-Myers, New York (USA), Rompun from Bayer, Leverkusen (Germany) and urethane from Fluka, Buchs (Switzerland). ^{125}I-Fibrinogen was obtained from Amersham International, Amersham (England).

Procedures
Cannulated rats: The right carotid as cannulated one day before a clot lysis experiment was performed. Blood was taken from the conscious animals via the implanted cannula. These rats were used for control experiments without anaesthesia.
  Anaesthesia-studies The anaesthetics Nembutal (70 mg/kg, ip), Hypnorm (1.5 mg/kg, im), Ketaset/Rompun (45 mg/kg, im; 0.5 mg/kg, sc) and urethane (1.25 g/kg, ip) were administered to male Wistar rats (180–200 g) 20 min before blood was taken from the abdominal aorta. Ether and CO_2 anaesthesia were induced immediately before blood sampling. All experiments were done with groups of 3 rats.
  Lysis experiments The clot lysis experiments were performed as described by

Chohan et al (1975) with some modifications. Briefly: blood was immediately diluted with 3 volumes of cold sodium acetate buffer (0.12 M, pH 7.4) and stored on ice for 30 min. After adding ^{125}I-fibrinogen a blood clot was prepared by addition of thrombin to an appropriate volume of diluted blood.

Immediately after mixing, a blood sample was taken for radioactive counting (100% lysis); 10 min later the clot was detached from the plastic vial wall and a second sample from the supernatant was taken for radioactive counting (0% lysis).

After 1, 2 and 5 hours additional samples were taken. The %-lysis was calculated on the basis of soluble iodinated fibrinogen fragments.

RESULTS AND COMMENTS

As no obvious signs of stress were noticed even during blood sampling, the rats with the chronically implanted cannulas were considered as the control group.

For practical purposes the assay was limited to 5 hours and the dilution of blood from control rats was therefore varied so that a significant degree of fibrinolysis oocurred within this period. As can be seen from Figure 40.1 this was achieved with a blood clot consisting of 17.5% blood.

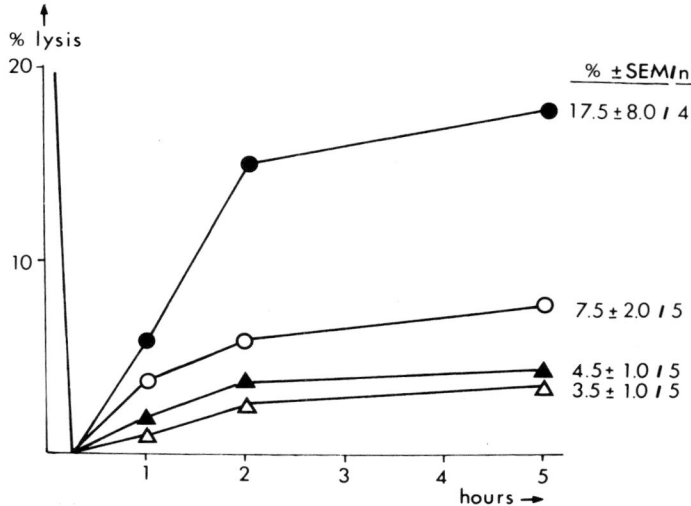

Fig. 40.1 The lysis of blood clots consisting of different percentages blood of control rats. The %-lysis after 5 hours is given: 15% blood clot (●), 17.5% blood clot (o), 20% blood clot (▲) and 22.5% blood clot (Δ).

In Figure 40.2, the effects of the anaesthetics on the fibrinolytic activity are shown. The fibrinolytic activity was considerably increased after ether or urethane anaesthesia but a more dramatical increase was obtained with CO_2. The combination Ketaset/Rompun slightly increased the fibrinolytic activity whereas no difference was observed after Hypnorm or Nembutal anaesthesia as compared with control rats.

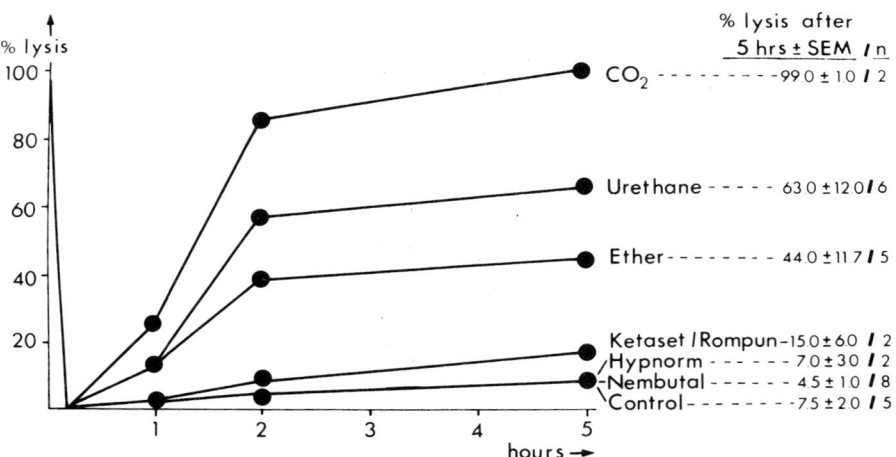

Fig. 40.2 The effect of several anaesthetics on the lysis of a 17.5% blood clot.

It can be concluded that the measured fibrinolytic activity of rats can be strongly influenced by anaesthetics. On the basis of the results a Hypnorm or Nembutal anaesthesia is recommended at least for studies where effects on fibrinolysis have to be measured.

REFERENCES

Chohan I S, Vermylen J, Singh I, Balakrishnan K, Verstraete M 1975 Sodium acetate buffer: a diluent of choice in the clot lysis time technique. Thrombosis et Diathesis Haemorrhagica 33: 226–229
Oyama T, Takiguchi M, Nagayama M, Maki M 1975 The coagulation-fibrinolysis system in man during ethrane anaesthesia and surgery. Canadian Anaesthetics Society Journal 22: 349–357
Simpson P J, Radford S G, Forster S J, Cooper G M, Hughes A O 1982 The fibrinolytic effects of anaesthesia. Anaesthesia 37: 3–8

41. Functional assay for endothelial cell-produced plasminogen activator in the presence of excess inhibitor

J. J. Emeis, C. M. van den Hoogen and V. W. M. van Hinsbergh

INTRODUCTION

Cultured endothelial cells will produce both plasminogen activator (PA) and PA inhibitor. It was previously shown (Emeis et al, 1983) that human and porcine endothelial cells secrete a greater measure of inhibitor, thus impeding the straightforward functional determination of PA activity. Still, PA activity is demonstrable in endothelial cell-conditioned media (ECCM) after sodium dodecyl sulphate/polyacrylamide gel electrophoresis (SDS/PAGE) by fibrin autography (e.g., Loskutoff and Mussoni, 1983). In addition, Levin (1983) described an activator activity in previously inactive purified endothelial activator-inhibitor complexes after treatment with SDS.

In the following we describe a simple procedure for the measurement of PA activity in ECCM containing inhibitor in excess over activator.

METHODS AND RESULTS

Human and porcine ECCM were obtained as described (Emeis et al, 1983; Rijken et al, 1984).

PA activity was determined by the spectrophotometric parabolic rate assay of Verheijen et al (1982).

ECCM showed no spontaneous activity. After treatment (37°C, one hour) with SDS, however, the ECCM showed PA activity. Optimal (final) concentrations of SDS were determined for the various types of ECCM, and would depend on both the cellular source, and the composition of the conditioned media (Table 41.1). Since the spectrophotometric assay will be influenced by the presence of SDS, all assays were performed at a constant final 0.25 mM SDS concentration in the incubation mixture. At higher SDS concentrations PA activity decreased, thus limiting the amount of SDS-treated sample that could be assayed.

In order to be able to express the measured activity of a sample in activator units, a reference curve was constructed. Increasing amounts of t-PA (obtained from Bowes melanoma cells) were added to a fixed volume of (diluted) ECCM, or

Table 41.1 Optimal SDS concentrations for the incubation of ECCM

Medium	Final SDS concentration
	% (mM)
Porcine ECCM, serum-free	0.1 (3.5)
Porcine ECCM, 20% fetal calf serum	0.6 (21)
Human ECCM, serum-free	0.6 (21)
Human ECCM, 10% fetal calf serum	0.6 (21)
Human ECCM, 10% human serum	1.2 (42)

ECCM were incubated with the indicated concentrations of SDS for one hour at 37°C. In the spectrophotometric parabolic rate assay, the final SDS concentration was 0.25 mM.

non-incubated control medium. After pre-incubation in either the presence or absence of SDS, the resultant PA activity was spectrophotometrically determined. As shown in Figure 41.1 for porcine serum-free ECM, approximately two units of t-PA were needed in order to titrate the excess inhibitor present in one ml of (diluted) ECCM (line A), whereas all t-PA added to the control medium was recovered (line B). After treatment with SDS, a partial but stoichiometric recovery of the t-PA added was obtained in both the ECCM

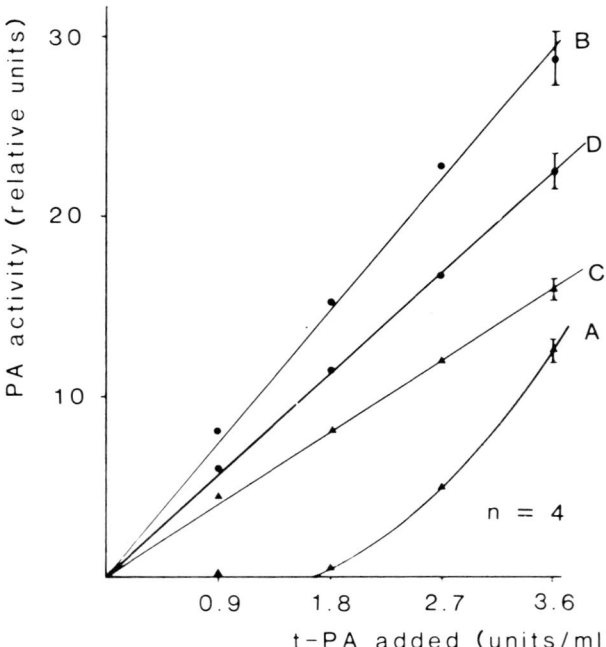

Fig. 41.1 PA activity (as determined by the spectrophotometric parabolic rate assay) in non-incubated control medium and in porcine serum-free ECCM after the addition of increasing amounts of t-PA.
Line A: ECCM, no pretreatment with SDS
Line B: control medium, no pretreatment with SDS
Line C: ECCM, after pretreatment with SDS
Line D: control medium, after pretreatment with SDS.
Line C has been corrected for the endogenous PA activity present in ECCM after pretreatment with SDS.
Results (expressed in relative units) are the mean of four determinations.

(line C) and the control medium (line D). Line C can now be utilized for the conversion of activity measurements into activator units. Similar lines were constructed for the various other types of ECCM used, as well as for urokinase replacing t-PA (data not shown). Also, in human ECCM t-PA antigen concentrations were determined by enzyme-immunoassay (Rijken et al, 1984). Antigen concentrations showed a good correlation with activity determinations after SDS-treatment (r = 0.96). The absolute amount of activity recovered was, however, lower than expected on the basis of antigen measurement: 70% in human serum-freee ECCM; 90% in human ECCM containing 10% fetal calf serum; and only 20% in human ECCM containing 10% pooled human serum.

DISCUSSION

Incubation of ECCM containing excess PA inhibitor with SDS results in the appearance of PA activity in the previously inactive media. The SDS presumably acts by re-activating inactive activator-inhibitor complexes, as, after SDS/PAGE (Weber and Osborn system) followed by fibrin autography, t-PA activity is only found at $M_r = 95\,000$, but not at the position of free t-PA ($M_r = 65\,000$).

The method described here is a quick and simple one, and applicable to ECCM of various species. Also, after SDS treatment, PA activity can be quenched by specific antibodies, thus allowing the analysis of various types of PA present in ECCM. In porcine ECCM, PA activity was completely quenched by anti t-PA IgG (data not shown).

The absolute amount of activity recovered in human ECCM is, however, lower than expected on the basis of antigen determinations, especially in media containing human serum. Whether this is due to the formation of activator-inhibitor complexes that can not be reactivated by SDS; to the formation of complexes with other inhibitors (e.g. α_2-antiplasmin) that can not be reactivated by SDS; or to the presence of degraded t-PA, remains to be established.

ACKNOWLEDGEMENT

The authors are indebted to Dr D C Rijken for performing the t-PA antigen determinations.

REFERENCES

Emeis J J, van Hinsbergh V W M, Verheijen J H, Wijngaards G 1983 Inhibition of tissue-type plasminogen activator by conditioned medium from cultured human and porcine vascular endothelial cells. Biochemical and Biophysical Research Communications 110: 392–398

Levin G 1983 Latent tissue plasminogen activator produced by human endothelial cells in culture: evidence for an enzyme-inhibitor complex. Proceedings of the National Academy of Sciences (USA) 80: 6804–6808

Loskutoff D J, Mussoni L 1983 Interactions between fibrin and the plasminogen activators produced by cultured endothelial cells. Blood 62: 62–68

Rijken D C, van Hinsbergh V W M, Sens E H C 1984 Quantitation of tissue-type plasminogen activator in human endothelial cell cultures by use of an enzyme-immunoassay. Thrombosis Research 33: 145–153

Verheijen J H, Mullaart, Chang G T G, Kluft C, Wijngaards G 1982 A simple, sensitive spectrophotometric assay for extrinsic (tissue-type) plasminogen activator applicable to measurements in plasma. Thrombosis Haemostasis 48: 266–269

42. Half quantitative determination of micro-quantities of plasminogen activator activity

E. P. Pâques, H. A. Stöhr and N. Heimburger

Activity assays for plasminogen activators are based on the activation of plasminogen in the presence of fibrin or fibrin degradation products.

Two different methods are actually available for the determination of plasminogen in the presence of fibrin degradation products.

Two different methods are actually available for the determination of plasminogen activators:

1. The solid-phase-method, consisting of a fibrin film, makes use of the fibrin degradation as signal to quantify plasminogen activators (Astrup and Müllertz). This assay requires radiolabelled fibrin to reach a high sensitivity.

2. The other method generally used allows the quantification of plasminogen activators in the fluid phase. The amount of plasminogen activator (PA) correlates with the quantity of cleaved synthetic substrate by activated plasminogen, namely plasmin (Drapier et al, Rånby and Wallén).

We report here an alternative method which allows the semiquantitative determination of very small amounts of PA in a short time.

PRINCIPLE

Plasminogen and PA are incubated in fibrin coated tubes. Fibrin serves as stimulator for PA as well as substrate for plasmin. In addition the liberated fibrin degradation products are used as signal and quantified using a Staphylococcus clumping test (Fig. 42.1).

METHODS

A. Coating of styrene tubes with fibrin

40 μl of a bovine fibrinogen solution (2%) were mixed with 20 μl of bovine thrombin (10 NIH/ml) in styrene tubes. The mixture was stirred for 30 sec. in order to allow fibrinogen molecules to deposit and coagulate along the tube wall; then the tubes were dried for 24 hours at 37°C. This procedure results in coating of the tubes with a fibrin film. Subsequently, the tubes were extensively washed with buffer until complete removal of FDP. The fibrin coated tubes were stored at 4°C.

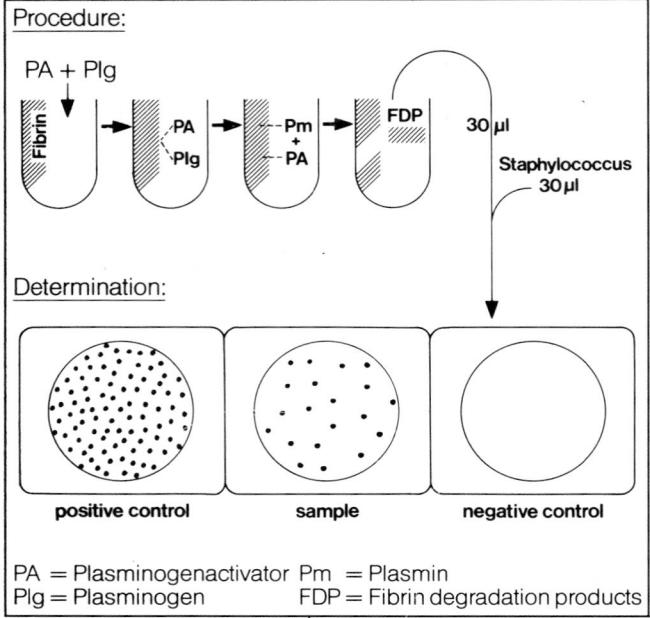

Fig. 42.1 Test principle for plasminogen activator activities.

B. Assay procedure

100 μl of the sample were added into a fibrin coated tube containing 100 μl human plasminogen (10 CTA/ml). The mixture was incubated by 37°C for 1 to 5 hours. At definite intervals of time 30 μl aliquots were removed and the liberated amount of FDP quantified by means of the Staphylococcus clumping test (SCT). All reagents are products of Behringwerke AG (Marburg, W. Germany).

RESULTS

Samples of u-PA (Urokinase) and t-PA (tissue plasminogen activator) containing 0,05 to 0,0001 IU/ml were analysed using the above described procedure.

As shown in Table 42.1, the methods allow the determination of amounts as small as 0,0001 IU/ml. The liberated amount of FDP, as determined with SCT,

Table 42.1 Measurement of t-PA activity.

	Staphylococcus Agglutination								
t-PA (UK-like-international units/ml)								controls	
time h	0.05	0.01	0.005	0.001	0.0005	0.0001	Plg	t-PA 0.05 U	buffer
1	+	−	−	−	−	−	−	−	−
2	+	+	+	+	−	−	−	−	−
3	+	+	+	+	+	−	−	−	−
4	+	+	+	+	+	+	−	−	−

+ = agglutination; − = no agglutination

172

correlates well with the PA activity. All controls were negative during the test performance.

In addition to the above reported results it was possible to discriminate between fibrin binding and non-binding activators. 0,05 units of u-PA and t-PA were incubated for 30 min in fibrin coated tubes, afterwards the solution was removed and the tubes washed with buffer. Subsequently the tubes were incubated for 1 hour at 37°C after addition of 200 μl plasminogen (5 CTA/ml). In control experiments, the same amounts of activators were added and directly incubated with plasminogen. As shown in Table 42.2, this procedure allows to distinguish between fibrin binding and non-binding activators.

Table 42.2 Discrimination between fibrin bindng and non-binding activators.

	Staphylococcus agglutination (1 h)
u-PA control	+
t-PA control	+
u-PA	−
t-PA	+

+ = agglutination; − = no agglutination

CONCLUSIONS

The present method allows the determination of very small amounts of plasminogen activator and is suitable to discriminate between fibrin binding and non-binding plasminogen activator activities.

REFERENCES

Astrup T, Müllertz S 1952 The fibrin plate method for estimating fibrinolytic activity. Archs. Biochem. Biophys. 40: 346–351
Drapier I C, Tenu J P, Lemaine G, Petit J F 1979 Regulation of plasminogen activator secretion in mouse peritoneal macrophages. Biochinie 61: 463–471
Rånby M, Wallén P 1981 A sensitive parabolic rate assay for the tissue plasminogen activator. In: Davidson J F, Nilsson I M, Asted B (eds) Progress in fibrinolysis. Churchill Livingstone, Edinburgh, vol 5, p 233–235

43. Sensitive assays for tissue plasminogen activator (t-PA) and its specific inhibitor (t-PA/INH)

M. Mahmoud, J. Pring and P.J. Gaffney

INTRODUCTION

Since tissue plasminogen activator (tPA) is present in blood taken from human subjects at rest in the low nanogram per millilitre range, sensitive assays have been developed for the specific assay of the tPA molecule (1–4). Some of these assays measure functionally active tPA (3,4) while others measure immunologically reacting material only (1,2). Functionally active tPA methods seem to depend on the presence of fibrin or fibrinogen/fibrin fragments to stimulate the tPA-plasminogen interaction (3–6). We here report on an assay for tPA which does not depend on the presence of fibrin or its fragments and which gives a true reflection of the levels of active tPA in a biological fluid. This assay is also of particular use in rapidly determining the level of the specific fast-acting tPA inhibitor (tPA/INH) in biological fluids.

MATERIALS AND METHODS

Materials

Plasma was obtained from individual donors and from pooled donations all taken into 3.8% sodium citrate. A solution of highly purified tPA (200 μg/ml) and the IgG fraction (10 mg/ml) from a rabbit antiserum to human melanoma tPA were kindly donated by Dr D. Rijken (Leiden, Holland). Human plasminogen (glutamic acid-type) is subsequently referred to as glu-plasminogen and was supplied by KabiVitrum (Stockholm, Sweden) as a 3.1 mg/ml frozen solution. The plasmin-specific chromogenic tripeptide substrate H–D–VAL–LEU–LYS–pNA (denoted S-2251) was purchased from Flow Laboratories (Ayr, Scotland). Flat bottomed polyvinyl chloride (PVC) microtitre plates were purchased from Flow Laboratories (Ayr, Scotland). Horse serum was obtained from Gibco (Paisley, Scotland) and Tween-80 from Koch-Light Laboratories (Colnbrook, Berkshire, UK). All other routine reagents were Analar grade.

174

Methods

Bioimmunoassay for t-PA
Principle:
1. Extrinsic plasminogen activator was adsorbed on the wells of polyvinylchloride micro-titer plate previously coated with the IgG fraction of an antiserum against tPA.
2. The adsorbed t-PA was measured by the conversion of plasminogen into plasmin. The plasmin formed is measured with the synthetic tripeptide substrate H–D–Val–Leu–Lys–pNA (S-2251).

Method
1. Ninety-six well flat bottom micro-titre plate was coated with the IgG fraction (10 μg/ml in 0.1 M phosphate buffer pH 7.4, 150 μl per well) of rabbit antiserum against tPA. The plate was covered and incubated at 37°C for 2 hr.
2. After the incubation the plate was washed 3 times with the washing buffer (0.1 M phosphate buffer pH 7.4, 0.1% Tween 80, 0.1% bovine albumin).
3. 200 μl of coating buffer (1% bovine albumin-phosphate buffer) was pipetted into each well and the plate was incubated for one hour at 37°C. The plate was washed 3 times with washing buffer.
4. Test samples were measured in duplicate; 100 μl of tPA standard was pipetted into micro-titre plate in various dilutions (50 ng, 25, 12.5, 6.25, 3.12, 1.56, .78, .39 ng); plasma (euglobulin fraction at pH 5.9 normally used) and other biological test fluids, were used directly or in a diluted form (100 μl) in place of the above standards.
5. After the addition of the standard and the samples, the plate was covered and incubated at 37°C for 3 hr. After the incubation the plate was washed 3 times and charged with 0.7 nM S-2251 (120 μl) and 2 μM glu-plasminogen (40 μl) in Tris-Tween buffer pH 7.4. Incubate for 1–2 hr at 37°C; read on a Titertek plate reader at 405 nm.
6. The standard curve is constructed from the log tPA versus O.D. generated after an appropriate time (see Fig. 43.1).

Assay of tPA/INH
1. To 1 ml of citrated plasma add 50 ngs of tPA. Incubate at 37°C for 5 minutes and perform a euglobulin precipitation at pH 5.9.
2. Apply 10 μl of reconstituted (1 ml) euglobulin precipitate to the BIA procedure at point 4 as outlined above.
3. The tPA recovered in the euglobulin precipitate can be read from the appropriate standard curve in Figure 43.1. If this figure is less than 50 ng the difference is adjudged to be due to the inhibition of tPA by the tPA/INH and the latter is expressed as 'ngs of tPA inhibited per ml of plasma' (see Table 43.1).

Euglobulin fraction. The euglobulin precipitate from human plasma was obtained by the method of Nilsson and Olow (6) and the precipitate was dissolved in a 0.4% sodium citrate — 0.085% sodium chloride (pH 7.4) buffer containing 0.1% Tween-80.

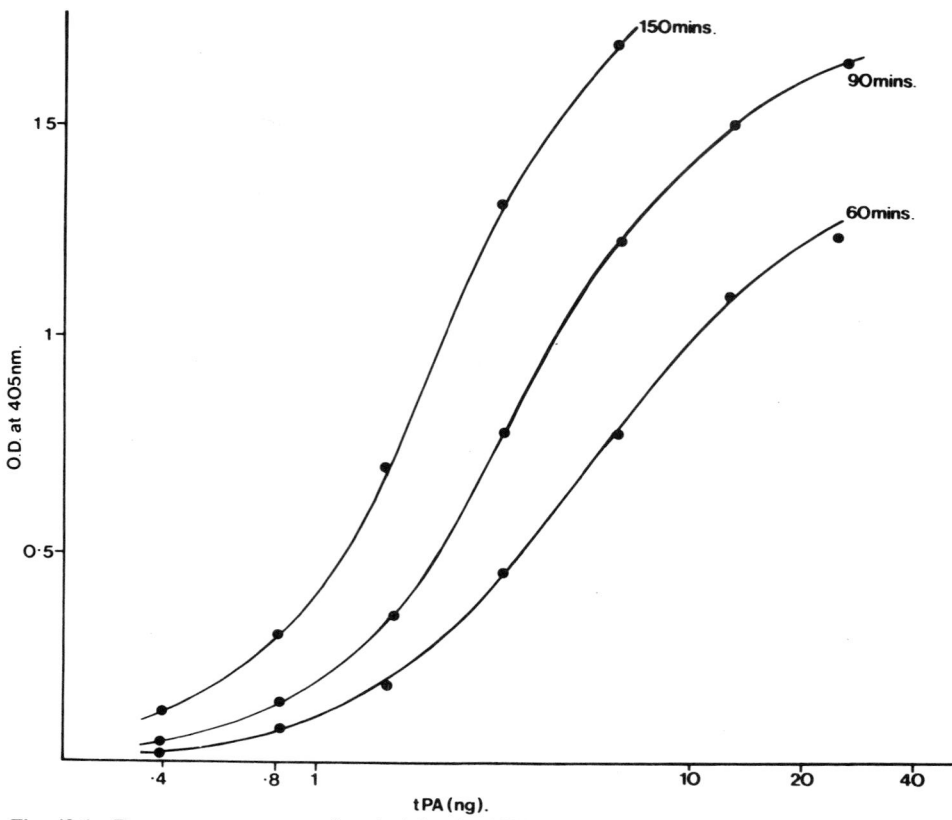

Fig. 43.1 Dose response curves of optical density (OD) at 405nm wavelength versus the log of the tPA concentration in ngs/ml. The data obtained at various incubation times (150, 90 and 60 minutes) of the immobilised tPA with glu-plgn and S-2251 indicate that the sensitivity of the assay can be manipulated to accommodate the levels of tPA in the test materials.

RESULTS

Figure 43.1 shows dose response curves of a tPA using the above described bioimmunoassay (BIA). The dose response range was 0–50 ng/ml. Sigmoid curves resulted from the graphical presentation of the logarithm of the tPA

Table 43.1   TPA/INH levels in some single donor plasmas using the BIA procedure

Subject No.	TPA/INH (ngs TPA inhibited by 1 ml plasma)		
1	11,	10,	10
2	6,	7,	6
3	5,	7,	5
4	8,	8,	7
5	14,	15,	15
6	5,	5,	6
7	5,	5,	5
8	7,	8,	8

176

concentration in ng/ml and the relevant absorbance at 405 nm of the hydrolysis product of S-2251, namely free p-nitroaniline. The times of incubation shown in Figure 43.1 were 60, 90 and 150 minutes. When low levels of tPA (e.g. 0.5–10 ngs/ml) were being measured the longer incubation time is recommended.

The use of this assay to measure the specific rapid-acting tPA inhibitor (tPA/INH) in plasma was investigated. Plasma contains an excess of this inhibitor which is removed in the supernatant following precipitation of plasma at pH 5.9. Following the addition of various levels of tPA to plasma, precipitates were generated at pH 5.9 after 5 minutes of tPA-plasma incubation at 37°C. Control concentrations of tPA were incubated with 2% horse serum buffered solution under the same circumstances. The tPA-plasma curve is displaced from the control curve and the extent of this displacement is constant throughout the dose-response curve suggesting that the inhibitor binds the same amount of tPA over a wide range of excess tPA. Thus the addition of an excess of tPA to plasma and the assay of residual tPA in the 5 minutes euglobulin fraction by the BIA assay is a reliable measure of the tPA/INH in plasma. Using this approach (the detail of which is outlined in the Methods Section) Table 43.1 shows some tPA/INH data obtained in plasma from a variety of healthy subjects.

DISCUSSION

Since many biological fluids (including plasma) contain low levels (nanogram) of both tPA and its specific fast acting inhibitor (tPA/INH) highly sensitive assays are required to measure both these components. Some of these assays (1,2) are advantageous in distinguishing tPA from its companion plasminogen activator, Urokinase (uPA), but they suffer from the drawback that inactive degradation products of tPA and tPA-inhibitor complexes cannot be distinguished from the biologically active tPA molecules. The bioimmunoassay (BIA) for tPA described above satisfies demands for sensitivity and specificity, while allowing a distinction to the made between tPA and uPA by the use of an immobilised specific t-PA antibody.

Our BIA data indicates that plasma contains no measurable free tPA and this finding is at variance with much of the data presented in the literature using assays which are fibrin based (3,4). While there is no doubt that plasma contains immunologically reactive tPA it seems that it is totally inhibited by the variety of tPA inhibitors present in the plasma. The fast acting specific inhibitor (tPA/INH) (7,8) may be the most important of these, but Tijken et al (9) have indicated that α_2-antiplasmin, α_1-antitrypsin and α_2-macroglobulin may also play a part in the slower inhibition of t-PA. The inhibitor data (Table 43.1) was generated using a five minute incubation period following the addition of t-PA to the plasma in an effort to specifically measure only the tPA/INH in the plasma.

REFERENCES

Rijken D C, Juhan-Vague I, De Cock F, Collen D 1983 Measurement of human tissue-type plasminogen activator by a two-site immunoradiometric assay. Journal of Laboratory & Clinical Medicine 101: 274–284

Rijken D C, Van Hinsbergh V W M, Sens E H C 1984 Quantitation of tissue-type plasminogen activator in human endothelial cell cultures by use of an enzyme immunoassay. Thrombosis Research 33: 145–153

Verheijen J H, Mullaart E, Chang G T G, Kluft C, Wijngaards G 1982 A simple sensitive spectrophotometric for extrinsic (tissue-type) plasminogen activator applicable to measurements in plasma. Thrombosis & Haemostas 48: 226–269

Ranby M, Norman I B, Wallén P 1982 A sensitive assay for tissue plasminogen activator. Thrombosis Research 27: 743–749

Haverkate F, Brakman P 1975 Fibrin plate assay. In: Davidson J F, Samama M M, Desnoyers P C (eds) Progress in chemical fibrinolysis and thrombosis. Raven Press, New York, vol 1, pp 151–159

Nilsson I M, Olow B 1962 Fibrinolysis induced by SK in man. Acta Chir Scand 123: 247–266

Kruithof E K O, Ransijn A, Bachmann F 1982 Inhibition of tissue-plasminogen activator by human plasma. Haemostasis 11: 60 (abstr)

Wiman B, Chmielewska J, Ranby M 1984 Inactivation of tissue plasminogen activator in plasma. Demonstration of a complex with a new rapid inhibitor. Journal of Biological Chemistry 259: 3644–3647

Rijken D C, Juhan-Vague I, Collen D 1983 Complexes between tissue-type plasminogen activator and proteinase inhibitors in human plasma identified with an immunoradiometric assay. Journal of Laboratory & Clinical Medicine 101: 285–294

44. Tissue plasminogen activator measured by radioimmunoassay in human endothelial cell cultures

N. R. Hunter, I. R. MacGregor,
M. M. McArthur, P. M. Taylor, C. V. Prowse
and D. S. Pepper

Tissue plasminogen activator (t-PA) can be detected in cultured human endothelial cells (Booyse et al, 1981; Hunter et al, 1983 and Rijken et al, 1983) but is secreted mainly in an inactive form (Levin, 1983). This renders quantitative functional assays of t-PA impractical, and we describe here the measurement of t-PA synthesis and secretion by cultured endothelial cells using a radioimmunoassay (RIA) which detects t-PA inhibitor complexes as well as active t-PA.

METHOD

Human umbilical vein endothelial cells (HUVEC) and adult saphenous vein endothelial cells (SAPEC) were isolated and grown to confluent density on fibronectin-coated plastic tissue culture wells or on gelatin-coated microcarrier beads. The cells were treated with a variety of stimuli, and t-PA secretion into serum free medium and intracellular levels of t-PA were measured by RIA (MacGregor and Prowse, 1983).

RESULTS

With the addition of 2 μg/ml of cycloheximide HUVEC secretion of t-PA after 24 hours was 7 ng/10^6 cells in the control. The cell lysate value was 7 ng/10^6 cells with cycloheximide and 19 ng/10^6 cells in the control. The lysate value at zero hours was 15 ng/10^6 cells. Therefore, the total amount of t-PA (supernatant plus lysate) after 24 hours in the presence of cycloheximide was equivalent to the amount of t-PA in the lysate at zero hours.

t-PA antigen was secreted by late passage cells at a greater rate than early passage cells. At 24 hours HUVEC 5 at passage 18 secreted 90–108 ng t-PA/10^6 cells while HUVEC 5 at passage 3 secreted 18.5 ng t-PA/10^6 cells (Fig. 44.1).

Confluent monolayers of endothelial cells in plastic tissue culture wells were treated with thrombin (0.1, 1.0 and 10 u/ml), calcium ionophore (10^{-6} M and 10^{-5} M), adrenalin (10^{-6} M, 2.5×10^{-5} M 10^{-4} M) and rat anterior pituitary extract (1,

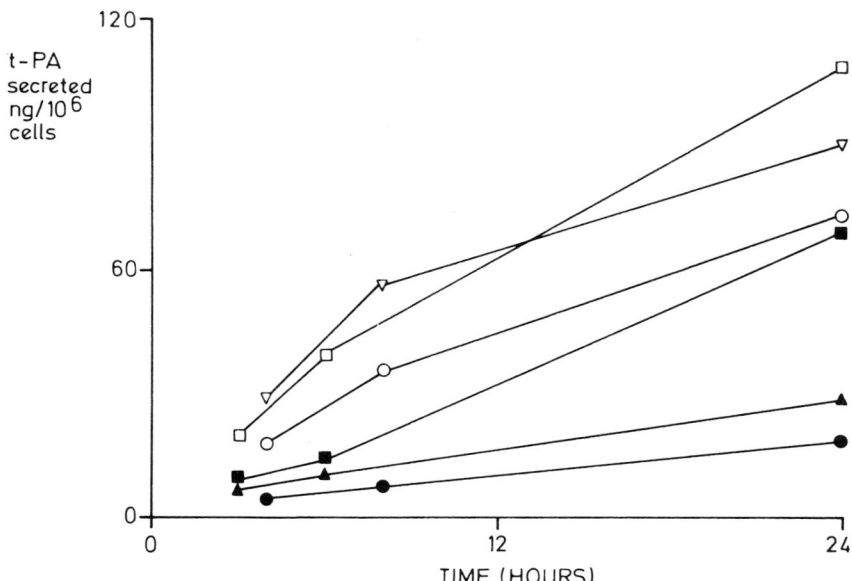

Fig. 44.1 Relationship between passage number of HUVEC 5 cell line and secretion of t-PA.
●——● P3; ▲——▲ P6; ■——■ P8; o – o P12; ▽——▽ P18; □——□ P18;
where P = passage number.

10 and 100 μg/ml). None of these agents potentiated the synthesis or secretion of t-PA over a 24 hour period (tested at 3, 6 and 24 hours). Short term release could not be tested for, due to the low cell surface to medium volume ratio.

HUVEC, on microcarrier beads, were placed in small columns and perfused with serum-free medium to which drugs could be added. The cell surface to medium volume ratio was such that short term release could, in theory, be measured. The carriers were perfused at 0.2 ml/minute and some evidence of t-PA release was found with addition of 10 u/ml of thrombin plus 1% human serum. The basal secretion of t-PA increased three fold after an initial pulse of thrombin plus serum while a steady increase to twice that of basal levels was observed with continuous perfusion of agonist.

CONCLUSIONS

Cycloheximide dimished secretion of t-PA by endothelial cells into serum-free medium, and we conclude that measured t-PA is a synthetic product of endothelial cells and not t-PA previously taken up from serum-containing growth medium.

The difference in rate of secretion of t-PA between early and late passage cells suggests that basal secretion is regulated by factors related to the number of population doublings the cells have undergone.

The small cell surface area to medium volume ratio (8 cm^2/ml) in flat well culture dishes did not permit measurement of short term t-PA release.

Microcarriers provided a relatively large cell surface area to medium volume ratio (300 cm^2/ml of packed beads which house approximately 10^7 cells/ml of beads) and can allow measurement of short term release of t-PA in perfused columns.

REFERENCES

Booyse F M, Scheinbuks J, Radek J, Ositowicz G, Feder S, Quarfoot A J 1981 Immunological identification and comparison of plasminogen activator forms in cultured normal human endothelial cells and smooth muscle cells. Thrombosis Research 24: 495–504

Hunter N R, Dawes J D, MacGregor I R, Pepper D S 1983 Synthesis and secretion of thrombospondin, plasminogen activators and heparin sulphate by endothelial and other cell types. Thrombosis and Haemostasis 50: 296

Levin E 1983 Latent tissue plasminogen activator produced by human endothelial cells in culture: evidence for an enzyme-inhibitor complex. Proceedings of the National Academy of Science USA 80: 6804–6808

MacGregor I R, Prowse C V 1983 Tissue plasminogen activator in human plasma measured by radioimmunoassay. Thrombosis Research 31: 461–474

Rijken D C, Sens E H C, van Hinsbergh V W M 1983 An enzyme immunoassay for human tissue type plasminogen activator. Thrombosis and Haemostasis 50: 269

45. Tissue plasminogen activator (t-PA) or vascular plasminogen activator (v-PA)? Its localization in normal human tissues as defined by a monoclonal antibody

A. Balaton, E. Angles-Cano and Y. Sultan

Plasminogen activator (PA) activity of human tissues has been shown to be associated with the vascular endothelium by means of the histochemical slide technique (Todd, 1959; Warren, 1963). However, the two major drawbacks of this technique, lack of discrimination between t-PA and urokinase (UK) activity, and the presence of tissue fibrinolytic inhibitors have led to controversies concerning the distribution of PA activity in different segments of the vascular system and in different tissues. Modified techniques have been derived (Noordhoek Hegt and Brakman, 1974) to cope with the presence of inhibitors. Immunohistological techniques that have the advantage of by-passing the inhibitor and that by definition are specific have been rarely used.

MATERIAL AMD METHODS

Production of monoclonal antibody

EA- 12D, the monoclonal antibody used in these experiments was produced as described elsewhere (Angles-Cano et al, 1984). A highly purified tissue-type PA separated from post-occlusion human venous plasma (v-PA) as previously described (Angles-Cano et al, 1979) was used for the immunization of mice and for the screening of hybridoma supernatants (Angles-Cano et Sultan, 1984). EA- 12 D is a single subclass IgG_1 antibody not having PA inhibitory activity. Its purification from culture supernatants was obtained by 45% ammonium sulphate precipitation and affinity chromatography on a goat to mouse Ig immunoadsorbant.

Indirect immunoperoxidase technique

Cryostat sections (5 μm) of several human tissues were air-dried for 10 min, at 4°C and washed in PBS for 10 min. EA- 12D diluted 1:25 was overlaid on the tissue and incubated for 6 h at 4°C. Following a wash in PBS (10 min), a rabbit antibody to mouse Ig peroxidase conjugated (Nordic), diluted 1:50, was then applied for 30 min at room temperature. Sections were washed in PBS, the peroxidase activity was demonstrated with diaminobenzidine-H_2O_2. A slight counterstaining with methyl green was performed. Control were performed omitting the first or the second antibody and substituting normal mouse serum or t-PA preabsorbed EA- 12D to EA- 12D.

RESULTS AND DISCUSSION

We have screened a wide range of normal human tissues: ovary, prostate, uterus, lung, liver, placenta, kidney and heart. In all cases there was exclusive localization of EA12D in the cytoplasm of endothelial cells lining capillaries, venules, arterioles, veins and arteries, binding was completely absent in other cell types. Two examples are shown in Figure 45.1

Our results set new evidence for the strict endothelial cell localization of tissue plasminogen activator and demonstrate also that t-PA is not restricted to the

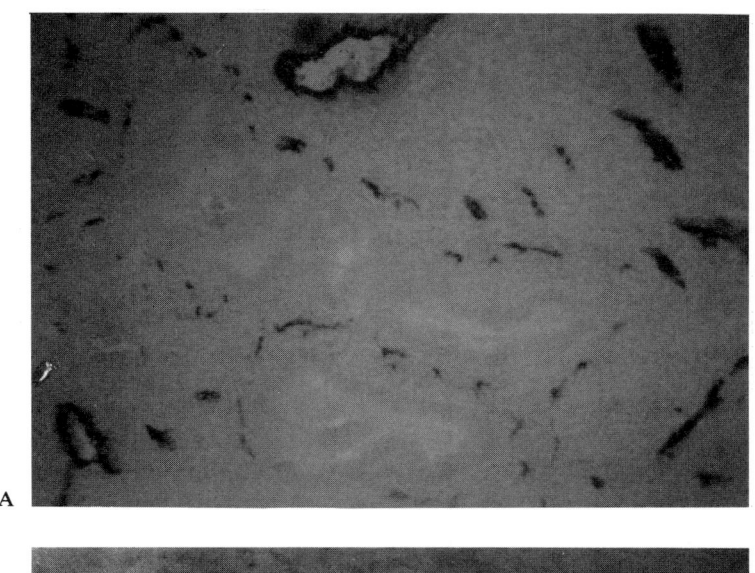

A

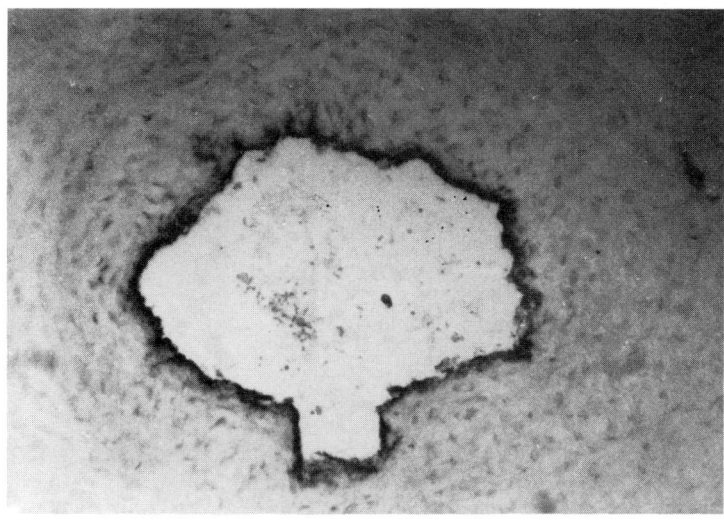

B

Fig. 45.1 Cryostat section of human prostate (A) and ovary (B) stained with monoclonal antibody EA- 12D. A diffuse and granular staining is observed in endothelial cells of venules and arterioles. Note the absence of staining in other cell types (including the glandular epithelium of the prostate).

capillary bed: endothelial cells from vessels of different sizes and types were all able to bind EA- 12D. As this monoclonal antibody was produced against the PA present in plasma after venous occlusion our results provide new and definitive evidences of the identity between the t-PA present in tissues, the endothelial cell PA or vascular-PA and the high fibrin affinity PA of human plasma. Furthermore this identity sets definately the endothelial cell origin of the PA found in plasma after venous occlusion and other stimuli.

REFERENCES

Todd A S 1959 The histological localization of fibrinolysin activator. Journal of Pathology and Bacteriology 78: 281–283
Warren B A 1963 Fibrinolytic properties of vascular endothelium. British Journal of Experimental Pathology 44: 365–371
Noordhoek Hegt V, Brakman P 1974 Inhibition of fibrinolysis by the human vascular wall related to the presence of Smooth muscle cells. Haemostasis 3: 118–128
Angles-Cano E, Balaton A, Sultan Y 1984 Production and immunolocalization of monoclonal antibodies to the high fibrin affinity plasminogen activator of human plasma. Submitted to publication
Angles-Cano E, Sultan Y, Bernard J 1979 Purification de l'activateur du plasminogene d'origine vasculaire. Compte Rendu de l'Académie des Science Paris. 289 (24 Septembre): 485–487
Angles-Cano E, Sultan Y 1984 A solid-phase fibrin immunoassay for the specific detection of monoclonal antibodies against different epitopic.determinants of tissue-plasminogen activators. Journal of Immunological Methods 69: 115–127

46. Immunological cross reactivity of antiurokinase antibodies with tissue plasminogen activator

S.A. Cederholm-Williams, J.M. Marshall and H. Chissic

INTRODUCTION

Urokinase (u-PA) and tissue plasminogen activator are products of different genes, exhibit different physico-chemical properties and are presumed to play different physiological roles. Both enzymes exhibit similar substrate specificities (plasminogen) and display sequence homology in the C-terminal regions forming the B chain and in the N-terminal kringle regions of the A chains. Very low levels of these enzymes can be detected by fibrin plate assay and fibrin zymography and these enzymes can be discriminated in complex mixtures by activity quenching with specific IgG fractions. Using a direct antibody binding technique we have shown that different antibodies are capable of recognising similar antigenic determinants in the different enzymes.

METHODS AND RESULTS

Human uterine t-PA was purified by the method of Rijken et al (1) and purified urokinase was kindly supplied by Dr F Toulemonde, Institute Choay, Paris. u-PA and t-PA were each reacted with Sepharose bound GLU-GLY-ARG-CH_2-Cl according to Schleuning (2). Final coupling ratios of 6.2 μg t-PA/100mg Sepharose and 15 μg u-PA/100 μg Sepharose were obtained. The coupled enzymes were washed thoroughly with urea-5mol/l, sodium dodecyl sulphate-20g/l to remove non-covalently bound materials. Antibodies to the Sepharose bound plasminogen activators were raised in rabbits.

Purified rabbit IgG fractions exhibited quenching activities such that equal volumes anti-uPA would completely inhibit the activity of 1 μg/ml u-PA and anti-tPA IgG would completely inhibit the activito of 0.2 μg/ml t-PA. No inhibition of t-PA (60ng/ml) could be produced using anti-uPA IgG and no inhibition of u-PA (100ng/ml) could be induced by anti-tPA IgG fraction.

Direct antibody binding was assessed as follows: varying dilutions of t-PA or u-PA were coated on to plastic microtitre wells and the plates blocked with bovine albumen. Coated plates were incubated with a predetermined dilution of specific rabbit IgG fraction then thoroughly washed. Bound rabbit IgG was detected using goat antirabbit peroxidase coupled IgG and the colour development assessed after incubation. Blank values were determined with non-immune rabbit IgG fraction. Colour development was proportional to the dilution of coating antigen for each antibody.

Positive binding results were also obtained when the IgG fractions were exchanged (Fig. 46.1). Prior adsorption of anti-t-PA IgG with u-PA (1 μg/ml) reduced the extent of reaction with t-PA indicating common cross reactivity.

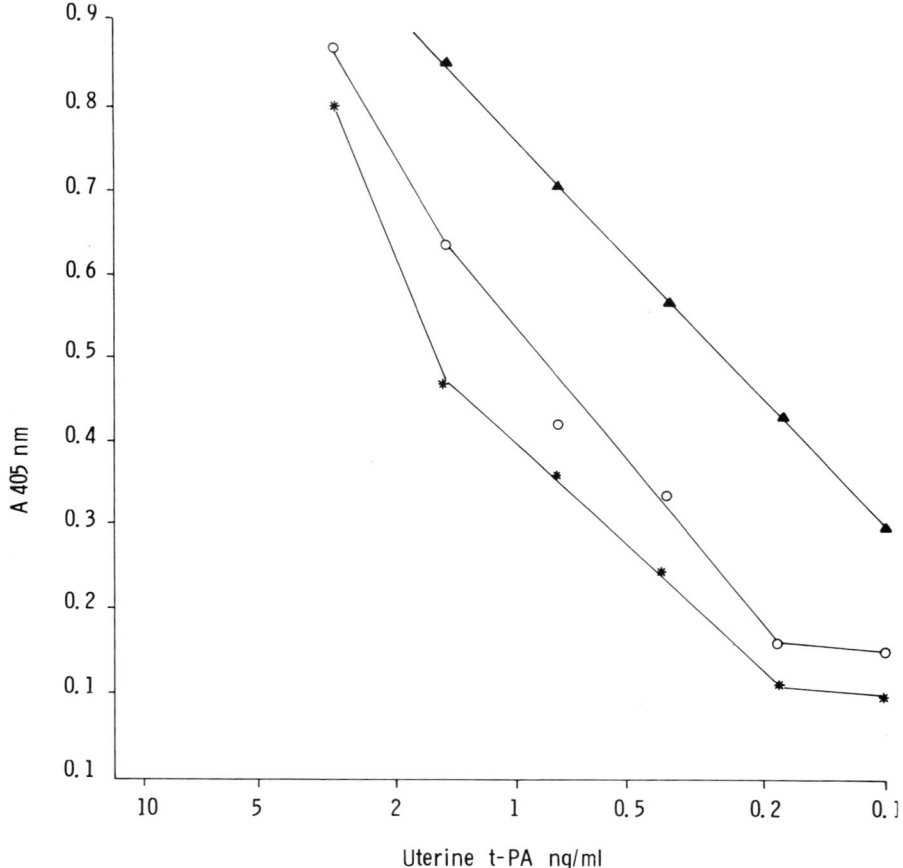

Fig. 46.1 Figure showing the amount of IgG (A405nm) bound to varying dilutions of t-PA coated to microtitre plates. 0 — anti-tPA IgG; * — anti-tPA IgG following prior adsorption with 1μg u-PA; ▲ — anti-uPA IgG.

CONCLUSION

It is evident that the two antibodies, though showing no common quenching activities do nevertheless show direct binding. It is possible that the specific method of immunogen preparation (reaction with inhibitor, followed by denaturation) may have exposed common determinants which are not normally exposed in the enzymes.

ACKNOWLEDGEMENT

This work is supported by the British Heart Foundation. H. Chissic is college supervisor for postgraduate students.

REFERENCES

Rijken D C, Wijngaards G, Zaal-DeJong M, Welbergen J 1979 Purification and partial characterisation of plasminogen activator from human uterine tissue. Biochemica et Biophysica Acta 580: 140–153
Schleuning W D, Shaw E 1983 A new approach for the generation of anti plasminogen activator antibodies. Progress in fibrinolysis. Churchill Livingstone, Edinburgh, vol 6, p 186–190

47. Isolation and partial characterization of an antibody crossreacting with urokinase and vascular plasminogen activator

J. Kirchheimer and B.R. Binder

INTRODUCTION

It is generally assumed that two distinct plasminogen activator entities can be distinguished physiocochemically, functionally and immunologically: a urokinase-type plasminogen activator (u-PA) and a tissue-type plasminogen activator (t-PA).

Despite these differences (Rijken et al, 1981) comparison of the amino-acid sequences of the two plasminogen activators reveals some similarities in their structure (Bachmann et al, 1984) and it is established that both activators share common domains, like a kringle and a growth factor structure.

In the present study we report on an antibody crossreacting with both urokinase (UK) as well as vascular plasminogen activator (VPA).

METHODS

Preparation of the antibody

A New Zealand white rabbit was immunized with a plasminogen activator from human prostate tissue (Kirchheimer et al, 1984). Th IgG-fraction of the immune serum was prepared by ammonium sulfate precipitation, ion exchange chromatography on DEAE-Sephacel and gel filtration on S-200.

Characterization of the antibody

Purity and molecular weight of the purified products were determined by SDS polyacrylamide gel electrophoresis. After electrophoresis the slab gel was stained for protein with the silver stain method.

In order to separate crossreacting antibodies, the purified IgG was adsorbed onto an immobilized UK-Sepharose column (0.1M potassium phosphate buffer, pH 7.4, containing 1.0M sodium chloride). IgG was collected in the non-bound effluent as well as in the 3.5M KSCN elution fractions. The latter fraction analyzed by preparative isoelectric focusing in a sucrose density gradient.

Precipitating antibodies were analyzed by Ouchterlony double immune

188

diffusion technque using human plasma, 10-fold concentrated human urine, prostate plasminogen activator, LMW-UK, HMW-UK and VPA as antigens.

In the column effluents reactivity of the purified antibodies with HMW-UK and the VPA was analyzed by incubation of 10 I.U. UK or 10 units VPA in 20ul with equal volumes of column effluents for 30 min at 37°C. Thereafter the incubated samples were centrifuged for 15 min at 8000xg and plasminogen activator activity of the supernatant was tested on fibrin plates.

The activity was expressed in % inhibition of the respective plasminogen activator activities treated with buffer instead of sample.

RESULTS

The IgG-fraction of the immune sera reacted in an Ouchterlony double immune diffusion with one line of complete identity with prostate plasminogen activator, concentrated human urine, HMW and LMW-UK and exhibited a line of partial identity with human VPA (Fig. 47.1).

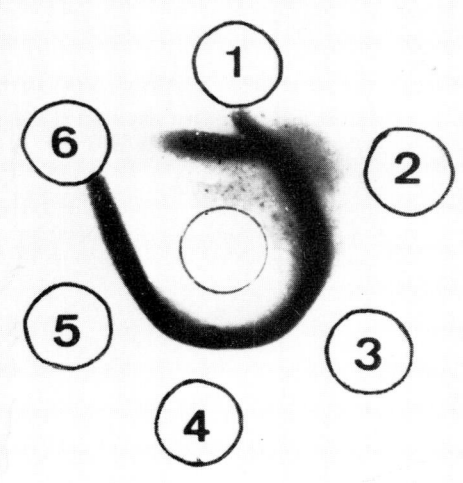

Fig. 47.1 Ouchterlony double immune diffusion of the crossreacting antibody against 1, vascular plasminogen activator; 2, HMW-urokinase; 3, LMW-urokinase; 4, prostate plasminogen activator; 5, concentrated human urine: 6, human plasma.

Adsorption of the purified IgG onto an immobilized UK-Sepharose and elution of the bound antibody with 3.5M KSCN revealed two peaks of antibody activity. One in the non-bound fraction, which inhibited VPA to about 10% and a second in the bound fraction, which inhibited HMW-UK completely and VPA to about 50%.

Isoelectric focusing of the antibody bound to UK-Sepharose resulted in two cross-reacting fractions (pI 8.86 and 8.67) and one fraction (pI 7.57) reacting only with UK.

DISCUSSION

Immunisation of rabbits with purified prostate plasminogen activator resulted in a purified antibody preparation which exhibited cross reactivity versus UK and VPA. This cross reactivity could be seen in an Ouchterlony double immune diffusion as well as in an assay system in which direct functional inhibition and functional inhibition by precipitating antibodies was tested. By binding of the antibodies to UK the majority of the protein associated with a small amount of functionally active antibodies which exclusively inhibited VPA became separated from an antibody population, which still reacted with both, VPA and UK, and which could be further separated by isoelectric focusing into 3 antibody fractions, two of which still reacted with both, UK and VPA. Since these two antibody entities did bind to UK-Sepharose it is unlikely that different antibodies reacting either with UK or with VPA had been copurified.

The data obtained might serve as indicative that these two IgG-fractions could react with common antigenic sites contained both in VPA and UK. However, without determination of the specific antibody binding site in the molecule no definite conclusion can be drawn.

REFERENCES

Bachmann F, Kruithof E K O 1984 Tissue plasminogen activator: chemical and physiological aspects. In: Seminars in Thrombosis and Haemostasis 10: 6–17
Kirchheimer J, Köller A, Binder B R 1984 Isolation and characterization of plasminogen activators from hyperplastic and malignant prostate tissue. Biochim. Biophys. Acta 797: 256–265
Rijken D C, Wijngaards G, Welberger J 1981 Immunological characterization of plasminogen activator activities in human tissues and body fluids. J. Lab. Clin. Med. 97: 477–486

48. Generation of plasmin inhibitor-plasmin complexes in plasma by tissue plasminogen activator and urokinase

P. C. Harpel, D. Weil, R. I. Levin and D. B. Rifkin

INTRODUCTION

We have recently developed an enzyme-linked immunosorbent assay (ELISA) that quantifies the complex formed between plasmin and α_2-plasmin inhibitor or between plasmin and α_2-macroglobulin (α_2M) in plasma (Harpel 1981). Using this assay we have documented that α_2-plasmin inhibitor-plasmin (PIP) complexes are formed in vivo. To further define the mechanisms of such complex formation, we have examined the generation of PIP complexes in plasma by tissue plasminogen activator (TPA) and urokinase (UK) under a variety of experimental conditions. These studies have led to a new methology for quantifying TPA or UK-type activator activity in plasma.

METHODS

Plasma was mixed with 0.1M Tris-HCl, pH 7.4, containing 0.01 EDTA, and varying concentrations of TPA or UK diluted in the same buffer containing 0.05% Tween 20. The mixtures were incubated at 37°C with or without the addition of Reptilase (0.1 ml/ml plasma). The final volume achieved a 1/2 dilution of the starting plasma. The supernatants were diluted 1/20 in 0.1 M EACA-PBS-Tween buffer and assayed for inhibitor-plasmin complexes as described (Harpel, 1981).

RESULTS AND DISCUSSION

The addition of TPA to plasma followed by clotting with Reptilase and incubation at 37°C led to the formation of PIP and α_2M-plasmin complexes that increased with time and were proportional to the amount of TPA added (Fig. 48.1).

Standard curves were prepared for the conversion of the absorbance values as measured in the ELISA to nM complexes formed by adding increasing concentrations of plasmin to plasma depleted of either α_2-PI or α_2M by

191

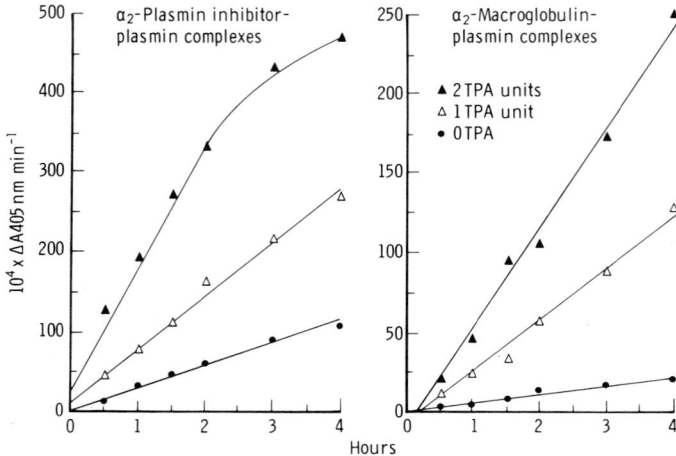

Fig. 48.1 Time-dependent generation of α_2-plasmin inhibitor-plasmin and α_2-macroglobulin-plasmin complexes in Reptilase-clotted plasma by TPA.

immunoaffinity chromatography. From these curves the total amount of complex formed at each time point in Fig. 48.1 was determined. In the plasma clotted without added TPA, a total of 5.5 nM complexes h^{-1} were generated. For the plasma clotted in the presence of 1 or 2 units TPA, 15.9 activity in TPA-treated as well as in post-venous occlusion plasma but not in UK-treated plasma, thereby confirming the specificity of the assay.

The methods presented in this study provide a new quantitative technique for measuring plasminogen activator activity in whole plasma and for distinguishing between TPA and UK-type activity.

REFERENCES

Harpel P C 1981 α_2-Plasmin inhibitor and α_2-macroglobulin-plasmin complexes in plasma. Quantification by an enzyme-linked differential antibody immunosorbent assay. J. Clin. Invest. 68: 46–55

49. An amidolytic assay of α_2-antiplasmin using a centrifugal analyser

J. Jespersen, J. Gram and J. Sidelmann

α_2-Antiplasmin (α_2-AP) is the most important of the plasmin inhibitors in plasma as it reacts rapidly and irreversibly with plasmin in a 1:1 stoichiometric binding. The physiological importance of disturbed plasma levels of α_2-AP has been demonstrated in patients (Brommer et al, 1983; Kluft et al, 1982; Koie et al, 1978). Manual methods for the determination of α_2-AP in plasma are cumbersome and time-consuming and therefore not suitable for use in large series or in the routine laboratory. To overcome these problems we have automated and modified the immediate plasmin inhibition test described by Gallimore et al (1979) and Teger-Nilsson et al (1977) for application on a centrifugal analyser.

MATERIALS

Urokinase activated human plasmin (KabiDiagnostica) labelled 25 casein units (CU) was dissolved in 50% 2 mmol/l HC1, 50% glycerol and 5 g/l polyethylene glycol (M_r 6000) to give a concentration of 1.0 CU/ml in the stock solution. For assay a further dilution with the same solution was done giving a concentration of 0.3 CU/ml. Chromozym Pl® (Boehringer Mannheim) or S-2251® (Kabi-Diagnostica) was dissolved in distilled water giving a concentration in the stock solution of 3.5 mmol/l. For assay the stock solution was further diluted in buffer (0.05 mol/l Tris, 0.11 mol/l NaCl, adjusted to pH 7.4 with 0.1 mol/l HCl, ionic strength 0.15) to a concentration of 1.17 mmol/l.

EXPERIMENTS AND RESULTS

Assay procedure

The Cobas Bio® (Hoffmann-la Roche) centrifugal analyser and initial rate enzyme kinetics in a single step assay procedure was used: to 30 μl diluted plasma (diluted 1:6 in the Tris/HCl buffer) and 30 μl distilled water are added 180 μl of substrate solution (Chromozym P1 or S-2251) with concentration 1.17 mmol/l. After addition of 60 μl human plasmin (0.3 CU/ml) the increase in optical density per min (ΔA/min) at 405 nm is recorded with readings beginning after 10 sec. Six points plasmin inhibition dilution curves (Fig. 49.1) were constructed from a pool of EDTA-stabilized plasma from 20 healthy volunteers. Large series for determination of α_2-antiplasmin could easily be run by means of the centrifugal analyser. Precision studies gave coefficients of variation about 3% (day-to-day) and 1.9% (within series, n = 4).

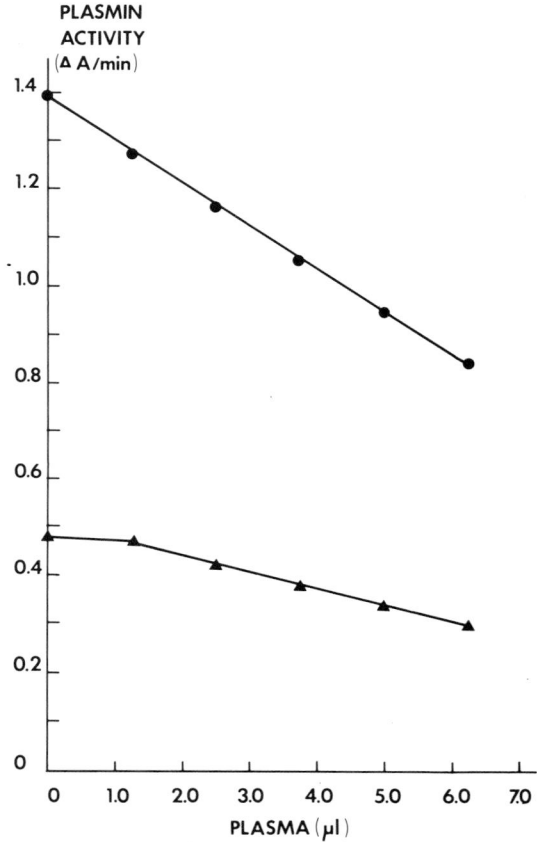

Fig. 49.1 Reference curves using Chromozym P1 and S-2251 without addition of non-ionic detergents.

Addition of non ionic detergents
As a downward deflection was observed at the origin of the six points dilution curve using S-2251 (Fig. 49.1) experiments with addition of polyethylene glycol 0.05% (v/v) (M_r 6000, Merck) and Tween 80 0.01% (v/v) (M_r 1310, Merck) to the buffer (Fig. 49.2) were performed. The effect of keeping the substrate solution S-2251 at room temperature (0–4 hours) prior to the assay was also investigated.

194

Addition of heparin and/or AT-III concentrate

The possible influence of heparin and/or antithrombin III (AT-III) on the assay of α_2-antiplasmin was investigated as follows: 1. heparin was added to the assay

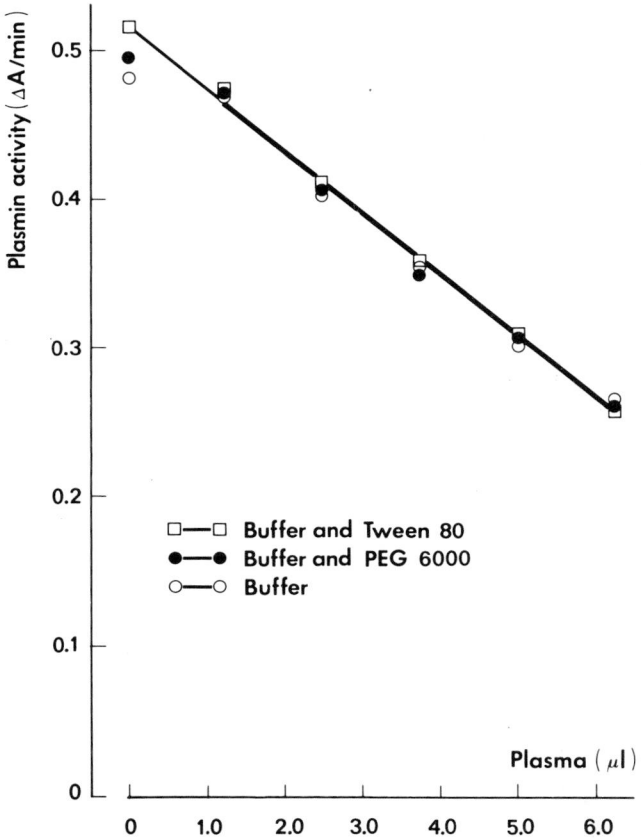

Fig. 49.2 Reference curve using S-2251 after addition of polyethylene glycol (0.05%) or Tween 80 (0.01%).

system in concentrations 0.24–12 IU/ml plasma (Fig. 49.3), 2. plasma was enriched by addition of AT-III concentrate (KabiDiagnostica) corresponding to final concentrations (herparin co-factor) between 100% and 200% of normal plasma (Fig. 49.4), and 3. repetition of 2 in the presence of heparin 2 IU/ml plasma (Fig. 49.4).

CONCLUDING REMARKS

As seen in Figure 49.1 the reference curve obtained with Chromozym P1 yields a completely linear and more steep curve than that obtained with S-2251 indicating

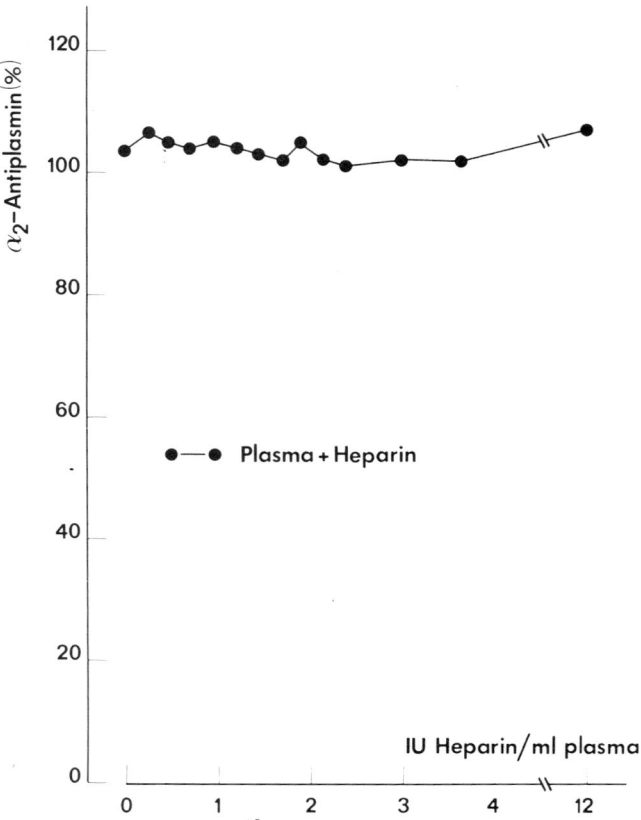

Fig. 49.3 Addition of heparin in concentrations 0.24–12 IU/ml plasma.

a higher affinity of plasmin for Chromozym P1 than for S-2251. This is compatible with the ratio of V_{max} for human plasmin for the two substrates as 2:1.

The reference curve for S-2251 represents a problem since deviations from linearity occur at zero concentration of α_2-AP causing a downward deflection at the origin of the reference curve is significantly reduced by addition of polyethylene glycol (0.05%), and complete linearity is obtained with Tween 80 (0.01%) (Fig. 49.2; Jespersen et al, 1984; Kluft et al, 1984). The same goal is reached when the substrate solution is kept at room temperature for at least 4 hours. This difference in the behaviour of the two substrates suggests differences in solubility as a cause of the assay problems, agreeing well with the higher solubility of Chromozym P1 (6–7 times) in comparison with S-2251 and with its lower content of hydrophobic aminoacids.

Neither heparinized plasma (Fig. 49.3) nor the presence of At-III in different concentrations (Fig. 49.4) interfered with the assays using Chromozym P1 or S-2251 (not shown) as substrate.

Financial support was received from KabiVitrum, Stockholm and Boehringer, Mannheim.

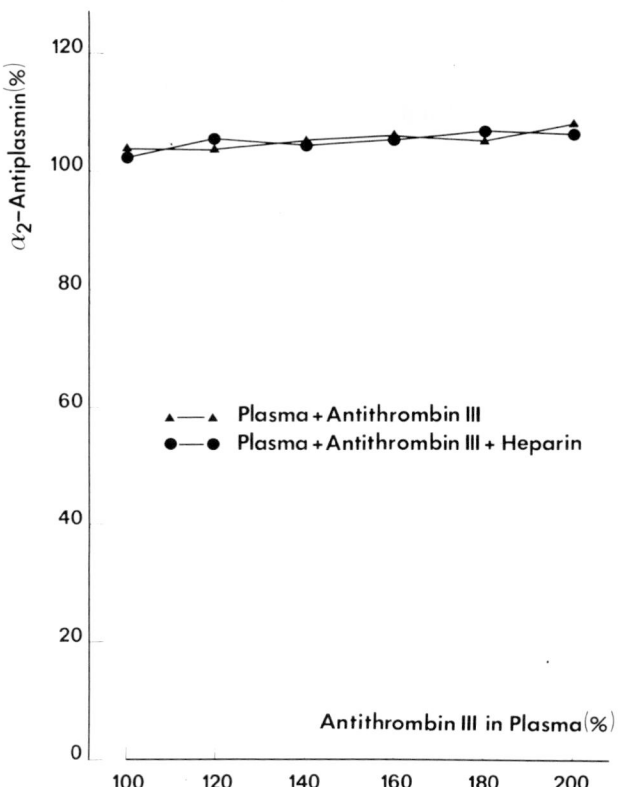

Fig. 49.4 Addition of AT-III (100%–200% of normal plasma) without and with heparin (2 IU/ml plasma).

REFERENCES

Brommer E J P, Leuven J A G, Kluft C, Wijngaards G 1983 Fibrinolytic inhibitor in type II hyperlipoproteinaemia. Lancet 2: 1066

Gallimore M J, Amundsen E, Aasen A O, Larsbraaten M, Lyngaas K, Svendsen L 1979 Studies on plasma antiplasmin activity using a new plasma specific chromogenic tripeptide substrate. Thrombosis Research 14: 51–60

Jespersen J, Sidelmann J 1983 Individual levels of plasma α_2-anti-plasmin and α_2-macroglobulin during the normal menstrual cycle and in women on oral contraceptives low in oestrogen. Thrombosis and Haemostasis 50: 581–585

Jespersen J, Gram J, Sidelmann J Modification of the immediate plasmin inhibition assay to secure linearity of the reference curve with the chromogenic substrate S-2251. Thrombosis and Haemostasis (in press)

Kluft C, Wijngaards G, Van Voorthuizen H Revised reference curve for the α_2-antiplasmin assay by the addition of detergents. Thrombosis and Haemostasis (in press)

Kluft C, Vellenga E, Brommer E J P, Wijngaards G 1982 A familial haemorrhagic diathesis in a Dutch family: An inherited deficiency of α_2-antiplasmin. Blood 59: 1169–1180

Koie K K, Kamiya T, Ogata K, Takamatsu J 1978 α_2-Plasmin-inhibitor deficiency (Miyasato Disease). Lancet 2: 1334–1336

Teger-Nilsson A C, Friberger P, Gyzander E 1977 Determination of a new rapid plasmin inhibitor in human blood by means of a plasmin specific tripeptide substrate. Scandinavian Journal of a new rapid plasmin inhibitor in human blood by means of a plasmin specific tripeptide substrate. Scandinavian Journal of Clinical and Laboratory Investigation 37: 403–409

Section 7
GENETIC CONTROL OF PLASMINOGEN AND PLASMINOGEN ACTIVATORS

50. Cloning and structural characterization of the gene for human plasminogen

J. E. Sadler, D. P. Malinowski and E. W. Davie

Plasminogen (Sottrup-Jensen et al, 1978a), prothombin (Magnusson et al, 1975), tissue plasminogen activator (Pennica et al, 1983) and high molecular weight urokinase (Günzler et al, 1982) are four proteins thus far identified that contain kringle structures. As the number of kringle-containing proteases has increased, so has our interest in defining structural, functional, and evolutionary relationships between these proteins and their kringle structures. These considerations have led us to characterize the gene for human plasminogen, which contains five kringles, and to compare it with the gene for prothrombin, which contains two kringles.

MATERIALS AND METHODS

A human liver cDNA library in pBR322 was provided by Dr. Savio L. C. Wo (Chandra et al, 1983). A human genomic DNA library prepared by partial *Hae*III/*Alu*I digestion and carried in the Charon 4A lambda phage was kindly provided by Dr. Tom Maniatis (Lawn et at, 1978; Maniatis et al, 1978).

The procedures employed for screening by colony and plaque hybridization, and for DNA sequencing, have been described elsewhere (Sanger et al, 1980; Rixon et al, 1983).

RESULTS AND DISCUSSION

A human liver cDNA library cloned into pBR322 was screened with a nick-translated radiolabeled fragment of a bovine plasminogen cDNA clone (Malinowski & Davie, 1983; Malinowski et al, 1984). Hybridization and washing were in 6 X SSC, 2 X Denhardt's (Southern, 1975), 0.5% SDS, 1mM EDTA at 58°C. Among 18,000 recombinants, six plasmids hybridized to the bovine cDNA probe and subsequently were shown to contain cDNA sequences for human plasminogen. The largest of the cDNA inserts contained 1850 base pairs, and was sequenced by the procedure of Maxam and Gilbert. The cDNA codes for amino acid residues 272 through 790 of plasminogen. The coding sequence is followed by a stop codon (TAA) and 224 base pairs of 3'-noncoding sequence, including a processing signal of AATAAA and a poly(A) tail. There are two minor disagreements with the reported protein sequence (Sottrup-Jensen et al, 1978b), including a Gln rather than Glu at residue 341, and Asp rather than Asn at residue 452 (Malinowski et al, 1984).

A fragment of the human plasminogen cDNA was then radiolabeled by nick-translation and used to screen a genomic library in the Charon 4A lambda phage (Benton & Davis, 1977; Woo, 1979). Out of 10^6 phage screened, ten isolates have been partially characterized by restriction mapping and DNA sequencing. A composite restriction map developed from three overlapping phage is shown in Figure 50.1, together with the approximate location of exons for kringle 3 and the 3'-noncoding region as determined by Southern blotting.

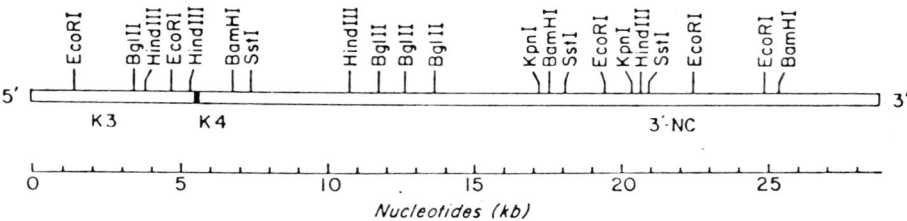

Fig. 50.1 Restriction map of the human plasminogen gene. The approximate location of exons for kringle 3 and the 3'-noncoding region of the mRNA, and the precise location of an exon for kringle 4 are indicated.

An exon for kringle 4 has been placed precisely by DNA sequencing and shown by the solid bar. The length of the partial gene is over 21 kilobases. All of the restriction sites shown lie in introns. Thus far, approximately eight kilobases of the genome have been sequenced, including three exons and six associated splice junctions. The placement of these exons and introns relative to the amino acid sequence of plasminogen is shown schematically in Figure 50.2.

The structure of the plasminogen gene can be compared with that of the prothrombin gene (Degen et al, 1983; S.J.F. Degen and E.W. Davie, unpublished results). Plasminogen kringles 4 and 5 appear to be encoded by two exons, as is kringle 1 of prothrombin. The same is true of the two kringles in tissue plasminogen activator (Ny et al, this volume, Ch. 51). In contrast, kringle 2 of prothrombin is encoded by a single exon. Similarly, there are (at least) two introns in the genomic region between exons encoding the active site residues Asp and Ser in plasminogen and prothrombin. Additional sequence data will be necessary to allow detailed comparisons among the genes for plasminogen, prothrombin, tissue plasminogen activator, urokinase, factor IX, other coagulation factors and related serine proteases. These comparisons will increase our understanding of the evolution and possibly the transcriptional regulation of these enzymes.

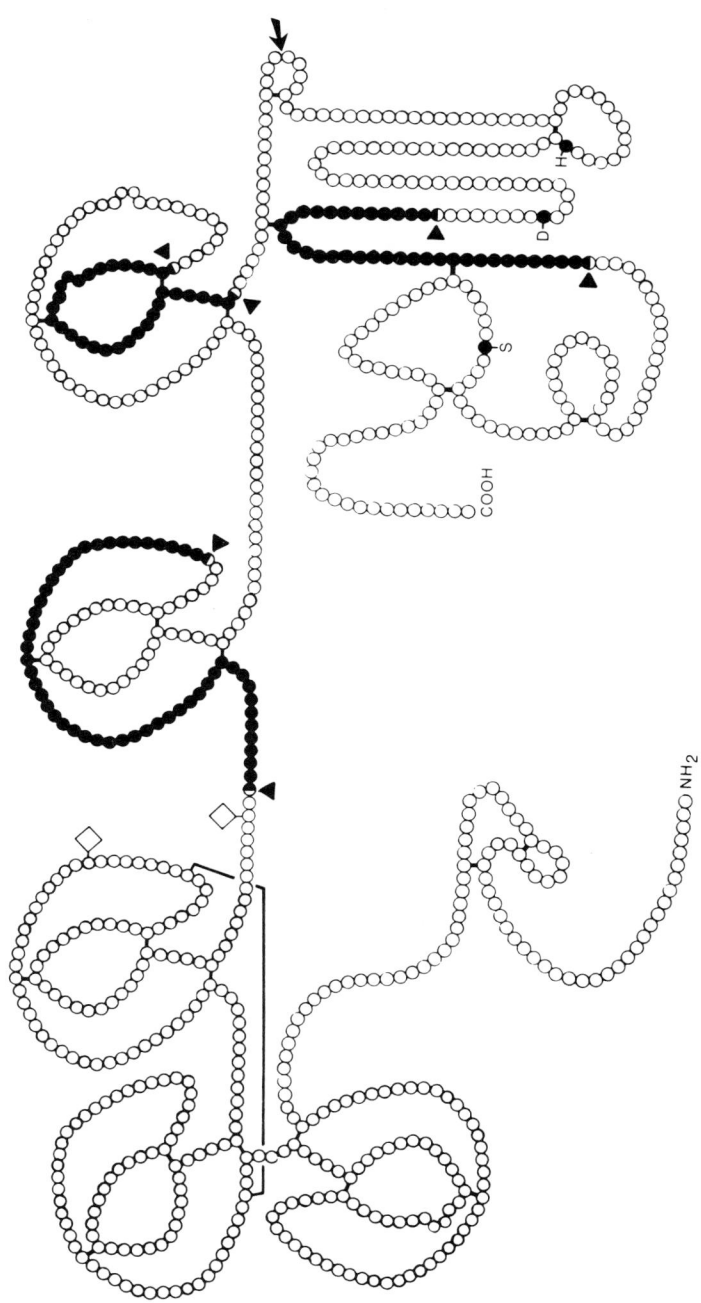

Fig. 50.2 Splice junctions in the plasminogen gene. The regions of the protein encoded by the exons that have been sequenced so far are shown by solid circles (● ● ●), and the locations of the known intervening sequences are shown by solid triangles (▲). These introns interrupt the coding sequence at amino acid residues 346, 399, 509/510, 541, 653, and 689. The arrow (←) indicates the site of cleavage during the conversion of plasminogen to plasmin. The carbohydrate attachment sites in plaminogen form 1 (Hayes and Castellino, 1979a,b) are shown by the open diamonds (◇). Active site residues are indicated by ●-H, ●D, and ●-S.

REFERENCES

Benton W D, Davis R W 1977 Screening λgt recombinant clones by hybridization to single plaques in situ. Science 196: 180–182

Chandra T, Stackhouse R, Kidd V J, Woo S L C 1983 Isolation and sequence characterization of a cDNA clone of human antithrombin III. Proceedings of the National Academy of Sciences (U.S.A.) 80: 1845–1848

Degen S J F, MacGillivray R T A, Davie E W 1983 Characterization of the complementary deoxyribonucleic acid and gene coding for human prothrombin. Biochemistry 22: 2087–2097

Günzler W A, Steffens G J, Ötting F, Kim S-M A, Frankus E, Flohé L 1982 The primary structure of high molecular mass urokinase from human urine: The complete amino acid sequence of the A chain. Hopee-Seyler's Zeitschrift für physiologische Chemie 363: 1155–1165

Hayes M L, Castellino F J 1979a Carbohydrate of the human plasminogen variants: II. Structure of the asparagine-linked oligosaccharide unit. The Journal of Biological Chemistry 254: 8772–8776

Hayes M L, Castellino F J 1979b Carbohydrate of the human plasminogen variants: III. Structure of the O-glycosidically linked oligosaccharide unit. The Journal of Biological Chemistry 254: 8777–8780

Lawn R M, Fritsch E F, Parker R C, Blake G, Maniatis T 1978 The isolation and characterization of linked α- and β-globin genes from a cloned library of human DNA. Cell 15: 1157–1174

Magnusson S, Petersen T E, Sottrup-Jensen L, Claeys H 1975 In: Reich E, Rifkin D B, Shaw E (eds) Proteases and Biological Control, Cold Spring Harbor Laboratories, Cold Spring Harbor, New York, pp 123–249

Malinowski D P, Davie E W 1983 Construction of a cDNA clone coding for plasminogen. In: Davidson J F, Bachmann F, Bouvier C A, Kruithof E K O (eds) Progress in Fibrinolysis, Vol. VI, Churchill Livingstone, Edinburgh, ch 71, pp 321–326

Malinowski D P, Sadler J E, Davie E W 1984 Characterization of a complementary deoxyribonucleic acid coding for human and bovine plasminogen. Biochemistry 23: in press

Maniatis T, Hardison R C, Lacy E, Lauer J, O'Connell C, Quon D, Sim G K, Efstratiadis A 1978 The isolation of structural genes from libraries of eucaryotic DNA. Cell 15: 687–701

Pennica D, Holmes W E, Kohr W J, Harkins R N, Vehar G A, Ward C A, Bennett W F, Yelverton E, Seeburg P H, Heyneker H L, Goeddel D V, Collen D 1983 Cloning and expression of human tissue-type plasminogen activator cDNA in *E. coli.* Nature 301: 214–221

Rixon M W, Chan W Y, Davie E W, Chung D W 1983 Characterization of a complementary deoxyribonucleic acid coding for the α chain of human fibrinogen. Biochemistry 22: 3237–3244

Sanger F, Coulson A R, Barrell B G, Smith A J H, Roe B A 1980 Cloning in single-stranded bacteriophage as an aid to rapid DNA sequencing. Journal of Molecular Biology 143: 161–178

Sottrup-Jensen L, Claeys H, Zajdel M, Petersen T E, Magnusson S 1978a In: Davidson T F, Rowan R M, Samama M M, Desnoyer P C (eds) Fibrinolysis and Thrombolysis, Vol. 3, Raven Press, New York, pp 191–209

Sottrup-Jensen L, Petersen T E, Magnusson S 1978b In: Dayhoff M O (ed) Atlas of Protein Sequence and Structure, Vol. 5, Suppl. 3, National Biomedical Research Foundation, Silver Spring, Maryland, p 91

Southern E M 1975 Detection of specific sequences among DNA fragments separated by gel electrophoresis, Journal of Molecular Biology 98: 503–517

Woo S L C 1979 A sensitive and rapid method for recominant phage screening. Methods in Enzymology 68: 389–395

51. Isolation and characterization of the genomic region carrying the human tissue plasminogen activator gene

T. Ny, A. Bäckman, F. Elgh, K. Engvist,
C. Fredriksson, S. Järvinen and B. Lund

INTRODUCTION

Protein and DNA sequence analyses have revealed that the tissue-type plasminogen activator (t-PA) is composed of a light and a heavy chain derived from the COOH-terminal and NH_2-terminal parts respectively. The light chain contains the serine protease part of the molecule (Pennica et al, 1983) and the heavy chain exhibits a number of structures homologous to those found in other plasma proteins. Thus, the heavy chain of t-PA contains two kringle structures (Pennica et al, 1983), a growth factor-like domain (Banyai, L. et al, 1983), and a domain that shows homology to the fibrin-binding finger-like structures of fibronectin (Banyai et al, 1983).

Eucaryotic genes are fragmented: the coding regions (exons) are interrupted by untranslated segments (introns) that are removed from the initial RNA transcript by a splicing system. The exons are jointed to form an mRNA molecule that is translated into the protein product. It has been postulated that exons represent genetic building blocks which code for structural or functional domains of the protein (Gilber 1978 and Blake, 1978). The t-pA gene codes for a protein with different structural or functional domains and thus would be a model to verify this hypothesis.

In order to characterize the human t-PA gene, cosmids carrying the genomic region coding for t-PA were isolated. The report summarizes the characteristics of the human t-PA gene.

MATERIALS AND METHODS

1. A cDNA clone (pPAOl; Edlund et al, 1983) containing sequences from human t-PA mRNA was ^{32}P-labeled and used as probe to isolate the t-PA gene from a cosmid library (Lindenmaier et al, 1982).

2. One of many identical cosmids, pcos PAUOl, was selected and analyzed by restriction mapping, Southern blotting, and DNA sequence analysis.

RESULTS AND DISCUSSION

1. The cosmid pcos PAUOl contains all the coding parts of the t-PA message but lacks the first 58 nontranslated nucleotides in the 5′ end of the mRNA.

2. The length of the t-PA gene is more than 20 kb and it is separated into at least 14 exons (I-XIV) by at least 13 introns (A-M) (Table 51.1). The number of exons and introns is tentative because the cosmid did not contain the first 58 nucleotides of the mRNA. However, the exons are numbered assuming that these 58 nucleotides are encoded by exon I.

3. All exons present on the cosmid have been sequenced and all intron/exon boundaries are found to follow the GT/AG rule.

4. The exons of t-PA seem to code for structural and functional domains. Thus, the signal peptide, the pro-peptide, the finger domains, and the growth factor domain all are encoded by separate exons. The two kringle regions are both coded by two exons which are cleaved by introns at identical positions. The light chain of the molecule comprising the serine protease part of the molecule is split by four introns. These introns interrupt the coding sequence such that the three active site amino acids (his 322, asp 371, and ser 478) are located in different exons. Comparing the gene structures of t-PA and three other serine proteases, chymotrypsin, trypsin, and elastase (Craik et al, 1983) reveals a conserved intron-exon pattern. The fact that there is a conserved intron-exon structure in these serine proteases, supports the theory that they all belong to a gene family derived from a common ancestor (Hartley, B.S., 1971). The position of three introns in the human urokinase (u-PA) gene is known (Verde et al, 1984). These three introns map at similar positions in the protein structure as introns E, I, and J of the t-PA gene (Table 51.1). Further analysis of genomic clones for urokinase most likely will reveal more similarities between the gene structure of these structurally and functionally similar proteins.

Table 51.1. Properties of human t-PA gene:
The size of the exons I-XIV and introns (A-M) of the human t-PA gene are shown in base pairs (bp) and kilobase pairs (kb), respectively. The approximate size of the first exon is determined from the cDNA data of Pennica et al. The DNA sequence around the spliced junctions is shown and intron sequences are underlined.

| Exon | | Intron | | Sequence at Splice |
Number	Size (bp)	Number	Size (kb)	Junction
I	≥ 58	A	> 0.7	GCCGTGXXX - CAGAATTTA
II	98	B	1.6	AGCCAGGTT - CAGGAAATC
III	43	C	2.1	ACCAAGGTC - TAGTGATCT
IV	138	D	0.8	TCAAAAGTA - CAGGTTGCA
V	111	E	0.3	AAATAGGTG - CAGATACCA
VI	175	F	2.1	CTGCAGGT - CAGAAACCC
VII	92	G	2.2	CTGAGGGTA - TAGGAAACA
VIII	172	H	1.0	CTGCTGTA - TAGGAATCC
IX	86	I	1.1	CCTGCTGTA - CAGCCACCT
X	196	J	0.2	GGAGAGGTA - CAGGTTTCC
XI	137	K	0.2	ACATTGGTA - CAGCGCTGC
XII	141	L	0.8	AGGCCTGTA - CAGTGTCTC
XIII	167	M	2.8	TGCCAGGTA - CAGGGCGAT
XIV	913–918			

ACKNOWLEDGEMENTS

Support was obtained from Kabigen AB, The National Board for Technical Development (Dnr 825463). T.N. was supported by EMBO for part of the time.

REFERENCES

Bányai L, Vardi A, Patthy L 1983 Febs Lett L63: 37–41
Blake C C F 1978 Nature London 273: 267
Craik C S, Rutter W J, Flettrick R 1983 Science 220: 1115–1129
Edlund T et al 1983 Proceedings of the National Academy of Science USA 80: 349–352
Gilbert W 1978 Nature London 271: 501
Hartley B S, Shotton D M 1971. In: Boyer P D (ed) The enzymes. Academic Press, New York, vol 3, pp 323–373
Lindenmaier W, Hauser H, Greiser de Wilke I, Schutz G 1982 Nucleic Acids Res. 10: 1243–1256
Pennica D et al 1983 Nature 301: 214–221
Verde P, Stoppelli P, Galeffi P, Di Nocera P, Blasi F 1984 Proceedings of the National Academy of Science USA 81: In press (August 1984)

52. Messenger RNAs coding for plasminogen activators are enhanced by ultraviolet light and by caffeine in human fetal fibroblasts

R. Miskin, N. Rotem and J. H. Axelrod

INTRODUCTION

Ultraviolet light has previously been shown to enhance the synthesis of plasminogen activator (PA) in human skin fibroblasts which exhibit characteristics related to inefficient repair of UV-induced lesions in the DNA. Thus, while no PA enhancement has been detected after irradiation in non-embryonic repair proficient cells, a considerable PA induction has been measured in embryonic fibroblasts which display a slow rate of excision repair (Ben Ishai et al, 1984), and in non-embryonic cells derived from patients with hereditary disorders related to DNA repair deficiency (Miskin and Ben Ishai, 1981). Enhancement of PA activity occurs also if impairment of DNA repair is caused experimentally by the addition of repair inhibitors immediately after cell irradiation (unpublished results). Caffeine, one of the inhibitors utilized, has been found to increase PA activity also when given alone to non-irradiated fetal fibroblasts (GM-11). Caffeine enhances both urokinase-type PA (u-PA) and tissue-type PA (t-PA) to considerable extents, whereas UV light increases mostly u-PA, as it appears from zymographic analyses (Miskin and Ben Ishai, 1981, Ben Ishai et al, 1984).

In the present study we have tested whether inductions of PA by UV light and by caffeine occur at the level of transcription of PA genes. We show that in GM-11 cells both reagents increase the steady state levels of u-PAmRNA and of t-PAmRNA.

RESULTS AND DISCUSSION

As specific probes to detect and to quantify PAmRNA we have used ^{32}P-labelled synthetic oligodeoxyribonucleotides coding for selected sequences of u-PA or t-PA. Such oligomers of 15–17 bases were deduced from the published amino acid sequence of u-PA (Steffens et al, 1982, Gunzler et al, 1982) and were synthesized chemically as mixtures containing all possible DNA sequences (Beaucage and Caruthers, 1981), as indicated by the redundancy of the genetic code. Oligomers of 21 bases coding for t-PA sequences were synthesized according to the published c-DNA sequence of the enzyme (Pennica et al, 1983). Control experiments have shown that the synthetic oligomers indeed provide specific probes for qualitative and quantitative analyses of PAmRNAs. For example, it can be seen in Figure 52.1 that the u-PA specific probe reacts strongly with total mRNA derived from the epidermoid carcinoma HEp-3 which is rich in u-PAmRNA (Miskin and Soreq, 1981). The same probe does not react with mRNA isolated from the t-PA rich Bowes melanoma cells. By contrast, the t-PA probe hybridizes extensively to mRNA from the melanoma, but only very poorly to mRNA from the carcinoma. As expected, the active band in the carcinoma (calculated to contain 2300 nucleotides) migrates somewhat faster than the melanoma active band (2450 nucleotides).

The effects of UV light and of caffeine on PAmRNAs were studied in skin fibroblasts derived from an 8 week fetus (GM-11). Cells were irradiated with UV

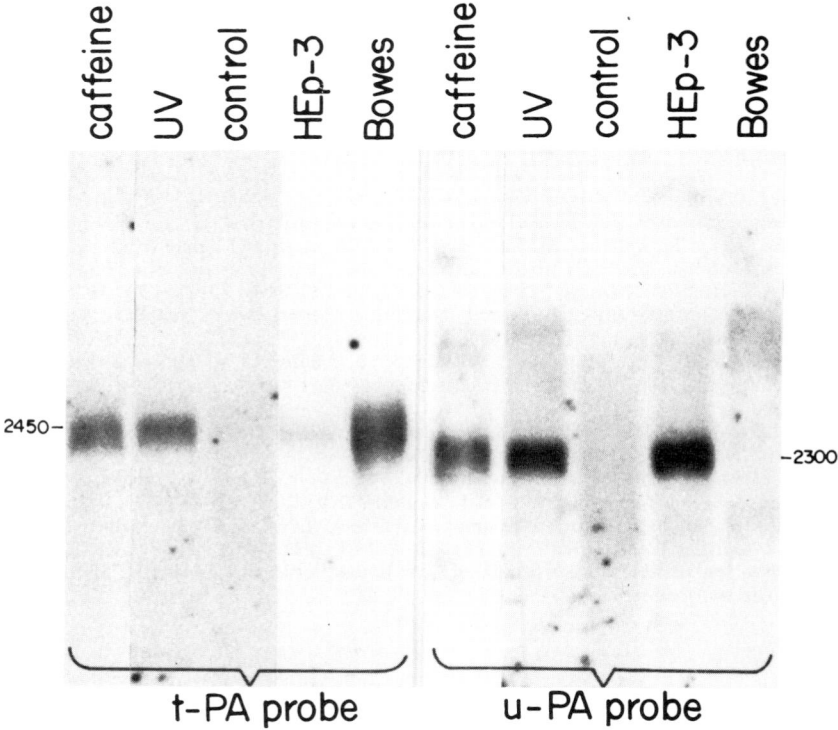

Fig. 52.1 Northern hybridization analysis of mRNA from GM-11 cells treated with UV light or with caffeine. GM-11 cells (Human Genetic Mutant Cell Repositary, Camden, N.J.) were irradiated (20 Jm^{-2}) and further incubated for 2 days as described by Ben-Ishai et al (1984). Total RNA was then extracted from the irradiated cells and from counterpart control cells and passed twice on oligo dT column to isolate poly(A) containing RNA. Total mRNA was extracted also from caffeine treated cells (3 mM, 3 days). Northern hybridization analysis was performed with 10 microgram samples of the indicated mRNAs, and with $5'-^{32}P$-labelled oligomers. The hybridization reactions were incubated for 16–20 h at 42°, in buffer containing $4 \times SSC$, $10 \times Denhart$ solution, 0.1% Na pyrophosphate, 0.1% SDS and 150 μg/ml sonicated salmon sperm DNA. The filters were then washed twice for 30 min at 45° (u-PA probe) or 65° (t-PA probe) in $2 \times SSC$ and 0.1% SDS and autoradiographed. For quantitative determination the films were scanned with Beckman DU-8 spectrophotometer.

light or treated with caffeine as described in the legend to Figure 52.1, so that each one of the reagents enhanced PA activity about 35 fold. Total poly(A) containing RNA was isolated from the treated cells and from control non-treated cells, and the levels of PAmRNAs in these preparations were compared by Northern blot hybridization (Fig. 52.1). Hybridization analysis first performed with a u-PA specific probe indicated that the level of uPAmRNA in both the irradiated and the caffeine treated cells was about 10 fold higher than in the control cells. After the analysis the u-PA probe was washed off the filters (70°, 0.1 SSC) and the same filters were subjected to a second hybridization with a t-PA specific probe. It is evident that both treatments enhanced also t-PAmRNA (4-7 fold) in GM-11 cells. Thus, enhancement of PA activity by UV light and by caffeine in GM-11 cells is to a large extent a consequence of an increase in the steady state levels of mRNAs coding for u-PA and for t-PA. The sensitivity of PA genes to caffeine appeared to be developmentally associated, as caffeine alone was effective in GM-11 cells but not in cells derived at 12 weeks of gestation of 3 days postnatally.

REFERENCES

Beaucage S L, Caruthers M H 1981 Deoxynucleotide phosphoramidites — a new class of key intermediates for deoxypolynucleotide synthesis. Tetrahedron Letters 22: 1859–1862
Ben-Ishai R, Sharon R, Rothman M, Miskin R 1984 DNA repair and induction of plasminogen activator in human fetal cells treated with ultraviolet light. Carcinogenesis 5: 357–362
Gunzle W A, Steffens G J, Otting F, Kim S-M A, Frankus E, Flohe L 1982 The primary structure of high molecular mass urokinase from human urine. Hoppe-Seyler's Zeitschrift für Physiologische Chemie 363: 1155–1165
Miskin R, Ben-Ishai R 1981 Induction of plasminogen activator by UV light in normal and xeroderma pigmentosum fibroblasts. Proceedings National Academy of Sciences USA 78: 6236–6240
Miskin R, Soreq H 1981 Microinjected Xenopus oocytes synthesize active human plasminogen activators. Nucleic Acids Research 9: 3355–3363
Pennica D, Holmes W E, Kohr W J, Harkins R N, Vehar G A, Ward C A, Bennett W F, Yelverton E, Seeburg P H, Heyneker H L, Gooddel D V, Collen D 1983 Cloning and expression of human tissue-type plasminogen activator cDNA in E. coli. Nature 301: 214–221
Steffens G J, Gunzler W A, Otting F, Frankus E, Flohe L 1982 The complete amino acid sequence of low molecular mass urokinase from human urine. Hoppe-Seyler's Zeitschrift Für Physiologische Chemie 363: 1043–1058

53. Preliminary studies on the structure and regulation of the human urokinase gene. Effect of tumour promoter, EGF and transformation by SV$_{40}$

P. Verde, M. P. Stoppelli, P. Galeffi, A. Riccio,
G. Grimaldi, E. K. Locatelli, S. Bullock, S. Boast,
G. Sebastio, P. P. Di Nocera and F. Blasi

Urokinase is a two-chain PA deriving from an inactive single chain prourokinase (Wun et al, 1982; Nielsen et al, 1982; Ferraiuolo et al, 1984) which in turn, derives from an intracellular precursor of slightly higher MW (Salerno et al, 1984).

We have undertaken the cloning of human PA genes. So far we isolated several cDNA fragments and the complete gene for human urokinase. Initially a cDNA clone (pHUK-1) of a partially unspliced polyadenylated precursor of urokinase mRNA was isolated (Verde et al, 1984), from a cDNA library of human fibroblasts transformed with SV40. Unexpectedly, the nucleotide sequence of pHUK-1 (2,900 bp insert) revealed unspliced intervening sequences interspersed with coding regions. The interrupting sequences in fact 1) lack colinearity with the amino acid sequence and present in-phase stop signals; 2) present consensus sequences at the exon-intron junctions; 3) separate functionally different domains of the protein within the urokinase mRNA.

The derived aminoacid sequence fully agrees with that determined experimentally (Günzler et al, 1982) and shows that the two chains are joined by a lysine residue (lys 157) which is evidently lost during activation of the two-chains urokinase, as previously hypothesized by Günzler et al, (1982). The coding regions in pHUK-1 starts with amino acid 46 of the light chain and proceeds throughout amino acid 411 where the stop codon is encountered. The light chain of urokinase is the N-terminal segment of the single-chain pro-urokinase precursor. At the end of the coding region a 933 bp long 3' untranslated sequence precedes the poly A tract. The knowledge of the nucleotide sequence of the unspliced urokinase mRNA precursor and the position of three introns greatly facilitated the isolation and structure determination of the human urokinase gene and the identification of urokinase mRNA. The entire coding region is contained within less than 8kb of DNA of a recombinant lambda phage. The restriction map of the insert coincides with that of total human genomic DNA.

The level of PA is known to be increased several fold by oncogenic transformation, tumour promoters and growth factors (see Reich, 1978, for a review). We have noticed that SV$_{40}$, EGF and TPA increase the transcription of the urokinase gene. Transformation of human fibroblasts with an origin-defective mutant of SV_{40} (Boast et al, 1982) induced the synthesis of urokinase mRNA and of urokinase itself. Potent tumour promoter PMA (Phorbol-myristate-acetate) increases urokinase synthesis in both A431 (human epidermoid carcinoma of the vulva) and A1251 (human kidney carcinoma) cells. EGF however, does so only in A431 cells. The increase in mRNA occurs within sixty minutes after the addition of the effectors.

The precocious enhancement of transcription of the urokinase gene suggests it to be a direct response of the cell to the growth stimulus and not a consequence of growth enhancement. This in turn suggests some hitherto unknown yet primary role for the urokinase gene product in determining the final response of a cell to these growth factors.

REFERENCES

Boast S, LaMantia G, Lania L, Blasi F 1983 High efficiency of replication and expression of foreign genes in SV_{40}-transformed human fibroblasts. EMBO Journal 2: 2327–2331
Ferraiuolo R et al 1984 Transcriptional induction of urokinase by tetra-decanoyl-phorbol-acetate in human kidney carcinoma cells. J. Cellular Physiology, in press
Günzler W A, Steffen G J, Otting F, Kim S M, Frankus E, Flohe L 1982 The primary structure of high molecular mass urokinase from human urine. The complete amino acid sequence of the A chain. Hoppe-Seyler's Zeitschrift fur physiologische Chemie 363: 1155–1165
Nielsen L S et al 1982 Purification of zymogen to plasminogen activator from human glioblastoma cells by affinity chromatography with monoclonal antibody. Biochemistry 21: 6410-6415
Reich E 1978 Activation of plasminogen. A general mechanism for producing localized extracellular proteolysis. In: Berlin R et al (eds) Molecular Basis of Biological Degradative Processes. Academic Press, N.Y., p 155–169
Salerno G et al 1984 Monoclonal antibodies to human urokinase identify the single-chain prourokinase precursor. Proceedings National Academy of Sciences, USA 81: 110–114
Verde P et al 1984 Identification and primary sequence of an unspliced human urokinase poly A$^+$ RNA. Proceedings National Academy of Scenes USA, in press
Wun T, Ossowski L, Reich E 1982 A proenzyme form of human urokinase. Journal of Biological Chemistry 257: 7262–7268

54. Insight into biosynthesis of human urokinase forms

L. Flohé, G. J. Steffens, W. A. Günzler,
F. Ötting, H. Heyneker, W. E. Holmes, M. Rey,
P. Seeburg, J. Hayflick and G. Vehar

The molecular identity of urokinase-type plasminogen activators and the interrelationship of different urokinase (UK) forms have been debated for years. At least three distinct forms of urokinase have been characterized: a high molecular mass form consisting of a single peptide chain (SC-UK), a high molecular mass form consisting of two disulfide-linked peptide chains (HUK), and a low molecular mass form (LUK) also consisting of two peptide chains (Günzler et al, 1982a). The complete primary structures of HUK and of LUK have been determined (Steffens et al, 1982; Günzler et al, 1982b). Moreover, the entire cDNA coding for UK has been sequenced (Heyneker et al, 1983). A synopsis of the information available now allows valid conclusions as to the structure of the physiological UK precursor and its conversion into the various UK forms.

Comparison of the amino acid sequences of HUK and LUK reveals that LUK is generated from HUK by limited proteolysis of its A chain, as the A_1 chain of LUK is contained in the A chain of HUK near its C-terminus. The relationship of HUK and LUK with SC-UK is evident from the sequence of cDNA reconstructed from overlapping cDNA fragments coding for UK sequences (Heyneker et al, 1983). The codes for both UK chains are present in a single coherent coding area of 1293 base pairs, as schematized below:

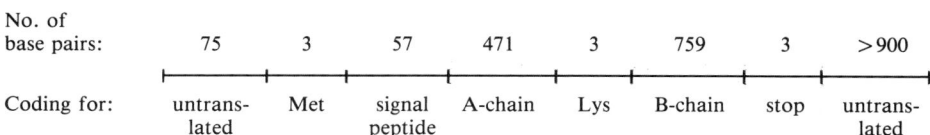

No. of base pairs:	75	3	57	471	3	759	3	>900
Coding for:	untrans-lated	Met	signal peptide	A-chain	Lys	B-chain	stop	untrans-lated

Figure 54.1 shows the amino acid transcript of the entire coding area. It is consistent with the amino acid sequences determined chemically, as far as they are retained in mature UKs. The sites of putative proteolytic processing of the primary expression product (arrows) suggest involvement of trypsin-type activities in most instances. The resulting sizes and N-termini of the most

213

```
           -20↓                                              -10                                    ↓ 1
      H-Met-Arg-Ala-Leu-Leu-Ala-Arg-Leu-Leu-Leu-Cys-Val-Leu-Val-Val-Ser-Asp-Ser-Lys-Gly-Ser-Asn-Glu-
                        10                                    20
      Leu-His-Gln-Val-Pro-Ser-Asn-Cys-Asp-Cys-Leu-Asn-Gly-Gly-Thr-Cys-Val-Ser-Asn-Lys-Tyr-Phe-Ser-
                        30                                    40                      ↓
      Asn-Ile-His-Trp-Cys-Asn-Cys-Pro-Lys-Lys-Phe-Gly-Gly-Gln-His-Cys-Glu-Ile-Asp-Lys-Ser-Lys-Thr-
           50                                    60                                    70
      Cys-Tyr-Glu-Gly-Asn-Gly-His-Phe-Tyr-Arg-Gly-Lys-Ala-Ser-Thr-Asp-Thr-Met-Gly-Arg-Pro-Cys-Leu-
                        80                                    90
      Pro-Trp-Asn-Ser-Ala-Thr-Val-Leu-Gln-Gln-Thr-Tyr-His-Ala-His-Arg-Ser-Asp-Ala-Leu-Gln-Leu-Gly-
                        100                                   110
      Leu-Gly-Lys-His-Asn-Tyr-Cys-Arg-Asn-Pro-Asp-Asn-Arg-Arg-Arg-Pro-Trp-Cys-Tyr-Val-Gln-Val-Gly-
           120                                   130                    ↓                        140
      Leu-Lys-Pro-Leu-Val-Gln-Glu-Cys-Met-Val-His-Asp-Cys-Ala-Asp-Gly-Lys-Lys-Pro-Ser-Ser-Pro-Pro-
                        150                            ↓   ↓   ↓    160
      Glu-Glu-Leu-Lys-Phe-Gln-Cys-Gly-Gln-Lys-Thr-Leu-Arg-Pro-Arg-Phe-Lys-Ile-Ile-Gly-Gly-Glu-Phe-
                        170                                   180
      Thr-Thr-Ile-Glu-Asn-Gln-Pro-Trp-Phe-Ala-Ala-Ile-Tyr-Arg-Arg-His-Arg-Gly-Gly-Ser-Val-Thr-Tyr-
                        190                                   200            *                   210
      Val-Cys-Gly-Gly-Ser-Leu-Ile-Ser-Pro-Cys-Trp-Val-Ile-Ser-Ala-Thr-His-Cys-Phe-Ile-Asp-Tyr-Pro-
                        220                                   230
      Lys-Lys-Glu-Asp-Tyr-Ile-Val-Tyr-Leu-Gly-Arg-Ser-Arg-Leu-Asn-Ser-Asn-Thr-Gln-Gly-Glu-Met-Lys-
                        240                                   250                            *
      Phe-Glu-Val-Glu-Asn-Leu-Ile-Leu-His-Lys-Asp-Tyr-Ser-Ala-Asp-Thr-Leu-Ala-His-His-Asn-Asp-Ile-
                        260                                   270
      Ala-Leu-Leu-Lys-Ile-Arg-Ser-Lys-Glu-Gly-Arg-Cys-Ala-Gln-Pro-Ser-Arg-Thr-Ile-Gln-Thr-Ile-Cys-
           280                                   290                                   300        CHO
      Leu-Pro-Ser-Met-Tyr-Asn-Asp-Pro-Gln-Phe-Gly-Thr-Ser-Cys-Glu-Ile-Thr-Gly-Phe-Gly-Lys-Glu-Asn-
                        310                                   320
      Ser-Thr-Asp-Tyr-Leu-Tyr-Pro-Glu-Gln-Leu-Lys-Met-Thr-Val-Val-Lys-Leu-Ile-Ser-His-Arg-Glu-Cys-
                        330                                   340
      Gln-Gln-Pro-His-Tyr-Tyr-Gly-Ser-Glu-Val-Thr-Thr-Lys-Met-Leu-Cys-Ala-Ala-Asp-Pro-Gln-Trp-Lys-
           350                        *                    360                                   370
      Thr-Asp-Ser-Cys-Gln-Gly-Asp-Ser-Gly-Gly-Pro-Leu-Val-Cys-Ser-Leu-Gln-Gly-Arg-Met-Thr-Leu-Thr-
                        380                                   390
      Gly-Ile-Val-Ser-Trp-Gly-Arg-Gly-Cys-Ala-Leu-Lys-Asp-Lys-Pro-Gly-Val-Tyr-Thr-Arg-Val-Ser-His-
                        400                                   410
      Phe-Leu-Pro-Trp-Ile-Arg-Ser-His-Thr-Lys-Glu-Glu-Asn-Gly-Leu-Ala-Leu-OH
```

Fig. 54.1 Amino acid transcript of the cDNA coding for urokinase. Arrows indicate putative cleavage sites of the primary expression product. Asterisks mark amino acid residues constituting the catalytic center. Positive position numbers start with the amino terminus of the A chain as determined in isolated HUK.

important urokinase species SC-UK, HUK and LUK are evident from Figure 54.2.

From these data the following conclusions can be drawn:

1. UK like other serine proteases is biosynthesized as a single chain protein.
2. Newly synthesized UK starts with an N-terminal hydrophobic amino acid sequence (Fig. 54.1; positions − 19 through − 1) never seen in the isolated enzyme and most probably representing a signal peptide to be expected for a secreted protein. It appears to be obligatorily eliminated during excretion.
3. In SC-UK, the A chain (positions 1–157) represents the N-terminal and the B chain (positions 159–411) and C-terminal part of the sequence.

214

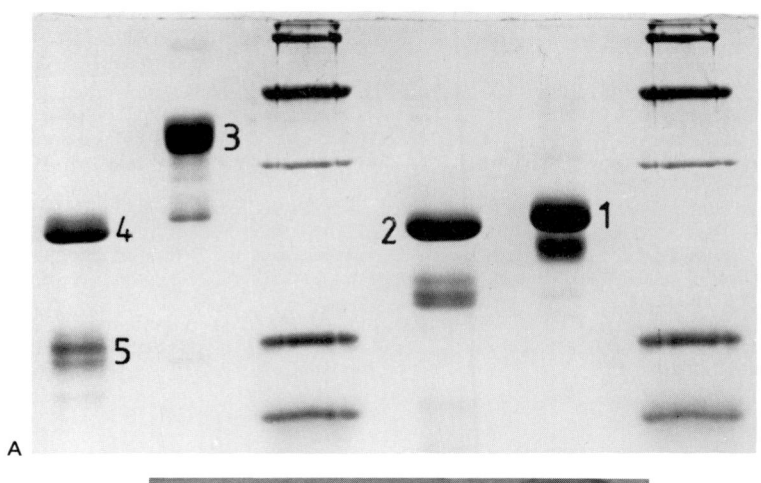

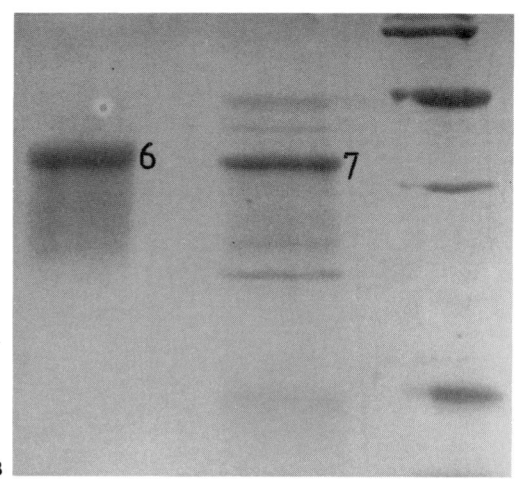

Fig. 54.2 SDS PAG electrophoresis of LUK, HUK and SC-UK in native (nat.) and reduced (red.) state. LUK and HUK were commercial products obtained from Ares and Hypolab, respectively; SC-UK was isolated from a recombinant E. coli strain described by Heyneker et al (1983). The numbered protein bands shown are further characterized as follows:

Band	1	2	3	4	5	6	7
Sample	nat.	red.	nat.	red.	red.	nat.	red.
	LUK	LUK	HUK	HUK	HUK	SC-UK	SC-UK
Apparent MW (kda)	32	31	49	31	19	48	48
N-Termini	Lys,Ile	Ile	Ser,Ile	Ile	Ser	Ser	Ser
Chain(s)	A_1-B	B	A-B	B	A	AB	AB

4. Limited proteolysis of a lysyl-isoleucine bond (positions 158–159) and elimination of lysine 158 yields fully activated HUK from SC-UK.

5. A_1 chain of LUK is generated from the A chain by a kind of tryptic cleavage of the 'growth factor domain' (positions 1–46) and the 'kringle domain' (positions 47–135) and loss of the C-terminal Phe 157.

Supported by the BMFT of the FRG (Grant PTB 8239).

REFERENCES

Günzler W A, Steffens G J, Ötting F, Buse G, Flohé L 1982a Structural relationship between human high and low molecular mass urokinase. Hoppe-Seyler's Z. Physiol. Chem. 363: 133–141

Günzler W A, Steffens G J, Ötting F, Kim S-M A, Frankus E, Flohé L 1982b The primary structure of high molecular mass urokinase from human urine. Hoppe-Seyler's Z. Physiol. Chem. 363: 1155–1165

Heyneker H, Holmes W, Rey M, Pennica D, Shepard H M, Seeburg P, Hayflick J, Ward C, Vehar G, Steffens G J, Günzler W A, Ötting F, Flohé L 1983 Functional expression of the human urokinase gene in Escherichia coli. In: Proceedings of the IVth international symposium on genetics of industrial microorganisms 1982, organizing committee of GIM, Kyoto, pp 214–221

Steffens G J, Günzler W A, Ötting F, Frankus E, Flohé L 1982 The complete amino acid sequence of low molecular mass urokinase from human urine. Hoppe-Seyler's Z. Physiol. Chem. 363: 1043–1058

55. Molecular characterization of human low molecular mass urokinase obtained from recombinant E. coli bacteria

G. J. Steffens, W. A. Günzler, H-H. Hennies, W. Henninger, S-M. A. Kim, F. Ötting, E. Frankus, M. Blaber, M. Winkler and L. Flohé

Recombinant E. coli bacteria transformed by the use of a cDNA coding for human urokinase (Heyneker et al, 1983) were used as a source for the preparation of low molecular mass urokinase (cLUK). This investigation aimed at a comparison of the molecular properties of cLUK and of low molecular mass urokinase from human urine (uLUK) in order to check the correctness of expression and posttranslational processing of the enzyme produced by bacteria.

As evident from Figure 55.1, the cLUK sample used in this study exceeds 95% in purity and shows somewhat lower apparent molecular mass than uLUK. Amino acid analyses obtained from cLUK and uLUK were quite similar and in good agreement with previous data (Steffens et al, 1982). However, no hexoseamines were detected in the case of cLUK indicating that, in contrast to uLUK, the bacteria-produced enzyme lacks the carbohydrate side chain.

N-terminal analyses gave identical of PTH-derivatives of lysine and isoleucine in the first and of proline and isoleucine in the second step of Edman degradation using cLUK and uLUK samples, respectively. After reduction and S-carboxymethylation of cLUK and uLUK the corresponding peptide chains, A_1 and B, were separated by gel filtration as reported previously (Günzler et al, 1982). The A_1 chains of uLUK and cLUK proved to be identical in their amino acid sequence. The resulting peptides of tryptic digestion of the B chains of cLUK and uLUK were separated by reversed phase HPLC and further characterized by their amino acid sequences. As evident from Figure 55.3, the characterized tryptic peptides indicated in the elution profiles (Fig. 55.2) cover almost the complete sequences of the B chains of uLUK and cLUK. The only major differences between the elution patterns shown in Figure 55.2 are explained by the carbohydrate moiety residing in peptide T_{15-16} of the urine enzyme. In the case of cLUK the lack of the carbohydrate side chain retards the elution of the corresponding peptide T_{15-16}. Furthermore, the adjacent tryptic cleavage site was not shielded by the carbohydrate side chain and gave rise to two additional peptides T_{15} and T_{16} (cf. Fig. 55.3).

It is concluded that the amino acid sequences of uLUK and cLUK are identical and that uLUK differs from cLUK only by the carbohydrate moiety attached to Asn in position 144 of its B chain.

Supported by the BMFT of the FRG (Grant PTB 8477).

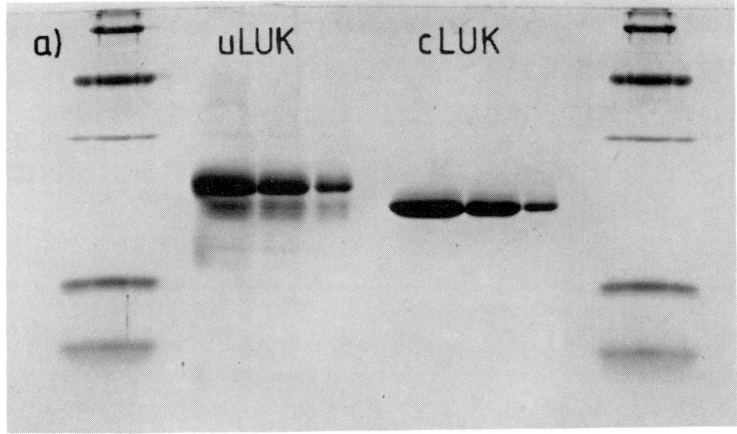

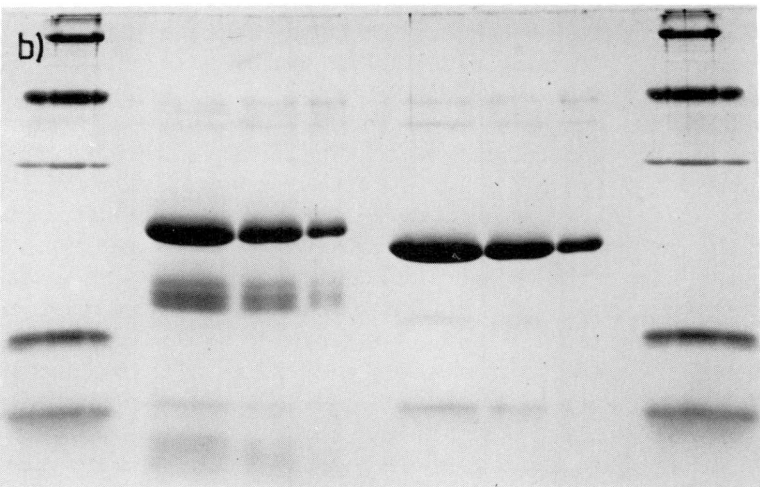

Fig. 55.1 SDS PAG electrophoresis of a) native and b) reduced samples of uLUK (Ares, Geneva, batch JJPL-2) and cLUK (Grüenthal GmbH, batch 54/6061/8), 10, 5, and 1 µg, respectively. Protein standards: 155, 68, 39, 21.5, and 12.5 kDa; stain: Coomassie brilliant blue.

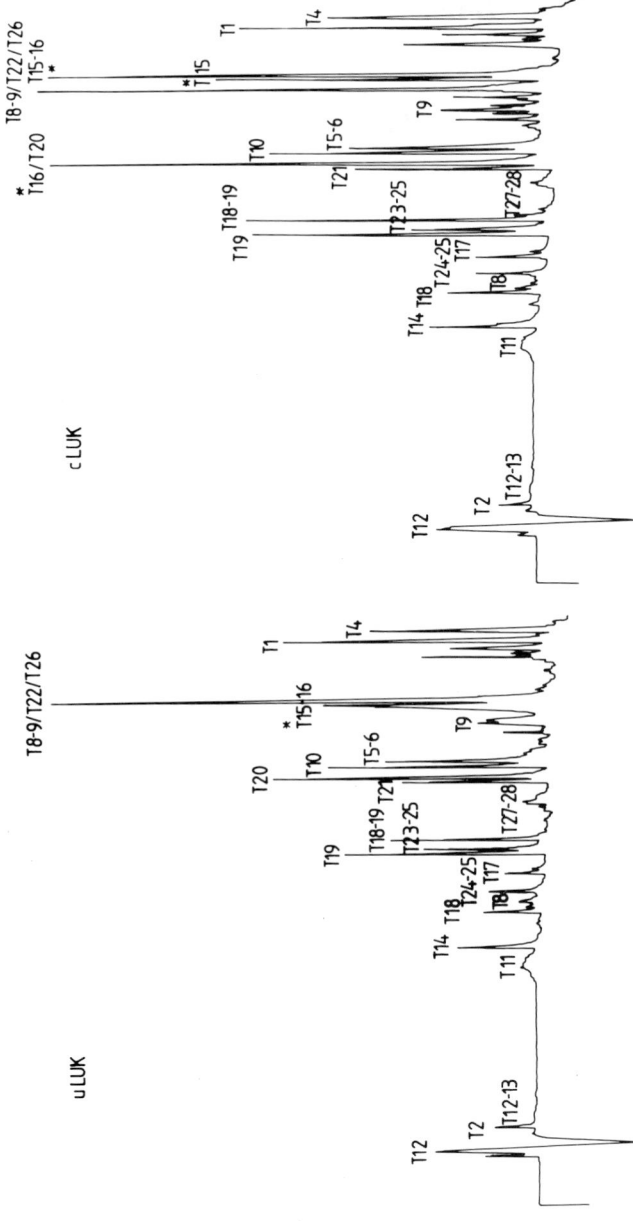

Fig. 55.2 Separation by reversed-phase HPLC of tryptic peptides of S-carboxymethylated B chains of uLUK and cLUK. Conditions: Nucleosil 5-C18 (0.72 × 25 cm); 50°C; solvent A (0.1% aqueous trifluoroacetic acid) 10 min; gradient 0–50% of solvent B (acetonitrile) 50 min; constant flow rate 1.4 ml/min. Asterisks mark major differences in elution patterns. For assignment of peaks see Fig. 55.3.

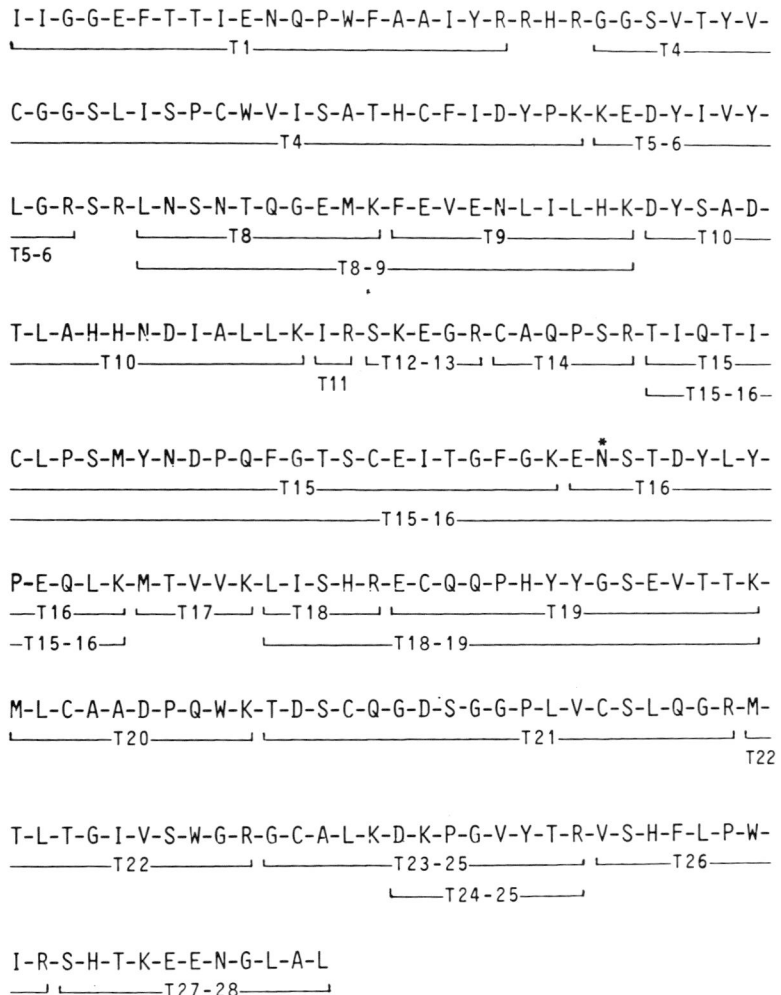

I-I-G-G-E-F-T-T-I-E-N-Q-P-W-F-A-A-I-Y-R-R-H-R-G-G-S-V-T-Y-V-
|————————————————T1————————————————| |————T4————|

C-G-G-S-L-I-S-P-C-W-V-I-S-A-T-H-C-F-I-D-Y-P-K-K-E-D-Y-I-V-Y-
|————————————————————T4—————————————————————| |———T5-6————|

L-G-R-S-R-L-N-S-N-T-Q-G-E-M-K-F-E-V-E-N-L-I-L-H-K-D-Y-S-A-D-
|————| |————————T8————————| |————T9————| |————T10———
T5-6 |————————————————T8-9————————————————|

T-L-A-H-H-N-D-I-A-L-L-K-I-R-S-K-E-G-R-C-A-Q-P-S-R-T-I-Q-T-I-
|—————————T10—————————| |—| |—T12-13—| |—T14———| |————T15———
                        T11 |————T15-16—

C-L-P-S-M-Y-N-D-P-Q-F-G-T-S-C-E-I-T-G-F-G-K-E-Ṅ-S-T-D-Y-L-Y-
|—————————————————T15—————————————————| |————T16————|
|——————————————————————T15-16——————————————————————|

P-E-Q-L-K-M-T-V-V-K-L-I-S-H-R-E-C-Q-Q-P-H-Y-Y-G-S-E-V-T-T-K-
|—T16———| |—T17——| |—T18——| |————————T19————————|
|—T15-16—| |————————————T18-19————————————|

M-L-C-A-A-D-P-Q-W-K-T-D-S-C-Q-G-D-S-G-G-P-L-V-C-S-L-Q-G-R-M-
|————————T20————————| |————————————————T21————————————————| |—
                                                              T22

T-L-T-G-I-V-S-W-G-R-G-C-A-L-K-D-K-P-G-V-Y-T-R-V-S-H-F-L-P-W-
|——————————T22——————————| |—————————T23-25—————————| |———T26———
                          |———————T24-25———————|

I-R-S-H-T-K-E-E-N-G-L-A-L
|—| |———————T27-28————————|
T26

Fig. 55.3 Amino acid sequence of the B chain or urokinase. Tryptic peptides identified after separation by HPLC (cf. Fig. 55.2) are indicated. The asterisk marks the glycosylation site in uLUK; note the adjacent tryptic cleavage site Lys-Glu.

REFERENCES

Günzler W A, Steffens G J, Ötting F, Buse G, Flohé L 1982 Structural relationship between human high and low molecular mass urokinase. Hoppe-Seyler's Z. Physiol. Chem. 363: 133–141

Heyneker H, Holmes W, Ray M, Pennica D, Shepard H M, Seeburg P, Hayflick J, Ward C, Vehar G, Steffens G J, Günzler W A, Ötting F, Flohé L 1983 Functional expression of the human urokinase gene in Escherichia coli. In: Proceedings of the IVth international symposium on genetics of industrial microorganisms 1982, organizing committee of GIM, Kyoto, pp 214–222

Steffens G J, Günzler W A, Ötting F, Frankus E, Flohé L 1982 The complete amino acid sequence of low molecular mass urokinase from human urine. Hoppe-Seyler's Z. Physiol. Chem. 363: 1043–1058

220

56. Functional characterization of human low molecular mass urokinase obtained from recombinant E. coli bacteria

W. A. Günzler, H-H. Hennies, W. Henninger,
F. Ötting, J. Schneider, E. Friderichs, H. Giertz,
M. Blaber, M. Winkler and L. Flohé

In pursuit of our goal to make human urokinase available in bulk quantities via bacterial fermentation, human-type low molecular mass urokinase (cLUK) was obtained from E. coli bacteria genetically transformed by recombinant techniques (Heyneker et al, 1983). This investigation was to provide evidence for functional equivalence in vitro and in vivo of cLUK with uLUK, the corresponding form of human urinary urokinase.

As shown in Figure 56.1 plasminogen-activating activity is attributed to the

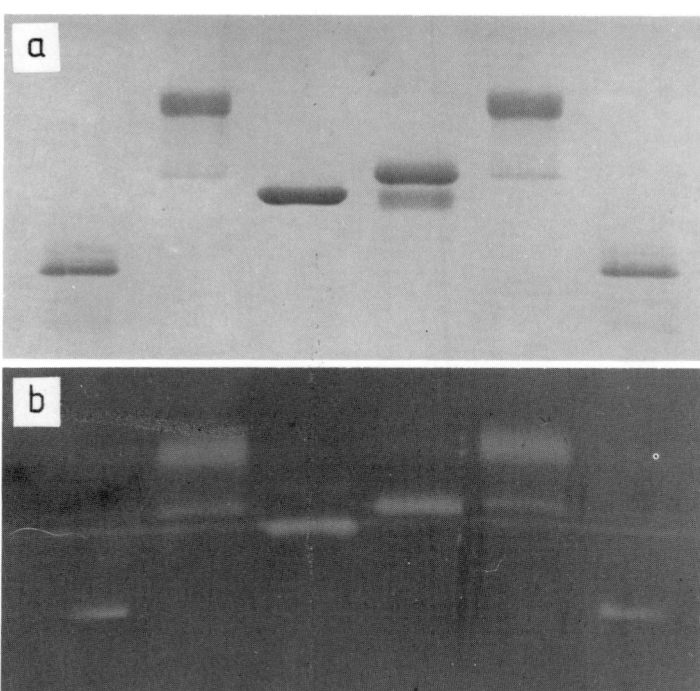

Fig. 56.1 Attribution of plasminogen-activating activity to protein bands in electrophoresis: a) Disc SDS PAGE (Laemmli, 1970); protein bands stained; b) plasminogen/gelatine disc SDS PAGE (Heussen & Dowdle, 1980); cleared area indicates proteolytic activity. No comparable gelatinolysis occurred when plasminogen was omitted (not shown).

single protein band of cLUK observed in electrophoresis as is to uLUK and uHUK (urinary high molecular mass urokinase).

Using the chromogenic peptide Glp-Gly-Arg-PNA (S-2444, Kabi) as a substrate, K_m values of 49 and 46 μmol/l were found for cLUK and uLUK, respectively. Moreover, a good agreement of the pronounced substrate specificities of cLUK and uLUK was observed when different chromogenic peptides were assayed. Further, the amidolytic activities of cLUK and uLUK were affected by low or high molecular mass inhibitors or by antibodies against uLUK to a similar degree as shown by comparable IC_{50} values (Table 56.1).

Table 56.1 Inhibition of amidolytic activity; substrate: S-2444 (0.3 mmol/l): control: 50 Ploug-U/ml

Inhibitor	IC_{50}			
	uLUK		cLUK	
Benzamidine	0.17 mM		0.24 mM	
Human placental urokinase				
inhibitor (Calbiochem)	100	U/ml	86	U/ml
Anti-LUK; rabbit IgG protein fraction	152	μg/ml	150	μg/ml

When assayed with the fibrin/agar plate according to Schumacher & Schill (1972) or with the fibrin plate according to Jespersen & Astrup (1983), consistently higher apparent activities were obtained with cLUK than with equal amidolytic activities of uLUK (Fig. 56.2). In contrast, similar plasminogen-activating efficacies of cLUK and uLUK were found when the urokinase-induced generation of plasmin from human or porcine plasminogen was monitored in solution.

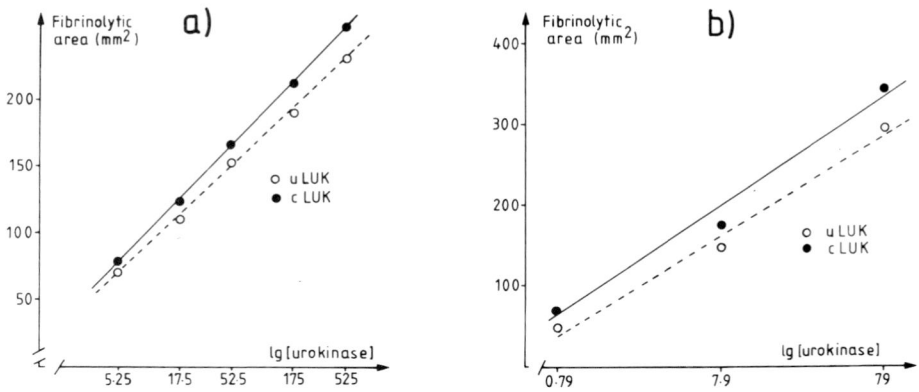

Fig. 56.2 Assays of cLUK and uLUK using a) a bovine fibrin/agar plate b) a human fibrin plate. Amidolytic (S-2444) activities are given on the abscissae.

Therefore, the discrepancy of activities in the diffusion-controlled fibrinolytic assays may be explained by a higher diffusion rate of cLUK, due to its lack of the carbohydrate side chain which is attached to the B chain in uLUK (Steffens et al, this volume).

In addition to these investigations in vitro, adequate thrombolytic activity of cLUK was also demonstrated in vivo. Thrombi (396 ± 2 mg) produced in vitro from autologous blood samples were injected into the jugular veins of anaesthetized rabbits. Saline or equal amidolytic activities of cLUK and uLUK (200 000 Ploug-U) were infused during 2 hours. Thrombolysis was determined from weight reduction of clots retrieved by dissection of pulmonary vasculature. Significant thrombolysis was observed with cLUK as was with uLUK (Fig. 56.3).

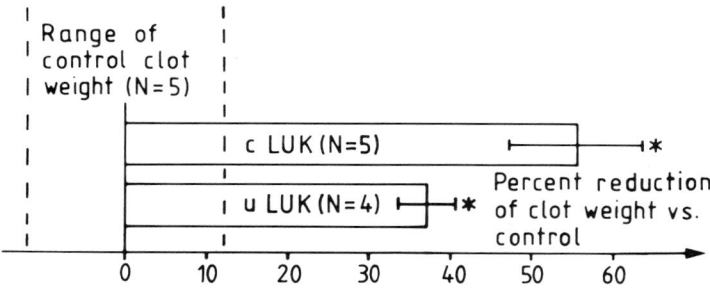

Fig. 56.3 Thrombolytic activity in rabbits in vivo; columns give means ± SEM; significance vs control: * $p < 0.05$.

It is concluded that cLUK is equivalent to uLUK in terms of its amidolytic. plasminogen-activating, and fibrinolytic activities in vitro and its thrombolytic activity in vivo. Therefore, the lack of the carbohydrate moiety in cLUK is considered not to interfere with its intended use as a thrombolytic drug.

Supported by the BMFT of the FRG (Grant PTB 8477).

REFERENCES

Heussen C, Dowdle E B 1980 Electrophoretic analysis of plasminogen activator in polyacrylamide gels containing sodium dodecyl sulfate and copolymerized substrates. Analytical Biochemistry 102: 196–202
Heyneker H. Holmes W, Ray M, Pennica D, Shepard H M, Seeburg P, Hayflick J. Ward C. Vehar G, Steffens G J, Günzler W A, Ötting F, Flohé L 1983 Functional expression of the human urokinase gene in Escherichia coli. In: Proceedings of the IVth international symposium on genetics of industrial microorganisms 1982, organizing committee of GIM, Kyoto, pp 214–222
Jespersen J, Astrup T 1983 A study of the fibrin plate assay of fibrinolytic agents. Haemostasis 13: 301–315
Laemmli U K 1970 Cleavage of structural proteins during the assembly of the head of bacteriophage T4. Nature (London) 227: 680–685
Schumacher G F, Schill W B 1972 Radial diffusion in gel for micro determination of enzymes. Analytical Biochemistry 48: 9–26
Steffens G J, Günzler W A, Hennies H H, Henninger W, Kim S M A, Ötting F, Frankus E, Blaber M, Winker M, Flohé L 1984 Molecular characterization of human low molecular mass urokinase obtained from recombinant E. coli bacteria. This volume.

Section 8
ACYL ENZYME DERIVATIVES

57. Structure-activity relationships for the formation and breakdown of acylated fibrinolytic enzymes

R. A. G. Smith, A. J. Garman and
G. S. Morgan

INTRODUCTION

A simple kinetic formulation of the mechanism of action of serine proteases is:

$$E + S \underset{}{\overset{K_s}{\rightleftharpoons}} E.S. \overset{k_2}{\rightarrow} E - A \overset{k_3}{\rightarrow} E.P. \underset{}{\overset{K_p}{\rightleftharpoons}} E + P$$

where E-A is the acyl-enzyme intermediate. We have recently proposed that stabilised acyl-fibrinolytic enzymes, derived from substrates for which $k_2 > > k_3$, may be used as thrombolytic pro-drugs (Smith et al, 1981; Smith, 1983a). The substrates used for the preparation of such acyl-enzymes are amidinophenyl esters of substituted benzoic acids with the general structure [I] (Markwardt et al, 1972; Tanizawa et al, 1977). This presentation analyses the reactivity of 'inverse' substrates [I] towards three fibrinolytic enzymes in terms of (a) the apparent second order rate constant for acylation, k_2/K'_s and (b) the first order rate constant for deacylation, k_3.

MATERIALS AND METHODS

Materials

Activator-free human plasmin (Batch DtB 25) was supplied by KabiVitrum, Stockholm, Sweden.

Activator-free porcine plasmin (Batch P70509Y) was a product of Novo, Copenhagen, Denmark.

Streptokinase-human plasmin activator complex (Batch 9018) was supplied by Behringwerke, Marburg, W. Germany.

Enzymes were stored as stock solutions (c. 2 μM) in 0.1 M Tris.HCl, 0.9% w/v NaCl, 20% v/v glycerol pH 7.4 [TGS buffer] at $-40°$C. Acylating agents were prepared by standard procedures (Smith, 1983b).

Acylation

A chromogenic substrate assay using substrate S-2251 (D-Val. Leu.Lys p-nitroanilide, KabiVitrum. 1.0 mM in 0.1 M triethanolamine pH 8.0) was employed. Substrate (1.0 ml) was placed in 4 cuvettes of a Pye Unicam SP6-350 visible spectrophotometer fitted with an autocell changer interfaced to a Hewlett-Packard HP 97S calculator. The acylating agent under study (stock: 0.1–2.5 mM in DMSO) was added to the substrate at six different concentrations in the range 1–80 μM. Enzyme (10–50 pmol) was added to each cuvette and the decrease in the rate of S-2251 cleavage studied as a function of time. This was accomplished by running the autocell changer on a cycle of 1.0 min for 7–20 cycles. (Pye Unicam software, 4 cell rate program.) After one cycle the rate of reaction in each cuvette (measured as $\Delta \mathrm{OD}_{405\,\mathrm{nm}}^{1\,\mathrm{cm}}$) was used as the initial rate and the subsequent rate at 1.0 min intervals was computed automatically. First order inactivation rate constants (k_{inact}) were calculated for each concentration of acylating agent from plots of $1\,\mathrm{n}\left(\frac{[E]_t}{[E]_0}\right)$ against time. Bender et al (1966) and Chase & Shaw (1969) have shown that provided $k_2 >> k_3$, double reciprocal plots of $1/_{\mathrm{kinact}}$ against $1/_{\mathrm{[acylating\ agent]}}$ have slopes of K_S'/k_2 and intercepts of $1/k_2'$. K_S' is an apparent substrate dissociation constant because inactivation of the enzyme is observed in the presence of a competing substrate (S-2251). Estimates of k_2/K_S' and, in some cases, k_2 were obtained by linear regression analysis of the above plot.

Deacylation
Acyl-enzymes which deacylated slowly ($k_3 < \sim 8 \times 10^{-4}\,\mathrm{s}^{-1}$) were prepared from stock enzyme solution (see above) and 0.1–1.0 mM acylating agent at 0°C for 1 h, desalted on small Sephadex G-25 columns into TGS buffer, diluted approximately 10-fold in TGS and brought to 37°C. Rapidly deacylating acyl-enzymes were generated by treating stock enzyme with an equimolar quantity of acylating agent at 0°C for 10–30 min. Acyl-enzyme was then divided into pre-warmed TGS at 37°C and samples taken at short intervals. In both cases, the S-2251 chromogenic substrate was used and k_3 calculated from plots of $1\,\mathrm{n}\left(1 - \left[\frac{(A_t - A_0)}{(A_{\mathrm{max}} - A_0)}\right]\right)$ against time. A_{max} was derived either from the activity of the enzyme before acylation (slow deacylating acyl-enzymes) or the maximum activity attained on deacylation at 37°C (fast deacylating derivatives).

RESULTS AND DISCUSSION

Acylation
The apparent second order rate constants for acylation of the three enzymes are shown in Table 57.1.
Three points are noteworthy:
(i) The most reactive acylating agents were those with electron-withdrawing substituents in *either* the 4-position of the benzoic acid *or* the R2-position of the amidinophenyl ring. (Fig. 57.1). The most efficient *titrant* was compound 11 which also releases a chromophore (ϵ (395 nm): 4807 M cm^{-1}) on acylation of the enzymes. Conversely, electron-releasing benzoyl substituents retarded acylation but this effect could be overcome by esterification with an electron-withdrawing amidinophenol (c.f. compounds 5, 9, 11).
(ii) Analysis of k_2 and K_S' (data shown for pig plasmin) suggested that in

228

Table 57.1 Apparent acylation rate constants for inverse substrates

Compound no.	R_1	R_2	R_3	n	Human plasmin k_2/K_S $M^{-1}s^{-1}$	SK. human plasmin k_2/K_S $M^{-1}s^{-1}$	Porcine plasmin k_2/K_S $M^{-1}s^{-1}$	k_2 s^{-1}	K_S μM
1	NO_2	H	H	O	8474	4083	1659	0.0045	2.7
2	Cl	H	H	O	2990	3022	1037	0.0057	5.5
3	H	H	H	O	552	1648	568	0.0139	24.4
4	CH_3	H	H	O	529	1149	288	0.0153	53.2
5	CH_3O	H	H	O	199	289	189	0.0550	31.6
6	NH_2	H	H	O	57	189	65	0.0033	50.5
7	CH_3O	I	H	O	1459	5038	1060	0.0254	24.0
8	CH_3O	Br	H	O	1937	4623	1143	0.0174	13.6
9	CH_3O	Cl	H	O	1857	4992	1147	0.0140	10.6
10	CH_3O	Cl	Cl	O	—	~5	~7	0.0009	129.0
11	CH_3O	NO_2	H	O	8511	12863	7576	0.0411	5.4
12	CH_3O	H	H	1	~3	—	—	—	—
13	CH_3O	3-amidinophenyl			~5	—	—	—	—

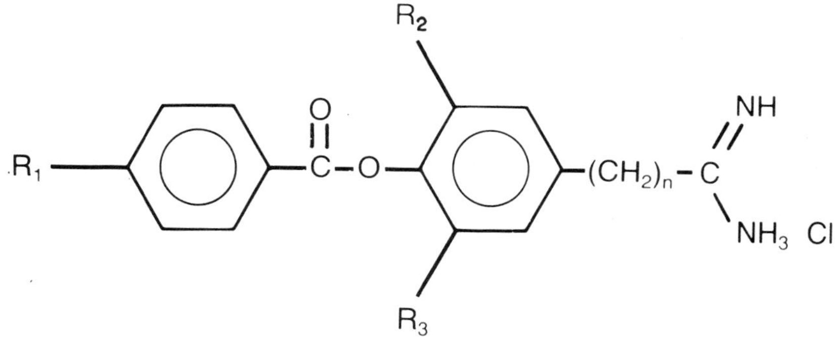

Fig. 57.1 General structure of inverse acylating agents.

electronegative esters, reactivity was increased more by a decrease in K_S' (tighter enzyme binding) than by an increase in k_2 (more rapid acyl transfer).

(iii) The reactivity of compounds [I] is critically dependent on the position of the amidine function in relation to the cleaved ester linkage. Insertion of a methylene unit between the benzene ring and the amidine or moving the amidine to the 3-position greatly decreased the deacylation rate as did substitution in both ortho positions (compound 10).

Deacylation

Figure 57.2 shows a plot of log (k_3) against Hammett constant σ_ϱ for 4-substituted benzoyl derivatives of the three enzymes. Linear regression analysis gave correlation coefficients of 0.992 (human plasmin), 0.994 (pig plasmin) and 0.957 (SK. plasmin). The slopes of these plots (Hammett ϱ values) were respectively 1.69, 2.32 and 1.83 — values which suggest only partial negative change in the change relay system during the deacylation step (Zannis & Kirsch, 1978). In general, the 4-aminobenzoyl and 4-guanidinobenzoyl enzymes

229

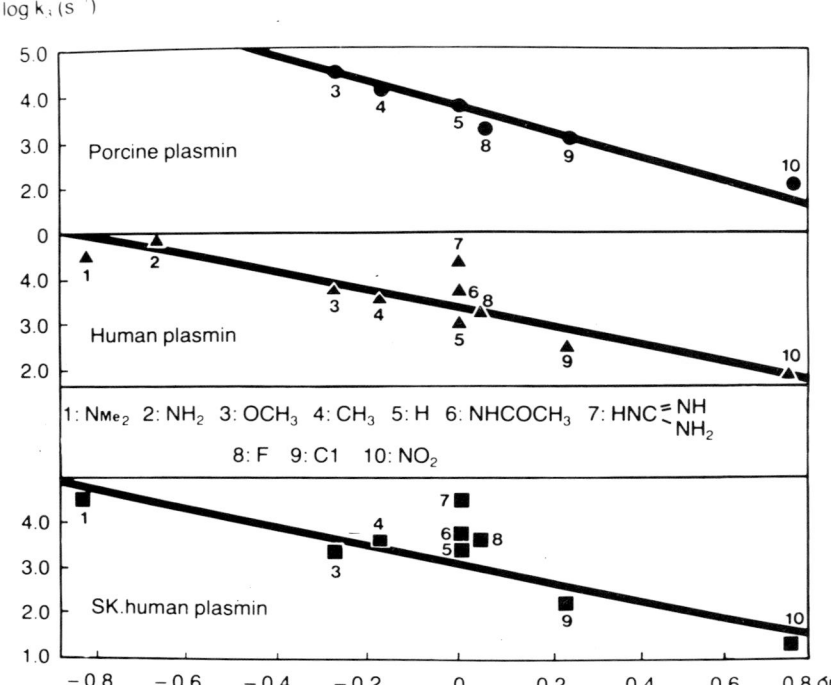

Fig 57.2 Hammett plots for the deacylation rates of 4-substituted benzoyl porcine and human plasmins and SK.human plasmin.

deacylated more slowly than would be predicted from these relationships. In addition, a comparison of 4-anisoyl derivatives of SK. plasmin(ogen) species revealed only slight differences in k_3, between the SK.plasmin and SK.(glu) plasminogen or SK.(lys) plasminogen derivatives. However, 4-anisoyl (Val$_{442}$) plasmin ('mini' BRL 26921) deacylated significantly faster ($k_3 = 7.7 \times 10^{-4} \, sec^{-1}$) than the other acyl-enzymes.

CONCLUSIONS

(i) Unlike other reagents which have been used for the generation of acyl-enzymes from serine or cysteine proteases (e.g. benzoyl imdazoles or 4-nitrophenyl esters), the inverse substrates [I] are not intrinsically reactive compounds capable of acylating proteins non-specifically. The most reactive ester studied (11) acylated human serum albumin more than 10^3-fold more slowly than it acylated SK.plasmin (data not shown). The specificity constants for acylation by most of these esters permit the generation of acyl-enzymes from plasmins and plasminogen activators at sub millimolar concentrations of [1] in a few minutes at room temperature.

(ii) The apparent second-order acylation rate constants are increased by electron-withdrawing substituents in the 4-position (R_1) of the benzoyl moiety or the R_2 (R_3) positions of the alcohol moiety (Fig. 57.1). By manipulation of the latter, rapid transfer to the enzyme of even electron-rich benzoyl functions can be achieved.

(iii) The stability of benzoyl-fibrinolytic enzymes is strongly correlated with the electron-releasing character of the benzoyl substituents, as has been found for other proteases (Wang & Shaw, 1972; Zannis & Kirsch, 1978). The half-lives of acyl-enzymes isolatable by lyophilisation range from less than 10 min to more than 12 hours. This flexibility and predictability allows the design of acylated fibrinolytic enzymes which can regenerate activity at a wide range of rates under physiological conditions.

ACKNOWLEDGEMENT

We are grateful to Mr R. Stevenson and Dr S.B. Kalindjian for providing some of the amidines used in this study.

REFERENCES

Bender M L, Bégue-Cantón M L, Blakeley R L, Brubacher L J, Fender J, Gunter C R, Kezdy F J, Killheffer J V Jr, Marshall T H, Miller C G, Toeske R W, Stoops J K 1966 The determination of the concentration of hydrolytic enzyme solutions: α-chymotrypsin, papain, elastase, subtilisin and acetyl-cholinesterase. Journal of the American Chemical Society 88: 5890–5913

Chase T Jr, Shaw E 1969 Comparison of the esterase activities of trypsin, plasmin and thrombin on guanidinobenzoate esters. Titration of the enzymes. Biochemistry 8: 2212–2224

Markwardt F, Wagner G, Waismann P, Horn H, Stürzbecher J 1972 Inhibition of trypsin and thrombin by amidinophenyl esters of aromatic carboxylic acids. Acta Biologica et Medica Germanica 28: K19–K25

Smith R A G, Dupe R J, English P D, Green J 1981 Fibrinolysis with acyl-enzymes: a new approach to thrombolytic therapy. Nature 290: 505–508

Smith R A G 1983a Acyl-enzymes as fibrinolytic pro-drugs. In: Davidson J F, Bachmann F, Bouvier C A, Kruithof E K O (eds) Progress in Fibrinolysis 6: 232–239

Smith R A G 1983b Proenzymes European Published Patent No 0 009 879

Tanizawa K, Kasaba Y, Kanaoka Y 1977 'Inverse substrates' for trypsin. Efficient enzymic hydrolysis of certain esters with a cationic center in the leaving group. Journal of the American Chemical Society 99: 4485–4888

Wang C-C, Shaw E 1972 A comparison of the deacylation rates of para-substituted benzoyl trypsins and chymotrypsins. Archives of Biochemistry and Biophysics 150: 259–268

Zannis V I, Kirsch J F 1978 Effects of substituents on the rates of deacylation of substituted benzoyl papains. Role of a carboxylate residue in the catalytic mechanism. Biochemistry 17: 2269–2674

58. Evidence for a sustained fibrinolytic response to BRL 26921 (p-anisoyl-streptokinase human lys-plasminogen activator complex) in vitro

R. Fears, P. Walker, R.A.G. Smith and J. Green

INTRODUCTION

BRL 26921 is the first of a new class of thrombolytic agents, the fibrinolytic pro-drugs, and can regenerate activity in vivo with the potential advantages of extended half-life, diminished side-effects and resistance to neutralisation by anti-proteases. Previous results from rabbit experiments (Smith et al, 1982) suggest that progressive activation of thrombus-bound plasminogen allows continuing activity even when systemic levels of agent are low. Acylation of the active centre does not diminish the fibrin-affinity of streptokinase-based activators (Smith, 1983) and the present studies used normal human plasma clots to attempt to define more precisely the importance of thrombus-binding in the fibrinolytic response to BRL 26921.

MATERIALS AND METHODS

The preparation of BRL 26921 and the sources of other materials used have been described elsewhere (English et al, 1981; Smith et al, 1982).

Pooled human plasma with a low streptokinase-resistance was obtained from volunteers, and aliquots (0.5 ml) were supplemented with 0.1 μCi [^{125}I]-human fibrinogen, purified by ammonium sulphate precipitation (Dupe et al, 1981) and clotted onto a supporting Nickel-chrome wire coil (Alkjaersig et al, 1959) using 2.5 units of bovine thrombin. Clots were matured at 25° for 30 minutes, washed in 6 vols 0.1 M phosphate buffer pH 7.6 at 0° for one hour and the [^{125}I]-fibrin content measured. The partially cross-linked clots were then either incubated in homologous plasma (3–5 ml) at 37° for up to 5 hours or were briefly exposed to the fibrinolytic agent in plasma, washed and returned to unsupplemented plasma or to buffer for incubation at 37°. Clot lysis was monitored by the measurement of the release of fibrin degradation products as [^{125}I] in aliquots of the incubation medium.

RESULTS AND DISCUSSION

When human plasma clots were incubated with BRL 26921 in plasma there was a concentration-dependent response with maximum lysis essentially complete by 5 hours at 2×10^{-8} M (2.8 μg, 100 SKU/ml). When clots were incubated with BRL 26921 in plasma for much shorter periods and then transferred to unsupplemented plasma, lysis continued for up to 3 hours. Uptake of BRL 26921 was competitive with plasminogen and the response was concentration-dependent. For example, after exposure of clots for only one minute, BRL 26921 induced 25% of that final lysis supported by incubation with agent for 5 hours. This sustained lysis could not be explained by transfer of loosely-associated surface material or by dissociation of agent from clot with rebinding from a dilute systemic pool since a virgin clot incubated concomitantly did not lyse ($< 3\%$).

The effect of a standard concentration of BRL 26921 (2×10^{-8} M) was potentiated approx. 3-fold and prolonged (> 5 hours) when clots were returned to buffer instead of plasma (Expt. 1, Table 58.1) and an intermediate degree of lysis was obtained in α_2-antiplasmin-depleted plasma (results not shown). The net lysis induced by streptokinase was similar to BRL 26921 although, as expected,

Table 58.1 Maintenance of human plasma clot lysis in vitro after initial exposure to fibrinolytic agent for one minute

Incubation conditions	Number of replicates	%Clot lysis (mean $\pm$ SEM)	
		30 minutes	5 hours
Expt. 1: Incubation with BRL 26921 (2×10^{-8} M) and return of washed clots to:			
Plasma	6	13.6 ± 1.8	26.4 ± 2.5
Buffer	6	25.0 ± 2.3	60.0 ± 5.1
Expt. 2: Return of clots to buffer after exposure to agent:			
BRL 26921 (2×10^{-8} M)	4	16.4 ± 1.0	41.1 ± 2.6
Streptokinase (2×10^{-8} M)	4	23.6 ± 1.9	35.8 ± 3.0
Urokinase (1.5×10^{-8} M)	6	1.8 ± 0.2	5.6 ± 2.0
Plasmin (1×10^{-6} M)	4	13.0 ± 1.1	11.9 ± 2.0
Control	6	1.8 ± 0.2	3.5 ± 1.5

initial activity was no greater (Expt. 2, Table 58.1). However, unlike the response to BRL 26921, the effect of streptokinase was associated with and dependent on the activation of plasminogen in the surrounding plasma during clot exposure. A concentration of urokinase (1.5×10^{-8} M) that was equiactive on 5 hours incubation was inactive after exposure of clots for one minute; a much higher concentration of urokinase (3×10^{-7} M) did induce some lysis but this was again associated with early activation of plasminogen in the surrounding plasma. A high concentration of plasmin (1×10^{-6} M) in buffer gave only initial activity.

These present results suggest that the processes within a clot that lead to fibrinolysis can occur relatively independently of systemic proteolytic activity and they extend the findings of Whitaker et al (1980) obtained using streptokinase and fibrin clots (5 minute exposure period). For the brief duration of exposure and low concentration of BRL 26921 used in the present studies, the sustained fibrinolysis achieved by initial uptake of activator is at least partly explained by specific fibrin-binding with activator entry into the clot followed by activation of endogenous plasminogen. This is a valuable property and although there are additional relevant factors in vivo including, for example, the age of the thrombus, it seems likely that a simplified system in vitro is useful to compare certain attributes of the various classes of activators. It has not yet been determined whether the mechanism of action of BRL 26921 involves processive migration along the fibrin network or sequential dissociation and rebinding locally from the fibrin interstices but in either event the consequences may contribute to clinical efficacy.

REFERENCES

Alkjaersig N, Fletcher A P, Sherry S 1959 The mechanism of clot dissolution by plasmin. Journal of Clinical Investigation 38: 1086–1095
Dupe R J, English P D, Smith R A G, Green J 1981 The evaluation of plasmin and streptokinase activator complexes in a new rabbit model of venous thrombosis. Thrombosis and Haemostasis 46: 528–534
English P D, Smith R A G, Dupe R J, Green J, Hibbs M J 1981 The thrombolytic activity of streptokinase in the rabbit. Thrombosis and Haemostasis 46: 535–537
Smith R A G 1983 Acyl-enzymes as fibrinolytic pro-drugs. In: Davidson J F, Bachman F, Bouvier C A, Druithof E K O (eds) Progress in Fibrinolysis, Churchill Livingstone, Edinburgh. 6: 232–239
Smith R A G, Dupe R J, English P D, Green J 1982 Acyl-enzymes as thrombolytic agents in a rabbit model of venous thrombosis. Thrombosis and Haemostasis 47: 269–274
Whitaker A N, Rowe E A, Masci P P, Joe F, Gaffney P J 1980 The binding of glu- and lys-plasminogens to fibrin and their subsequent effects on fibrinolysis. Thrombosis Research 19: 381–391

59. Pharmacokinetic and pharmacodynamic comparisons of acylated streptokinase-plasminogen complexes with different deacylation rate constants

A. F. Esmail, R. J. Dupe,
P. D. English and R. A. G. Smith

INTRODUCTION

It has been proposed that active-centre acylated derivatives of fibrinolytic enzymes may be used as pro-drugs of thrombolytic agents and that the pharmacokinetic and pharmacodynamic properties of such derivatives may be chemically manipulated to suit different clinical situations where fibrin removal is required (Smith et al 1981). There is evidence that temporary inactivation of the active centre blocks at least one major pathway of physiological clearance of streptokinase (SK).plasmin[ogen] complexes (Gonias et al 1982; Smith, 1983). Two acylated SK.plasminogens, the 4-anisoyl derivative (BRL 26921), and the 4-aminobenzoyl compound (BRL 33575) have been prepared with deacylation half-lives in vitro of about 40 min and 17 hours respectively. The very different stabilities of these acyl-enzymes suggest that they may be appropriate for the treatment, respectively, of acute and chronic thrombotic disease. This study reports data on clearance of the agents in rabbits and on efficacy in two rabbit models of thrombosis.

METHODS AND MATERIALS

^{125}I-human lys$_{77}$-plasminogen was prepared using the Iodogen method (Fraker & Speck, 1978) from highly purified lys-plasminogen (KabiVitrum). ^{125}I-SK.human plasmin (Type 2) was prepared by the method of Dupe et al (1981) using the above ^{125}I-plasminogen which was also used to prepare ^{125}I-(plasminogen)-BRL 26921 and BRL 33575 by the previously described method (Smith et al 1982). Unlabelled BRL 26921 and BRL 33575 were pharmaceutical grade materials prepared as previously described (Smith et al 1982).

Clearance studies
Male New Zealand White rabbits were anaesthetised with pento-barbitone and

the femoral artery cannulated. Agents (c. 45 µg/kg in fibrinolytic experiments) were injected rapidly (< 60 sec) into a marginal ear vein. Arterial blood samples (2.0 ml) were taken within 1 min of administration to determine an initial level and at various intervals thereafter. Blood ^{125}I levels were determined by γ-scintillation counting. Euglobulin precipitate was prepared by a standard procedure (Austen & Rhymes, 1975). The assay of euglobulin precipitate for total potential plasminogen activator activity and the calibration of this assay will be presented elsewhere.

Rabbit inferior vena cava thread-supported thrombus model
This model has been described previously (Dupe et al 1981).

Rabbit jugular vein thread-supported thrombus model
This model is similar to that used by Collen et al (1983). Male New Zealand White rabbits (2.5–3.0 kg) were anaesthetised with Hypnorm (0.5 ml/kg i.m.). A 2.0 cm segment of the right jugular vein was isolated and a single woollen thread inserted within the vessel lumen. ^{125}I-human fibrinogen was used to form a labelled clot according to previously described protocols (Dupe et al 1981). The clot was allowed to age in the conscious animal for 24h. Agents were injected into the contralateral ear vein and blood samples (1.0 ml) taken from the central ear artery under Hypnorm sedation (0.15 mg/kg). ^{125}I-FDP was determined by γ-scintillation counting of whole blood. 24h after administration of the enzyme, clots were removed for determination of final lysis. No anticoagulation was used in these experiments.

RESULTS AND DISCUSSION

Clearance
Figure 59.1 shows the clearance of SK.plasmin, BRL 26921 and BRL 33575 measured by radiometric assay. Agents were radiolabelled in the plasminogen moiety and fibrinolytic activity of diluted euglobulin fraction was estimated on fibrin plates under conditions which allowed deacylation of the acyl-enzymes. The radiometric studies show that acylation of the active centre of SK.plasmin(ogen) prolonged the plasma residence time of the plasmin(ogen) protein in agreement with the results of Gonias et al (1982) who studied the clearance of p-guanidinobenzoyl SK.plasmin in mice. Although there is a rank correlation of radiometric clearance rate with deacylation rate in vitro, the radiometrically determined half-lives were found to be longer than the functional half-lives. The latter were about 2.7 min for SK.plasmin, 45 min for BRL 26921 and 120–130 min for BRL 33575. The discrepancy may be due to diversion of activator complex radiolabel into slowly cleared complexes with plasma inhibitors or to selective catabolism of the SK moiety or to both. Nevertheless, slowing the deacylation rate of the acyl-activator appeared to increase the availability of potential fibrinolytic activity in the plasma of rabbits.

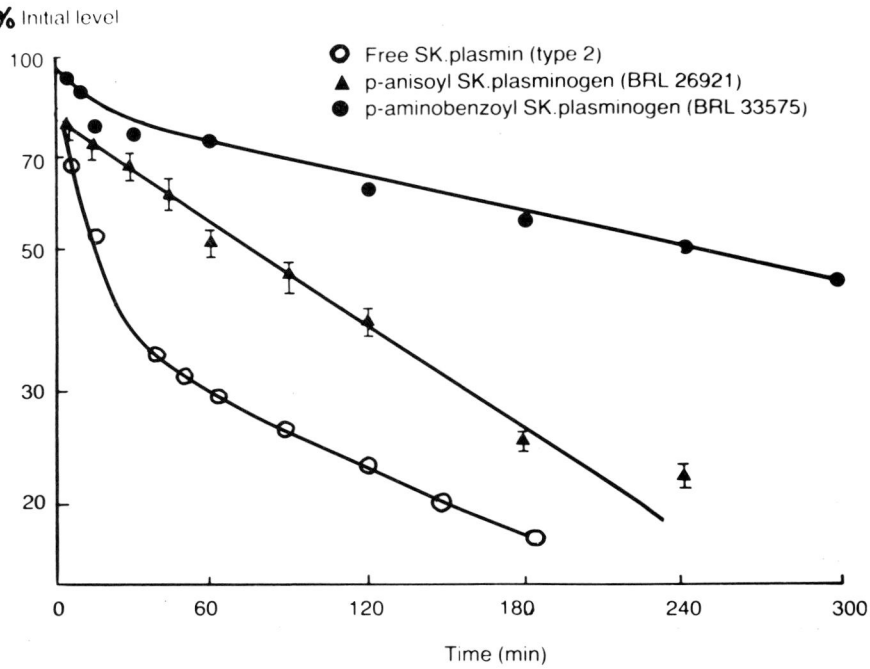

% Initial level

Legend:
○ Free SK.plasmin (type 2)
▲ p-anisoyl SK.plasminogen (BRL 26921)
● p-aminobenzoyl SK.plasminogen (BRL 33575)

Time (min)

Fig. 59.1 Clearance of unmodified and active centre-acylated forms of SK.plasminogen from the bloodstream of rabbits Radiochemical determination using ^{125}I-plasminogen labelled agents.

Thrombolytic activity

Figure 59.2 shows the release of ^{125}I-fibrin degradation products (^{125}I-FDP) from fresh experimental venous thrombi following single bolus doses of thrombolytic agents. Unmodified SK.plasmin generated a short-lived and rapid lytic response in which the peak ^{125}I-FDP level occurred earlier than 30 min post-dose whereas BRL 26921 produced maximum ^{125}I-FDP levels after 2–3 hours. There was no significant difference between lysis induced by BRL 26921 after 5h (51 ± 4%) and that produced by the same dose after 10h (63 ± 10%) and plasma ^{125}I-FDP continued to decline between 3 and 10h after dosing. However, no clear-cut peak in ^{125}I-FDP could be observed within 5–10h of dosing with BRL 33575 and lysis caused by this agent after 10h (41 ± 7%) was significantly greater (P < 0.05) than that produced after 5h (20 ± 4%).

Figure 59.3 shows the response to fibrinolytic agents of a rabbit model of venous thrombosis in which experimental thrombi were allowed to age in vivo for 24h. Lysis was assessed radiochemically 24h after single bolus dosage. SK.plasmin complex gave only slight lysis in this model although SK alone was more active, possibly reflecting a slower clearance rate for the uncomplexed protein and the effect of fibrin on SK-induced fibrinolysis in the rabbit (English et al 1981). BRL 26921 at an equivalent dose was also active. BRL 33575 was more active than BRL 26921 at the same dose and showed maximum activity at around 280 μg/kg.

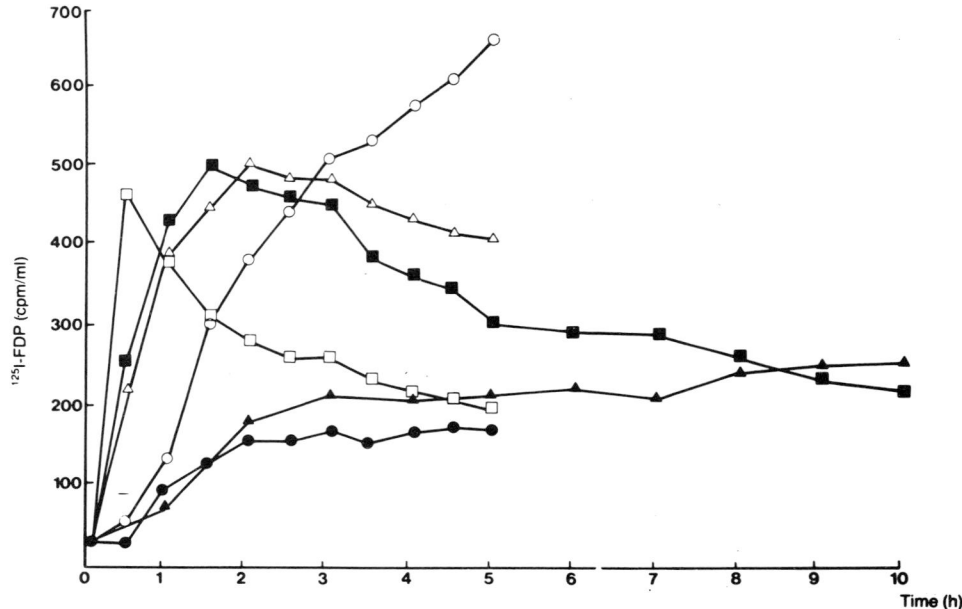

Fig. 59.2 Release of ^{125}I-FDP from experimental thrombi in the rabbit inferior vena cava treated with various agents.

[Agent, dose, % end lysis: mean ± SEM, group size].

Δ:	BRL 26921	70 μg/kg	51 ± 4 after 5 h,	8
●:	BRL 33575	70 μg/kg	20 ± 4 after 5 h,	7
■:	BRL 26921	70 μg/kg	63 ± 16 after 10 h,	3
▲:	BRL 33575	70 μg/kg	41 ± 7 after 10 h,	8
O:	BRL 33575	840 μg/kg	63 ± 10 after 5 h,	3
□:	SK.plasmin	280 μg/kg	32 ± 5, 5	

For clarity, error bars have been omitted from the individual FDP levels

CONCLUSIONS

(i) Acylation of the active centre of SK.plasmin(ogen) decreases the clearance rate of radiolabelled agent and of total potential fibrinolytic activity in the plasma euglobulin fraction. The decrease in clearance rate correlates with the deacylation half-life for the acyl-enzyme in vitro.

(ii) Kinetics of lysis of fresh experimental thrombi by acyl-enzymes suggest that the duration of thrombolytic action correlates with the half-life for total potential fibrinolytic activity in plasma.

(iii) The efficacy of BRL 33575 against aged experimental thrombi suggests that this slow-acting acyl-enzyme may be appropriate for the treatment of established deep venous thrombosis in man.

ACKNOWLEDGEMENT

We are very grateful to Dr B. Nunn for performing the functional clearance assay.

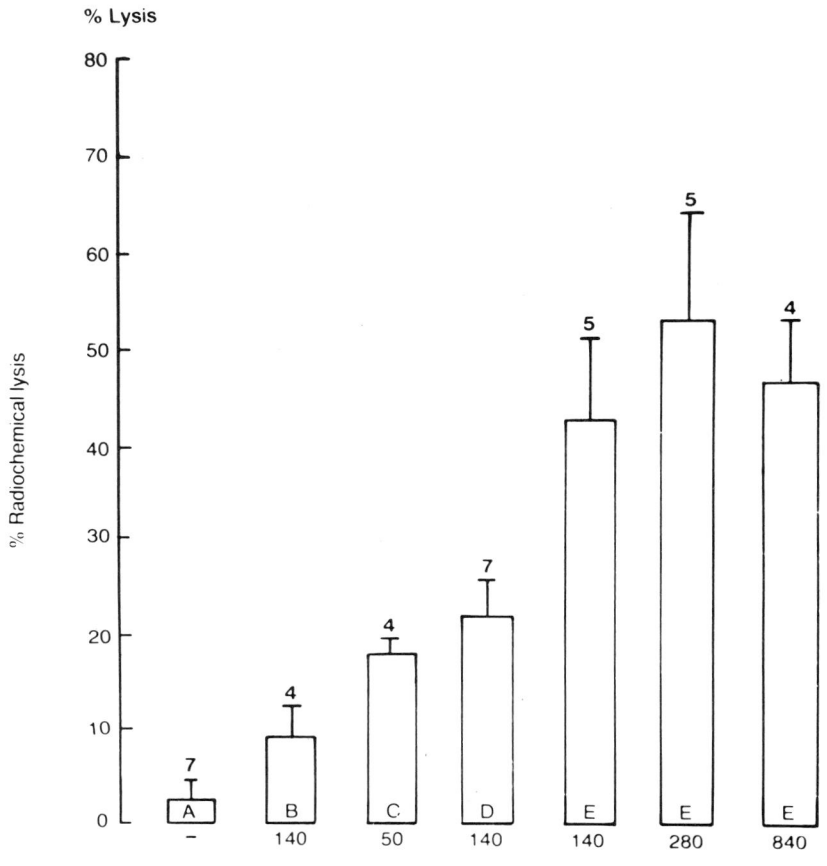

% Lysis

Fig. 59.3 Efficacy of thrombolysis induced by various agents acting on 24h old jugular vein clots in the rabbit.
A: Saline controls; B: SK.human plasmin: C: Streptokinase; D: BRL 26921; E: BRL 33575

REFERENCES

Austen D E G, Rhymes I L 1975 A laboratory manual of blood coagulation. Blackwell, Oxford, p 80
Collen D, Stassen J-M, Verstraete M 1983 Thrombolysis with human extrinsic (tissue-type) plasminogen activator in rabbits with experimental jugular vein thrombosis. In: Davidson J F, Bachmann F, Bouvier C A, Kruithof E K O (eds) Progress in fibrinolysis. Churchill Livingstone, Edinbugh, vol 6, p 227–231
Dupe R J, English P D, Smith R A G, Green J 1981 The evaluation of plasmin and streptokinase activator complexes in a new rabbit model of venous thrombosis. Thrombosis and Haemostasis 46: 528–534
English P D, Smith R A G, Dupe R J, Green J, Hibbs M J 1981 The thrombolytic activity of streptokinase in the rabbit. Thrombosis and Haemostasis 46: 535–537
Fraker P J, Speck J C 1978 Protein and cell membrane iodinations with a sparingly soluble chloroamide; 1,3,4,6-tetrachloro-3a,6a-diphenyl glycouril. Biochemical and Biophysical Research Communications 80: 849–857

Friberger P, Knös M, Gustavsson S, Aurell L, Claeson G 1978 Methods for the determination of plasmin, antiplasmin and plasminogen by means of substrate S-2251. Haemostasis 7: 138–145

Gonias S L, Einarsson M, Pizzo S V 1982 Catabolic pathways for streptokinase, plasmin and streptokinase activator complex in mice. Journal of Clinical Investigation 70: 412–423

Smith R A G, Dupe R J, English P D, Green J 1981 Fibrinolysis with acyl-enzymes: a new approach to thrombolytic therapy. Nature 290: 505–508

Smith R A G 1983 Acyl-enzymes as fibrinolytic pro-drugs. In: Davidson J F, Bachmann F, Bouvier C A, Kruithof E K O (eds) Progress in fibrinolysis.Churchill Livingstone, Edinburgh, vol 6, p 232–239

60. Responses of experimental venous clots, aged in vivo in dogs, to acylated and unmodified streptokinase–plasmin(ogen) complexes

R. J. Dupe, R. A. G. Smith and J. Green

INTRODUCTION

In order to explore the therapeutic potential of acyl-enzyme fibrinolytic pro-drugs, we have developed several models of venous and arterial thromboembolism in the beagle dog. The responses of such models to one such acyl-enzyme, 4-anisoyl streptokinase–plasminogen complex (BRL 26921) have been described previously (Dupe et al 1983). The experimental thrombi in these models were established for 24h or less. We were therefore interested in the effect of acyl-enzymes on experimental thrombi which were older, more highly organised and possibly more representative of established deep venous thrombi in man. This report describes a method for the establishment and aging in vivo of thread-supported thrombi in dogs and the responses of these thrombi to various thrombolytic agents, including the slow-deacylating acyl-enzyme BRL 33575 (4-aminobenzoyl SK.plasminogen complex, deacylation $t_{\frac{1}{2}}$ in vitro c. 17h).

METHODS AND MATERIALS

Materials

BRL 26921 and BRL 33575 were prepared as previously described (Smith et al 1982). SK plasmin complex was prepared freshly by continuous infusion of highly purified streptokinase and lys-plasminogen (KabiVitrum) in equimolar concentrations through the arms of a Y piece at a rate calculated to permit complex formation in the stem of the Y immediately before entry into the venous system.

Methods

The general methodology for the establishment of venous thrombosis in the *femoral* vein of the dog has been described (Dupe et al 1983, 1984). The femoral vein model, however, proved most suitable for aging periods up to 24h. Attempts to age femoral vein clots for longer periods resulted in hyperplasia and collateral development, leaving a stenosed chord-like vessel. Better results were obtained when similar techniques were applied to the jugular vein. Full details of the procedures will be presented elsewhere.

Fibrinogen
This was determined by the turbidimetric method of Burmester et al (1973).

Scanning electron microscopy
Two thrombi were formed, one in each jugular vein of a dog and one was removed 20 min after clotting while the other was removed after 72h aging, as described above. Clots were rinsed in 0.9% w/v saline, fixed in glutaraldehyde (3% w/v, 0.1 M sodium cacodylate pH 7.2, 2–4h), washed in the buffer, dehydrated with ethanol, dried and sectioned. Sections were gold sputter coated and examined at various magnifications.

RESULTS AND DISCUSSIONS

(i) Nature of the experimental thrombi
Fig. 60.1A shows two sections of a fresh experimental clot. The clot consisted primarily of erythrocytes in a loose fibrin mesh with strands less than 200 nm thick. Some batches of more dense fibrin could be observed on the surface of the clot. Fig. 60.1B shows sections of a three-day old clot derived from the same

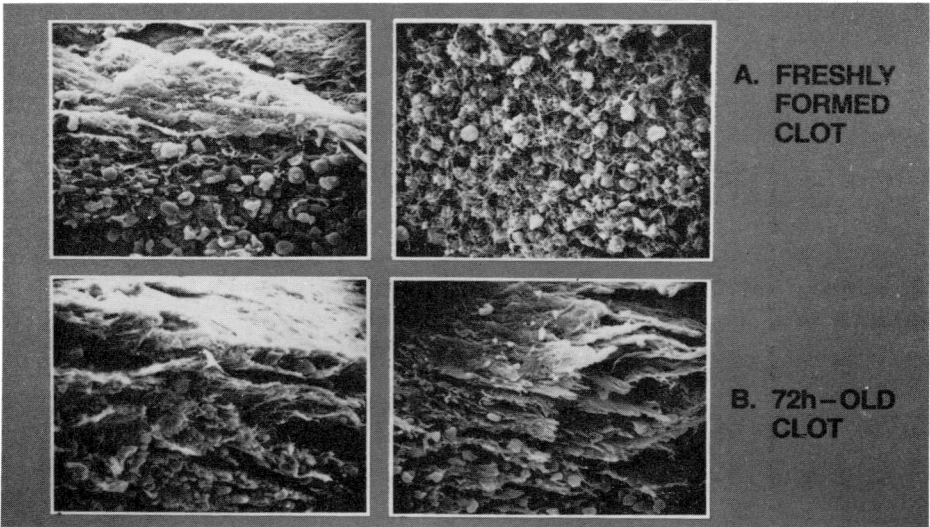

A. FRESHLY FORMED CLOT

B. 72h–OLD CLOT

Fig. 60.1 Scanning electron micrographs of experimental jugular vein clots. Magnification × 1250.

animal. The mesh was replaced by dense fibrin mats, particularly near the surface. The erythrocyte content was lower than in the fresh clots and some leukocytes were evident. The major difference between aged and fresh clots in this model appeared to be the greater quantity and density of fibrin fibrils in the former.

(ii) Controls and unmodified SK.plasmin
72h-old experimental thrombi showed good radiochemical stability over the next 24h (15% loss of label — Table 60.1). Venography (not shown) revealed that the thrombi remained occlusive over this period; in several cases there was evidence of distal thrombus extension and development of collateral circulation.

Table 60.1 Effects of single and multiple doses of BRL 26921, BRL 33575 and infusion of SK–Pm activator complex in a 72 h aged clot model of venous thrombosis in the dog

Agent	Total dose (μg/kg)	Dosing regimen (μg/kg)	Group size	Thrombolysis (mean $\pm$ SEM)	Selectivity ratio††
Saline control	—	Single dose	6	15 $\pm$ 5	—
BRL 26921	280	1 $\times$ 280	6	39 $\pm$ 8	0.8
BRL 26921	420	1 $\times$ 420	5	46 $\pm$ 10	0.8
BRL 33575	280	1 $\times$ 280	10	77 $\pm$ 6	2.4
BRL 33575	420	1 $\times$ 420	5	99 $\pm$ 1	2.3
BRL 26921	420	3 $\times$ 140*	6	86 $\pm$ 5	1.3
BRL 33575	420	2 $\times$ 210**	7	59 $\pm$ 13	2.3
BRL 33575	420	3 $\times$ 140**	4	95 $\pm$ 5†	2.8
SK–Pm	420	28 μg/kg/h for 15 h	4	29 $\pm$ 7	0.3

* 6 h intervals between doses
** 12 h intervals between doses
† Thrombolysis measured after 36 h (24 h in all other groups)
†† % radiochemical lysis/maximum fibrinogen depletion (%) during experiment

Preliminary experiments with SK (data not shown) indicated that the thrombi were resistant to this agent at 20,000 IU/kg. Therefore, an infusion of freshly prepared SK.human plasmin was studied. At 2800 IU/kg/h for 15h, the activator complex failed to give significant lysis (Fig. 60.2 and Table 60.1) despite producing severe fibrinogen depletion (Fig. 60.3).

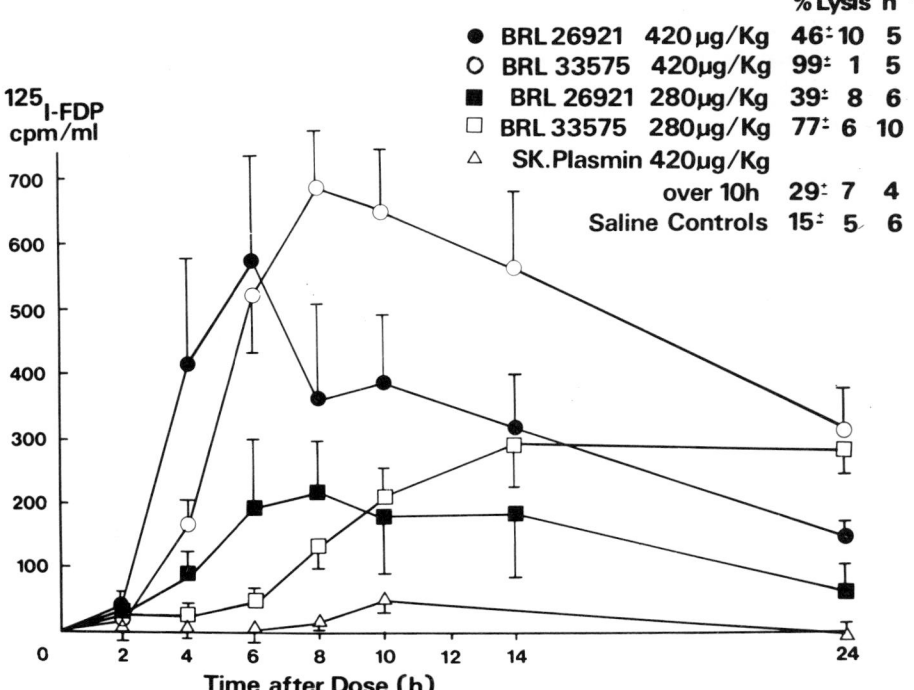

Fig. 60.2 Dog 72hr jugular vein model: FDP release following bolus dose BRL 26921 and BRL 33575 and SK.plasmin infusion.

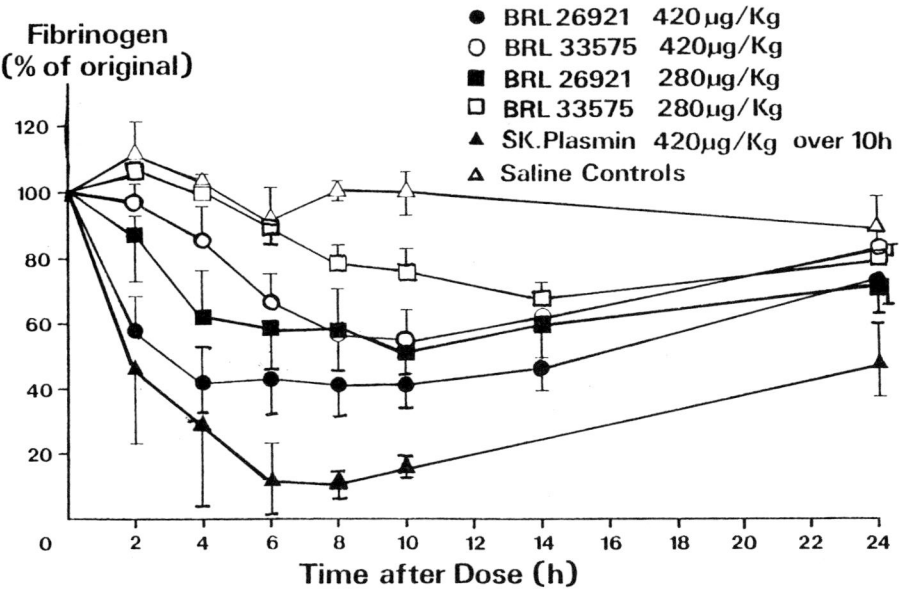

Fig. 60.3 Dog 72h jugular vein model: effect on fibrinogen: BRL 26921, BRL 33575 and SK.plasmin.

(iii) **BRL 26921**

This agent was given as a bolus injection at two doses, 280 and 420 μg/kg, the latter being equivalent to the total infused dose of SK.plasmin. BRL 26921 gave a significant release of ^{125}I-FDP from the experimental thrombi, peak levels being achieved 6–8h post-dose. Although BRL 26921 gave more lysis (measured radiochemically) than SK.plasmin, venographic evidence of recanalisation was only obtained when radiochemical lysis exceeded 80% (three dose regime — Table 60.1). The agent also produced significant fibrinogen depletion at the doses used (Fig. 60.3) although the apparent specificity could be increased by dividing the dose (Table 60.1).

(iv) **BRL 33575**

When given as single injections at 280 and 420 μg/kg, BRL 33575 gave significant ^{125}I-FDP release with peak levels respectively at 8 h and greater than 14h post-dose. This response is consistent with the relatively long plasma half-life of this acyl-enzyme in dogs (c. 7h — unpublished). At 420 μg/kg, venographic evidence of total vessel clearance was obtained in 4/5 dogs. BRL 33575 caused moderate fibrinogen depletion at lytic doses (Fig. 60.3) but its selectivity was greater than that of BRL 26921 and could be increased slightly by splitting the dose and increasing the treatment time (Table 60.1).

CONCLUSIONs

(i) Thread-supported experimental clots can be aged in the jugular veins of dogs to give a thrombus-like structure with dense layered fibrin. Such clots are resistant to lysis by the endogenous fibrinolytic system and by a regime of SK. human plasmin activator complex capable of inducing a systemic 'lytic state'.

(ii) These clots may be lysed by the active-site acylated SK.plasminogen complexes BRL 26921 and BRL 33575. The rate of lysis appears to be dose-dependent and related to the deacylation rate of the acyl-enzyme. The efficacy of BRL 26921 (but not BRL 33575) could be increased by dividing the dose.

(iii) Both acyl-enzymes were more selective (in terms of the ratio of fibrinolysis to fibrinogenolysis) than the unmodified complex. The slow-deacylating acyl-enzyme (BRL 33575) showed the higher selectivity.

(iv) On the basis of these results, the more appropriate agent for the treatment of established deep venous thrombosis in man would appear to be BRL 33575 given by intermittent bolus dosage at 12h intervals.

ACKNOWLEDGEMENTS

We are very grateful to Dr. A. J. Garman, Dr G. R. Parish and Mr J. K. Warrack for the electron microscopy study and to Miss V. McCartney for technical assistance.

REFERENCES

Burmester H B C, Aulton K, Horsfield G I 1970 The evaluation of a rapid method for the determination of plasma fibrinogen. Journal of Clinical Pathology 23: 43–46
Dupe R J, English P D, Smith R A G, Green J 1983 The activity of an acylated streptokinase.plasminogen complex (BRL 26921) in dog models of thrombosis. In: Davidson J F, Bachmann F, Bouvier C A, Kruithof E K O (eds) Progress in fibrinolysis. Churchill Livingstone, Edinburgh, vol 6, p 240–244
Dupe R J, English P D, Smith R A G, Green J 1984 Acyl-enzymes as thrombolytic agents in dog models of venous thrombosis and pulmonary embolism. Thombosis and Haemostasis (Stuttgart) 51: 248–253
Smith R A G, Dupe R J, English P D, Green J 1982 Acyl-enzymes as thrombolytic agents in a rabbit model of venous thrombosis. Thrombosis and Haemostasis (Stuttgart) 47: 269–274

61. Experience with the streptokinase-plasminogen-complex BRL 26921 in the treatment of deep vein thrombosis

G. Trübestein, J. Schatz, M. Ludwig, Th. Harder and N. Müller

Recently an acylated form of the streptokinase-plasminogen-complex has been synthesised (BRL 26921*) and in animal studies this exhibited a potent fibrinolytic activity, without the fibrinogenolytic effects of streptokinase. This specificity was explained as due to binding of the inactive acylated complex to thrombus fibrin, followed by spontaneous deacylation to form a plasminogen activator on the thrombus, allowing a local rather than systemic lysis (1,2,3).

In the years 1982 and 1983, 18 patients with deep vein thrombosis were treated with the streptokinase-plasminogen-complex BRL 26921 (SKPLC) in the Medical University Policlinic of Bonn. 16 patients had an acute, 3–5 day old deep vein thrombosis, 2 patients had a subacute, 10 and 14 day old deep vein thrombosis. Two groups were formed. Group I, including 11 patients received 15 mg SKPLC daily, group II, including 7 patients received 30 mg SKPLC daily.

Two standardized dosage schemata were used. Patients of group I received an initial dose of 5 mg SKPLC and a maintenance dose of 15 mg SKPLC/24h, administered as 5 mg at an 8 hours interval. Patients of group II received an initial dose of 10 mg SKPLC and a maintenance dose of 30 mg SKPLC/24h, administered as 10 mg at an 8 hours interval. Heparin was added simultaneously after 24 hours when the thrombin time was less than 3 times of the normal.

Apart from the daily controls of blood count and urinalysis, the fibrinogen (method according to Vermylen), the reptilase time, the PTT and the thrombin time were determined. Moreover we examined the Quick prothrombin test, the thrombelastogram and the factors II, V, VIII and X. Plasma was frozen for examination of plasminogen and alpha$_2$-antiplasmin. The thrombelastogram and the factors analysis were examined every 24 hours, all other parameters were examined at an 8 hours interval.

A phlebography was performed in all patients before starting fibrinolytic treatment. First control phlebographies were usually performed after 3 days of SKPLC treatment; the second control phlebography was performed after 6 days or at the end of therapy. The duration of treatment was between 2 and 7 days, and in 2 patients with bleeding complications 1 and 2 days.

In group I, 3 patients and in group II 2 patients had a bleeding complication limiting the fibrinolytic therapy.

*Beecham Pharmaceuticals Research Division, G.B.

246

The evaluation of the hemostaseological parameters showed in both the groups a sharp drop of the plasminogen within the first 24 hours to 33% and 23% respectively staying depressed during the treatment period. The fibrinogen dropped from 5.9 g/l and 4.8 g/l to 1.3 g/l in both the groups within the first 24 hours and stayed depressed during the treatment period. The reptilase time increased within the first 24 hours and was clearly prolonged during the treatment period. The alpha$_2$-antiplasmin also dropped sharply in both the groups and was continuously decreased over the treatment period.

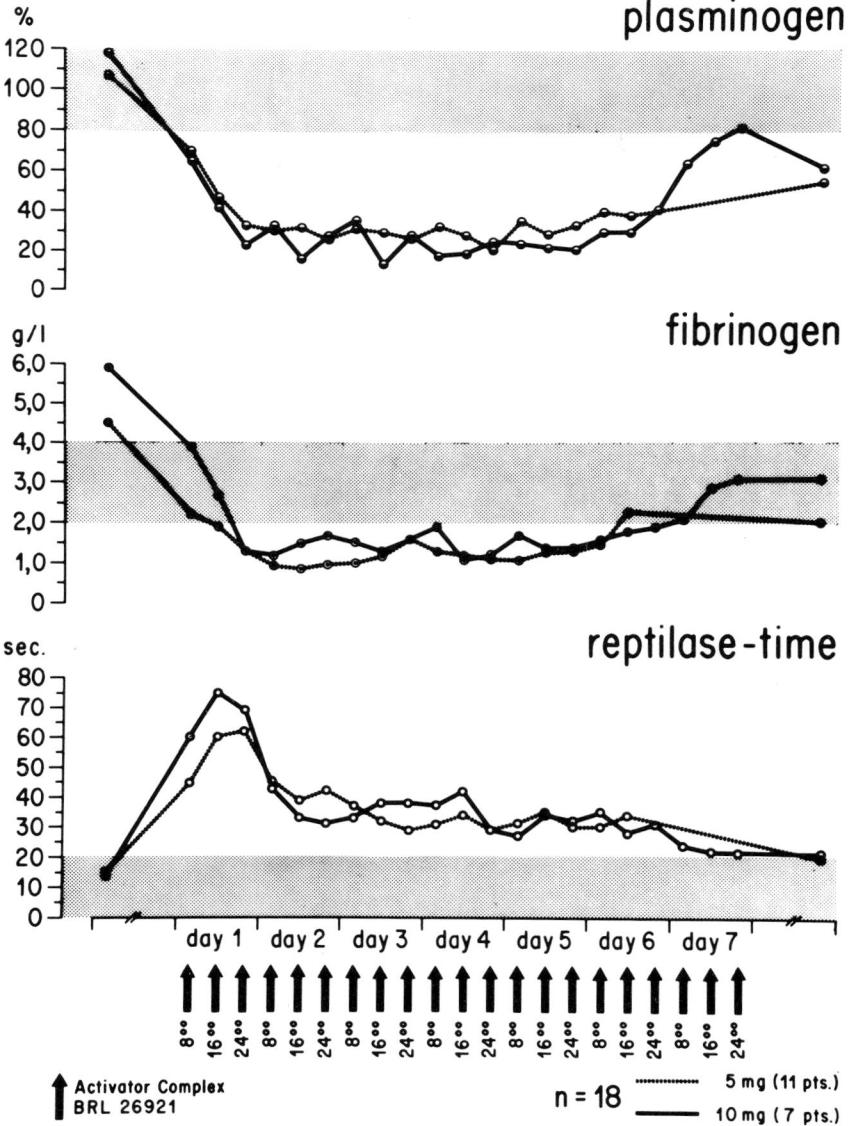

Fig. 61.1 Plasminogen, fibrinogen and reptilase time during the two dosage schemata with BRL 26921.

In both the groups there was only a small variation and no significant difference was found for the 4 parameters. Other parameters as the Quick prothrombin test, the factors II, V, and VIII showed a smaller decrease too.

RESULTS

In the 11 patients of group I the thromboses could be dissolved completely in 5 patients and partially in 4 patients. 2 patients of group I showed no improvement in the phlebograms. In the 7 patients of group II the thromboses could be dissolved completely in 4 patients and partially in 1 patient. 2 patients of group II showed no improvement in the phlebograms.

CONCLUSION

Summarizing we can state, that the streptokinase plasminogen complex BRL 26921 is effective in the treatment of deep vein thrombosis. But, in spite of its high affinity to thrombus fibrin a clear systemic effect on the fibrinolytic system was found. A new compound BRL 33575 with a high affinity to thrombus fibrin and a slow deacylation in order to produce a less stronger systemic effect on the fibrinolytic system is now ready for clinical trials.

REFERENCES

1. Smith R A G, Dupe R J, English P D, Green J 1981 Fibrinolysis with acyl-enzymes: a new approach to thrombolytic therapy. Nature 290 (5806): 505–508
2. Prowse C V, Hornsey V, Ruckley C V, Boulton F E 1982 A comparison of acylated streptokinase-plasminogen complex and streptokinase in healthy volunteers. Thrombosis Haemostasis 47 (2): 132–135
3. Staniforth D H, Smith R A G, Hibbs M 1983 Streptokinase and anisoylated streptokinase plasminogen complex. Their action on haemostasis in human volunteers. European Journal of Clinical Pharmacology 24: 751–756

62. Thrombolysis with acylated enzymes in deep vein and arterial thrombosis

F. Duckert, B. Lämmle, G. A. Marbet, G. Noll, A. Lohri, P. Huber, L. Biland, L. K. Widmer, R. Ritz and H. E. Schmitt

INTRODUCTION

To reduce the hazards of thrombolytic therapy Smith et al (1981) have introduced the acyl-enzymes. The acylated streptokinase-plasminogen complex (SK-Plg) should have enough time to attach itself to the thrombus fibrin thus developing its thrombolytic action in situ after hydrolysis of the acyl-group and reducing systemic fibrinolysis. BRL 26921 (BRL = Beecham Research Laboratory, England) and BRL 33575 are acylated with a p-anisoyl residue and p-amino benzoic acid with deacylation rates of $t_{\frac{1}{2}} = 44$ min and $t_{\frac{1}{2}} = 17$ hrs respectively. BRL 33575 has a plasma $t_{\frac{1}{2}}$ of 5–8hrs and should be less fibrinolytic.

TREATMENT

The patients have been treated by 12 hourly injections of 5–10 mg BRL 26921. Generally, doses of 5–10mg BRL 33575 were given preferably as a short infusion to avoid side effects, because this dose represents an equivalent of 310 000U SK. All patients were concomitantly anticoagulated with 12 500 to 35 000U Heparin in 24 hrs. A patient with high SK tolerance has received 25 mg as starting dose and as little as 2.5 mg have been infused once to another patient because of a high fibrinolytic response. With BRL 26921 exclusively patients with deep vein thrombosis (DVT) have been treated (Lämmle et al 1984). Whereas 7 DVT patients (results reported in only 5) 1 with portal vein thrombosis and 2 with arterial occlusions have received BRL 33575.

CLINICAL RESULTS

The segment by segment vein evaluation shows a clearance in 52% with BRL 26921 and 30% with BRL 33575. It is naturally too early to make any comparison at this stage. In DVT the clinical effects of BRL 33575 for individual patients were first disappointing (Table 62.1). However, treatment of additional patients, not included in this first report has been a complete success. The patient with the portal vein thrombosis was clinically greatly improved.

Table 62.1 Effects of thrombolysis in patients with deep vein thrombosis

	Complete success	Partial success	No effect/ worsened
BRL 26921	5/12	3/12	4/12
BRL 33575	0/5	3/5	2/5
p-Plasmin-Streptokinase	47/101	31/101	23/101

In 2 patients treated with BRL 26921 a thrombus extension was observed. This adverse effect was not seen with BRL 33575. Extension of thrombi was very rare with the sequential treatment porcine plasmin and streptokinase (Marbet et al 1982, a and b).

Today we have treated only 2 patients with arterial occlusions. In one a 53cm long totally occluded segment was fully reopened in about 36 hrs. In the second patient the treatment was stopped due to bleeding (Table 62.2). These results clearly show that BRL 33575 is able to clear thrombosed vessels. It is much too early for a comparison with other types of thrombolytic treatment.

Table 62.2 Side effects of thrombolysis

	Haemorrhagic complications				Incompatibility reaction		
	Macro- haematuria	Cutaneous haematoma	Other organ	Intra- cranial	Temp. $>38°C$	Catheter phelebitis	Headache muscular pain
BRL 26921 n = 12	1	4	0	0	9	5	1
BRL 33575 n = 8	0	0	2*	0	7	1	2**
p–Plasmin→SK n = 114	30	29	14	1	52	16	33

* At an arterial puncture site and sternocleidomastoid muscle bleeding
** Leucopenia in one case before and accentuated during treatment. Granulocytes were always sufficient.

The side effects with the acylated compounds are different from those seen with streptokinase (Table 62.2). Bleeding is certainly less frequent especially macrohematuria. Bleeding in the sternocleidomastoid muscle was the cause of premature stop, but haemorrhages at unusual locations are occasionally seen during thrombolysis.

In opposition the incompatibility reactions seem more frequent, for example a temperature rise above 38°C, than in the sequential treatment with porcine plasmin followed by low dose streptokinase (Marbert et al 1982b). All patients recovered rapidly after cessation of treatment. These results show that BRL derivatives are efficient lytic agents with less disturbing side effects than streptokinase itself.

LABORATORY RESULTS

The point of interest with acylated enzymes is the presence or absence of systemic lytic effects.

250

Systemic fibrinolytic effects cannot be avoided. They are less pronounced than with SK alone or with porcine plasmin followed by streptokinase. The fibrinogen concentration measured with a functional assay (Clauss, 1957) reaches low values, as well as plasminogen and particularly α_2-antiplasmin, probably due to the higher molar concentration of plasminogen (Table 62.3). There is a close parallelism in the decrease of concentration, respectively activity of the measured parameters. The reduction is much less marked than with the sequential treatment. The smallest effect is seen with BRL 33575 (Table 62.3) which is clearly less fibrinogenolytic.

Table 62.3 Behaviour of fibrinogen, plasminogen and α_2-antiplasmin during thrombolysis

	Fibrinogen		Plasminogen		α_2-antiplasmin	
	before	during[1]	before	during[1]	before	during[1]
BRL 26921 n = 12	3.25	0.57	113[2]	30[2]	96[3]	26[3]
BRL 33575 n = 8	3.60	1.32	113	65	103	31
p–Plasmin SK[4] n = 114	—	0.36	116	10	95	10

[1] mean values during treatment; [2] values for 9 patients only; [3] values for 11 patients; [4] Marbet et al, 1982a

It must be pointed out that the response to the acylated compounds varies from patient to patient. The reason for the individual variations has not yet been found.

In vitro experiments with BRL 33575 confirm the very slow deacylation rate of 17 hrs in buffer which is not modified in human plasma (Beecham, unpublished data). At the same time they demonstrate that the very slow deacylation releases traces of a potent SK-plasminogen complex able to activate plasminogen. The large amounts of SK (5 mg BRL 33575 are equivalent to 160 000 SK U) are able to completely neutralize SK antibodies which thus do not interfere with the deacylated compounds.

The acylated streptokinase-plasminogen complexes are very promising lytic agents. The choice of the acyl group will depend on the target of thrombolysis, for instance DVT or pulmonary embolism.

REFERENCES

Clauss A 1957 Gerinnungsphysiologische Schnellmethode zur Bestimmung des Fibrinogens. Acta Haematologica 17: 237–246
Lämmle B, Duckert F, Noll G, Lohri A, Marbet G A, Huber P, Biland L, Schmitt H E 1984 Thrombolyse mit acylierten Streptokinase-Plasminogen-Komplexen (BRL 26921 und BRL 33575). In: Beck E A, Duckert F, Lüscher E F, Straub P W, van de Loo J (eds) Thrombose und Haemostase Forschung 1984. Schattauer Verlag, Stuttgart
Marbet G A, Eichlisberger R, Duckert F, da Silva M A, Biland L, Widmer L K, Ritz R, Schmitt H E 1982a Sequential treatment of deep leg vein thrombosis with porcine plasmin and low dose streptokinase. Thrombosis and Haemostasis 48: 190–195

Marbet G A, Eichlisberger R, Duckert F, Ritz R, da Silva M A, Biland L, Widmer L K, Schmitt H E 1982b Side effects of thrombolytic treatment with porcine plasmin and low dose streptokinase. Thrombosis and Haemostasis 48: 196–200

Smith R A G, Dupe R J, English D P, Green J 1981 Fibrinolysis with acyl-enzymes: a new approach to thrombolytic therapy. Nature 290: 505–508

63. Thrombolytic effects of acylated urokinase

F. Markwardt, H-P. Klöcking and J. Stürzebecher

During the development of synthetic, low molecular weight inhibitors of serine proteinases a series of 4-amidino-phenyl benzoates have been found to act as temporary inhibitors of trypsin, plasmin, thrombin, kallikrein and urokinase (Markwardt et al 1972, 1974, 1984; Tanizawa et al 1981; Smith, 1983). 4-Amidinophenyl esters of arylcarboxylic acids behave like substrates of trypsin-like enzymes but acylation is much more rapid than deacylation. The result is accumulation of a comparatively stable acyl-enzyme. On deacylation the active enzyme is reactivated. In plasma, an acyl-enzyme behaves like an inert form of the enzyme and is protected from being inactivated by natural plasma inhibitors.

This principle has been made use of in the development of acyl-plasmin and acylated streptokinase-plasmin activator complex as delivery systems for fibrinolytic agents in vivo (Smith et al 1981; Markwardt et al 1983a, b). We used this concept for preparation of acylated urokinase. The thrombolytic effect of the urokinase preparation was studied in an artificial circulating system and in experimental venous thrombosis.

MATERIALS AND METHODS

4-Amidinophenyl esters of substituted benzoic acids were prepared according to Wagner & Horn (1973). The urokinase preparation used was Ukidan® (Urokinase Serono, molecular weight 54,000). The enzymatic activity was determined by means of cleavage of the chromogenic peptide substrate Z-Gly-Pro-Arg-pNA (Boehringer, Mannheim).

Acyl-urokinase was prepared by incubation of urokinase with amidinophenyl ester. The mixture was dialysed against 0.154 mol/l NaCl (pH 3.0).

The in vitro experiments were carried out in an artificial circulating system composed of a radioactive thrombus consisting of a ^{125}I-fibrinogen-labelled human plasma clot suspended in human plasma according to Matsuo et al (1981). Dissolution of the plasma clot was followed by continuous measurement of radioactivity in plasma. The degree of thrombolysis was estimated from the released radioactivity and expressed as per cent of that of the original thrombus.

Plasma samples were taken before the addition of activator and at 1 h intervals for 4 h. Fibrinogen and fibrin(ogen) degradation products in the plasma samples were measured as described previously (Markwardt et al 1979), plasminogen and α_2-antiplasmin, as described by Mussoni et al (1979) and Teger-Nilsson et al (1977).

The thrombolytic effect in vivo was studied in rabbits with a radioactive thrombus produced in the infra-renal segment of the inferior vena cava as described by Dupe et al (1981). The radioactivity over the occluded venous segment was measured by a scintillation probe fitted with a collimator adapted to the anatomical conditions. Changes in the impulse rate were recorded. The degree of thrombolysis was calculated as the difference in isotope content of the thrombus before and after the injection of activator.

RESULTS AND DISCUSSION

By the use of 4-amidinophenyl benzoates acyl residues can be introduced into urokinase (UK) active site. The deacylation rate constant of the acyl-enzymes increases with the electron accepting potency of the benzoic acid substituent. Therefore, a variety of acyl-urokinase intermediates with different deacylation rates can be designed.

For thrombolytic studies benzoyl urokinase (BUK) was chosen. The residual activity of the acyl-enzyme preparation was about 5 per cent of that of the original enzyme, while almost complete reactivation as a result of deacylation was observed on incubation of the acyl-enzyme at pH 7.5. The time course of inactivation and reactivation of BUK is shown in Figure 63.1.

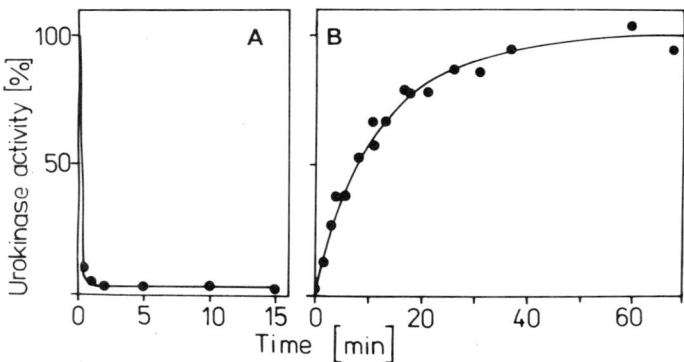

Fig. 63.1 Time course of inactivation of urokinase (10,000 IU/ml) by 0.3 mmol/l of 4-amidinophenyl benzoate (A) and reactivation of benzoyl urokinase (B) (4500 IU/ml) at pH 7.5.

BUK is reactivated in plasma. Therefore, thrombolysis in the artificial system may be induced by UK and BUK (Fig. 63.2).

Table 63.1 shows the extent of thrombolysis induced by different amounts of UK and BUK. Significant thrombolysis was obtained with 50 IU or more of UK or with 10 IU or more of BUK/ml plasma. From these experiments it is concluded that the thrombolytic effect of BUK is twice that of UK.

254

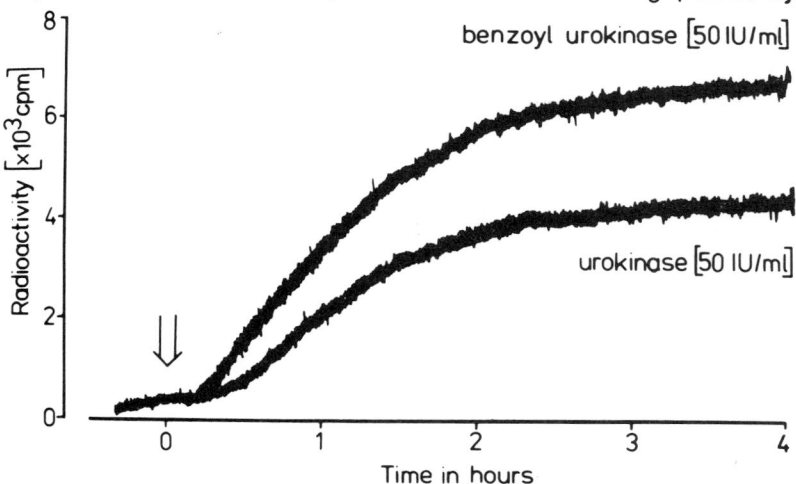

Fig. 63.2 Thrombolysis of radioactive human plasma clots induced by urokinase and benzoyl urokinase (50 IU/ml plasma) in the circulating plasma system.

Table 63.1 Extent of thrombolysis of radioactive human plasma clots in the artificial circulating system

	n	Thrombolysis [+] (%)
Control	3	16.6 ± 2.2
Urokinase 10 IU/ml	3	9.2 ± 6.3
Benzoyl urokinase 10 IU/ml	4	28.6 ± 3.3
Urokinase 50 IU/ml	2	55.6 ± 10.9
Benzoyl urokinase 50 IU/ml	3	85.0 ± 9.1
Urokinase 200 IU/ml	2	90.5 ± 2.3
Benzoyl urokinase 200 IU/ml	2	92.6 ± 2.0

[+] after 4 hours

Changes of the main fibrinolytic parameters in the circulating system are shown in Figures 63.3a-d. Activation of the fibrinolytic system was evident from the decrease in plasminogen as a consequence of its conversion to plasmin and from the consumption of antiplasmin. The fibrinolytic effect was shown by formation of degradation products which were considered to be formed from the fibrin clot since the fibrinogen level did not drop significantly.

The comparatively pronounced thrombolytic effect of the acyl form of the enzyme (BUK) may be due to the fact that irreversible interactions with plasma inhibitors are blocked by acylation and that the acylated enzyme retains its affinity for fibrin.

Comparison of equivalent doses of UK and BUK in a model of venous thrombosis showed that the acyl form of the enzyme was significantly more active than the free enzyme.

The release of radioactivity from labelled thrombi suggested that a bolus of

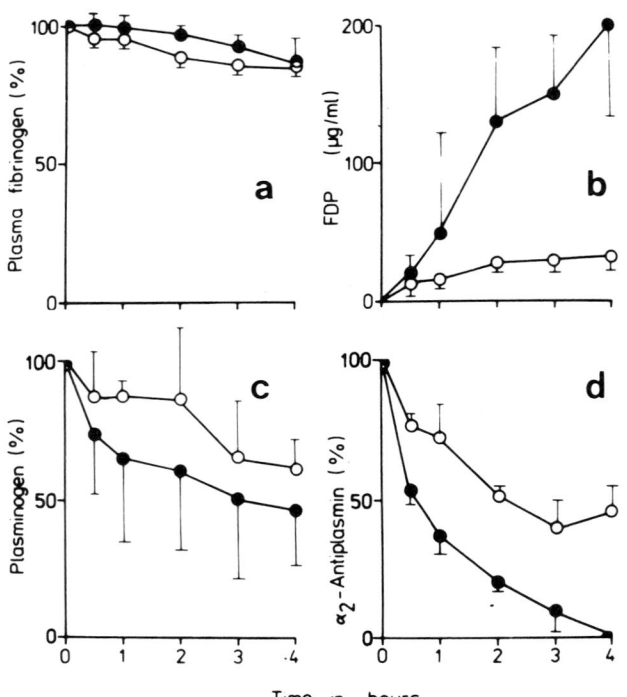

Fig. 63.3 Changes of fibrinolytic parameters in the artificial circulating system induced by 50 IU urokinase (O) and benzoyl urokinase (●) per ml plasma. a) Fibrinogen, b) fibrin degradation productions, c) plasminogen, d) α_1-antiplasmin.

both UK and BUK produced fibrinolysis of like duration. Due to its relatively rapid deacylation ($t_\frac{1}{2}$ about 8 min) BUK does not exert a markedly delayed fibrinolytic action which has been shown with other acylated fibrinolytic enzymes (Smith et al 1982). By the correct choice of acyl groups the deacylation rate of acylated UK can be modified as to meet the specific requirements of a delivery system. Further experiments with acyl-urokinase preparations from which the enzyme is comparatively slowly generated have to be done.

REFERENCES

Dupe R J, English P D, Smith R A G, Green J 1981 The evaluation of plasmin and streptokinase activator complexes in a new rabbit model of venous thrombosis. Thrombosis and Haemostasis 46: 528–534
Markwardt F, Drawert J, Perlewitz J 1979 Pharmakologische Beeinflussung einer sekundären generalisierten Fibrinolyse. Acta Biologica et Medica Germanica 38: 1201–1209
Markwardt F, Drawert J, Walsmann P 1974 Synthetic, low molecular weight inhibitors of serum kallikrein. Biochemical Pharmacology 23: 2247–2256
Markwardt F, Nowak G, Stürzebecher J 1983a Experimental therapy of microthrombosis with acyl-plasmin. Thrombosis and Haemostasis 50: Abstr No 1208
Markwardt F, Nowak G, Stürzebecher J 1983b Experimental therapy of disseminated intravascular coagulation in the lung by fibrinolytic agents. In: Davidson J F, Bachmann F, Bouvier C A, Kruithof E K O (eds) Progress in fibrinolysis. Churchill Livingstone, Edinburgh, vol 6, p 249–253

Markwardt F, Stürzebecher J, Müller H 1984 Acyl-kallikrein — a delivery system for the kinin liberating enzyme. Experimentia in press

Markwardt F, Wagner G, Walsmann P, Horn H, Stürzebecher J 1972 Inhibition of trypsin and thrombin by amidinophenyl esters of aromatic carboxylic acids. Acta Biologica et Medica Germanica 28: K19-K25

Matsuo O, Collen D, Verstraete M 1981 On the fibrinolytic and thrombolytic properties of active-site p-anisoylated streptokinase-plasminogen complex (BRL 26921). Thrombosis Research 24: 347-358

Mussoni L, Roczka E, Chmielewska J, Donati M B, Latallo Z S 1979 Plasminogen assay in rabbit, rat and mouse plasma using the chromogenic substrate S-2251. Thrombosis Research 15: 341-349

Smith R A G 1983 Acyl-enzymes as fibrinolytic prodrugs. In: Davidson J F, Bachmann F, Bouvier C A, Kruithof E K O (eds) Progress in fibrinolysis. Churchill Livingstone, Edinburgh, vol 6, p 232-239

Smith R A G, Dupe R J, English P D, Green J 1981 Fibrinolysis with acyl-enzymes: a new approach to thrombolytic therapy. Nature 290: 505-508

Smith R A G, Dupe R J, English P D, Green J 1983 Acyl-enzymes as thrombolytic agents in a rabbit model of venous thrombosis. Thrombosis and Haemostasis 47: 269-274

Tanizawa K, Nakayama H, Fujioka T, Nozawa M, Nakaona M, Kanaoka Y 1982 Inverse substrates: novel synthetic substrates for trypsin and related enzymes. Folia Haematologica (Leipzig) 109: 61-66

Teger-Nilsson A-C, Friberger P, Gyzander E 1977 Determination of a new rapid antiplasmin in human blood by using a plasmin specific tripeptide substrate. The Scandinavian Journal of Clinical and Laboratory Investigation 37: 403-409

Wagner G, Horn H 1973 Synthese antiproteolytisch wirksamer Arylcarbon-, Aralkylcarbon- und Arylsulfonsäureester von Amidinophenolen. Pharmazie 28: 427-431

64. Thrombolysis with acyl enzyme derivatives

J. F. Davidson and I. D. Walker

INTRODUCTION

Streptokinase and urokinase have been available for the past two decades but despite extensive clinical use these two thrombolytic agents have had limitations. The main limitation has been the systemic activation of fibrinolysis which is produced if thrombolysis is to be achieved and this is frequently associated with a bleeding tendency. Also streptokinase is antigenic and urokinase expensive.

Recent years have seen considerable advances in our understanding of the molecular biology of fibrinolysis. These developments have encouraged investigators to seek other safer means of achieving thrombolysis. As it became clear that the molecular mechanisms of thrombolysis were to a degree self-limiting outwith the immediate environment of the thrombus, investigators sought to utilise these concepts to achieve localised pharmacological thrombolysis.

Attempts were made to 'enhance' fibrinolysis. Numerous chemical compounds had been shown in vitro to bring about thrombolysis but this could not be translated to in vivo. Only the anabolic steroids offered some promise. The anabolic steroids as a group and stanozolol in particular were shown to 'enhance' fibrinolysis. The problem was, was this of any therapeutic relevance. This effect of anabolic steroids has been known for more than ten years. So far clear evidence of clinical benefit from this form of therapy is awaited.

More recently intense effort has gone into the development and production of tissue plasminogen activator (t-PA). Recent advances in recombinant technology have made this possible. This 'natural' t-PA has great promise for fibrinolysis. The outcome of clinical studies with t-PA is eagerly awaited.

Also in recent years attempts have been made to improve existing thrombolytic agents to make them inactive in the general circulation and able to bind selectively to fibrin. The objective was to produce a thrombolytic agent which would 'target' onto fibrin without systemic activation of fibrinolysis.

Smith et al (1981) and Smith (1983) have addressed this problem and have endeavoured to produce such an agent. They took a series of enzymes with thromboytic activity and modified them chemically to enable them 'target' on fibrin without significant systemic effects. This was achieved by acylation of the

258

active serine site without damaging the fibrin binding properties. In this way the acyl enzyme derivatives were developed for fibrinolysis. Several acyl enzyme derivatives were prepared each with different deacylation kinetics and thus different physiological characteristics.

THE ACYL ENZYME DERIVATIVES

The currently available acyl enzyme derivatives are shown in Table 64.1. The three compounds BRL 26920, BRL 26921 and BRL 33575 were developed at the Beecham Research Laboratories in England. The acyl-plasmin derivative has been studied in vitro and in animals. The two acyl-SK-plasminogen activator complexes, BRL 26921 and BRL 33575 have now been studied in man. Almost all the clinical experience to date is with BRL 26921. Acyl-urokinase has been studied in vitro and in animals (Markwardt et al 1984).

Table 64.1 Acyl-enzyme derivatives

acyl-plasmin	:	BRL 26920
acyl-SK-plasminogen activator complex	:	BRL 26921
		BRL 33575
acyl-urokinase		

ACYL-SK-PLASMINOGEN ACTIVATOR COMPLEX — BRL 26921

BRL 26921 is supplied as a freeze dried powder in vials containing 5 mg of the complex together with albumin, D-mannitol and L-lysine. 30 mg is approximately equivalent to 1 million units streptokinase activity and when administered as an iv bolus this 30 mg releases the equivalent of 18 000 units streptokinase activity per minute. The compound has a half-life in vivo of 1–2 hours and a deacylation half-life of 44 minutes (Smith, 1983). See Table 64.2. When deacylated, its clearance in vivo is the same as streptokinase.

Table 64.2 BRL series acyl-enzyme derivatives

BRL 26921	—	$t_{\frac{1}{2}}$ deacylation	=	44 min in vivo
	—	$t_{\frac{1}{2}}$ activity	=	1–2 hrs in vivo
BRL 33575	—	$t_{\frac{1}{2}}$ deacylation	=	17 hrs in vivo
	—	$t_{\frac{1}{2}}$ activity	=	5–8 hrs in vivo

This compound has therefore relatively rapid deacylation kinetics and lends itself to the situation where fast lysis is required. It has therefore been evaluated in acute myocardial infarction and to a lesser extent in deep vein thrombosis and in pulmonary embolism.

BRL 26921 in acute myocardial infarction

To date more than 80 cases of acute myocardial infarction have been treated in a number of centres by the intra-coronary route. Doses varying from 5mg to 30mg have been used as a slow intra-coronary bolus given within several hours of infarction. Where the dose has been between 15mg and 30mg, reperfusion rates similar to that achieved by streptokinase given in a similar manner have been attained.

More recently more than 120 cases of acute myocardial infarction have been treated in a number of centres by the iv bolus method. Again doses ranging from 5 mg to 30 mg have been used and again the higher doses have achieved good reperfusion rates. Latterly a dose of 30 mg has been used and this in several centres has achieved reperfusion rates of around 90%.

At the present time therefore it seems that a 30 mg iv dose of BRL 26921 given within a few hours of acute myocardial infarction will achieve reperfusion in the majority of cases.

BRL 26921 in deep vein thrombosis

To date more than 60 cases of deep vein thrombosis have been treated in a number of centres with iv doses ranging from 5 mg to 10 mg twice or three times a day for up to five days. The number of cases treated by an individual regimen is small but if the results are taken overall they would appear to be similar to that which can be achieved by streptokinase.

BRL 26921 in pulmonary embolism

The experience in pulmonary embolism is more limited. More than 20 cases have been treated in several centres in doses ranging from 5 mg to 10 mg twice or three times daily iv or via a pulmonary artery catheter for up to three days. Some good results have been obtained but the data is insufficient to draw even tentative conclusions.

ACYL-SK-PLASMINOGEN ACTIVATOR COMPLEX — BRL 33575

BRL 33575 is presented in a similar fashion to BRL 26921. Its kinetics are however quite different and are much 'slower' (Table 64.2). Its half-life for deacylation is 17 hours in vivo which means if it is not bound to fibrin it will circulate for a long time in its inactive form.

With these relatively slow deacylation kinetics this compound seems well suited to the treatment of venous thrombosis. Clinical experience is so far very limited and is insufficient to allow comment on its efficacy.

CONCLUSION

The acyl enzyme derivatives are a promising innovation in the treatment of thrombosis. The compound most extensively studied, BRL 26921, holds promise for the treatment of acute myocardial infarction. If given iv in a bolus dose of 30 mg, reperfusion can be achieved in the majority of early acute myocardial infarcts. At this dose of 30 mg, systemic activation of fibrinolysis is inevitable — a little disappointing because lack of systemic activation was what was sought initially. Nevertheless at this dose level, haemorrhagic complications appear to be unusual. Doses of 7.5 mg and below do not cause systemic fibrinolysis but fail to achieve the same level of therapeutic efficacy as the higher doses. The results of controlled trials of BRL 26921 in acute myocardial infarction are awaited with great interest.

BRL 33575 has much slower deacylation kinetics and seems well suited to the treatment of DVT. With these kinetics it is to be expected that thrombolysis can be achieved without significant systemic activation. The early clinical studies with BRL 33575 which are under way at the present time are awaited with great interest.

While recombinant t-PA has been held out as the great hope for thrombolytic therapy the acyl enzyme derivatives would appear to have quite a significant role to play in the thrombolytic therapy of the future.

REFERENCES

Markwardt F, Klocking H P, Sturzebecher J 1984 Thrombolytic effects of acylated urokinase. Haemostasis 14:55
Smith R A G 1983 Acyl-enzymes as pro-drugs. In: Davidson J F, Bachmann F, Bouvier C A, Kruithof E K O (eds) Progress in fibrinolysis. Churchill Livingstone, Edinburgh, vol 6 p 232–9
Smith R A G, Dupe R J, English P D, Green J 1981 Fibrinolysis with acyl enzymes: a new approach to thrombolytic therapy. Nature 290: 505–8

Section 9
FIBRINOLYSIS AND TUMOURS

65. Effect of estrogens and antiestrogens on plasminogen activator and progesterone receptor levels of MCF-7 human breast cancer cells

W. F. Mangel and
B. S. Katzenellenbogen

INTRODUCTION

Plasminogen activator activity is induced by estrogens in estrogen-responsive cells (Kneifel et al 1982; Peltz et al 1983; Katzenellenbogen et al 1984). trans-Hydroxytamoxifen, a triphenylethylene antiestrogen, is widely used in the treatment of endocrine-responsive human breast cancer (Fisher et al 1981). Here we compare in human breast cancer cells, the effect of estradiol and of two geometric isomers of tamoxifen and of hydroxytamoxifen on the levels of plasminogen activator activity and of progesterone receptor, a widely used marker for estrogen action (Eckert and Katzenellenbogen, 1982). For these studies we used the MCF-7 cell line, a line that is frequently studied as a model for estrogen-responsive human breast cancer. The results indicated that cell-associated plasminogen activator activity may serve as a good marker for estrogen/antiestrogen in human breast cancer cells.

RESULTS

Plasminogen activator

Plasminogen activator activity was stimulated by low, physiological concentrations of estradiol in MCF-7 cells, Figure 65.1. Maximal stimulation, about 4-fold over control cells, was achieved with 10^{-9} M estradiol. Time course studies (data not shown) indicated that optimal stimulation of plasminogen activator activity by estradiol occurred on Day 1 of hormone treatment and remained constant through Day 8. cis-Tamoxifen stimulation of plasminogen activator activity also peaked on Day 1 but remained constant only through Day 4, after which it began to decrease substantially. Because of these observations, all studies with the tamoxifen derivatives were performed after a 4-day exposure to hormone. cis-Tamoxifen behaved as an estrogen, albeit a weak estrogen. At the highest concentration tested, 3×10^{-6} M, stimulation was about 75% that maximally observed with estradiol. trans-Tamoxifen, trans-hydroxytamoxifen and cis-hydroxytamoxifen markedly suppressed plasminogen activator activity below the levels exhibited by the control cells. In addition, these three compounds

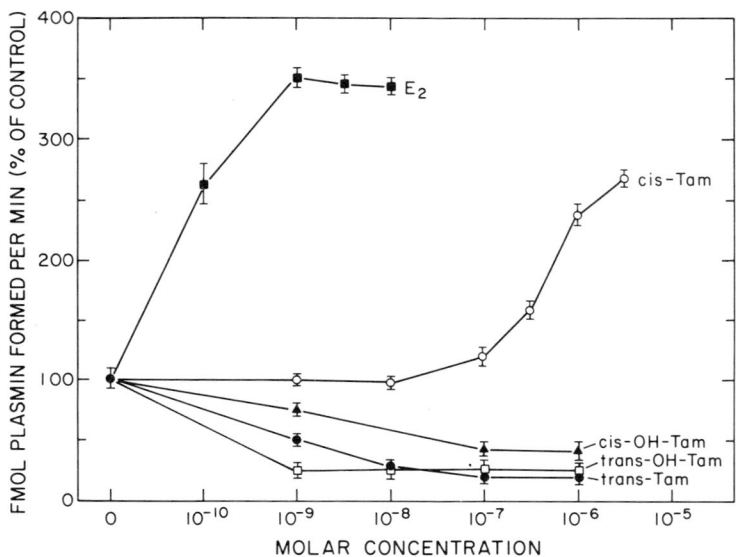

Fig. 65.1 Effect of the cis- and trans-isomers of tamoxifen and hydroxytamoxifen and estradiol (E_2) on the plasminogen activator activity of MCF-7 cells. Cells were incubated with the indicated concentrations of compound for 4 days, with fresh media and hormone renewed every 48 hr. Cells were then harvested, distributed to microwells, and assayed for plasminogen activator activity as described in Katzenellenbogen et al 1984. Values represent the initial velocity of the reaction in fmol of plasmin formed per min and are expressed as the percentage of control of 3 separate determinations. The control value was 1.1 ± 0.1 fmol of plasmin formed per min. cis-Tam, cis-tamoxifen; cis-OH-Tam, cis-hydroxytamoxifen, trans-OH-Tam, trans-hydroxytamoxifen; trans-tam, transtamoxifen. Bars, S. E.

at 10^{-8} to 10^{-6} M suppressed to very low levels, about 10–25%, the stimulation of plasminogen activator activity induced by 10^{-9} M estradiol or by 10^{-6} M cis-tamoxifen (data not shown). Thus, these three tamoxifen compounds not only suppressed plasminogen activator activity to below that of the control cells but also appeared to be effective antagonists to the induction of plasminogen activator activity by estrogenic compounds.

Progesterone receptor
Progesterone receptor was also stimulated by low, physiological concentrations of estradiol in MCF-7 cells, Figure 65.2. In studies on the time course of progesterone receptor stimulation by the different compounds, maximal stimulation was achieved by Day 3 and remained constant through Day 6. Because of this, all studies were performed after a 5-day exposure to hormone. Estradiol was a potent stimulator of progesterone receptor levels, a 600% increase at 10^{-10} M estradiol. At a much higher concentration, 10^{-6} M, cis-tamoxifen stimulated progesterone receptor levels to the same extent as that observed with 10^{-10} M estradiol. trans-Hydroxytamoxifen and cis-hydroxy-tamoxifen elicited submaximal, i.e., 2- to 3-fold, increases in progesterone receptor at 10^{-10} and 10^{-8} M concentrations, and trans-hydroxytamoxifen elicited a very weak stimulation of progesterone receptor at 10^{-7} M.

266

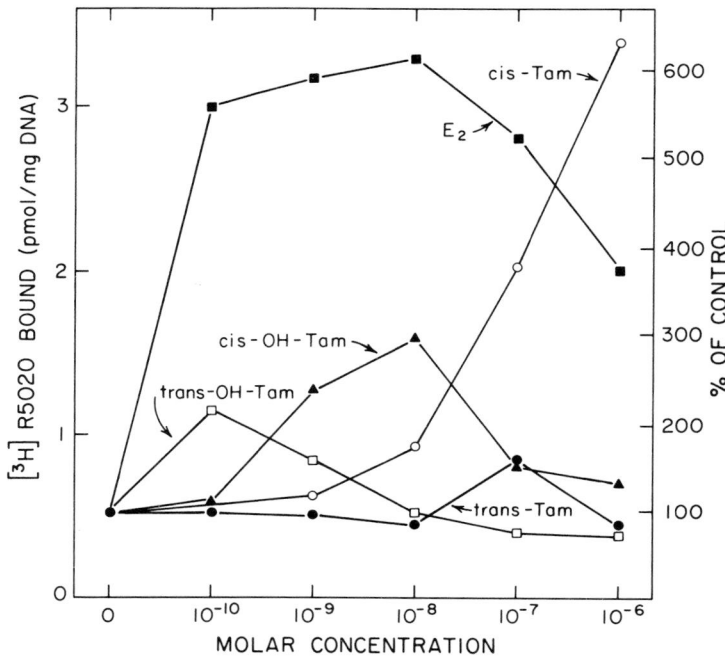

Fig. 65.2 Dose-response curves for stimulation of progesterone receptor in MCF-7 cells by tamoxifen and hydroxytamoxifen isomers and by estradiol (E_2). Cells were incubated for 5 days with compounds at the concentrations indicated. Fresh media and hormone were added daily during the 5-day period. The cells were then harvested and fractionated, and the cytosol was assayed for progesterone receptor utilizing 10 nM [^{3}H]R5020 in the absence and presence of a 100-fold excess of radioinert R5020. Bound radioactivity was determined as described in Katzenellenbogen et al 1984, using hydroxylapatite. Each point represents data obtained in duplicate from one near-confluent T-150 flask of cells. Values obtained in 2 additional experiments did not vary by more than 15%. cis-Tam, cis-tamoxifen; cis-OH-Tam, cis-hydroxytamoxifen; trans-OH-Tam, trans-hydroxytamoxifen; trans-Tam, trans-tamoxifen.

DISCUSSION

Plasminogen activator activity appeared to be a good marker of estrogen action and could be used to distinguish estrogens from antiestrogens. Plasminogen activator activity was stimulated by low, physiological concentrations of estradiol, and antiestrogens such as trans-tamoxifen and trans-hydroxytamoxifen did not stimulate plasminogen activator activity. cis-Tamoxifen increased the plasminogern activator activity of MCF-7 cells. We had expected cis-hydroxytamoxifen also to be estrogenic, but instead it appeared to be antiestrogenic. However, we observed that the cis- and trans-hydroxytamoxifens readily underwent isomer interconversion upon exposure to our cell culture conditions (data not shown). The relative binding affinities of cis-tamoxifen, trans-tamoxifen, cis-hydroxytamoxifen, and trans-hydroxytamoxifen for the cytosol estrogen receptor were 0.3, 2.5, 1.8, and 310%, respectively, in which the affinity of estradiol was defined as 100% (data not shown). Thus, the paradoxical behaviour of cis-hydroxytamoxifen was due to some of its conversion to trans-hydroxytamoxifen, an antiestrogen with a very high affinity for the estrogen receptor. Under similar cell culture conditions, we observed no isomer interconversion with the cis- and trans-tamoxifens.

That plasminogen activator activity is a preferable marker for distinguishing estrogens from antiestrogens is seen by comparing the effects of antiestrogens on plasminogen activator activity and on progesterone receptor levels. Whereas the antiestrogens trans-tamoxifen and trans-hydroxytamoxifen did not stimulate plasminogen activator activity, but actually suppressed it to levels below that of the control cells, these compounds slightly stimulated progesterone receptor levels 2- to 3-fold above that of the control cells. Plasminogen activator activity may also be a good marker for the suppression of growth of the MCF-7 cells by antiestrogens. Under our conditions of assay of our MCF-7 cells, estradiol did not stimulate cell growth but trans-tamoxifen and trans-hydroxytamoxifen were effective inhibitors (data not shown). Consistent with their estrogen receptor binding affinities, trans-hydroxytamoxifen was 100-fold more potent than its nonhydroxylated form in inhibiting the growth of MCF-7 cells. cis-Tamoxifen, like estradiol, did not stimulate or suppress growth of these cells but cis-hydroxytamoxifen, presumably due to some isomer interconversion, appeared to be a potent inhibitor of cell growth, being about 10-fold more potent than was trans-tamoxifen.

REFERENCES

Eckert R L, Katzenellenbogen B S 1982 Effects of estrogens on estrogen receptor dynamics and the induction of progesterone receptor in MCF-7 human breast cancer cells. Cancer Research 42: 139–144
Fisher B, Raymond C, Brown A and other NSABP investigators 1981 Treatment of primary breast cancer with chemotherapy and tamoxifen. New England Journal of Medicine 305: 1–6
Katzenellenbogen B S, Norman M J, Eckert R L, Peltz S W, Mangel W F 1984 Bioactivities, estrogen receptor interactions, and plasminogen activator-inducing activities of tamoxifen and hydroxytamoxifen isomers in MCF-7 human breast cancer cells. Cancer Research 44: 112–119
Kneifel M A, Leytus S P, Fletcher E, Weber T, Mangel W F 1982 Uterine plasminogen activator: Modulation by steroid hormones. Endocrinology 111: 493–500
Peltz S W, Katzenellenbogen B S, Kneifel M A, Mangel W F 1983 Plasminogen activators in tissues of the immature and estrogen stimulated rat uterus and in uterine luminal fluid: characterization and properties. Endocrinology 112: 890–897

66. Glucocorticoid induction of an inhibitor of plasminogen activator in hepatoma cells

T. D. Gelehrter, P. L. Coleman and B. J. Cwikel

Incubation of HTC rat hepatoma cells in tissue culture with the synthetic glucocorticoid, dexamethasone, causes a rapid decrease in cellular plasminogen activator (PA) activity. Mixing experiments indicated the presence of PA inhibitory activity in the hormone-treated cells (Seifert and Gelehrter, 1978). HTC cells appear to contain both PA and inhibitor in apparent equilibrium with an enzymatically inactive complex. The objective of this study was to determine whether the observed decrease in PA activity and increase in inhibitor activity in dexamethasone-treated cells result from an induced increase in total inhibitor without a decrease in the amount of PA; to a decrease in the amount of activator, hereby making constitutively-produced amounts of inhibitor appear elevated; or to some combination of both mechanisms. To distinguish among these alternatives, we have utilized the observation that HTC PA and its inhibitor can be dissociated during SDS-polyacrylamide gel electrophoresis under non-reducing conditions. Renaturation (by exchanging Triton for SDS) and elution of proteins from gel slices allows separate quantitation of both activator and inhibitor activities. PA activity was assayed by the solubilization of ^{125}I-labeled fibrin, and inhibitor activity by titrating the inhibition of urokinase.

HTC PA is present in two major electrophoretic forms of 64 000 and 110 000 daltons. Incubation of cells with dexamethasone for 4 hours decreases cellular PA activity to 10 ± 3% of that in control cells (n = 6) but does not decrease the total amount of activator activity eluted from the gel (115 ± 28% of control). Dexamethasone does alter the relative abundance of the two PA species, however, decreasing the 64 KDa form and increasing the 110 KDa form (Cwikel et al, 1984).

The same gel dissociation method was used to measure the amount of inhibitor in mixtures in which it is present with PA. The inhibitory activity from cell extracts migrates as a single peak of about 50 KDa. Its activity and mobility are unaffected by sulfhydryl reducing agents which inactivate PA. Incubation of cells with dexamethasone for 4 hours causes a 10.5 ± 3.1 fold increase in gel-dissociated inhibitor (n = 9). In variant hepatoma cells selectively resistant to the dexamethasone inhibition of PA activity (Seifert and Gelehrter, 1979), basal amounts of inhibitor are present, but dexamethasone fails to increase the amount of inhibitor in these variants (Cwikel et al, 1984). These results suggest that the hormonally-induced increase in inhibitory activity and decrease in net PA activity in wild-type cells are due primarily, if not solely, to an increase in total inhibitor without a decrease in total activator.

The increase in inhibitor activity in dexamethasone-treated cells requires concomitant RNA and protein synthesis, and is blocked by actinomycin D and by cycloheximide. Half-maximal induction of inhibitor is observed at 5 nM dexamethasone, the same concentration which produces half-maximal stimulation of other glucocorticoid responses in these cells. Thus, the induction of PA inhibitor appears to be mediated by the glucocorticoid receptor.

The glucocorticoid-induced inhibitor inhibits HTC PA (which is antigenically of the tissue-type) without irreversibly inactivating the enzyme. In contrast, the same inhibitor appears to irreversibly inhibit urokinase (UK) and forms a covalent complex with it which is stable to SDS and sulfhydryl reducing agents. Incubation of 35 KDa ^{125}I-labeled UK with conditioned medium from dexamethasone-treated cells, for 30 minutes at 37°, results in conversion of approximately 60% of the radioactive UK to a complex of 85 KDa. The covalent complex does not form when the incubation is performed at 0°, when conditioned medium from control cells is used, when the active site of UK is blocked with Phe-Ala-Arg CH$_2$Cl, or in the presence of an excess of unlabeled UK. In contrast, plasmin, thrombin and trypsin do not block complex formation. The dexamethasone-induced inhibitor of PA is clearly different from protease nexin in that it is acid stable, does not inhibit plasmin or thrombin, and the inhibition of UK is not accelerated by heparin (Coleman, Barouski and Gelehrter, 1982; Coleman et al, 1983).

There is a growing awareness of the biological importance of specific inhibitors of plasminogen activator. Our studies over the past several years indicate that in rat hepatoma cells such an inhibitor is under hormonal regulation, and that the induction of this inhibitor is the major mechanism by which glucocorticoids regulate plasminogen activator in HTC hepatoma cells.

REFERENCES

Coleman P L, Barouski P A, Gelehrter T D 1982 The dexamethasone-induced inhibitor of fibrinolytic activity in hepatoma cells — cellular product which specifically inhibits plasminogen activation. Journal of Biological Chemistry 257: 4260–4264
Coleman P L, Cwikel B J, Shafer J A, Gelehrter T D 1983 A covalent complex forms between urokinase and the hormonally-induced inhibitor of plasminogen activator from hepatoma cells. Federation Proceedings 42: 1950
Cwikel B J, Barouski-Miller P A, Coleman P L, Gelehrter T D 1984 Dexamethasone induction of an inhibitor of plasminogen activator in HTC hepatoma cells. Journal of Biological Chemistry 259: June/July, in press
Seifert S C, Gelehrter T D 1978 Mechanism of glucocorticoid inhibition of plasminogen activator in rat hepatoma cells. Proceedings of the National Academy of Sciences USA 75: 6130–6133
Seifert S C, Gelehrter T D 1979 Isolation of variant rat hepatoma cells selectively resistant to glucocorticoid inhibition of plasminogen activator. Journal of Cellular Physiology 99: 333–341

67. Characterization of the plasminogen activators synthesized by human fetal liver and by two different transformed human liver cell lines

G.H. Barlow, S.L. Firestone and K.C. Robbins

The availability of cell lines from human liver has made possible the characterization of the plasminogen activator(s) synthesized by this organ. This information could give a valuable insight on the plasma activator activity since it is well established that most of the plasma proteins are known to be synthesized in the liver.

EXPERIMENTAL

Human fetal liver (HFL) as well as the transformed human liver cell lines SKHEP1 (1) and HEP 3B (2) were grown to confluency in E-199 media containing 10% fetal calf serum. At confluency, the media was changed to one that was serum-free or low (1%) in fetal calf serum. The conditioned media was sampled at selected times following confluency and the media was totally replaced at five day intervals.

The conditioned media showed little or no plasminogen activator activity when measured directly on fibrin plates, but developed activity following chromatography on fibrin celite, or phenyl sepharose, or following separation by SDS-PAGE. Molecular weight determination by SDS-PAGE followed by slicing, extraction and fibrin plate showed activator activity corresponding to molecular weights of 48 000, 80 000, and > 100 000.

Quantitation of the rate of production of activator is shown in Figure 67.1.

The human embryonic liver produced less than the transformed cell lines while the more heterogeneous SKHEP-1 line was a better producer than the HEP 3B which is very parenchymal in morphology. These results are in agreement with the report by Markus (3) who showed higher plasminogen activator activity in transformed tissue than in the normal tissue located nearby.

Conditioned media was pooled and absorbed directly to immunoabsorbent columns of either anti-urokinase or anti-tissue activator. The H.F.L. and HEP 3B showed approximately 85% of the activity as urokinase-like and 15% tissue activator-like, while the SKHEP-1 showed only urokinase-like activity.

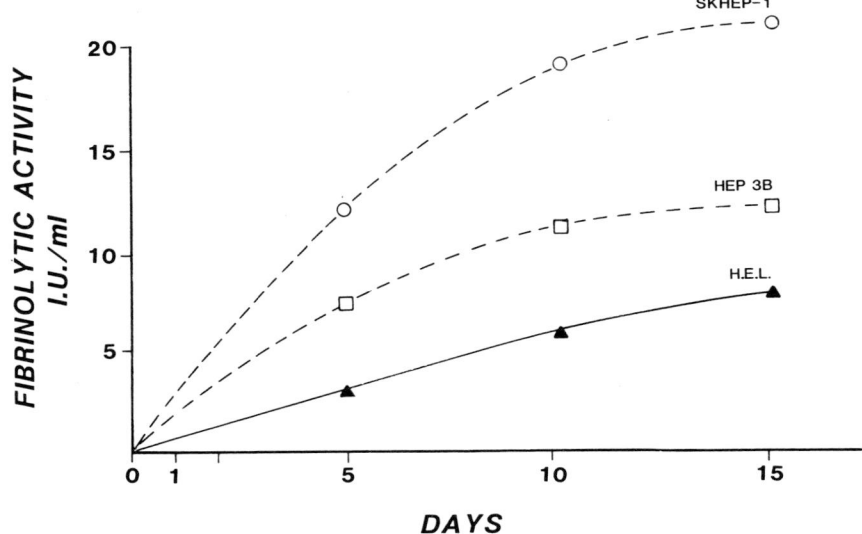

Fig. 67.1 Plasminogen activator activity, as urokinase, as a function of time following confluency for the several liver cell lines.

DISCUSSION

All the liver cell line studies are shown to produce primarily urokinase-like activator with some lines also producing a small amount of tissue-like activator. Levin et al (5) reported on the transformed cell line HEP G2 and found only urokinase-like activity similar to our findings with the SKHEP-1 line.

We have not determined the chain structure of our urokinase-like activity, but based on the fact that it binds to fibrin celite, we assume it is most likely the one-chain form (6).

The absence of activity in the conditioned media when assayed directly but its presence following a purification step is interpreted to be the results of the presence of high levels of inhibitors in the media; since it is well established that the liver is the site of synthesis for most of the plasma protease inhibitors, this is a feasible explanation.

Since these results show the liver synthesizes primarily a urokinase-like activator, it still leaves the endothelial cell as the source of tissue-like activator.

ACKNOWLEDGEMENT

Supported by USPHS grants HL-04366 and HL-29913.

REFERENCES

1. Fogh J, Trempe G 1975 New human tumor cell lines. In: Fogh J (ed) Human tumor cells in vitro, Plenum Press, New York pp 115–159

272

2. Aden D P, Fogel A, Plotkin S, Damjanov I, Knowles B B 1979 Controlled synthesis of HBsAg in a differentiated human liver carcinoma-derived cell line. Nature 282: 615–616
3. Markus G, Hiroshi T, Camiolo S M, Carasanti J G, Evers J L, Hohika G H 1980 Content and characterization of plasminogen activator in human lung tumours and normal lung tissue. Cancer Research 40: 841–848
4. Barlow G H, Firestone S L, Robbins K C 1983 Identification of the plasminogen activator(s) produced by the transformed liver cell line, SK-HEP-1. Thrombosis Research 32: 29–34
5. Levin E G, Fair D S, Loskutoff D J 1983 Human hepatoma cell line plasminogen activator. Journal Laboratory and Clinical Medicine 102: 500–508
6. Husain S S, Gurewich V, Lipinski B 1983 Purification and partial characterization of a single chain high molecular weight form of urokinase from human urine. Archives of Biochemistry and Biophysics 220: 31–38

68. Plasminogen activators produced by malignant tissues in culture

S.A. Cederholm-Williams, S. Houlbrook,
N.W. Porter and H. Chissic

INTRODUCTION

Plasminogen activators are widely distributed through normal human tissues and many cells continue to secrete these enzymes in cell culture. The enzymes, which are usually firmly bound to cell structures, may be solubulised with strong chaotropic solutions or low pH (4.0). Of the two types of specific plasminogen activators present in human tissues, tissue-type plasminogen activator (t-PA) predominates in extracts. Significant amounts of urokinase (u-PA) are found only in urine. The role of t-PA and u-PA in normal tissue physiology are uncertain though it has been suggested that they contribute to the invasive properties of certain cells (1) and take part in normal tissue reorganisation processes.

Malignant tumours are known to produce high levels of plasminogen activators which may contribute to the natural history of that tumour (2). In order to measure the production of plasminogen activators, malignant tissues have been grown in culture and enzyme production assessed under standard conditions.

METHODS

Biopsy samples from malignant tissues were disaggregated by trypsin-EDTA digestion, or grown as explants. Cells were grown in DMEM supplemented with 10% calf serum, L-glutamine, penicillin and streptomycin and buffered with 10 mmol/l HEPES. This procedure leads to mixed cell cultures in many instances but occasionally single cell types are obtained at first attempt. Once the cells achieve confluence the media is replaced with serum free media for 24h. The released plasminogen activator was measured.

Plasminogen activator was assayed using bovine fibrin-agar plates supplemented with human plasminogen. This assay was calibrated using urokinase standard curves and was linear over a range from 1–100 CTA units/ml.

Plasminogen activators were characterised by mixing media aliquots with IgG fraction against urokinase or uterine t-PA. These antibodies could inhibit 50 CTA units of t-PA or u-PA respectively.

RESULTS AND CONCLUSIONS

Only the results from single cell type cultures are reported in the Table. Proteolytic activity was not detected when plasminogen was omitted from the fibrin-agar plates.

Table 68.1 Showing amounts and types of plasminogen activators produced

Cell type	PA activity CTA units/ml	t-PA %	u-PA %
Endometrium	>100	0	100
Ascitic fluid	80	0	100
Endometrium	20	0	90
Endometrium	20	0	95
Endometrium	12	0	98
Endometrium	3.7	0	81
Breast	0.6	0	77
Melanoma	7.0	100	0
Melanoma	30	100	0
Ascitic fluid	3.2	90	0
Squamous cells	2.5	100	0
Breast	1.3	100	0
28 others	<1.0	—	—

It is apparent that some malignant cells in culture can produce very high levels of plasminogen activator. Generally the high producers secrete u-PA whereas the low producers secrete t-PA.

It is very difficult to obtain quantitative data on PA production from cultured cells. PA production is influenced by growth rate, cell numbers, metabolic effects of the serum, age of culture, inhibitor synthesis, as well as specific cell characteristics. Despite these problems it is evident that certain malignant tissues in culture do secrete high levels of plasminogen activators. However, it must be considered that PA release may be an artifact of tissue culture and perhaps bears no relation to *in vivo* synthesis.

ACKNOWLEDGEMENTS

This work was supported by the Cancer Research Campaign, UK. H. Chissic is supervisor for post graduate students.

REFERENCES

1. Cederholm-Williams S A 1981 Molecular mechanism of fibrinolysis: A system involved with malignant cells. Invasion and Metastasis: 1: 85–98
2. Bernik M B, Wijngaards G, Rijken D C 1981 Production by human tissues in culture of immunologically distinct multiple molecular weight forms of plasminogen activator. New York Academy Sciences 370: 592–608

69. Fibrinolytic activity of human invasive tumours and derived primary cultures

F. Carretero, A. Fabra, J. Adán, D. Tugues, M. Borrell, L. Vila, J. Garcia, C. De Castellarnau and M.L. Rutllant

INTRODUCTION

Plasminogen activator (PA) production and secretion by human solid tumours are important factors in tumour growth and characterization, as has been reported (Markus, 1983; Evers et al, 1982; Corasanti et al, 1980; Wilson et al, 1980; Tissot and Bachmann, 1983; Markus et al, 1983).

This work presents a further contribution to the study of PA type produced by three human tumour biopsies kind (breast and colon adenocarcinoma and melanoma) and derived cell lines in culture.

MATERIAL AND METHODS

Source of samples
Tumour biopsies were obtained by surgery and collected under aseptic conditions.

Culture methods
Part of the biopsy was set up in culture by explant technique or enzyme disgregation with a mixture of trypsin, collagenase and DNase. Cultures were grown in Eagle's MEM with 20% FBS, at 37°C in 7.5% CO_2. Subcultures were performed by 0.25% trypsin treatment. Conditioned medium was obtained by incubation of a monolayer in Eagle's MEM without FBS, for 24 h and kept at −80°C until use.

Cellular extracts
Tumour tissues, kept at −80°C, were thawed, homogenized with 0.25% TritonX-100, treated by sonication and subjected to alternate freezing and thawing. Cellular extracts from semiconfluent monolayers were obtained by washing with PBS and scraping in presence of 0.25% TritonX-100, followed by alternate freezing and thawing.

Fibrinolytic activity and type determination

Total fibrinolytic activity (FA) were determined by the amidolytic assay with S-2251 chromogenic substrate and fibrin monomers, in microtiter wells (Wiman et al, 1983). Activity was related to a standard urokinase curve carried out in the same conditions as the samples. Protein concentration was determined by the Bradford method. The type of activator was elucidated in parallel assays in the presence of rabbit IgG-anti-UK or IgG-anti-T-PA and the percentage of lost activity was determined with respect to total FA.

Molecular weight determinations

The molecular weight (MW) of PA was determined by SDS-polyacrilamide gel electrophoresis followed by a transfer onto a fibrin matrix (Granelli-Pipperno and Reich, 1978). Parallel determinations were performed onto fibrin matrix with specific IgG against UK or T-PA for the determination of UK-type and T-PA-type species.

RESULTS AND DISCUSSION

Cell lines derived from breast (MAM), colon (REC) adenocarcinomas and melanomas (MEL), present an increase of FA with respect to their original biopsies (Table 69.1), specially in MEL lines. And in two cases there is a loss of FA.

Predominant PA-types are T-PA-related in biopsies regardless of their origin, although there is a component of UK-type in REC and MAM.

Cellular extracts, from cell lines in passages greater than 30 and up to 120, present some changes depending on the tumour origin. REC lines show a change in PA pattern with respect to the main activity (74.3% T-PA-type in biopsies and 73.7% UK-type in cell lines). MAM and MEL conserve the main PA-type (T-PA-type) though they present a loss of the secondary activity in MAM and a gain of minor one in a MEL line.

The molecular species related to T-PA (Fig. 69.1) present the usual range of 65–70 KD and two higher ones of 100–110 and 120 KD. The former range is present in MAM and MEL biopsies as well as in one MEL cell line. On the other

Table 69.1 Fibrinolytic activity and PA-type composition of biopsies and derived cell lines

	FA (UCTA.MG^{-1})	UK-related (%)	T-PA related (%)	Number of samples
Biopsies:				
MAM	0.3 ± 0.02	10.1	90.3	15
REC	0.6 ± 0.19	41.3	74.3	12
MEL	0.27 ± 0.1	—	100	8
Cellular extracts:				
MAM	1.25 ± 1	—	93	3
REC	0.95 ± 0.5	73.7	—	3
MEL	4.2 ± 1.4	15.8	75.8	4

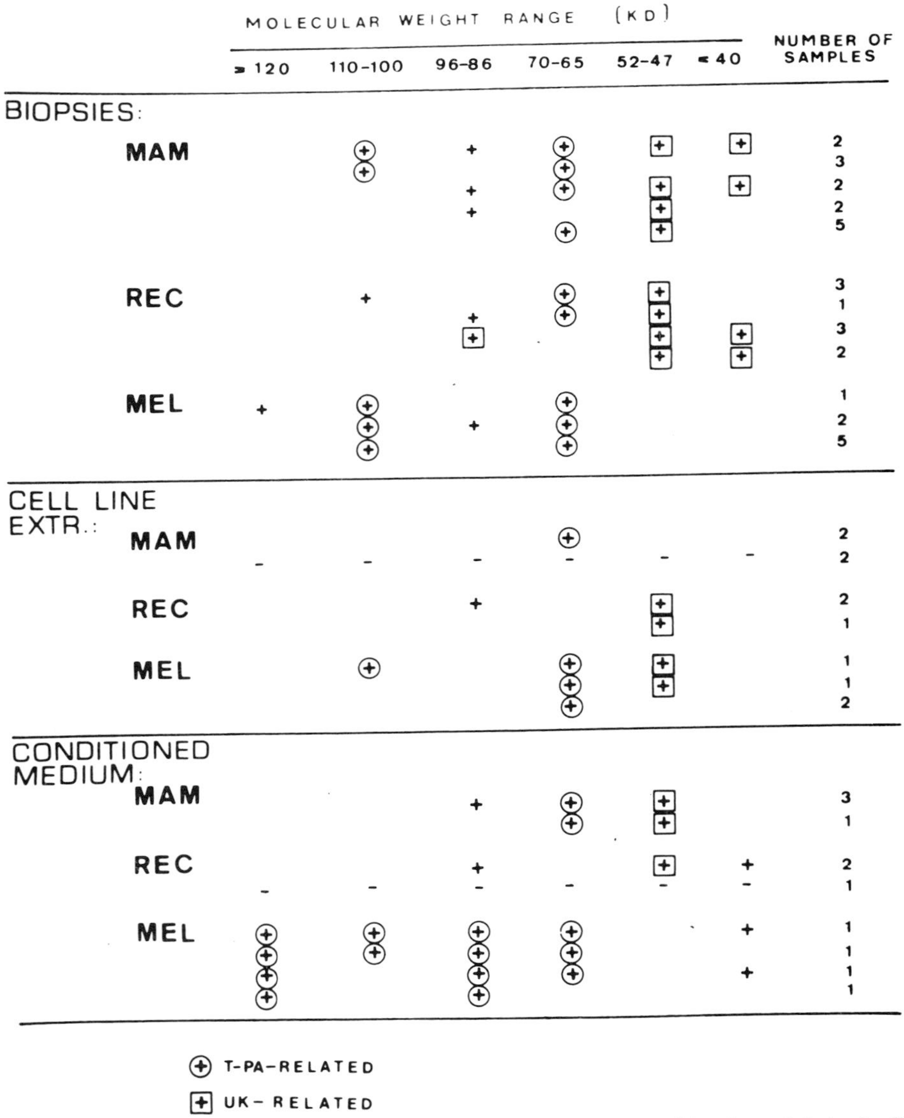

MOLECULAR WEIGHT RANGE (KD)

	≥120	110–100	96–86	70–65	52–47	<40	NUMBER OF SAMPLES
BIOPSIES:							
MAM		⊕	+	⊕	⊞	⊞	2
		⊕		⊕			3
			+	⊕	⊞	⊞	2
			+		⊞		2
				⊕	⊞		5
REC		+		⊕	⊞		3
				⊕	⊞		1
			+⊞		⊞		3
					⊞	⊞	2
MEL	+	⊕		⊕			1
		⊕	+	⊕			2
		⊕		⊕			5
CELL LINE EXTR.:							
MAM				⊕			2
	–	–	–	–	–	–	2
REC			+		⊞		2
					⊞		1
MEL		⊕		⊕	⊞		1
				⊕	⊞		1
				⊕			2
CONDITIONED MEDIUM:							
MAM			+	⊕	⊞		3
				⊕	⊞		1
REC			+		⊞	+	2
	–	–	–	–	–	–	1
MEL	⊕	⊕	⊕	⊕		+	1
	⊕	⊕	⊕	⊕			1
	⊕		⊕	⊕		+	1
	⊕		⊕			+	1

⊕ T-PA–RELATED

⊞ UK–RELATED

Fig. 69.1 Molecular weight pattern of PA produced by human tumour biopsies and derived cell lines.

hand, MEL cell line derived conditioned medium show a higher MW range of 120 KD and a new group of bands located in a 86–96 KD range.

UK-related molecular species are located in the usual MW ranges of 47–52 and 30KD. In addition three REC biopsies present a band in a MW range of 86–96 KD, which is lost in derived lines.

A series of FA bands non inhibited by IgG-anti-UK and IgG-anti-T-PA appear at a MW range of 86–96 KD, 100–110 KD and 120 KD. The former one is present in the three kinds of tumour biopsies and is partially conserved in cell lines derived from MAM and REC. The two other ranges seem be lost in cell lines.

REFERENCES

Corasanti J G et al 1980 Plasminogen activator content of human colon tumours and normal mucosa. Journal of National Cancer Institute 65: 345–351

Evers J L 1982 Plasminogen activator activity and composition in human breast cancer. Cancer Research 42: 219–226

Granelli-Pipperno A, Reich E 1978 A study of proteases and protease-inhibitor complexes in biological fluids. Journal of Experimental Medicine 148: 223–243

Markus G 1983 Plasminogen activators in malignant growth. In: Davidson J F, Bachmann F, Bouvier C A, Kruithof E K O (eds) Progress in fibrinolysis. Churchill Livingstone, Edinburgh, vol 6, p 587–604

Markus G, Camiolo S M, Hohga S, Madeja J M, Mittelman A 1983 Plasminogen activator secretion of human tumours in short-term organ culture, including a comparison of primary and metastatic colon tumors. Cancer Research 43: 5517–5525

Tissot J D, Bachmann F 1983 Plasminogen activators of normal tissues and of carcinoma extracts. In: Davidson J F, Bachmann F, Bouvier C A, Kruithof E K O (eds) Progress in fibrinolysis. Churchill Livinstone, Edinburgh, vol 6, p 133–135

Wilson E L, Becker M L B, Hoal E G, Dowle E B 1980 Molecular species of plasminogen activators secreted by neoplastic and normal human cells. Cancer Research 40: 933–938

Wiman D, Mellbring G, Ranby M 1983 Plasminogen activator release during venous stasis and exercise as determined by a new specific assay. Clinica Chimica Acta 127: 279–288

70. Effect of dicarboxylic acids on plasminogen activator activity in supernatants of a human tumour cell line

O. F. Wagner, J. Wojta, H. Pehamberger, H. Leibl and B. R. Binder

INTRODUCTION

Acelaic acid (AA, C9-dicarboxylic acid) is used for the treatment of diseases involving abnormal melanocytes such as lentigo maligna and malignant melanoma (Nazzaro-Porro et al, 1979 and 1980). Based on the facts that melanoma cell lines are known to produce a plasminogen activator (PA) exhibiting the same physico-chemical, immunological and functional characteristics as tissue plasminogen activator (t-PA) and that plasminogen activators are thought to be involved in malignant processes it was our aim to describe the influence of AA on the fibrinolytic system of melanoma cells.

METHODS

Human melanoma cells (ATCC CRL1424) were grown for up to 24 hours and supernatants were tested for t-PA activity both as described (Wagner et al, 1983). To determine the effect of AA melanoma cells were grown in medium containing 2×10^{-2}M either AA or adipic acid, respectively, for 5, 12 and 24 hours.

For studies of t-PA synthesis ^{35}S-methionine was added and after 16 hours supernatants were precipitated with protein A-Sepharose immobilized anti-t-PA. The precipitated material was run in SDS polyacrylamide gel electrophoresis. Thereafter, the gels were applied to an autoradiographic plate.

Alpha-2-antiplasmin in supernatants was measured using S-2251 and human plasmin. Existence of specific PA inhibitor was measured by SDS gel electrophoresis and subsequent fibrin agarose overlay.

Cell viability was tested by Trypan Blue exclusion and all results were corrected for the respective cell count. A direct effect of AA on t-PA activity was excluded.

RESULTS

In Figure 70.1 the time dependent increase of PA activity (PAA) in supernatants of CRL1424 cells grown in the presence of either AA or adipic acid or normal

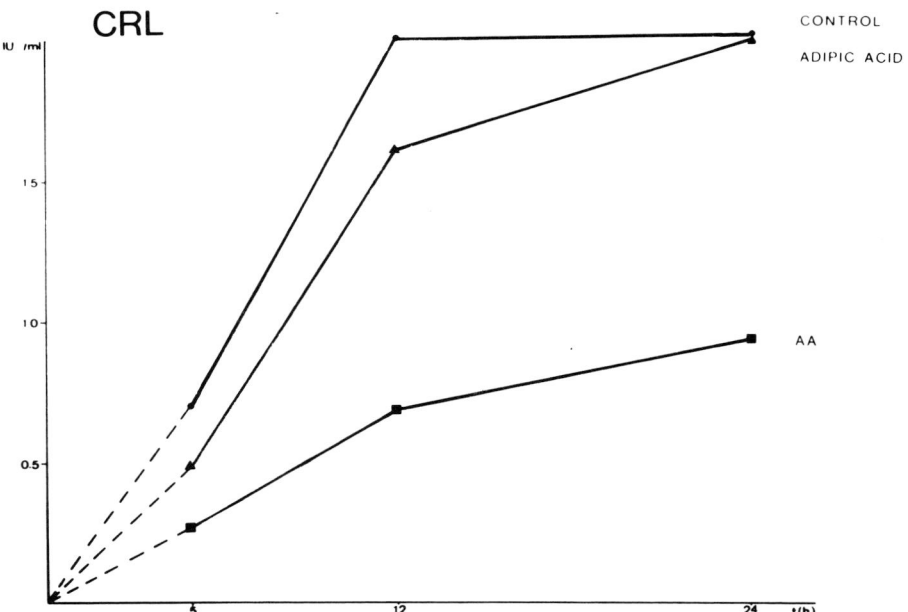

Fig. 70.1 Influence of AA and adipic acid on PAA of CRL1424 cell supernatants.

medium is shown. Values are corrected for equal cell count which was decreased in the case of AA marked cells by about 10 to 25% after 24 hours.

Figure 70.2 shows the autoradiogram of t-PA produced by controls or in the presence of AA and adipic adid, respectively. Total radioactivity in the 70 000,

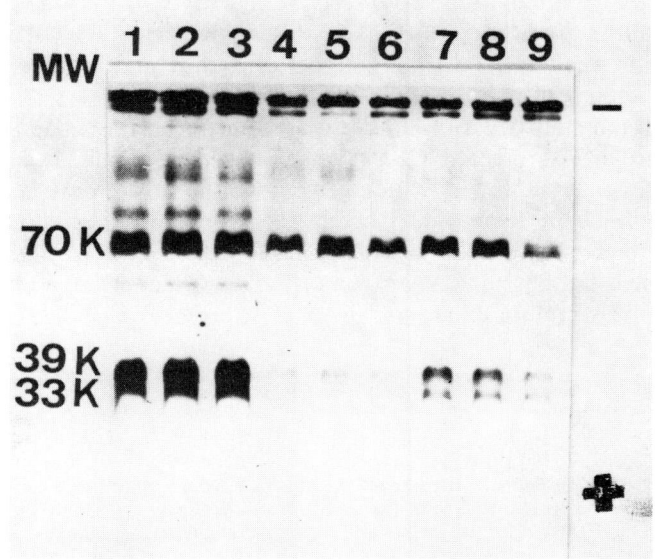

Fig. 70.2 Autoradiogram of t-PA produced by cells growing in normal growth medium (panels 1–3), by cells incubated with AA (panels 4–6) and incubated with adipic acid (panels 7–9).

33 000 and 39 000 radioactivity bands was not significantly different between control and treated cells. However, the relative proportion of the 33 000 and 39 000 band as compared to the 70 000 band was significantly shifted towards the low molecular bands in the supernatants of cells grown in normal growth medium.

There was no significant difference in the alpha-2-antiplasmin content in the supernatant between controls, AA and adipid acid treated cells. Also the specific anti-activator content appeared to be similar in all supernatants examined.

CONCLUSION

The present study indicates that AA significantly decreases PAA in supernatants of CRL cells. This decrease is already present after 5 hours and amounts to about 50% after 24 hours. Synthesis of t-PA antigen, however, seems not to be a major cause for that decreased activity, because the ^{35}S methionine radioactivity incorporated into t-PA by AA treated CRL cells was not significantly lower as compared to controls or adipic acid treated cells and the total cell count. In contrast, the relative contribution of single and double chain t-PA to total t-PA was significantly shifted towards single chain t-PA in AA treated CRL cells. The different forms alone should not explain the different activities found, since double chain t-PA has about the same fibrinolytic activity as single chain t-PA.

Also anti-plasmin activity as well as anti-activator activity was about the same in control and in AA treated CRL supernatants. However, because of the decreased cell count in the AA treated cell culture the relative amount of inhibitors might be increased and thereby contribute to the reduced activity because of different slopes at the dose-responding curves of PAA and inhibition. From our data it is clear that AA affects t-PA in CRL cells. The different forms alone should not explain the different activities found, since double chain t-PA has about the same fibrinolytic activity as single chain t-PA.

Also anti-plasmin activity as well as anti-activator activity was about the same in control and in AA treated CRL supernatants. However, because of the decreased cell count in the AA treated cell culture the relative amount of inhibitors might be increased and thereby contribute to the reduced activity because of different slopes at the dose-responding curves of PAA and inhibition. From our data it is clear that AA affects t-PA in CRL cells. The mechanisms involved, however, remain unclear.

REFERENCES

Nazzaro-Porro M, Passi S, Balus L, Breathnach A, Martin B, Morpurgo G 1979 Effect of dicarboxylic acids on lentigo maligna. The Journal of Investigative Dermatology 72: 296–305
Nazzaro-Porro M et al 1980 Effect of azelaic acid on human malignant melanoma. The Lancet, May 24: 1109–1111
Wagner O, Wojta J, Binder B R 1983 Analysis of the plasminogen activator production by two human tumor cell lines. In: Jespersen J, Kluft C, Korsgaard O (eds) Clinical aspects of fibrinolysis and thrombolysis. South Jutland University Press, Esbjerg, p 35–42

71. Effects of plasminogen activators on the promotion of RSV-induced cell transformation

G. De Petro, T. Vartio, E. Salonen, A. Vaheri and S. Barlati

INTRODUCTION

Transformation-enhancing factors (TEF) are found in vivo in human plasma cryoprecipitates of more than 90% of patients affected with different neoplastic diseases (leukemias, lymphomas and solid tumors), but rarely (5%) in healthy controls or in patients with non-neoplastic diseases. TEF activity in plasma cryoprecipitates appears to be of potential diagnostic and prognostic value (Varlati et al, 1978; Mignatti et al, 1980). Gelatin-binding fragments of fibronectin (gb-FNdp), obtained by proteolytic digestion of purified human plasma fibronectin, have TEF activity at nanomolar concentrations (De Petro et al, 1981) and the gelatin-binding fraction of tumor patients cryoprecipitates retains TEF activity and contains FN, FNdp and t-PA (Barlati et al, 1983; De Petro et al, 1983, 1984a). Agarose gel filtration of TEF-positive plasma cryoprecipitate revealed that one of the two TEF-positive peaks (mol.wt — 250 000) had associated plasminogen activator (PA) activity (Barlati and Mignatti, 1980) and that TEF-positive cell culture media induce normal or Rous sarcoma-virus-transformed cells to release PA (Mignatti and Barlati, 1982). These data led us to investigate whether purified t-PA and/or u-PA could exert TEF activity and whether the activity present in the plasma cryoprecipitate and/or in FNdp could be neutralized by α-FN, α-tPA and/or α-u-PA sera.

RESULTS AND DISCUSSION

Table 71.1 reports dose-effect experiments of purified t-PA, u-PA, tested for TEF activity. The TEF assay was performed as previously described (Mignatti et al, 1980). The results show that only t-PA was able to promote morphological cell transformation, at concentrations as low as 2 ng/ml (30 pM), while u-PA was TEF negative up to 8 μg/ml (148 nM). Table 71.1 reports for comparison also the TEF activity of the gelatin-binding fraction of plasminolytic fragments of FN.

Table 71.2 shows that α-FN, α-t-PA, and not α-u-PA or α-human albumin sera (HSA), are able to inhibit TEF activity present in either tumor cryo or in the FNdp; the antisera alone had no effect in the assay. The samples (10 μl of cryo or

Table 71.1 Assay of TEF activity associated with purified proteins

Samples tested	Concentrations in assay	Factor of enhancement of transformation (F.E.)	P ≤	TEF Activity
t-PA	0.2 ng/ml	0.9 ± 0.1	n.s.	−
t-PA	2 ng/ml	1.9 ± 0.2	0.001	+
t-PA	20 ng/ml	2.3 ± 0.2	0.001	+
t-PA	200 ng/ml	2.5 ± 0.2	0.001	+
u-PA	0.008 μg/ml	0.9 ± 0.1	n.s.	−
u-PA	0.08 μg/ml	1.1 ± 0.1	n.s.	−
u-PA	0.8 μg/ml	1.1 ± 0.1	n.s.	−
u-PA	8 μg/ml	1.3 ± 0.1	n.s.	−
gb-FNdp	1 ng/ml	1.1 ± 0.1	n.s.	−
gb-FNdp	5 ng/ml	1.3 ± 0.2	n.s.	−
gb-FNdp	100 ng/ml	2.2 ± 0.3	0.001	+
gb-FNdp	500 ng/ml	2.3 ± 0.3	0.001	+
gb-FNdp	750 ng/ml	2.3 ± 0.2	0.001	+
gb-FNdp	1000 ng/ml	2.3 ± 0.2	0.001	+

Table 71.2 Neutralizing effect of antibodies on TEF activity

Samples tested	F.E.	P ≤	TEF activity
0.2% Tumor CRYO + 0.1% Rabbit serum	2.4 ± 0.3	0.001	+
0.2% Tumor CRYO + 0.1% α-FN	1.0 ± 0.1	n.s.	−
0.2% Tumor CRYO + 0.1% α-t-PA	1.2 ± 0.1	n.s.	−
0.2% Tumor CRYO + 0.1% α-u-PA	2.2 ± 0.2	0.001	+
0.2% Tumor CRYO + .1.% α-HSA	1.8 ± 0.2	0.01	+
2 μg/ml FNdp + 0.1% Rabbit serum	2.1 ± 0.2	0.001	+
2 μg/ml FNdp + 0.1% α-FN	1.0 ± 0.1	n.s.	−
2 μg/ml FNdp + 0.1% α-t-PA	1.2 ± 0.1	n.s.	−
2 μg/ml FNdp + 0.1% α-u-PA	2.4 ± 0.1	0.001	+
2 μg/ml FNdp + 0.1% α-HSA	2.3 ± 0.1	0.001	+
0.1% α-FN	1.0 ± 0.1	n.s.	−
0.1% α-t-PA	1.3 ± 0.1	n.s.	−
0.1% α-u-PA	1.3 ± 0.1	n.s.	−
0.1% α-HSA	0.8 ± 0.2	n.s.	−

FNdp or control buffer + 5 μl of antiserum or control serum) were preincubated of 2 h at room temperature and then added to 5 ml of TEF assay medium.

The neutralization of TEF activity associated with FNdp by α-t-PA sera could be explained either with the observation by Banyai et al (1983) of structural homologies between t-PA and FN or considering the possibility of low levels of contamination of FNdp by t-PA. This could be possible since gb-FNdp are active at concentration 100 fold higher than t-PA and that the limit for evaluation of t-PA contamination is — 3% (De Petro et al, 1984b). On the other hand neutralization of the TEF activity with α-FN sera indicate a direct involvement of the FNdp.

Therefore the results reported in this study support the hypothesis that t-PA and FNdp might form a stable complex responsible for the TEF activity: this would be the case also for the activity recovered in the TEF positive plasma cryoprecipitate. Moreover the data point to a possible direct involvement of t-PA and FNdp on the appearance of the transformed cell morphology, *in vitro*.

We thank Prof. Desiré Collen for kindly providing t-PA and anti-t-PA serum. This work was supported by grants awarded by C.N.R., Special Project 'Oncologia' and 'Ingegneria Genetica e Basi Molecolari delle Malattie Ereditarie', by the Italian Ministry of Education; National Group of 'Biology and Pathology of the Cell Membrane' and by the Finnish Cancer Foundation.

REFERENCES

Barlati S, Mignatti P, Brega A, De Petro G, Ascari E 1978 Utilization of Rous sarcoma virus for the detection of transformation-enhancing and inhibiting factors in human cells. In: Barlati S, De Giuli C (eds) Avian RNS tumor viruses. Piccin, Padua, pp 331–348

Barlati S, Mignatti P 1980 Transformation-enhancing factors in the plasma of cancer patients. In: De Ausua L J, Levi-Montalcini R, Shields R, Iacobelli S (eds) Control mechanisms in animal cells. Raven P ess, New York, pp 269–277

Barlati S, De Petro G, Vartio T, Vaheri A 1983 Transformation enhancing factors and fibronectin degradation products as possible tumor markers. In: Chandra P (ed) Biochemical and biological markers of neoplastic transformation. Plenum, New York, pp 295–306

Banyai L, Varadi A, Patthy L 1983 Common evolutionary origin of the fibrin-binding-structures of fibronectin and tissue-type plasminogen activator. European Journal of Biochemistry F.E.B.S. 163(1): 37–41

De Petro G, Barlati S, Vartio T, Vaheri A 1981 Transformation enhancing activity of gelatin-binding fragments of fibronectin. Proceedings of the National Academy of Sciences (Wash.) 78: 4965–4969

De Petro G, Barlati S, Vartio T, Vaheri A 1983 Transformation-enhancing activity in plasma of tumor patients: relationship with fibronectin fragments. International Journal of Cancer 31: 157–162

De Petro G, Vartio T, Vaheri A, Barlati S 1984a Transformation-enhancing activity present in the plasma of cancer patients binds to gelatin. In: Peeters H (ed) Protides of the biological fluids, vol 31, p 731–734

De Petro G, Vartio T, Salonen E, Vaheri A, Barlati S 1984b Tissue type plasminogen activator, but not urokinase, exerts transformation-enhancing activity. International Journal of Cancer 33: 563–567

Mignatti P, Ascari E, Barlati S 1980 Potential diagnostic significance of the transformation-enhancing factor(s) in the plasma cryoprecipitate of tumor patients. International Journal of Cancer 25: 727–734

Mignatti P, Barlati S 1982 Enhancement of plasminogen activator activity by the culture medium of Rous sarcoma virus-transformed cells. Journal of General Virology 63: 365–373

72. Inhibition of cell-associated plasminogen activator of a tumorigenic cell by some neighboring cells but not others

W. F. Mangel and H-Y. Liu

INTRODUCTION

We recently began to study some of the factors that modulate the expression of the cell-associated plasminogen activator activity of cells growing *in vitro*. This was made possible by using a highly quantitative assay (Liu et al, 1980; Leytus et al, 1981) based upon the new active-site titrant for plasmin, 3',6'bis(4-guanidinobenzoyloxy)-5-[N'-(4-carboxyphenyl)thioureido]spiro[isobenzofuran-1-(3H), 9-'-[9H]xanthen]-3-one, abbreviated FDE for fluoresceindiester. The cells whose plasminogen activator activity we chose to study were isolated by Imada and Sueoka (1978) and Imade et al (1978) from a neurotumor of peripheral nerve origin, RT4, that was induced by subcutaneous injection of a newborn BDIX strain rat with ethylnitrosourea. Four cell types (AC, D, B and E) with four different morphologies were isolated from the tumor and adapted to grow in cell culture. The AC cells are stem cells capable of multipotential differentiation *in vitro* into cell types D, B, and E. When injected into syngenic animals, the AC and D cells are tumorigenic, and the B and E cells are nontumorigenic. However, AC cells may not be tumorigenic in the same way D cells are tumorigenic, i.e., AC cells may have to differentiate terminally *in vivo* into D cells before a tumor can arise. We found that the plasminogen activator activity of the D cells was almost inversely proportional to cell density at high cell densities and independent of cell density at low cell densities and that the presence of AC cells but not B cells severely inhibited the plasminogen activator activity of the D cells. In no case was inhibition of D cell plasminogen activator activity mediated by a soluble inhibitor; rather, some form of cell-cell contact seemed to be required.

RESULTS

Density

To determine the relationship between cell density and plasminogen activator activity per cell, we seeded microwells with 1 500 to 150 000 D cells and, after attachment, assayed the cell-associated plasminogen activator activity. The data, Figure 72.1, are presented as initial velocity per cell for the activation of

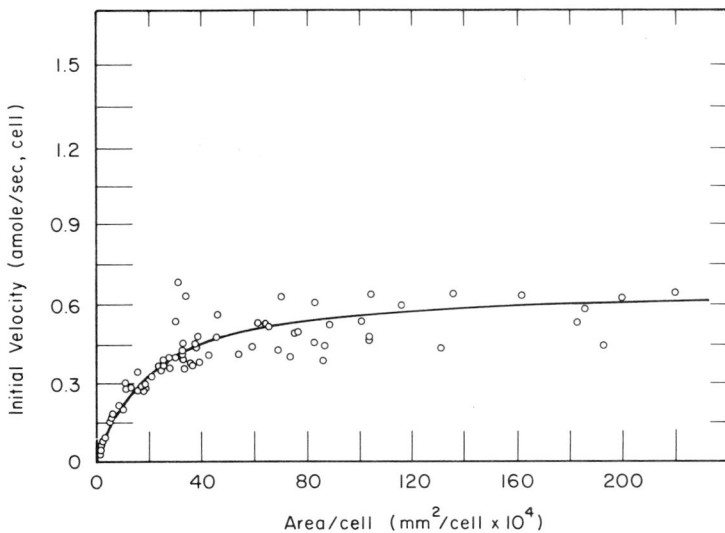

Fig. 72.1 Relationship between plasminogen activator activity per cell and cell density. Microwells (0.32-cm² growth area) were seeded with 1500 to 150 000 D cells. The medium was removed 16 hours later, and the cells were washed three times with PBS and then incubated with 11 μM dog plasminogen for 30 minutes. The amount of plasmin that had formed was then determined by an active-site titration with FDE as described in Liu et al (1982), and the number of cells in each microwell was counted. The initial velocities (attomoles of plasmin per second) for the activation of plasminogen were normalized per cell and plotted against the growth area divided by the cell number.

plasminogen to plasmin versus area per cell, the reciprocal of cell density. The amount of plasminogen activator activity per cell was dramatically influenced by cell density. As the area per cell was increased, there was an almost linear increase in the amount of plasminogen activator activity per cell. The slope of the line then began to decrease until eventually the amount of plasminogen activator activity per cell became independent of the area per cell. The plasminogen activator activity per cell became independent of the area per cell at approximately the same point that the cells ceased to be confluent. The range in plasminogen activator activity per cell as a function of the area per cell was quite dramatic. The plasminogen activator activity per cell of 10 000 cells was seven-fold greater than that for 150 000 cells growing in an area of the same dimensions.

Cocultivation
Although the D cells have a large amount of plasminogen activator activity, the AC cells have little or no plasminogen activator activity, Figure 72.2. Cocultivation of D cells with AC cells, under conditions in which the plasminogen activator activity of the D cells was not inhibited by cell density, dramatically affected the plasminogen activator activity of the D cells. When from 5000 to 20 000 D cells were seeded with from 1250 to 10 000 AC cells and then assayed for plasminogen activator activity 16 hours later, the initial velocity for the activation of plasminogen per D cell was decreased as the number of AC cells was increased. In the presence of constant numbers of D cells and increasing numbers of AC cells, the plasminogen activator activity progressively decreased,

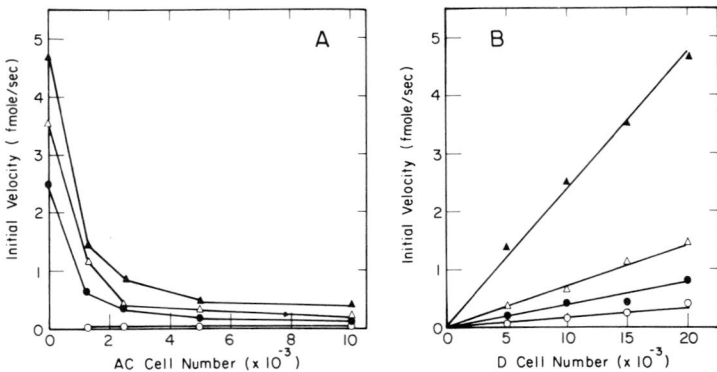

Fig. 72.2 Change in initial velocity for activation of plasminogen upon cocultivation of D and AC cells, with variation of AC cell number (A) or D cell number (B). (A) Microwells were seeded with the indicated number of AC cells and the following number of D cells: 20 000 (▲), 15 000 (△), 10 000 (●), or 0 (o). Sixteeen hours later, the cells were washed with PBS and incubated with 0.05 ml of 11 μM dog plasminogen for 20 min, and the resulting plasmin was titrated with FDE as described in Liu et al (1984). (B) Microwells were seeded with the indicated number of D cells and the following number of AC cells: 0 (▲), 1250 (△), 2500 (●), 5000 (o). The cells were treated and assayed as described in (A). The units for the initial velocity for the activation of plasminogen are femtomoles of plasmin produced per second.

Figure 72.2A. For example, the initial velocity for the activation of plasminogen by 20 000 D cells decreased by 79% by cocultivation with 1250 AC cells and by 89% by cocultivation with 5000 AC cells. In the presence of constant numbers of AC cells and increasing numbers of D cells, the plasminogen activator activity per D cell was constant, Figure 72.2B. As the AC cell number was increased, the plasminogen activator activity per D cell was decreased. In similar experiments with B cells, which have little or no plasminogen activator activity, no alteration of D cell plasminogen activator activity was observed (data not shown).

DISCUSSION

The major conclusions from these experiments are that the plasminogen activator activity of a tumorigenic cell, the D cell, can be severely inhibited by high cell densities but not low cell densities and by the presence of some cells, AC cells, but not others, B cells. In experiments not shown, the decrease in the plasminogen activator activity per D cell was the result of a decrease in the maximal velocity for the activation of plasminogen and not the result of a change in the Michaelis constant. Inhibition was not the result of the presence of a soluble inhibitor. Media from D cells growing at high cell density was not inhibitory when used to seed cells to grow at low cell density. When D cells were seeded in a drop adjacent but not touching a drop of AC cells and, after attachment, both cell types were covered by a common drop, no inhibition of D cell plasminogen activator activity was observed. Thus, inhibition by high cell density or by cocultivation seemed to require some sort of cell-cell contact.

These experiments define two major variables in assays of the plasminogen activator activity of cells growing in culture and may be relevant to the role of this enzyme in tumor formation and metastasis. The discrepancies among reports on the correlation between the plasminogen activator activity of cells in culture and the ability of those cells to form tumors and to metastasize may solely reflect differences in cell density or the presence of other cell types in the assay. If tumorigenic D cells were assayed at high densities and corresponding normal cells assayed at low densities, there would appear to be a lack of correlation between enhanced levels of plasminogen activator activity and tumorigenicity. Similarly, if tissue from the rat neurotumor RT4 were assayed for plasminogen activator activity, the presence of the AC cells might mask the high level of plasminogen activator activity of the D cells. The possible biological relevance of these experiments stems from the observation that the localization of a cell within a tumor influences its ability to metastasize and that for certain human neoplasms there is a secondary site preference for metastatic colonization (Nicolson, 1982).

REFERENCES

Imada M, Sueoka N 1978 Clonal sublines of rat neurotumor RT4 and cell differentiation. I. Isolation and characterization of cell lines and cell type conversion. Developmental Biology 66: 97–108
Imada M, Sueoka N, Rifkin D B 1978 Clonal sublines of rat neurotumor RT4 and cell differentiation. II. A conversion coupling of tumorigenicity and a glial property. Developmental Biology 66: 109–116
Leytus S P, Peltz G A, Liu H-Y, Cannon J F, Peltz S W, Livingston D C, Brocklehurst J R, Mangel W F 1981 A quantitative assay for the activation of plasminogen by transformed cells in situ and by urokinase. Biochemistry 20: 4307–4314
Liu H-Y, Peltz G A, Leytus S P, Livingston C, Brocklehurst J, Mangel W F 1980 Sensitive assay for plasminogen activator of transformed cells. Proceedings of the National Academy of Sciences USA 77: 3796–3800
Liu H-Y, Peltz S W, Mangel W F 1982 Modulation of the plasminogen activator activity of a transformed cell line by cell density. Molecular and Cellular Biology 2: 1410–1416
Liu H-Y, Yang P P, Toledo D L, Mangel W F 1984 Modulation of cell-associated plasminogen activator activity by cocultivation of a stem cell and its tumorigenic descendent. Molecular and Cellular Biology 4: 160–165
Nicolson G L 1982 Cancer metastasis: organ colonization and the cell-surface properties of malignant cells. Biochimica et Biophysica Acta 695: 113–176

73. Fibrinolysis and fibrin stabilizing factor (F.XIII) in patients with neoplasms

J. Kloczko, A. Zuch, M. Wojtukiewicz, M. Bielawiec and U. Buluk

The involvement of the intravascular fibrin deposition in tumor growth and metastasis has been strongly suggested by a number of clinical and experimental observations. The aim of our work was to estimate the relationship between plasma fibrinolytic activity and plasma factor XIII level against a background of other hemostasis parameters in patients with malignant neoplasms.

MATERIAL AND METHODS

The investigations were carried out on 198 patients (mean age — 57 ± 12) with inoperable malignant neoplasms. The following parameters were determined: factor XIII (FSF) level by measuring the plasma activity to convert fibrin polymers into insoluble clots in monochloroacetic acid (Buluk and Zuch), euglobulin lysis time — ELT (Chakrabarti et al), fibrin degradation products — FDP (Merskey et al), ethanol gelation test (Godal and Abildgaard), plasma fibrinogen as clottable protein by means of phenol reagent.

RESULTS

The patients revealed a significant prolongation of ELT, a substantial fall of FSF level and an elevation of FDP concentration (Table 73.1). Patients with positive ethanol test revealed significantly lower FSF level in comparison with not only healthy subjects but patients with a negative ethanol test as well.

Table 73.2 indicates different manners of both plasma fibrinolytic activity and FSF level in dependence on the localization of neoplasm. This comparison points out that a significant decrease of FSF level was present in the group of patients with ELT within the normal range as well as in the group with markedly inhibited fibrinolysis.

Table 73.3 points to the lack of correlation between ELT and FSF level in plasmas of patients with malignant neoplasms.

290

Table 73.1 Comparison of some coagulation–fibrinolytic parameters in patients with neoplasms and healthy persons

	Control (n = 37) Mean ± SD	Neoplasms (n = 198) Mean ± SD	Statistical significance
ELT (min)	184.3 ± 40.6	451.3 ± 301.8	t = 4.02 p<0.01
Factor XIII (units/ml)	49.8 ± 15.1	38.1 ± 19.9	t = 3.28 p<0.01
Fibrinogen (g/l)	3.0 ± 0.6	3.4 ± 1.9	t = 1.28 p>0.2
FDP (μg/ml)	6.7 ± 1.9	11.8 ± 11.6	t = 4.26 p<0.001
% of the positive ethanol tests	0	19.1	

Table 73.2 Euglobulin lysis time and factor XIII level in patients with different neoplasms

	No.	ELT (min) Mean ± SD	Factor XIII (units/ml) Mean ± SD
Ca mammae	37	417.4 ± 173.8	42.2 ± 17.5
Ca pulmonum	38	473.2 ± 248.2	43.1 ± 20.1
Ca ventriculi	19	268.0 ± 98.8	22.3 ± 12.6
Ca renis	11	655.0 ± 195.3	24.8 ± 12.4

Table 73.3 Correlations among the variables measured in 198 patients with neoplasms

Comparison	r	p
ELT/Factor XIII	−0.02	>0.1
ELT/Fibrinogen	+0.26	<0.01
ELT/FDP	+0.13	>0.1
Factor XIII/Fibrinogen	−0.24	<0.02

DISCUSSION

A markedly inhibited plasma fibrinolytic activity and a significant decrease of FSF level were found in patients with malignant tumors. These patients revealed an enhancement of FDP concentration and nearly 20% of them had a positive ethanol test. The analysis of the obtained results indicates different degree of inhibition of fibrinolysis as well as a decrease of FSF level in dependence on tumor localization. It allows us to think about dissimilarity of mechanisms leading to a defect of both of these enzymatic systems. In support of this suggestion a lack of correlation between ELT and FSF level was obtained.

A decreased fibrinolytic activity coexisting with an elevation of FDP concentration in the presence of correlation between ELT and fibrinogen concentration indicates that the observed changes could be a result of previous activation of the fibrinolytic system with a subsequent depletion of plasminogen activator in the blood stream. The largest decrease of FSF level in patients with a positive ethanol test in conjunction with negative correlation between FSF and fibrinogen concentration may indicate that an activation of coagulation causing consumption of both of these factors with secondary overproduction of fibrinogen was observed.

The ascertained discrepancies in manners of fibrinolytic activity and stabilization may exert an influence on the clinical course of neoplasm and metastasis formation through their modulating action on the hemostatic processes.

REFERENCES

Buluk K, Zuch A 1967 The possibility of proteolytic activation of the fibrin stabilizing factor. Biochimica et Biophysica Acta 147: 593–594
Chakrabarti R, Bielawiec M, Evans I F, Fearnley G R 1968 Methodological study and a recommended technique for determining the euglobulin lysis time. Journal of Clinical Pathology 21: 698–701
Godal H C, Abildgaard U 1966 Gelation of soluble fibrin in plasma by ethanol. Scandinavian Journal of Haematology 3: 342–350
Merskey G, Lalezari P, Johnson A J 1969 A rapid, simple, sensitive method for measuring of fibrinolytic split products in human serum. Proceedings of the Society for Experimental Biology and Medicine 131: 871–875

74. Immunological characterization of plasminogen activators in human prostatic tissue

H. Ljungnér and D. Bergqvist

Human prostatic tissue has a high content of plasminogen activators (PA) as determined by histochemical techniques (Kester, 1969). The activators are of two types, tissue like (t-PA) and urokinase like (UK). Using a sensitive enzyme-immunoassay Matsuo et al (1983) found a high concentration of t-PA in hyperplastic prostatic tissue extracts, whereas immunological histochemical techniques showed a relative high content of UK (Kirchheimer & Binder, 1983).

The aim of the present study was to characterize PA in human hyperplastic prostatic tissue by an immunologic histochemical fibrin slide technique.

MATERIAL AND METHODS

Tissue specimens were obtained from 20 men aged 65 to 82 years, all undergoing transvesical or transurethral prostatic resection. In all cases the histological diagnosis was hyperplasia.

PA activity was determined according to a modification of Todd's fibrin slide technique (Pandolfi et al, 1968). All specimens were incubated on fibrin films at 37°C for 45 min and fibrinolysis appeared after staining as white zones surrounded by bluish stained fibrin film.

Quenching of PA activity was studied using IgG antibodies, raised in goats, against t-PA (anti-t-PA) and against low molecular weight UK (anti-UK). The IgG fraction from a preimmune goat served as a control. The same concentration of the different IgG fractions were used (28 μg/ml) and 200 μl of each antiserum was incorporated into the fibrinogen solution. The method was described in detail by Ljungnér et al (1983).

RESULTS

There was no or very small areas of lytic zones in the fibrin slides when anti-t-PA was added, whereas the addition of anti-UK showed almost the same fibrinolytic activity as fibrin slides with and without IgG (control slide). A mixture of anti-t-PA and anti-UK quenched the activity completely.

293

COMMENTS

The results from the present study substantiate the finding that there are two types of PA responsible for activation of the fibrinolytic system in prostatic tissue. The first type, t-PA, is known to be confined in vein walls (Ljungnér et al, 1983). This activator is the main component of activators of blood after venous occlusion or the administration of DDAVP. The second type of PA, urokinase, which is demonstrable in most tissues in organ cultures (Holmberg et al, 1982) was found only in small amounts after an incubation period of 45 min. This finding further substantiates the suggestion that UK is present in tissues as an inactive precursor, 'pre-urokinase', which cannot be detected using histochemical techniques.

REFERENCES

Holmberg L, Kristoffersson A-C, Lecander I, Wallén P, Åstedt B 1982 Immunoradiometric quantification of tissue plasminogen activator secreted by fetal organs. Comparison with urokinase. Scandinavian Journal of Clinical and Laboratory Investigation 42: 347–354
Kester R C 1969 Plasminogen activator in the human prostate. Journal of Clinical Pathology 22: 442–446
Kirchheimer J, Binder B R 1983 Localization and immunological characterization of plasminogen activators in human prostate tissue. Haemostasis 13: 358–362
Ljungnér H, Holmberg L, Kjeldgaard A, Nilsson I M, Åstedt B 1983 Immunological characterization of plasminogen activators in the human vessel wall. Journal of Clinical Pathology 36: 1046–1049
Matsuo O, Kata K, Matsuo C, Matsuo T 1983 Determination of tissue plasminogen activator by an enzyme-immunoassay method. Analytical Biochemistry 135: 58–63
Pandolfi M, Robertson B, Isacson S, Nilsson I M 1968 Fibrinolytic activity of human veins in arms and legs. Thrombosis Diathesis Haemorrhagica 20: 247–256

75. Prolonged arrest of a spindle cell sarcoma by a proteolytic enzyme inhibitor: a case report

K.S. Zänker, G. Blümel, J. Lange and J.R. Siewert

Raised proteinase levels in tumour tissues are thought to play a role in tumorigenesis. Troll et al (1979) demonstrated that endogenous proteases are involved in the process of carcinogenesis, metastasis formation, tumour cell detachment and vascular invasion. It has been suggested that other antimetastatic agents, such as dimethyltriazenes, N-diazoacetyl-glycinamide and ICRT 159 may act through inhibitory effects on tumour proteinases (Giraldi et al, 1978). We have demonstrated in cell cultures that the synthetic protease inhibitor N,N-dimethylcarbamoylmethyl 4-(4-guanidinobenzoyloxy-) phenylacetate blocks protein- and DNA synthesis temporarily (Zänker, Trappe and Blümel, 1981). Based on our laboratory work and the reported effect on delayed appearance of 3-methylcholantrene induced skin tumours in mice, receiving the above mentioned protease inhibitor (Ohkoshi and Fujii, 1983), we decided to use this agent by informed consent in a 65-year-old lady.

CASE REPORT

The lady presented herself at our Hospital with multiple lung secondaries (chest x-ray) from a histologically verified spindle cell sarcoma of the right leg, which was treated surgically 18 months ago. At the time of admission, no other lesions could be imaged by CAT scans. The lady refused to be treated by chemotherapeutic agents, thus, no higher priority protocol existed.

The performance status of the patient was 90% on the Karnofsky scale. Estimated from experimental data in animals, the lady got 1,000mg of the protease inhibitor (FOY 305, Sanol Schwarz GmbH, Monheim, GFR) daily, divided into a 6 hour application cycle (250mg each).

CONFIRMATIONAL STUDIES

By means of fine needle aspiration biopsy, tumour material was obtained from one lung secondary (Scan picture A) and a cell culture was raised, the cells of which were mainly flattened (B) and showed plasminogen-dependent fibrinolysis.

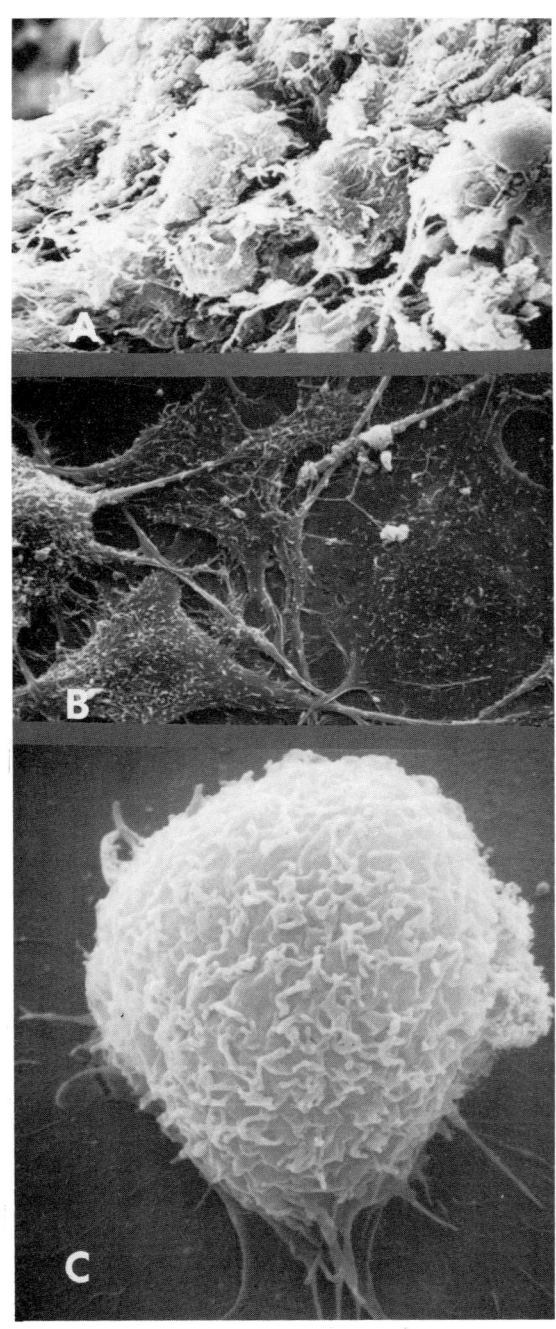

Fig. 75.1 Morphological heterogeneity of a spindle cell sarcoma (A) before (B) and after (C) treatment with a proteinase inhibitor. The cells in (C) were totally independent from plasminogen in respect to lyse a fibrin plate and not influenced in their capacity of lysis by FOY-305.

Consecutive x-ray pictures of the lung, taken for follow up, revealed that the initially faded-out tumour shadows become sharply edged and progression ceased; the Karnofsky index kept stable. The preponderant feature of a cell culture, cultivated from a second fine needle aspiration biopsy of an encapsulated lesion, likely by therapy, exposed spherical cells with membrane ruffling (C) and fibrinolysis was now independent from the presence of plasminogen in the assay system. The patient did well for nine months without any harmful side effects and enjoyed symptom-free life off chemotherapy. After that the secondaries escaped gradually from therapy and bone metastases developed, causing pathological fractures of the right femur and humerus; the patient died by disseminated disease.

COMMENTS

Metastasis as a selective process appears to be a relatively inefficient process so that only a few cells that invade the circulation survive the traumas of dissemination, arrest and extravasation. Moreover, if tissue degradation, which is mandatory for metastasis formation, can be prevented by proteolytic enzyme inhibition, cancer should be arrested. Because tumours progress in their host, it is reasonable to assume that tumour progression is also influenced by host homeostatic factors, selection pressures and biological diversity of the primary/metastases. The observation obtained by this case report suggests that proteinase inhibitor(s) might modify proteinase activity, necessary for tissue invasion, and, thus, preventing major metastases formation. However, prolonged time of tumour cell arrest does only mean tumour cell stasis and not tumour cell death. Once tumour cells dedifferentiate themselves in respect to realising and/or sessile degradative enzymes, rapid metastases formation becomes likely. It is to argue that the time of response, as seen in this case, is mostly influenced by the capability of a fraction of cells, within a given lesion, to grow 'silently', thus, escaping from the mode of action of the applied agent.

REFERENCES

Giraldi T, Houghton P J, Tayler D M, Nisi C 1978 Antimetastic action of some triazene derivatives against Lewis lung carcinoma in mice. Cancer Treatment Reports 62: 721–725
Ohkoshi M, Fujii S 1983 Effect of the synthetic protease inhibitor N,N-Dimehtylcarbamoylmethyl 4-(4-guanidinobenzoyloxy)- phenyl acetate methanesulfate on carcinogenesis by 3-methylcholantrene in mouse skin. Journal of National Cancer Institute 71: 1053–1057
Troll W, Belman S, Wiesner R, Shellabarger C J 1979 Protease action in carcinogenesis. In: Holzer H, Tschesche H (eds) Biological function of proteinases. Springer Verlag, Berlin, pp 165–170
Zänker K S, Trappe A, Blümel G 1981 Die Wirkung von FOY-305 auf Tumorzellen: Fakten und Fiktion. In: Grözinger K H, Schrey A, Wabnitz R W (eds) Proteinasen-Inhibition. Wolf and Sohn, München, pp 368–380

76. Plasminogen activator production by endothelial cells exposed to angiogenic stimuli

D.B. Rifkin and D. Moscatelli

PLASMINOGEN ACTIVATOR AND NEOVASCULARIZATION

One of the more intensely studied of normal invasive processes is neovascularization. During this process, the migrating endothelial cells degrade their basement membrane as well as stromal proteins such as collagen. In 1979, we postulated that when endothelial cells were stimulated by angiogenic factors to form new vessels they would secrete increased amounts of the proteases plasminogen activator (PA) and latent collagenase (Rohrlich and Rifkin). The PA secreted would then convert plasminogen to plasmin. Plasminogen is present in many tissue fluids and spaces and in its active form, plasmin, has been shown to be an effective activator of latent collagenase. Thus, two proteases are generated, plasmin and collagenase, and it is the combined activities of these two enzymes which is responsible for the degradation of the basement membrane proteins and collagen.

The hypothesis that exposure of endothelial cells to angiogenic factors induces the synthesis of PA and latent collagenase yields a number of predictions which can be tested using cultured endothelial cells as a model. One, capillary endothelial cells should respond to angiogenic factors or preparations by producing increased amounts of PA and latent collagenase. Two, this response should be specific to cells from the microvasculature and not to cells from large vessels since neovascularization occurs only from the microvasculature. Three, angiogenic factors can be identified and purified using the production of latent collagenase and PA as an assay.

When cultured bovine adrenal cortex capillary endothelial (BCE) cells are exposed to any of three different preparations, all of which are known to induce neovascularization in vivo, there is a significant increase in the amount of PA and collagenase produced by the cells (Table 76.1). The factors tested were an extract of bovine retinae (D'Amore et al), culture medium conditioned by mouse adipocytes (F 442A cells) (Castellot et al), and a sonicate from a human hepatoma cell line (Folkman). Each of these preparations induced both PA and latent collagenase in a dose responsive manner (Gross et al). The latent collagenase was shown to be a typical vertebrate collagenase capable of cleaving types I, II and III collagens. The PA made consisted of both the urokinase and tissue types.

Table 76.1

| Addition | PA (Fold stimulation over control) | | Collagenase | |
	BCE	BAE	BCE	BAE
Hepatoma lysate (0.86 mg)	9.9	4.3	55.3	2.4
Retinal extract (200 μg)	3.9	1.0	6.3	0
Adipocyte medium (150 μg/ml)	3.3	0.8	6.0	0
TPA (2×10^{-7}M)	4.8	2.3	17.5	0.9

BCE cells were grown to confluence in MEM supplemental with tumour conditioned medium and 10% donor calf serum. BAE cells were maintained until confluence in DME with 10% donor calf serum. The cells were then treated as described in Gross et al (1983).

When the responses of BCE cells were compared to those of bovine aortic endothelial (BAE) cells, it was observed that BCE cells are much more responsive to the angiogenic preparations than BAE cells (Table 76.1). The lack of response of the BAE cells was the most obvious when the levels of induced collagenase were compared between BAE and BCE cells. Similar results have been obtained comparing the responses of human umbilical vein endothelial cells to human foreskin capillary endothelial cells when exposed to angiogenic preparations (unpublished observations).

We have recently begun to isolate the protease inducing factor from the human hepatoma cells. The activity is non-dialyzable, heat labile, and stable within the pH range of 5.0–9.0. The activity from a crude sonicate elutes from Sephadex G-150 at a position slightly behind the void volume (Rifkin et al). However, if this material is rechromatographed in the presence of 1 M guanidine-HCl, the active fraction elute at a position corresponding to a molecular weight of about 20,000 daltons. Current efforts are concerned with the purification to homogeneity of this material so that studies can be performed on its mechanism of action, etc.

These studies have demonstrated that: (1) BCE cells respond to angiogenic preparations by producing PA and latent collagenase, (2) this appears to be a unique property of capillary endothelial cells, and (3) the ability to induce latent collagenase and PA may be used as an assay to isolated protease inducing factors. Although the correlation between protease induction and angiogenesis is strong, we have presented no proof that the in vitro assay of protease production is equivalent to the in vivo assay.

The ability to test in a quantitative way for specific biochemical changes that occur after cells are exposed to defined stimuli should permit the isolation of angiogenisis factors.

ACKNOWLEDGEMENT

This investigation was supported by grants from the NIH, American Cancer Society, and Kroc Foundation.

REFERENCES

Castellot J J, Karnovsky M J, Spiegelman B M 1980 Patent Stimulation of Vascular Endothelial Cell Growth by Differentiated 3T3 Adipocytes. Proceedings of the National Academy of Sciences (USA) 77: 6007–6011

D'Amore P A, Glaser B M, Brunson S K, Fenselau A H 1981 Angiogenic Activity from Bovine Retina: Partial Purification and Characterization. Proceedings of the National Academy of Sciences (USA) 78: 3068–3072

Folkman J 1974 Tumour Angiogenesis 1974 In: Klein G, Weinhouse S (eds) Advances in Cancer Research Vol 19 Academic Press, New York, p 331

Gross J L, Moscatelli D, Rifkin D B 1983 Increased Capillary Endothelial Cell Protease Activity in Response to Angiogenic Stimuli in vitro. Proceedings of the National Academy of Science (USA) 80: 2623–2627

Rifkin D B, Moscatelli D, Gross J, Jaffe E 1984 Proteases, Angiogensis, and Invasion. In: Nicolson G L, Milas L (eds) Cancer Invasion and Metastasis: Biologic and Therapeutic Aspects. Raven Press, New York, p 187

Rohrlich S T, Rifkin D B 1979 Proteases and Cell Invasion. In: Hess H-J (ed) Annual Reports in Medical Chemistry Vol 14, p 229

Section 10
EXTRACTIVE AND SEMI-SYNTHETIC FIBRINOLYTIC AGENTS

77. Fibrinolytic activity of heparin and low molecular weight heparin fractions

C. Doutremepuich, J.L. Gestreau, M.C. Kuttler,
A. Masse, F. Bousquet, F. Toulemonde,
E.G. Vairel and R. Quilichini

INTRODUCTION

In a previous study (1), it was shown that in an experimentally induced venous thrombosis in rats, heparin (M.W. = 14 000 d) and low molecular weight heparin fractions (LMWF) developed a thrombolysis.

The aim of this study was to specify this thrombolytic activity. Heparin and LMWF were administered alone or in association with an antifibrinolytic drug, Epsilon Amino Caproic Acid (EACA) to rats.

MATERIALS AND METHODS

Heparin and LMWF

Heparin was prepared from pig intestinal mucosa. Its anti-Xa activity was 170 units/mg.

LMWF were kindly provided by Choay Laboratory (CY 216 and CY 222).

* CY 216 had a molecular weight = 4000 d, an anti-Xa activity = 200 units/mg, an USP activity = 50 units/mg;

* CY 222 had a molecular weight = 2500 d, an anti-Xa activity = 250 units/mg, an USP activity = 20 units/mg.

Animals

90 male Wistar rats (200–250 g body weight) from Evic-Ceba Laboratory (Bordeaux, France) were used.

Experimentally induced venous thrombosis

An experimental venous thrombosis described by Reyers (3) had been modified for the purpose of this study.

Rats were anaesthetized by intraperitoneal injection of Ketalar (ND) (100mg/kg). The inferior vena cava was isolated and a ligature applied below the left renal vein branch. The abdomen was closed. Six hours later, the abdomen was reopened under Ketalar anaesthesia. The inferior vena cava was clamped 2 cms below the first ligature. This segment was emptied of blood and cut. The thrombus was removed and placed for 24 hours at 40°C.

Two control groups of untreated rats were studied. For the first control group, after six hours the mean thrombus dry weight was about twice the two hours (second control group). It reflects the thrombus extention.

Drug treatment
Nine groups of ten rats were randomly treated 90 min after the application of ligature. In the groups I to IV, only heparin (Gr I) or CY 216 (Gr II) or CY 222 (Gr III) or placebo (Gr IV) were subcutaneously injected at the dose of 10 mg/kg b.w. In the groups V to VIII, heparin subcutaneously injected at the dose of 10 mg/kg b.w. simultaneously with E.A.C.A. (1g/kg b.w.).

Assays
The anti-Xa activity was performed by the Yin-Wessler method modified by Stago Laboratory (Paris).(5)
The plasminogen activity was performed according to the method described by Marsh.(2)

RESULTS

The results of mean thrombus dry weight removed six hours after ligation are given in Figure 77.1. The mean thrombus dry weight removed two hours after ligation is: 1.22 + 1.20 mg.

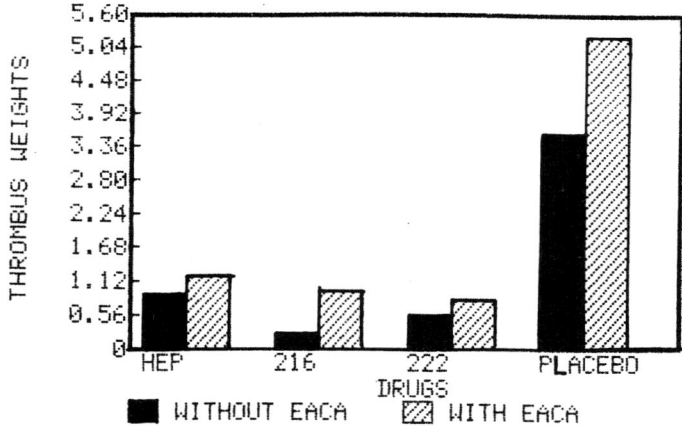

Fig. 77.1 Mean thrombus dry weight removed 6 hours after ligation of the vena cava, and 4 hours after drug administration.

The plasminogen activator values are given in Figure 77.2 and anti-Xa activity in Figure 77.3

COMMENTS

1. At high dosage, heparin and LMWF induced thrombolysis. This thrombolysis was inhibited by EACA. Indeed the mean thrombus dry weight of

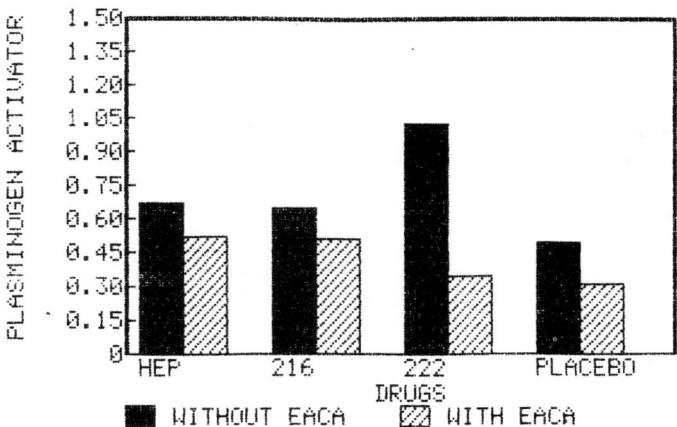

Fig. 77.2 Plasminogen activator value: 6 hours after ligation of the inferior vena cava and 4 hours after drug administration.

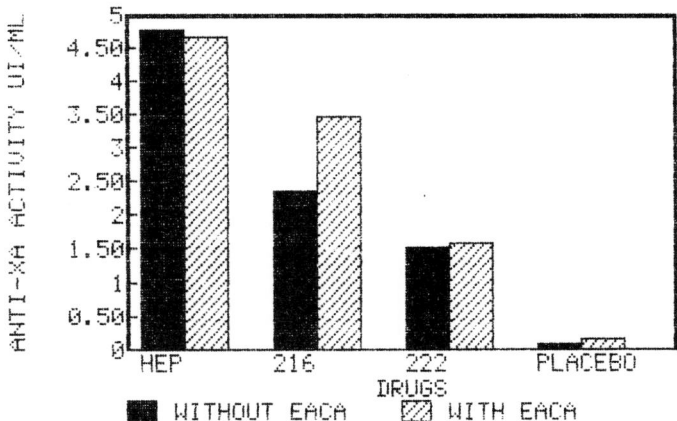

Fig. 77.33 Anti-Xa activity: 6 hours after ligation of the inferior vena cava and 4 hours after drug administration.

the treated groups with EACA gave the same results as the two hours control group. So in this situation we observed a limitation of the extention of the thrombus (anticoagulant effect) and an inhibition of the regression of the thrombus by EACA (thrombolysis effect).

2. Plasminogen activator was not so enhanced with heparin or LMWF as previously described. But in this situation, plasminogen activator was probably adsorbed on the thrombus.

IN CONCLUSION

Heparin and LMWF induced thrombolysis. Its mechanism is due, in first part to a release of plasminogen activator and in second part to its anticoagulant activity.
These studies suggest new possibilities for LMW heparin fractions.

305

REFERENCES

1. Doutremepuich C, Gestreau J L, Maury M O, Quilichini R, Boisseau M R, Toulemonde F, Vairel E G 1983 Experimental venous thrombosis in rats treated with heparin and a low molecular weight heparin fraction. Haemostasis 13: 109–112
2. Marsh M A, Gaffney P J 1977 The rapid fibrin plate-a method for plasminogen activator assay. Thrombosis-Haemostasis 38: 545–551
3. Reyers I, Mussoni L, Donati M B, De Gaetano G 1980 Failure of aspirin at different doses to modify experimental thrombosis in rats. Thromb. Res. 18: 669–674
4. Vairel E G, Bouty-Boye H, Toulemonde F, Doutremepuich C, Marsh N A, Gaffney P J 1983 Heparin and a low molecular weight fraction enhances thrombolysis and by this pathway exercises a protective effect against thrombosis. Thromb. Res. 30: 219–224
5. Yin E T, Wessler S, Buttler J V 1976 Plasma heparin unique practical submicrogram sensitive assay. J. Lab. Clin. Med. 81: 198–199

78. Enhancement of fibrinolysis by a low molecular weight heparin in patients with thromboembolism and defective response to venous occlusion

P.M. Molho, F.W. Dunn, T.L. Barzu, C. Soria, J. Soria, E. Dupuy and G.M. Tobelem

In addition to the main mechanisms of anticoagulant activity, the antithrombotic potency of heparin could be in relation to an enhanced fibrinolytic activity, specially in the case of low molecular weight heparin fractions (LMWH).(1) A defective response to venous occlusion (v.o.) and/or to de-amino-8-arginine vasopressine (DDAVP) infusion is frequently associated with recurrent thromboembolism (R.T.E.). It was therefore interesting to evaluate the profibrinolytic potency of heparin in patients with R.T.E., non responders to v.o. For the aim of this study, a LMWH was selected, for its longer half life and its great anti Xa/anti IIa activity ratio, lowering the bleeding risk.

MATERIAL AND METHODS

Patients and protocol

Eight patients with R.T.E., without signs of acute thrombosis were selected as non responders to v.o. (20 mn), at two subsequent determinations, and eventually (4/8 patients) non responders to DDAVP infusion. The LMWH, CY 222 (Institut Choay, Paris, Mw 1500–8000, anti IIa/anti Xa activity = 10) was administered at a daily dose of 1000 U anti Xa/kg in two subcutaneous injections, for four weeks. The kinetics of anti Xa activity for 24 hours was performed on day 2. The v.o. tests were performed always in the same conditions, 3 hours after the morning injection of CY 222, on day 0, day 2, every week during treatment, and one week after treatment was discontinued.

Methods

Anti Xa activity was measured on a chromogenic substrate (CBS 3139 from Diagnostic Stago).

Euglobulin lysis time (E.L.T.) and lysis area on fibrin plates (F.P.) were performed as previously described.(2,3)

Tissue plasminogen activator (tPA) was measured by a biological assay, according to a modification of Verheijen method.(4) The generation of plasmin in the presence of an excess of lys-plasminogen and fibrin monomers was measured each hour using S 2251 (Kabi, Stockholm, Sweden). A standard curve was established with purified tPA from melanoma (kindly provided by Dr. Lijnen). Results were expressed in mIU of urokinase (UK).

RESULTS AND COMMENTS

This study confirmed the high anti Xa/anti IIa activity and the long half life of a LMWH fraction, CY 222. 24 hours after a subcutaneous injection a significant anti Xa activity was still detectable. During the 4 weeks of treatment, no haemorhagic incident was registered, even with the high doses used in this protocol (1 000 U anti Xa/kg/day).

CY 222 enhanced the fibrinolytic response to v.o. in patients, as assessed by the shortening of the E.L.T. and the increase of the lysis area on F.P. observed in the blood samples taken after v.o. (Table 78.1). Apparently the effect was delayed, maximal on the third week, and disappeared soon after the treatment was discontinued.

Table 78.1   The fibrinolytic activity (ELT and FP tests) after venous occlusion in patients treated by CY 222

	Δ^* E.L.T. (in mn)			Δ^* Lysis area on F.P (in mm ^{2})		
Patients	Control before	CY 222 (3rd weeks)	Control after	Control before	CY 222 (3rd weeks)	Control after
1	15	120	0	77	281	13
2	30	125	90	48	275	200
3	15	165	NT	32	204	NT
4	40	130	80	39	172	75
5	0	135	60	0	200	48
6	10	160	40	57	145	100
7	40	15	50	38	75	20
8	50	20	0	36	29	16
$\overline{X}$	25	109	46	41	173	67.4
E.S.	± 6.1	± 20.5	± 11.9	± 7.8	± 31.3	± 21.9
P		< 0.01	> 0.1		< 0.01	> 0.3

*Δ: Difference between the values before and after venous occlusion

This profibrinolytic effect could be related to an increased release of tPA, as suggested by the biological assay (Table 78.2), or to an induced synthesis of tPA, especially in patients who were non responders to DDAVP.

Table 78.2   T.P.A. release after venous occlusion in the patients receiving CY 222

	Δ^* T.P.A. (in i.u. of U.K. $\times 10^{-3}$)		
Patients	Control	CY 222 (3rd weeks)	Control after
1	0	12.6	NT
2	5	117	NT
3	14	899	49
4	6.25	1655	2.1
X	6.4	680	25.5
	± 2.9	± 383	

*Δ: Difference between the value before and after venous occlusion

Our results are in agreement with previous studies in healthy volunteers(5) showing an indirect effect of LMWH heparin on the fibrinolytic system activity. Nevertheless, a crossover blind study is necessary to confirm these preliminary results.

REFERENCES

1. Vinazzer H, Stemberger A, Haas S, Blumel G 1982 Influence of heparin, of different heparin fractions, and of a low molecular weight heparin like substance on the mechanism of fibrinolysis. Thrombosis Research 27: 341–352
2. Marsh N A 1977 Measurement of fibrinolytic capacity by the euglobulin lysis time method — a problem of 'units'. Thrombosis Research 12: 197–200
3. Marsh N A, Gaffney P J 1977 The rapid fibrinplate — a method for plasminogen activator assay. Thrombosis Haemostasis 38: 545–551
4. Verheijen J H, Mullaart E, Chang G T G, Kluft C, Wijngaards G 1982 A simple, sensitive spectrophotometric assay for extrinsic (tissue type) plasminogen activator applicable to measurements in plasma. Thrombosis Haemostasis 48: 266–269
5. Vairel E G, Bouty-Boye H, Toulemonde, Doutremepuich C, Marsh N A, Gaffney P J 1983 Heparin and a low molecular weight fraction enhances thrombolysis and by this pathway exercises a protective effect against thrombosis. Thrombosis Research 30: 219–224

79. Alteration of haemostatic and fibrinolytic components during minor and major surgery. Effect of LMW heparin

E. Melissari, M.F. Scully, T. Paes and V.V. Kakkar.

In this present study we have 1) evaluated changes in haemostatic and fibrinolytic components in patients undergoing minor or major surgery (since these two forms of surgery may be expected to produce different degrees of trauma) and 2) examined the effect of prophylactic low molecular weight (LMW) heparin on these changes thereby relating them to the condition of hypercoagulability.

Patients

The series consisted of 44 patients: 22 undergoing minor elective surgery (average age 50 years) and 22 undergoing major abdominal surgery (average age 49 years). Half of the patients in each group received 5000 units (antifactor Xa units) of LMW heparin (Choay, Paris, France) subcutaneously 2 hours prior to sampling. In patients undergoing major surgery heparin was continued at a single dose per day for 7 days. Blood samples were withdrawn: pre-operation (PO), post-anaesthesia (PA), during operation (DO) and 24 hours after operation (24hr).

Methods

Plasminogen activator was measured by ECLT and on fibrin plates. Factor VIII:C by a modified APTT using haemophilic plasma (VIII:C $< 1\%$) in the presence of kaolin. Factor VIIIRiCoF was measured by agglutination of washed fixed platelets using fixed amounts of plasma and ristocetin. Factor VIIIR:Ag and protein C were quantitated by rocked immunoelectrophoresis. Fibrinogen was by clotting assay, APTT as usual, plasminogen, fast α2 antiplasmin by amidolytic assay using S2251 substrate. ATIII using S2238 and prekallikrein using S2302. Statistical analysis was by Mann-Whitney U test.

Results

Fibrinolytic activity: Release of activator by ECLT and on fibrin plates is seen at PA ($p < 0.05$) reaching a peak at DO ($p < 0.005$) and a depletion is observed at 24hr ($p < 0.05$) when compared to PO levels. Heparin prophylaxis did not change the pattern of activator release.

Factor VIII components: No significant changes were observed in factor VIII components at PA and DO stages. Thus at these stages the highest level of plasminogen activator was not associated with maximal release of factor VIII. A marked increase of factor VIII was observed at 24hr (VIIIR:Ag p<0.002 in minor and in major VIIIRiCoF p<0.002 VIIIR:Ag p<0.002). Heparin prophylaxis did not affect the changes in factor VIII components in minor operation but in major operation (greater degree of trauma) factor VIIIR:Ag was increased at DO in heparin treated patients (p<0.002) as opposed to the control group (p<0.02) perhaps through a thrombin mediated control mechanism. Also in the major control group the ratio factor VIII:C/VIIIR:Ag increased to 1.7-fold at DO and to 1.64-fold at 24hr but remained at 1 at similar stages in the treated group.

Other Haemostatic and Fibrinolytic Tested Components
Fibrinogen: Induction of anaesthesia decreased fibrinogen (p<0.002) and a further fall was observed at DO (p<0.002). The levels of fibrinogen in control and in heparin treated group were not different at any stage.

APTT: A significant shortening was observed at 24hr (p<0.05 in minor and in major p<0.002). Under heparin prophylaxis a marked prolongation of APTT was seen at all stages compared to control (PA, DO, 24hr p<0.002 in minor and in major DO p<0.05, 24hr p<0.002). The prolongation of APTT seen at 24hr was apparently unrelated to heparin concentration since at this stage the patients (undergoing minor operation) had received no heparin for 24 hours.

ATIII fell at all stages (PA, DO, 24hr p<0.05) while in the treated group ATIII fell to a lesser degree than in control (at DO p<0.005 in minor and in major at 24hr p<0.05).

Prekallikrein fell at all stages (PA, DO, 24hr p<0.002 in minor and in major PA p<0.004, 24hr p<0.004). In the treated group higher levels of prekallikrein were seen at all stages of operation compared to control (PA, DO, 24hr p<0.002 in minor and in major at 24hr p<0.005). The higher levels of ATIII and the lesser fall in prekallikrein under heparin prophylaxis may suggest that heparin minimised depletion of ATIII and in vivo activation of the contact system.

Plasminogen fell at PA and DO (p<0.005) but returned to PO level at 24hr stage. A similar pattern of changes was exhibited in the treated minor group whereas in major treated higher levels were observed at DO (p<0.05) compared to control group.

Fast α_2 antiplasmin fell at PA and DO (p<0.005) but became significantly higher than PO level at 24hr (p<0.005). Under heparin prophylaxis the pattern of change of fast α_2 antiplasmin was similar to control though lower levels were seen at DO (p<0.05) in minor and at 24hr (p<0.002) in major treated compared to control.

Protein C (Table 79.1) levels fell significantly at the 24hr stage in the control and in the treated group but the level in the heparin treated group at 24hr was

Table 79.1 % reduction of protein C levels at 24hr post-operation in relation to PO levels

	X ± SE	p values
Minor + major control	9.8 ± 3	p<0.014
Minor + major treated	14.8 ± 5	p<0.05
(Minor + major) control v (minor + major) treated		p<0.007

significantly lower than control suggesting perhaps that this stage depletion may not be entirely related to activation by thrombin and subsequent clearance (Esmon, 1983).

Comments
Heparin modified therefore the activation of coagulation although the lower level of fast α_2 antiplasmin and protein C seen under heparin prophylaxis may suggest some interaction of heparin with the fibrinolytic system or effect on acute phase synthesis.

REFERENCES

Esmon C T 1983 Protein C, Biochemistry, Phsyiology and Clinical Implications. Blood 62: 1155–1158

312

80. Pentosan polysulphate-induced release of plasminogen activator

H-P. Klöcking and F. Markwardt

Previous studies have shown that pentosan polysulphate is able to release plasminogen activator from the isolated pig ear (Markwardt & Klöcking, 1977). This communication is concerned with the effects of pentosan polysulphate in isolated preparations (rabbit ear, rat lung) and in the whole animal (rabbit, rat). Moreover, the antithrombotic effect of pentosan polysulphate is demonstrated.

MATERIAL AND METHODS

Pentosan polysulphate: SP 54 (Benechemie, München, FRG).

Perfusion: Activator release was studied at constant perfusion volume in the isolated perfused rat lung (Klöcking et al, 1981) and in the isolated perfused rabbit ear. The method used for rabbit ear was similar to that of perfusion of pig ear (Markwardt & Klöcking, 1981).

Determination of plasminogen activator activity: Plasminogen activator activity was assayed in euglobulin fractions prepared from plasma samples or perfusates on plasminogen-rich fibrin plates (Kluft & Brakman, 1975).

Venous stasis procedure: To assess the effect of pentosan polysulphate on clot formation in the absence and presence of an antifibrinolytic agent, the Wessler procedure (Wessler et al, 1954) was modified. Human serum was replaced by a thrombogenic prothrombin complex concentrate.

RESULTS

Pentosan polysulphate was found to release plasminogen activator from the isolated perfused rabbit ear and isolated perfused rat lung (Fig. 80.1). The release reaction could be induced several times. The activator released was characterised to be plasminogen activator of tissue type.

Following intravenous administration of 5 mg pentosan polysulphate/kg in rabbits and rats the fibrinolytic activity was enhanced (Fig. 80.2).

Activation of the intrinsic activator was of secondary importance for the

313

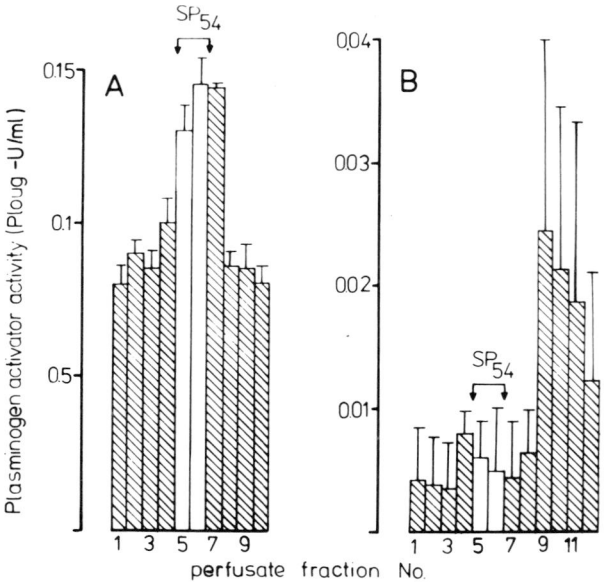

Fig. 80.1 Plasminogen activator release during perfusion of rabbit ear (A) and rat lung (B) with Tyrode's solution (▨) and Tyrode's solution containing pentosan polysulphate (SP 54) (▢) (A: 200 μg/ml, B: 10 μg/ml).

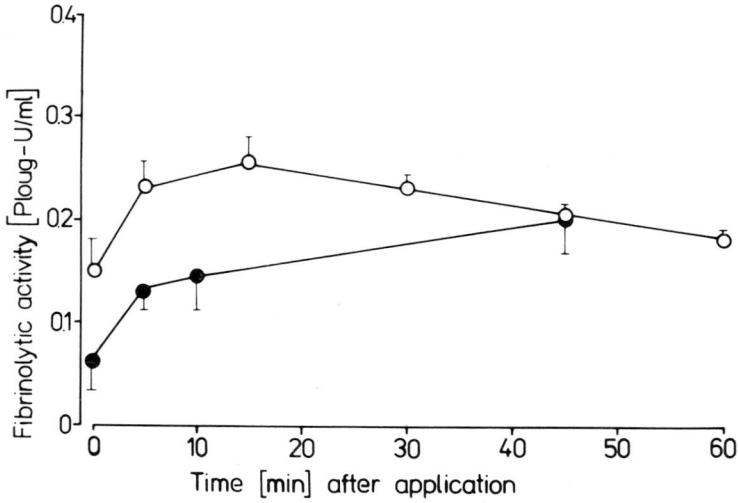

Fig. 80.2 Influence of pentosan polysulphate (5 mg/kg i.v.) on the fibrinolytic activity of plasma in rabbits (O) and rats (●).

fibrinolytic activity induced by pentosan polysulphate. Pentosan polysulphate inhibited the development of experimentally induced thrombi in the jugular vein of rats. This antithrombotic action was prevented by pre-treatment with the antifibrinolytic agent p-aminomethylbenzoic acid (PAMBA) (Table 80.1).

Table 80.1 Influence of pentosan polysulphate (SP 54) on clot formation induced by stasis and thrombogenic prothrombin complex concentrate (200 U F. IX/kg i.v.) in rats

Pretreatment	n	Mean score
Control	8	3.0
SP 54 (3.2 mg/kg i.v.)	8	0.125
PAMBA (100 mg/kg s.c.) + SP 54 (3.2 mg/kg i.v.)	8	3.0

CONCLUSIONS

The fibrinolytic state induced by pentosan polysulphate is mainly due to the release of vascular tissue-type plasminogen activator into the blood.

The antithrombotic effect of pentosan polysulphate may be explained in part by the activation of the fibrinolytic system.

REFERENCES

Markwardt F, Klöcking H-P 1977 Heparin-induced release of plasminogen activator. Haemostasis 6: 370–374
Klöcking H-P, Jablonowski Ch, Markwardt F 1981 Studies on the release of plasminogen activator from the isolated rat lung by serine proteinases. Thrombosis Research 23: 375–379
Markwardt F, Klöcking H-P 1978 Einfluß von Mediatoren auf die Freisetzung von Plasminogenaktivatoren. Acta Biologica et Medica Germanica 37: 1603–1610
Kluft C, Brakman P 1975 The effect of flufenamate on euglobulin fibrinolysis: involvement of C1-inactivator. In: Davidson J F, Samama M, Desnoyers P C (eds) Progress in chemical fibrinolysis and thrombolysis. Raven Press, New York, vol 2, p 375–381
Wessler S, Reimer S M, Sheps M C 1954 Biologic assay of thrombosis inducing activity in human serum. Journal of Applied Physiology 6: 943–946

81. Pentosan polysulfate (SP 54): mechanism of action on blood coagulation and fibrinolysis after intravenous injection of four different concentrations in healthy volunteers

J. Sampol, E. Angles-Cano, P. Benchimol, H. Diner, B. Boutiere and Y. Sultan

We studied the effects of Pentosan Polysulfate (PSP) on blood coagulation and fibrinolysis after IV injection in healthy volunteers.

MATERIAL AND METHODS

Healthy volunteers and PSP administration

8 men (30 ± 5 years) without any cardiovascular, hepatic or renal affection, and any haemostasis disorder.

PSP was injected at four concentrations (25, 50, 75 and 100 mg) with one week interval, samples were obtained from each volunteers as following: before injection (J0), after injection, 15′, 30′, 60′, 180′, 360′ post injection (J1) and 24 hours post injection (J2).

Methods

Coagulation studies were performed with classical methods and fibrinolytic activity was tested on fibrin agar plates and with the Euglobulin Lysis Time (ELT).

RESULTS

The variations (means ± s.e.m.) of the parameters significantly modified are shown in the Figure 81.1.

APTT presented a significant ($p < 0.005$) and dose dependent elevation with a peak level 15′ post injection and a return to normal level six hours after injection. PT showed a marked shortening ($p < 0.01$) with a minimum 15′ post injection. A maximum decrease of Factor V was observed 15′ after PSP injection. It isn't dose dependent but return to normal level is slower with high doses (75 mg, 100 mg). The effect of PSP on TT required at least 50 mg concentration ($p < 0.005$) with a peak level 15′ post injection, proportional to PSP concentration.

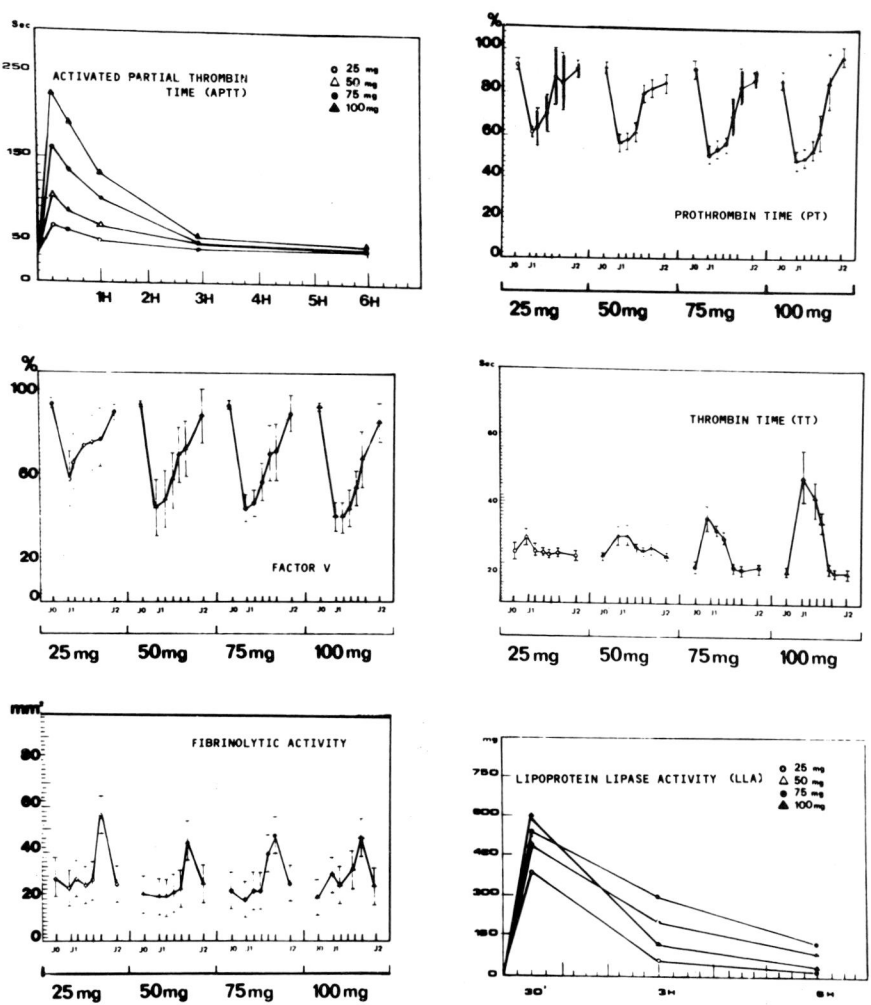

Fig. 81.1 Variations of APTT, PT, Factor V, TT, fibrinolytic activity and lipoprotein lipase activity.

Fibrinolysis activity of euglobulines on fibrin agar plates was weak but significantly increased six hours after injection ($p < 0.05$). LLA was significantly increased reacting a maximum 30′ post injection and was dose dependent.

COMMENTS

It is of interest to note the marked elevation of APTT which may be due to the inhibition of factor Xa generation.(1) This inhibition could be generated by the impairment of the complex IXa VIII Ca^{++} phospholipids or by the impairment of factor IXa generation.

The important lipoprotein lipase activity could also modify the phospholipids and contribute at the prolongation of APTT.

The decrease of factor V could be related to the polysulfate structure of PSP providing a high negative charge, in agreement with the data obtained in vitro by Boffa et al.(2)

The fibinolysis activity is weak and also delayed, compared to clotting modifications the plasminogen activator release from the vascular endothelium could suggest.(3) But the mechanism has to be determined according to the concentration and the ways of PSP injections.

REFERENCES

1. Fischer A M, Barrowcliffe W, Thomas D P 1982 A comparison of Pentosan Polysulfate (SP 54*) and Heparin. I: Mechanism of action on blood coagulation. Thrombosis and Haemostasis 47: 104–108
2. Boffa M C, Dreyer B, Pusineri C 1984 Plasma contact activation and decrease of factor V activity on negatively charged polyelectrolytes. Thrombosis and Haemostasis 51: 61–64
3. Bergqvist D, Nilsson I M 1981 A sulphated polysaccharid. The effect in vivo and in vitro on the haemostatic system in healthy volunteers. Thrombosis Research 23: 309–315

82. Clinical and experimental data on the fibrinolytic action of pentosan polysulphate

H. A. Vinazzer

A fibrinolytic action of heparin and of heparin analogues could be shown a long time ago (Halse 1950; Vinazzer 1951) but only recently detailed investigations were carried out (Markwardt 1977; Vinazzer 1981; Vairel 1983). An enhancement of fibrinolysis was also found when Polyanion SP 54, a low molecular weight heparin analogue obtained by sulfatation of Xylan, was examined. An in vitro effect on the euglobulin lysis time (ELT) was explained by an endogenous mechanism triggered by partial activation of factor XII (Vinazzer 1982; Marsh and Gaffney 1983).

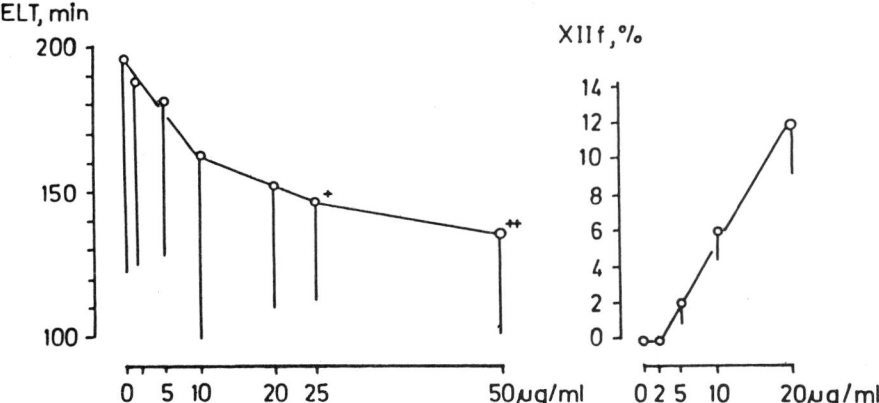

Fig. 82.1 Influence of Polyanion SP 54 on the ELT in vitro. n = 1, 0, M and SEM. Left: Euglobulin lysis time; right: activated soluble factor XII after addition of SP 54 to plasma samples.

An additional in vivo effect was found to be caused by an increase of the vascular activator of fibrinolysis (Gaffney 1982; Vinazzer 1982). Polyanion SP 54 was shown to shorten the ELT also after oral administration though the dose had to be considerably higher than after injection (Vinazzer 1982, Fig. 82.2).

The oral effect did not diminish during administration of the substance over a prolonged period of time (Marsh and Gaffney 1983).

After these results were known, a long term study with Polyanion SP 54 was carried out in patients suffering from cerebral thrombo-embolic episodes. A total

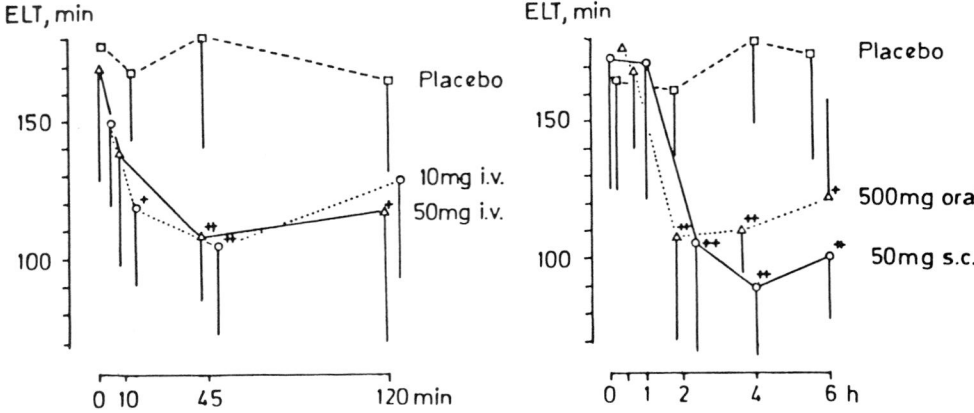

Fig. 82.2 Influence of SP 54 on ELT in vivo after i.v. and s.c. injection and after oral administration. +: p below 0.05, + +: p below 0.01.

of 231 cases was on a screening program for the detection of possible risk factors from thromboembolism. In all these cases ELT's before and after venous occlusion, assays of the activity of Antithrombin III and platelet aggregation tests were carried out. General data of the patients are given in Table 82.1.

Table 82.1 Patients after TIA, PRIND or cerebral thrombosis, general data

	male	female
n	164	67
age	58.5 ± 9.4	60.3 ± 7.7
TIA	126	47
PRIND	30	15
Cerebral Infarction	8	5

The results of the coagulation tests are shown in Table 82.2.

Table 82.2 Risk factors found in the clotting system.

	n
Activator of fibrinolysis diminished	45
Platelet aggregation increased	39
Hyperaggregation plus hypofibrinolysis	41
Antithrombin III below 70%	12
Other risk factors	49
No risk factor detectable	21
Not evaluable because of therapy	24

The original aim of this study was the wish to provide a more specific prophylactic therapy. For this reason, 86 patients in whom the main deficiency was a diminished activity of the vascular activator of fibrinolysis received a daily oral dose of 300 mg Polyanion SP 54. 58 patients with an increased platelet aggregation were given a daily dose of 250 mg ASA and 12 patients in whom AT III was diminished were anticoagulated and Phenprocoumone. In the former two groups ELT's were repeatedly carried out in order to examine the long term effect of Polyanion SP 54 on fibrinolysis. The ASA group served as controls. In 52 patients on SP 54 and in 39 patients on ASA controls could be made up to one year after the beginning of therapy (Table 82.3).

Table 82.3 Influence of therapy on ELT (ELT in units)

	SP 54 (n = 52)	ASA (n = 39)	p
Initial	5.77 ± 2.27	11.77 ± 2.72	0.001
1 month	12.87 ± 9.69	12.15 ± 6.24	n.s.
3 months	20.32 ± 15.60	12.19 ± 4.48	0.01
6 months	19.21 ¼ 13.40	13.17 ± 4.07	0.05
12 months	17.52 ± 13.07	11.54 ± 3.59	0.05

These results show that by a daily oral dose of 300 mg SP 54 the ELT could be significantly shortened and that this effect did not diminish within a period of one year. The study is still going on. It is therefore, too early for a clinical evaluation of the prophylactic value of this therapy in cases with a diminished fibrinolysis.

REFERENCES

Gaffney P J, Marsh N A, Thomas D P 1982 The influence of heparin and heparin-like substances on the fibrinolytic system in vivo. (Abstract) Haemostasis 12/1, 85
Halse Th 1950 Heparin und Heparinoide, Dicumarol. Hirzel S (ed) Zurich
Markwardt F, Klöcking H-P 1977 Heparin-induced release of plasminogen activator. Haemostasis 6, 370–374
Marsh N A, Gaffney P J 1983 The effect of pentosan polysulphate on the fibrinolytic system of man. (Abstract): Thrombos. Haemostas. 50, 83
March N A, Gaffney P J, Stiff G H, Doutremepuich C 1983 Pentosan polysulphate induced thrombolysis in an in vivo rat model. (Abstract) Thrombos. Haemostas. 50, 303
Vairel E G, Bouty-Boye H, Toulemonde F, Doutremepuich C, Marsh N A, Gaffney P J 1983 Heparin and a low molecular weight heparin fraction enhances thrombolysis and by this pathway exercises a protective effect against thrombosis. Thromb. Res. 30, 219–224
Vinazzer H 1951 Untersuchungen über die fibrinolytische Wirkung des Heparins. Wien.Z.Inn.Med. 32, 167–173
Vinazzer H, Stemberger A, Haas S, Merkel Ch 1981 Beeinflussung der Gerinnung durch niedermolekulare Heparinanaloge. In: Blümel, Haas S (ed) Mikrozirkulation und Prostaglandinstoffwechsel. F.K. Schattauer, Stuttgart — New York 415–420
Vinazzer H, Stemberger A, Haas S, Blümel G 1982 Influence of heparin, of different heparin fractions and of a low molecular weight heparin-like substance on the mechanism of fibrinolysis. Thromb. Res. 27: 341–352

83. Pharmacokinetics of defibrotide and of its profibrinolytic activity in different animal species. Effects on the levels of fibrinolysis inhibitors and of fibrinogen/fibrin degradation products (FDP) (*DCI)

R. Porta, R. Pescador, M. Mantovani, R. Niada, G. Prino and M. Madonna

Defibrotide, a natural polydeoxyribonucleotide, has significant profibrinolytic activities when injected i.v. into rabbits, cats and dogs (Fig. 83.1). Defibrotide increases both total plasmin and plasminogen (Fig. 83.2).

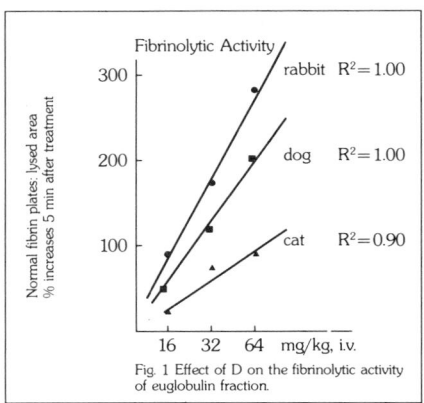

Fig. 1 Effect of D on the fibrinolytic activity of euglobulin fraction.

Fig. 83.1

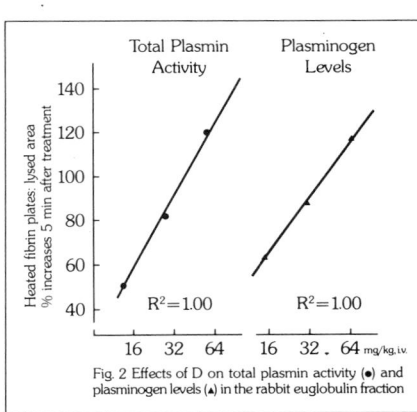

Fig. 2 Effects of D on total plasmin activity (●) and plasminogen levels (▲) in the rabbit euglobulin fraction

Fig. 83.2

R^2 indicate the reliability of the correlation.

These effects are present even when Defibrotide is injected i.v. into rabbits twice a day for 14 weeks (Fig. 83.3).

Moreover, under these experimental conditions Defibrotide progressively increases the plasminogen level (Fig. 83.4).

These assays were performed according to Astrup and Müllertz, Brakman, Hedner and Nilsson.

Defibrotide inactivates fibrinolysis inhibitors and returns experimentally enhanced antiplasmin activity to normal values (Fig. 83.5).

Antiplasmin activity was measured by the method of Bozzo et al, levels of inhibitors were increased in rats by Triton WR 1339 and in rabbits by thrombin. (Mantovani; Prino and Mantovani).

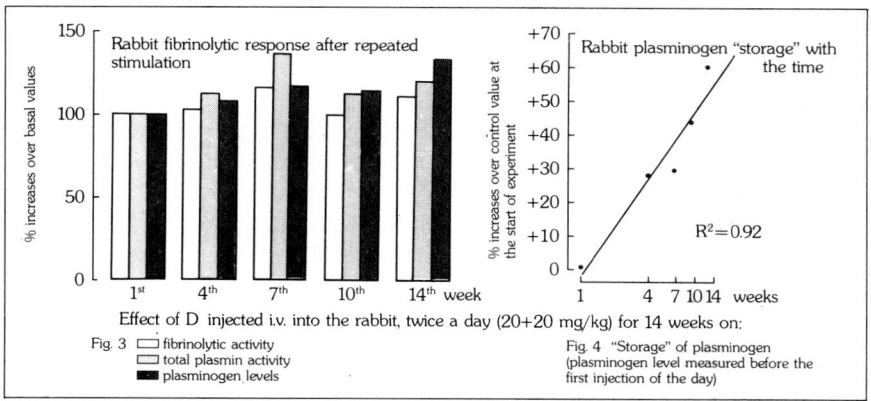

Rabbit fibrinolytic response after repeated stimulation

% increases over basal values

1st 4th 7th 10th 14th week

Rabbit plasminogen "storage" with the time

% increases over control value at the start of experiment

$R^2 = 0.92$

1 4 7 10 14 weeks

Effect of D injected i.v. into the rabbit, twice a day (20+20 mg/kg) for 14 weeks on:

Fig. 3 ☐ fibrinolytic activity
☐ total plasmin activity
■ plasminogen levels

Fig. 4 "Storage" of plasminogen (plasminogen level measured before the first injection of the day)

Fig. 83.3   **Fig. 83.4**

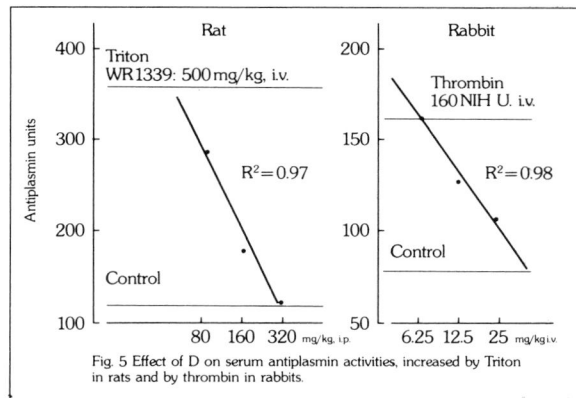

Rat

Triton
WR 1339: 500 mg/kg, i.v.

Antiplasmin units

$R^2 = 0.97$

Control

80 160 320 mg/kg, i.p.

Rabbit

Thrombin
160 NIH U. i.v.

$R^2 = 0.98$

Control

6.25 12.5 25 mg/kg i.v.

Fig. 5 Effect of D on serum antiplasmin activities, increased by Triton in rats and by thrombin in rabbits.

Fig. 83.5

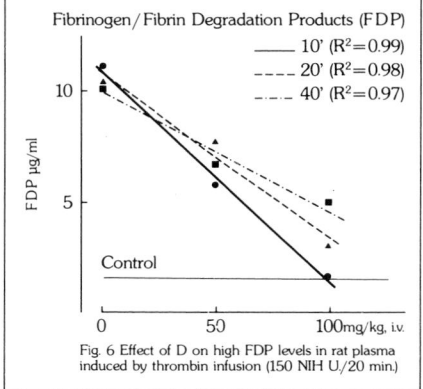

Fibrinogen / Fibrin Degradation Products (FDP)

———— 10' ($R^2 = 0.99$)
- - - - 20' ($R^2 = 0.98$)
—·—·— 40' ($R^2 = 0.97$)

FDP µg/ml

Control

0 50 100 mg/kg, i.v.

Fig. 6 Effect of D on high FDP levels in rat plasma induced by thrombin infusion (150 NIH U./20 min.)

Fig. 83.6

Defibrotide injected i.v. into rabbits, reduces the high FDP levels induced by thrombin infusion (Mantovani) (Fig. 83.6).

FDP were measured by the Staphylococcal Clumping Test (Biochemia Kit n. 126578), as suggested by Hawiger.

It must be emphasized that Defibrotide has no anticoagulant activity and, in particular, does not modify fibrinogen levels (Prino et al, 1977).

Curves of disappearance of Defibrotide from plasma after a rapid single i.v. injection into the rabbit and the cat, show a two compartment open model (Figs. 83.7, 83.10). Increasing the dose notably slows Defibrotide elimination, as shown by the decrease in β with increasing dose.

As a consequence of this, the $T\frac{1}{2}$ is also strongly dose-dependent (Figs. 83.7, 83.10). Since profibrinolytic activity is a function of plasma Defibrotide concentration (Figs. 83.9, 83.12) the kinetics of this activity are also dose-dependent. The decrease in this activity is clearly dose-dependent in the rabbit (Fig. 83.8) and to a lesser degree in the cat (Fig. 83.11).

The rapid appearance of fibrinolytic activity in blood (Figs. 83.8, 83.11) could be the result of either promotion by Defibrotide of release into the blood stream of tissue activators or antagonism of inhibitors of fibrinolysis (antiplasmin and anti-activators of plasminogen) already present in the blood stream, or both.

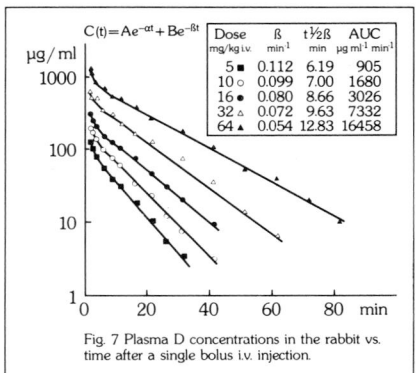

Fig. 7 Plasma D concentrations in the rabbit vs. time after a single bolus i.v. injection.

Fig. 83.7

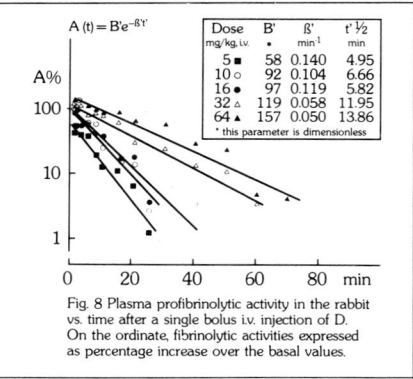

Fig. 8 Plasma profibrinolytic activity in the rabbit vs. time after a single bolus i.v. injection of D. On the ordinate, fibrinolytic activities expressed as percentage increase over the basal values.

Fig. 83.8

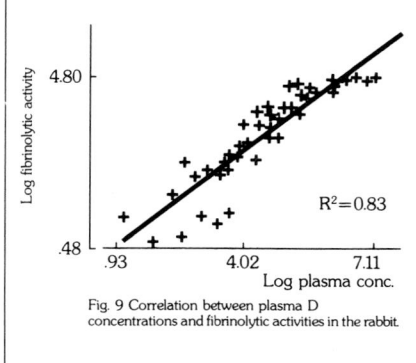

Fig. 9 Correlation between plasma D concentrations and fibrinolytic activities in the rabbit.

Fig. 83.9

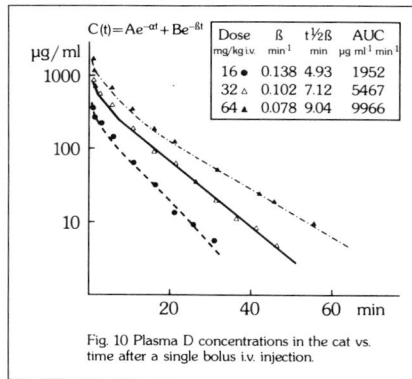

Fig. 10 Plasma D concentrations in the cat vs. time after a single bolus i.v. injection.

Fig. 83.10

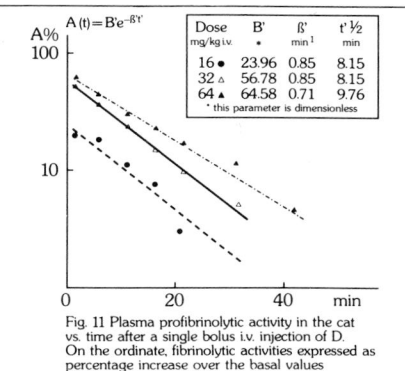

Fig. 11 Plasma profibrinolytic activity in the cat vs. time after a single bolus i.v. injection of D. On the ordinate, fibrinolytic activities expressed as percentage increase over the basal values

Fig. 83.11

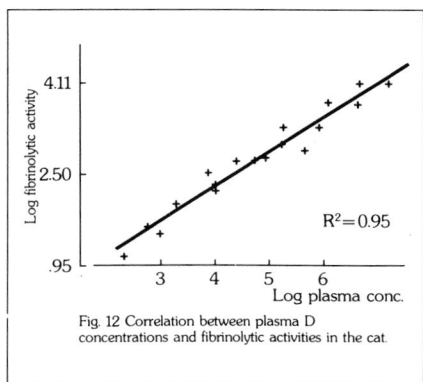

Fig. 12 Correlation between plasma D concentrations and fibrinolytic activities in the cat.

Fig. 83.12

Defibrotide in plasma was measured as described in Pescador et al. Fibrinolytic activity was determined by the methods of Astrup and Müllertz and Brakman.

REFERENCES

Astrup T, Müllertz S 1952 The fibrin plate method for estimating fibrinolytic activity. Archives of Biochemistry and Biophysics 40: 346–351

Bozzo A, Piomelli S, Schettini F 1956 Titolazione del potere antifibrinolitico del siero umano: descrizione di una nuova metodica. Rivista Istituto Sierotera pico Italiano 31: 362–367

Brakman P 1967 Fibrinolysis. A standardized fibrin plate method and a fibrinolytic assay of plasminogen. Scheltema and Holkema NV, Amsterdam

Hawiger J, Niewiarowski S, Gurewich V, Thomas D P 1970 Measurement of fibrinogen and fibrin degradation products in serum by staphylococcal clumping test. Journal of Laboratory and Clinical Medicine 75: 93–108

Hedner U, Nilsson I M 1974 Methods. In: Nilsson I M (ed) Haemorrhagic and Thrombotic Disease, John Wiley and Son, London, p 228–229

Mantovani M, unpublished data

Mussoni L, Evolvi C, Donati M B 1979 Activation of plasma and vascular fibrinolytic activity by a polydeoxyribonucleotidic substance, Fraction P, in rats and rabbits. VIIth Int. Congress on Thrombosis and Haemostasis (London, 15–20 July), Abs 0922, Poster Session. Thrombosis Haemostasis 42: 388

Pescador R, Mantovani M, Prino G, Madonna M 1983 Pharmacokinetics of Defibrotide and of its profibrinolytic activity in the rabbit. Thrombosis Research 30: 1–11

Prino G, Mantovani M 1970 Antiplasmin activity in rat serum after acidification, euglobulin precipitation and treatment with Triton or carbon tetrachloride. Coagulation 3: 273–278

Prino G, Mantovani M, Niada R, Coccheri S, Butti A 1977 Indagini preliminari sull'attività fibrinolitica, nell'animale e nell'uomo, di una nuova sostanza presente in diversi organi animali. In: La ricerca scientifica nell'industria farmaceutica in Italia. Simposio Internazionale (Roma, Ottobre 2–4 1975). Proceedings, Ferro Edizioni, Milano, p 557–560

84. Some observations in man with a new extractive drug: defibrotide

O.N. Ulutin, N. Ilhan-Berkel and
S. Balkuv-Ulutin

Defibrotide is a new extractive drug obtained from mammalian lung which has fibrinolytic and antithrombotic effect. The preventive effect of Defibrotide on electrically induced thrombosis was also shown (1,2,3 Mayo). These observations parallel to encouraging clinical results which we obtained in patients with peripheral obliterative vascular diseases such as atherosclerosis and Buerger's diseases (4).

The effect of Defibrotide on the venous stasis test (Cuff test) has been investigated.

Venous stasis test has been performed in 20 normal control and 22 atherosclerotic and 8 Buerger's cases. 600 mgr Defibrotide per day administered intravenously for ten days and then every second day for a month and then twice weekly for next two months. Before, one week and one month after the haemostatic parameters and Cuff test were tested. The results are summarized in the tables (Table 84.1 and 84.2).

Table 84.1 The effect of Defibrotide treatment of Cuff test using the difference before and after venous stasis comparing before treatment and one month after the treatment. The mean of 8 cases of Buerger's disease. And the results minutes in ELT and basis area in mm^2 in Fibrin plate

	Before	One week	One month
ELT	28.6 ± 17.47	p 0.05	42.7 ± 8.1
Fibrin plate (N = 8)	44.28 ± 28.3	p 0.02	97.71 ± 39.6

Table 84.2 The effect of Defibrotide treatment on Cuff test in the cases of atherosclerosis. The mean of 23 cases of atherosclerotic peripheric obliterative disorder

	Before	One week	One month
ELT % difference	15 ± 20.30 (N = 23)	30 ± 17.6 (N = 19)	40.2 ± 14.56 (N = 15)
	p 0.02		p 0.0005
Fibrin plate	36.1 ± 66.49	58.51	76.1 ± 38.29
	0.1 p 0.2		p0.01

It is difficult to explain the progressive effect of therapy by a short lived fibrinolytic effect. The tests show Defibrotide treatment causes a higher response in the Cuff test. Beside showing increase of PA secretion from endothelial cells in our laboratory Çizmeci observed an increase of the PGI$_2$ secretion and production (5). Results show that Defibrotide may be considered a drug which modifies and repairs the impaired vessel wall especially endothelial cell functions in atherosclerosis since we have already shown its positive effect on the release of PA and PGI$_2$ from endothelium.

REFERENCES

1. Ulutin O N, Tunali H, Giriskin G, Aytis S, Uğur M S, Balkuv-Ulutin S 1982 The effect of 'Fraction P' on electrically induced thrombus formation in dogs (Abs. 235) Haemostasis (Seventh International Congress on Thrombosis) 1, 130
2. Ulutin O N, Balkuv-Ulutin S 1983 The dog venous thrombosis model using electrical stimulation and some results using this model. In: Breddin K, Zimmermann R, Schattaurverlag F K (eds) Standardization of animal models of thrombosis. Stuttgart, New York, pp 83–90
3. Ulutin O N, Tunali H, Girisken G, Aytis S, Uğur M S, Balkuv-Ulutin S 1983 The effect of xanthinol-nicotinate and plasminogen or Defibrotide treatment on electrically induced thrombosis. XIIIth World Congr. of Internat. Union of Angiology, Sept. 11–17, Rochester, Minn. USA
4. Ulutin O N, Ilhan-Berkel N, Özer M, Önsel C, Uğur M S, Urgancioğlu I 1983 The effect of plasmin plus xanthinol nicotinate or Defibrotide therapy on Buerger's Disease and peripheric obliterative atherosclerotic disorders. XIIIth World Congr. of Internat. Union of Angiology Sept. 11–17, Rochester, Minn. USA
5. Çizmeci G 1984 In vivo effect of Defibrotide on platelet c-AMP and blood prostanoid levels. VIIIth International Congress on Thrombosis. June 4–7, Istanbul. (Abst. 100)

85. Effect of defibrotide* administered i.v., i.m. and per os on some fibrinolytic parameters in man. Controlled study versus placebo

A. Vittoria, G.L. Messa, F. Berri, F. De Giovanni, G. Buzzetti and T. Di Perri

Defibrotide (D), an antithrombotic and thrombolytic agent in animal (Niada et al; Pescador et al), has shown also in man the capacity to activate the fibrinolytic system (Coccheri et al). In this study we tested the profibrinolytic effect of the drug in a group of patients with peripheral obliterative arterial disease (POAD).

MATERIAL AND METHODS

Study design

12 patients with POAD and ipofibrinolytic activity (ELT over 120 min) were submitted to i.v. and oral trial. 6 patients began with placebo and then continued with Defibrotide 800 mg i.v. and per os administration, and 6 with placebo and then per os and i.v. supply, according to open cross-over design versus placebo. Each oral administration was repeated two times. 5 other POAD patients were submitted to three doses of D i.m. (800, 400 and 200 mgs in sequential manner) versus placebo again.

The interval between each experiment was three days.

Methods

In each patient before and after 60, 120, 240, 360, 480, 720 min of the oral supply of D, before and after 15, 60, 120, 240, 480, 720 min in i.v. experiments, and finally before and after 120, 240, 360, 480, 720 min in i.m. administration, we performed the following parameters: Euglobulin Lysis Time (ELT) in min (DADE), Fibrinogen as clottable protein in mg% (Boheringer-Biochemia-Robin), Plasminogen immunologic in mg%, α-2-Antiplasmin in I.U./ml, α-1-Antitripsin in mg%, α-2-Macroglobulin in mg%, Antithrombin III in U.I./ml (all as chromogen substrate Boheringer-Biochemia-Robin) and PTT, TT, Platelets as standard methods.

RESULTS

First group

Defibrotide, at the dose of 800 mgs, significantly decreased ELT, Fibrinogen, Plasminogen (Table 85.1) α-2-Antiplasmin, α-1-Antitripsin, whereas Antithrombin III concentration increased (Table 85.2). The effect began in one

* D.C.I.

Table 85.1 Behaviour of Euglobulin Lysis Time (ELT), Fibrinogen (Fib.) and Plasminogen (Plas) before and after Defibrotide 800 mg per os or i.v. in 12 POAD patients. Means ± S.E. and 't' values versus baseline

		Placebo	os 't'	Defibrotide	't'		Placebo	i.v. 't'	Defibrotide	't'
ELT min.	B	320.0 ± 15.2		308.5 ± 7.4		B	319.5 ± 13.3		322.0 ± 14.3	
	60'	314.1 ± 14.7	0.53	274.1 ± 8.8	2.73	15'	313.7 ± 12.5	0.48	311.6 ± 14.4	1.23
	120'	312.0 ± 17.4	0.98	270.4 ± 10.3	3.03	60'	306.6 ± 12.2	1.78	270.4 ± 20.2	2.00
	240'	317.5 ± 15.8	1.10	245.6 ± 9.2	5.13	120'	307.9 ± 13.4	0.42	172.9 ± 13.5	7.46
	360'	316.6 ± 13.4	0.52	260.4 ± 11.1	2.36	240'	313.3 ± 15.2	0.97	198.7 ± 17.8	5.15
	480'	317.9 ± 14.9	1.00	287.0 ± 9.7	0.96	480'	312.5 ± 14.5	1.07	248.3 ± 21.9	3.09
	720'	313.3 ± 16.0	1.36	309.7 ± 8.0	0.43	720'	320.4 ± 12.7	1.58	297.0 ± 14.7	2.26
Fib. mg%	B	289.8 ± 11.9		289.0 ± 9.0		B	294.8 ± 11.6		291.7 ± 13.3	
	60'	289.3 ± 13.5	0.66	277.8 ± 9.6	5.42	15'	291.1 ± 12.2	1.18	288.3 ± 14.9	1.13
	120'	288.8 ± 11.4	0.33	257.8 ± 8.7	4.91	60'	295.0 ± 13.3	0.24	283.0 ± 15.6	1.49
	240'	295.1 ± 12.2	2.56	249.3 ± 8.9	5.32	120'	289.1 ± 12.9	0.96	263.0 ± 19.1	2.63
	360'	294.3 ± 12.5	1.73	257.7 ± 9.5	6.85	240'	289.1 ± 13.1	1.19	250.0 ± 16.5	4.09
	480'	290.6 ± 12.5	0.04	272.0 ± 8.6	2.87	480'	289.2 ± 12.6	1.45	258.1 ± 16.1	3.85
	720'	294.8 ± 12.4	1.66	292.6 ± 9.1	1.15	720'	292.6 ± 11.6	2.89	284.8 ± 13.8	0.81
Plas. mg%	B	10.77 ± 0.29		10.76 ± 0.18		B	10.56 ± 0.25		10.56 ± 0.26	
	60'	10.48 ± 0.23	1.45	10.47 ± 0.22	2.26	15'	10.57 ± 0.26	0.26	10.45 ± 0.31	0.84
	120'	10.77 ± 0.33	0.15	10.25 ± 0.20	5.61	60'	10.62 ± 0.28	0.19	9.82 ± 0.32	2.28
	240'	10.74 ± 0.31	0.72	9.44 ± 0.21	4.13	120'	10.51 ± 0.32	0.83	9.18 ± 0.37	3.68
	360'	10.74 ± 0.28	0.73	9.99 ± 0.20	3.64	240'	10.49 ± 0.33	1.68	8.90 ± 0.36	3.64
	480'	10.73 ± 0.31	0.96	10.44 ± 0.20	2.31	480'	10.54 ± 0.26	0.28	9.50 ± 0.27	3.95
	720'	10.75 ± 0.29	0.41	10.71 ± 0.19	2.64	720'	10.62 ± 0.24	0.87	9.81 ± 0.26	2.61
	N = 24		't'		't'	N = 12		't'		't'

Table 85.2 Behaviour of Antithrombin III (A.T.III), Alpha-1-antitripsin (α-1a-Tr.) and Alpha-2-antiplasmin (α-2-Pl.) before and after Defibrotide 800 mg per os or i.v. in 12 POAD patients. Means ± S.E. and 't' values versus placebo

		os					i.v.			
		Placebo	't'	Defibrotide	't'		Placebo	't'	Defibrotide	't'
A.T.III U.I./ml		10.77 ± 0.29		10.73 ± 0.17			10.58 ± 0.25		10.76 ± 0.23	
	60'	10.50 ± 0.25	0.51	11.13 ± 0.22	3.66	15'	10.66 ± 0.27	1.53	11.50 ± 0.55	1.64
	120'	10.51 ± 0.24	0.50	11.48 ± 0.25	2.98	60'	10.58 ± 0.24	0.15	11.60 ± 0.30	2.43
	240'	10.58 ± 0.23	0.38	11.96 ± 0.27	4.36	120'	10.67 ± 0.23	0.22	12.53 ± 0.40	4.38
	360'	10.60 ± 0.26	0.69	12.02 ± 0.27	4.36	240'	10.83 ± 0.29	1.29	12.66 ± 0.42	5.17
	480'	10.61 ± 0.26	1.09	11.29 ± 0.20	2.14	480'	10.74 ± 0.23	0.93	12.02 ± 0.42	2.95
	720'	10.62 ± 0.26	1.73	10.83 ± 0.16	1.76	720'	10.59 ± 0.24	1.68	11.17 ± 0.38	1.58
α-1a.Tr. mg%		255.1 ± 2.79		254.9 ± 1.88			256.7 ± 3.73		253.4 ± 3.23	
	60'	249.0 ± 2.40	3.82	247.0 ± 2.68	2.22	15'	253.4 ± 3.34	0.43	249.8 ± 3.60	0.49
	120'	254.0 ± 3.40	0.29	243.6 ± 2.56	3.99	60'	255.9 ± 4.13	0.28	248.1 ± 3.94	1.41
	240'	255.4 ± 3.72	1.41	235.3 ± 1.46	3.27	120'	253.9 ± 4.23	0.77	236.0 ± 4.12	3.24
	360'	252.1 ± 2.95	0.43	239.2 ± 1.97	4.14	240'	251.7 ± 4.79	1.02	236.4 ± 2.50	5.19
	480'	254.1 ± 3.54	0.49	247.5 ± 2.48	1.43	480'	254.0 ± 3.71	1.72	244.2 ± 4.30	1.60
	720'	253.8 ± 2.99	1.27	256.1 ± 2.47	0.53	720'	256.9 ± 3.57	0.51	256.0 ± 4.01	0.23
α-2a.Pl. I.U./ml		0.96 ± 0.03		0.97 ± 0.02			0.96 ± 0.03		0.97 ± 0.02	
	60'	0.95 ± 0.03	1.75	0.86 ± 0.02	3.83	15'	0.96 ± 0.03	0.93	0.89 ± 0.02	1.64
	120'	0.95 ± 0.04	1.36	0.80 ± 0.03	4.04	60'	0.94 ± 0.02	1.70	0.80 ± 0.04	2.57
	240'	0.97 ± 0.03	0.27	0.77 ± 0.02	5.53	120'	0.92 ± 0.03	1.26	0.65 ± 0.05	4.79
	360'	0.95 ± 0.03	0.55	0.84 ± 0.01	5.78	240'	0.91 ± 0.03	0.92	0.58 ± 0.05	6.81
	480'	0.96 ± 0.03	0.45	0.88 ± 0.02	1.68	480'	0.93 ± 0.02	1.31	0.73 ± 0.04	5.12
	720'	0.96 ± 0.03	0.50	0.96 ± 0.02	0.65	720'	0.93 ± 0.02	0.92	0.86 ± 0.02	2.83
		N = 24	't'		't'		N = 12	't'		't'

hour and lasted for 8 hours both by oral route and i.v. infusion. α-2-Macroglobulin, PTT, TT and Platelets did not show any changes (data not indicated in Tables).

Second group
In this experimental model again the drug provided a significant decrease of ELT, Fibrinogen, Plasminogen (Table 85.3), α-2-Antiplasmin, α-1-Antitripsin and an increase of Antithrombin III concentration (Table 85.4) from the 2nd to 8th hour. The three doses (800–400–200 mgs) seemed to act on the fibrinolytic system in a concentration-dependent manner. PTT, TT, α2-Macroglobulin and Platelets did not change (data not indicated).

In the two groups of patients no changes were observed in previous parameters during placebo experiments.

DISCUSSION

Our data confirmed that Defibrotide has shown an effective profibrinolytic activity in POAD patients, according to Coccheri et al (1982), even if the doses used in our study were greater. In this trial we observed this effect not only by i.v. and i.m. administration, but also when we used the oral route: this point must be underlined because there are relatively poor drugs able to act on fibrinolytic system per os. In our groups of patients D has not influenced globally the clotting system, thus the increase of Antithrombin III, contrary to Coccheri et al (1982), was difficult to explain.

With regard to the mechanism of action we agree with the above mentioned hypothesis that D acts probably by decreasing some plasmatic inhibitors, especially α-2-Antiplasmin and α-1-Antitripsin and/or perhaps by the release of tissue plasminogen activator.

Finally the tolerance of the drug in this acute study was generally good after parenteral and oral administration.

Table 85.3 Behaviour of Euglobulin Lysis Time (ELT), Fibrinogen (Fib.) and Plasminogen (Plas) before and after several doses of Defibrotide (800, 400 and 200 mg i.m.) in 5 POAD patients. Means ± S.E. and 't' values versus baseline

		Placebo	't'	800 mg.	't'	400 mg.	't'	200 mg.	't'
ELT min.	B	305.0 ± 10.0		305.0 ± 7.4		310.0 ± 11.4		304.0 ± 10.6	
	120'	292.0 ± 13.2	2.15	254.0 ± 22.4	1.87	217.0 ± 9.6	6.59	270.0 ± 15.2	5.27
	240'	312.0 ± 7.1	0.91	164.0 ± 21.7	2.30	179.0 ± 16.3	7.45	257.0 ± 9.5	7.50
	360'	314.0 ± 6.7	1.26	204.0 ± 21.4	6.81	201.0 ± 32.1	4.13	269.0 ± 9.0	6.14
	480'	301.0 ± 12.7	0.83	251.0 ± 27.7	2.49	232.0 ± 24.9	4.25	287.0 ± 15.9	1.30
	720'	297.0 ± 10.4	3.14	286.0 ± 19.0	1.59	283.0 ± 20.5	1.80	298.0 ± 8.1	0.26
Fib. mg%	B	318.0 ± 29.6		318.8 ± 29.8		315.0 ± 27.7		310.6 ± 25.8	
	120'	316.4 ± 28.4	0.37	311.8 ± 29.0	1.99	309.0 ± 30.5	2.06	294.4 ± 28.0	3.92
	240'	319.4 ± 31.1	0.86	294.6 ± 31.7	5.12	287.2 ± 31.8	6.37	291.2 ± 29.5	4.21
	360'	319.0 ± 29.5	0.34	274.0 ± 29.9	4.63	283.6 ± 27.5	6.16	292.6 ± 29.3	3.76
	480'	317.8 ± 31.7	0.07	275.6 ± 30.9	5.57	298.2 ± 28.9	6.95	304.6 ± 30.5	1.13
	720'	320.2 ± 28.0	0.60	308.0 ± 26.7	1.82	307.8 ± 28.8	2.56	306.6 ± 26.3	1.52
Plas. mg%	B	10.64 ± 0.63		10.62 ± 0.54		10.62 ± 0.63		10.60 ± 0.59	
	120'	10.51 ± 0.59	1.46	10.00 ± 0.59	4.14	9.84 ± 0.59	10.61	9.96 ± 0.68	3.18
	240'	10.71 ± 0.60	0.72	9.18 ± 0.68	4.29	9.44 ± 0.61	7.71	9.94 ± 0.62	8.82
	360'	10.66 ± 0.64	0.53	9.68 ± 0.71	5.21	9.92 ± 0.71	3.91	10.18 ± 0.55	4.12
	480'	10.62 ± 0.61	0.32	9.80 ± 0.71	3.23	10.38 ± 0.64	3.54	10.30 ± 0.68	2.54
	720'	10.59 ± 0.60	1.29	10.18 ± 0.64	3.92	10.76 ± 0.55	1.06	10.36 ± 0.59	2.80

Table 85.4 Behaviour of Antithrombin III (A.T.III), Alpha-1-antitripsin (α-1a.Tr.) and Alpha-2-antiplasmin (α-2a-Pl.) before and after several doses of Defibrotide (800, 400 and 200 mg i.m.) in 5 POAD patients. Means ± S.E. and 't' values versus baseline

		Placebo	't'	800 mg.	't'	400 mg.	't'	200 mg.	't'
A.T.III U.I./ml		10.58 ± 0.93		10.66 ± 0.93		10.43 ± 0.95		10.59 ± 1.00	
	120'	10.51 ± 0.89	0.79	10.80 ± 0.85	0.68	10.59 ± 1.00	1.30	10.97 ± 1.03	4.50
	240'	10.60 ± 0.96	0.40	11.97 ± 0.94	4.25	11.38 ± 0.94	5.85	10.97 ± 0.95	2.94
	360'	10.60 ± 0.91	0.42	12.70 ± 0.37	3.08	11.92 ± 0.76	4.83	10.98 ± 0.90	3.01
	480'	10.49 ± 0.90	1.55	12.12 ± 0.50	2.75	11.62 ± 0.81	2.86	10.99 ± 0.90	1.99
	720'	10.53 ± 0.88	0.69	11.38 ± 0.76	2.46	11.24 ± 0.63	2.44	10.78 ± 0.93	1.14
α-1a.Tr. mg%		251.6 ± 12.3		245.6 ± 8.55		249.6 ± 14.4		247.0 ± 9.7	
	120'	249.6 ± 10.7	0.79	230.4 ± 7.99	3.99	239.8 ± 12.8	2.65	238.2 ± 10.2	4.68
	240'	250.8 ± 12.6	0.48	230.8 ± 8.87	4.98	233.8 ± 16.1	8.17	235.6 ± 5.53	2.15
	360'	251.4 ± 12.1	0.30	236.0 ± 9.71	3.84	237.6 ± 16.5	3.16	244.4 ± 7.59	0.78
	480'	251.6 ± 11.5	0.05	234.2 ± 5.71	2.97	243.8 ± 15.4	2.51	242.0 ± 9.79	1.27
	720'	250.8 ± 11.3	0.52	246.6 ± 4.26	0.17	251.6 ± 12.0	0.76	247.2 ± 9.74	0.08
α-2a.Pl. I.U./ml		0.97 ± 0.06		0.98 ± 0.05		0.97 ± 0.06		0.97 ± 0.05	
	120'	0.97 ± 0.07	0.35	0.72 ± 0.06	7.58	0.77 ± 0.06	5.85	0.80 ± 0.04	7.61
	240'	0.98 ± 0.06	0.59	0.61 ± 0.11	6.20	0.69 ± 0.10	5.81	0.77 ± 0.06	12.0
	360'	0.95 ± 0.06	1.03	0.66 ± 0.04	15.1	0.75 ± 0.04	11.4	0.78 ± 0.05	9.02
	480'	0.95 ± 0.06	2.27	0.75 ± 0.08	3.66	0.80 ± 0.02	3.71	0.86 ± 0.04	4.30
	720'	0.97 ± 0.07	0.28	0.88 ± 0.04	7.25	0.88 ± 0.03	2.47	0.98 ± 0.05	0.51

REFERENCES

Coccheri S et al 1982 Effect on fibrinolysis of a new antithrombotic agent: Fraction P (Defibrotide). A multicentre trial. International Journal of Clinical and Pharmacological Research. II(3), 227-245

Niada R, Mantovani M, Prino G, Pescador R, Porta R 1982 PGI_2-Generation and antithrombotic activity of orally administered Defibrotide. Pharmacological Research Communications, 14(10), 949-957

Pescador R, Mantovani M, Prino G 1983 Pharmacokinetics of Defibrotide and of its profibrinolytic activity in the rabbit. Thrombosis Research, 30: 1-11

86. Treatment of acute renal failure due to hemolytic-uremic syndrome and thrombotic thrombocytopenic purpura with a new fibrinolytic agent

V. Bonomini, A. Vangelista, G. Frascà,
C. Raimondi and G. L. D'Arcangelo

INTRODUCTION

Hemolytic uremic syndrome (HUS) and thrombotic thrombocytopenic purpura (TTP) are conditions where coagulation plays an important role in causing widespread vascular damage in various organs including the kidney, where thrombotic lesions are found in arterioles and glomeruli.

Prolonged anuria, hypertension, and neurological manifestations are signs of poor prognosis both for the recovery of renal function and patient survival. The therapeutic approaches until now employed failed to improve significantly the course of the disease and were sometimes associated with severe side-effects (Proesman & Eeckels, 1974; Brandt et al, 1981).

In the last 2 years we treated 8 patients with acute renal failure (3 HUS and 5 TTP) with Defibrotide (D), a polydeoxyribonucleotide salt obtained from mammalian lung, which displays considerable antithrombotic activity in various experimental models of thrombosis (Prino et al, 1976). This substance decreases the blood concentration of plasmin inhibitors and induces the release of plasminogen activator factors (Mantovani et al, 1978) and prostacyclin from vascular tissue (Niada, 1982).

PATIENTS AND METHODS

Four children (3–11 years old) and 4 adults (20–48 years old) with acute renal failure were included in the study. The clinical picture at admission, serum creatinine and pathological diagnosis are reported in Table 86.1. All but one patient underwent percutaneous renal biopsy before therapy. Coagulation studies included serial determinations of PT, PTT, fibrinogen, serum FDP, and platelets.

Defibrotide was initially administered by continuous intravenous infusion at a dosage of 10 mg/Kg/day for an average of 13 days. Oral administration was then continued at the same dosage for 1 to 6 months in 6 patients.

Table 86.1 Clinical picture at admission, pathological diagnosis, and outcome of the 8 patients treated with defibrotide

Patient	Sex/Age	Clinical picture at admission	Diagnosis	Serum creat. mg/dl	Duration of treatment i.v.	os	Follow-up (months)	Outcome
1	F 10	Anuria, coma, petechiae jaundice, melena, anemia, hypertension	TTP	6.4	16 d	1 m	14	Serum creat. 1.4, mild hypertension
2	M 7	Anuria, lethergia, fever, petechiae, jaundice, anemia, hypertension	TTP	7.2	8 d		16	RDT, hypertension
3	F 3	Anuria, seizures, petechiae, melena, anemia, hypertension	HUS	5.3	9 d	20 d	4	Serum creat. 0.8
4	F 11	Oliguria, hematuria, coma, petechiae, intestinal bleeding, hypertension	TTP	7.9	21 d	3 m	7	Serum creat. 1.2, mild hypertension
5	M 20	Fever, anuria, edema, jaundice, hypertension	HUS	8.5	13 d	1 m	21	RDT
6	M 48	Oliguria, petechiae, myalgia lethargia, anemia hypertension	TTP (polyarteritis)	10.2	11 d	4 d	13	Serum creat. 1.8, hypertension
7	M 42	Anuria, fever, pneumonia, petechiae, anemia, hypert.	TTP (Wegener granulomatosis)	14.9	12 d	6 m	18	Serum creat. 2.1
8	F 23	Oliguria, fever, petechiae, melena, lethargia	HUS	5.7	14 d	3 m	9	Serum creat. 1.0

RESULTS AND DISCUSSION

All patients had severe coagulation abnormalities with thrombocytopenia (11,000–110,000/mm^3) and rised serum FDP (30–80 μg/ml), which rapidly improved during treatment, while no significant change was observed in the other coagulation parameters.

Neurological manifestations, present in 6 patients (Table 86.1), showed a rapid improvement and/or disappearance during D administration.

Four patients had a complete recovery of renal function within 12 to 47 days, while a partial recovery was obtained in 2 patients.

Patient 2 and 5 (Table 86.1) did not show any improvement in renal function and entered a regular dialysis treatment programme. No side effect related to D administration was observed.

Both HUS and TTP are associated with high rate of mortality and development of chronic renal failure, particularly in adults and in patients with neurological involvement (Morel Maroger et al, 1979; Goldenfarb & Finch, 1973). The behaviour of renal function and rapid improvement of clinical symptoms observed in our patients, suggest that D might be useful in the management of these patients. The enhanced production of PGI$_2$ during D administration, may at least partially account for the therapeutic effect we observed, since in recent years it has been suggested that the deficiency of prostacyclin may be the primary defect in patients with HUS (Webster et al, 1980). Further studies, however, are needed to define the precise mode of action of D and to confirm its effectiveness in patients with HUS and TTP.

REFERENCES

Brandt P, Jespersen J, Gregersen G 1981 Post-partum hemolytic-uremic syndrome treated with antithrombine III Nephron 27: 15–18
Goldenfarb P B, Finch S C 1973 Thrombotic thrombocytopenic purpura. A ten year survey. J.A.M.A. 226: 644–657
Mantovani M, Prino G, Pescador R 1978 Activation of fibrinolytic process by a substance of polydesoxyribonucleotidic nature (fraction P). In: Strano A (ed) Advances in coagulation, fibrinolysis, platelet aggregation and atherosclerosis. C.E.P.I., Rome, p 274–281
Morel Maroger L, Kanfer A, Solez K, Sraer J, Richet G 1979 Prognostic importance of vascular lesions in acute renal failure with microangiopathic hemolytic anemia (hemolytic-uremic syndrome). Clinico-pathologic study in 20 adults. Kidney International 15: 548–558
Niada R, Mantovani M, Prino G, Pescador R, Porta R, Berti F, Folco G C, Omini C, Viganò T 1982 PGI$_2$ generation and antithrombotic activity of orally administered Defibrotide. Pharmacological Research Communications. 14: 949–957
Prino G, Mantovani M, Niada R 1976 Antithrombotic activity of a polidesoxyribonucleotidic-like substance (fraction P). In: Strano A (ed) Advances in coagulation, fibrinolysis, platelet aggregation and atherosclerosis. C.E.P.I., Rome, p 282–289
Proesman W, Eeckels R 1974 Has heparin changed the prognosis of the hemolytic-uremic syndrome? Clinical Nephrology 2: 169–173
Webster J, Rees A J, Lewis P J, Hensby C N 1980 Prostacyclin deficiency in haemolytic-uremic syndrome British Medical Journal ii: 271

Section 11
PLASMINOGEN ACTIVATORS FROM DIFFERENT SOURCES

87. Comparison of the properties of the epithelial with other tissue type plasminogen activators

A. Electricwala, P.M. Sutton, B. Griffiths, P.A. Riley and T. Atkinson

INTRODUCTION

Recently, there has been a great deal of interest in the field of tissue type plasminogen activators (tPA). Over the past few years, a number of activators have been purified from various tissues such as pig heart, hog ovaries and human uterus. However, one major drawback with these activators is that one requires large amounts of fresh tissue to obtain few milligrams of pure protein. As an alternative to tissue source, many research workers have used the cell culture technique for the production of tPA. Thus Rijken & Collen (1981) have reported the purification and properties of plasminogen activator from malignant melanoma cell line. This activator was immunologically identical to and possessed all the properties of human tissue plasminogen activator.

We have been working on the plasminogen activators derived not from malignant but from the normal and established *epithelial* cell lines, guinea pig keratocyte (GPK) and human breast epithelium (BEB). This report describes the purification of these activators and compares their biochemical properties with those of melanoma and human uterine activators.

MATERIALS AND METHODS

The epithelial cells were grown to sub-confluent monolayers on Cytodex 3 microcarrier beads (10 g/l) at 37°C in Eagles MEM growth medium. GPK and BEB derived plasminogen activators were isolated from serum-free conditioned medium by the procedure essentially as described by Rijken & Collen (1981), but in the absence of Aprotinin.

The fibrinolytic activity of the plasminogen activators was determined by the fibrin plates and the clot lysis time method as described by Rijken et al (1979).

Molecular weight and isoelectric point of the GPK activator have been reported earlier by Electricwala et al (1983). Similar procedures were used with the purified BEB activator.

The amidolytic activity of the purified activators was determined with the chromogenic substrate S-2322 in Tris/HCL buffer, pH 9.0. The kinetic constants were determined from Lineweaver-Burke plots.

Fibrin binding studies and immunological studies with both the epithelial activators have been performed according to the procedures described by Rijken & Collen (1981).

Amino acid sequences of the purified proteins were determined by automated Edman degradation using a gas phase sequencer. The PTH amino acids were identified by HPLC according to the method of Hunkapillar & Hood (1983).

RESULTS

Table 87.1 summarises the results obtained with GPK and BEB activators and compares the data with those of melanoma and human uterine tPA.

The specific activities of the purified GPK and BEB activators were relatively lower and estimated to be about 12500 and 6000 IU/mg, respectively.

The molecular weight and isoelectric point of both the epithelial activators were similar. However, there was no evidence of the two chain form for the epithelial activators on SDS-PAGE, as has been reported for melanoma and uterine tPA. The isoelectric point of 4.6 ± 0.2 for both GPK and BEB activators was significantly different from the values of other tPA as reported in the literature.

The values of the kinetic constants obtained with GPK and BEB activators were comparable with those of melanoma and uterine activators.

Table 87.1 Comparison of the properties of various tissue plaminogen activators

		GPK PA	BEB PA	Melanoma PA	Human uterine PA
Specific Activity (IU/mg)	Clot lysis time method	12500	6000		16000
	Fibrin plate method			90000	48000
Molecular weight (reduced)	One chain	62000	62000	72000	69000
	Two chain	—	—	39000 33000	38000 31000
Isoelectric point		4.6	4.6	—	—
Kinetic data with S-2322	K_m(mM)	1.9	1.2	1.0	1.3
	V_{max}(nmol/min/IU)	0.208	0.111	0.053	0.071
Affinity for fibrin		Yes	Yes	Yes	Yes
Cross reaction with urokinase/ anti-urokinase IgG		No	No	No	No
Quenching with autologous IgG		Yes	Yes	Yes	Yes
N-terminal sequence		XDTIVAVELD		SYQVICRDEK —	

Immunological studies indicate that none of the tissue activators cross react with urokinase and their fibrinolytic activities were quenched by autologous anti-IgG.

Preliminary results of the amino acid sequence studies indicate that both the epithelial activators have similar N-terminal sequences, but with no apparent homology to the sequence of melanoma tPA.

CONCLUSION

It is concluded that the plasminogen activators isolated from epithelial cell lines are tissue type plasminogen activators. These activators have some properties which are similar to, but others which are very different from, melanoma and human uterine activators. Thus, it seems that the epithelial activators are unique proteins and represent a different and previously unrecognised class of tissue plasminogen activator.

REFERENCES

Rijken D C, Collen D 1981 Purification and characterisation of the plasminogen activator secreted by human melanoma cells in culture. Journal of Biological Chemistry 256(13): 7035–7041

Rijken D C, Wijngaards G, Zaal-de-Jong M, Welbergen J 1979 Purification and partial characterisation of plasminogen activator from human uterine tissue. Biochimica et Biophysica Acta 580: 140–153

Electricwala A, Sutton P M, Griffiths B, Riley P M, Latter A, Atkinson T 1983 Purification and properties of the plasminogen activator secreted by guinea pig keratocyte cells in culture. In: Jespersen J, Kluft C, Korsgaard O (eds) Clinical aspects of fibrinolysis and thrombolysis. South Jutland University Press, Denmark, 85–91

Hunkapillar M W, Hood L E 1983 Analysis of phenylthiohydantoins by ultrasensitive gradient high performance liquid chromatography. Methods in Enzymology 91: 486–493

88. Plasminogen activators of isolated human glomeruli

E. Angles-Cano, E. Rondeau, A. Balaton,
F. Delarue, Y. Sultan and J.D. Sraer

The renal glomerulus is a complex structure formed by at least three cellular types: endothelial, epithelial and mesangial cells. This has hampered the precise localization and identification of glomerular plasminogen activators. Using different techniques we were able to circumvent this problem and we report here data on the quantitation and localization of urokinase (UK) and vascular plasminogen activator (v-PA) of isolated human glomeruli.

MATERIALS AND METHODS

Isolation of glomeruli

Glomeruli were isolated from normal human kidneys not used for transplantation, as previously described (Sraer et al, 1981) with minor modifications. The final preparation consisted of decapsulated glomeruli with less than 1% tubular contamination.

Glomerular PA release reaction

Glomeruli were washed immediately before use in 20 mM Tris-HCl buffer pH 7.5 containing 135 mM NaCl, 10 mM KCl and 5 mM glucose, and resuspended in the same buffer at a known density (10 to 20 mg/ml of glomerular protein). Incubations were carried out in buffer or in the presence of stimulators (Sraer et al, 1979): either 1 mM CaC12 or 10 μg/ml arachidonic acid (AA), final concentrations or both. After 30 min at 37°C, glomeruli were discarded by centrifugation at 2000 g for 2 min at 10°C. A glomerular suspension aliquot was made 0.1% for Triton $\times$ 100 and centrifugated after 5 min at 22°C. Supernatants were collected and immediately tested for PA activity.

Assay of plasminogen activator

Plasminogen activation by glomeruli-supernatants was detected spectrophotometrically by measuring para-nitroanilide liberation from the plasmin-sensitive chromogenic substrate S-2251 (A.B. Kabi). t-PA was detected using a solid-fibrin phase (SOFIA) plate (Angles-Cano and Sultan, 1984). Urokinase was detected using untreated polyvinylchloride (PVC) plates, Before testing glomeruli-supernatant were diluted 1:2 either with Tris-HCl buffer or with the Ig fraction (2 mg/ml) of a goat to UK serum kindly provided by Pr. F.

Bachmann. The assay mixture contained: 50 μl tris-HCl buffer pH 7.4, 25 μl 40 μg/ml plasminogen, 30 μl 1 mM S-2251 and 50 μl of glomeruli supernatant. After 3 h (PVC) or 1 h (SOFIA) incubation, the absorbance at 405 nm was measured using a micro Elisa counter. Absorbance readings were converted into I.U. by reference to curves made with either UK (PVC) or a t-PA (SOFIA) of porcine origin (see Angles-Cano and Sultan, 1981, for details).

Localisation of t-PA

Immunohistological localization of t-PA was carried out by an indirect immunoperoxidase procedure using EA-S12D, a monoclonal antibody to t-PA (Angles-Cano et al, 1984). Frozen-section of human renal cortex were used.

RESULTS AND DISCUSSION

Quantitation and identification of PA activity in glomeruli-supernatants are shown in Table 88.1. Figure 88.1 shows the specific and exclusive binding of

Table 88.1 Glomerular PA activity

Supernatant	u-PA + t-PA[1]	t-PA[2]	u-PA[3]
TX100	2.150[4]	1.250	0.610
Basal	0.650	0.560	0.010
CaCl$_2$	0.820	0.720	0.011
AA	0.715	0.540	0.024
CaCl$_2$ + AA	0.880	0.750	0.022

1. SOFIA test, supernatant + buffer
2. SOFIA test, supernatant + anti-UK
3. PVC test, supernatant + buffer. This activity was completely quenched by anti-UK Ig
4. Activity is given in I.U./ml by reference to UK and porcine t-PA

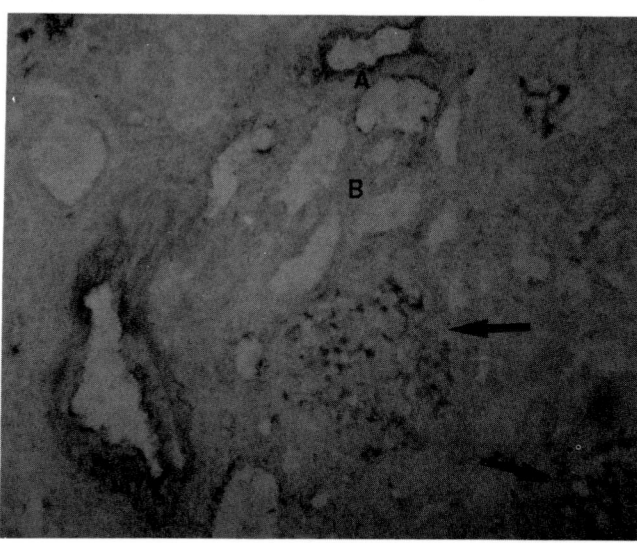

Fig. 88.1 Localization of t-PA in endothelial cells of a glomerulus (arrow) and venules[A] and arterioles[A] of human kidney. Note the absence of staining in tubular sections[B].

EA-δ12D to the endothelial cell lining of glomerular capillaries. Specific marquage of vascular endothelium is also seen in an arteriole. Our results demonstrate that the human glomerulus contains and is able to release both, UK and t-PA. This has been shown for t-PA by its fibrin associated PA activity, its absence of cross-reaction with anti-UK antibodies and its immunological identity with the vascular PA, as demonstrated with a monoclonal antibody. Urokinase was identified by the quenching of its fibrin-independent PA activity with antibodies to UK. The total glomerular content is constituted by at least 30% UK. The profiles were different in supernatants obtained under basal conditions and after stimulations. 95 to 98% of PA activity detected was due to t-PA; $CaCl_2$ stimulation was able to induce an increase in t-PA release exclusively. AA stimulation induced an important increase in the UK levels only. The significance of these specific stimulations are now under investigation.

The new data presented here can probably help to better understand the physiopathology of glomerular fibrin deposition. As glomerular UK is probably produced by the podocyte-epithelial cells, the persistance of extracapillary deposits of fibrin could be related to defective UK release by these cells. On this basis it is not astonishing to find a normal t-PA glomerular response in glomerular lesions resulting from immunological injury (Giroux et al, 1979) such as extracapillary glomerulonephritis, thrombotic microangiopathy or kidney allograft rejection.

REFERENCES

Giroux L, Verroust P, Morel-Maroger L, Delarue F, Delauche M, Sraer J D 1979 Glomerular fibrinolytic activity during nephotoxic nephritis. Laboratory Investigation 40: 415–422
Sraer J D, Moulonguet-Doleris L, Delarue F, Sraer J, Ardaillou R 1981 Prostaglandin synthesis by glomeruli isolated from rats with glycerol-induced acute renal failure. Circulation Research 49: 775–783
Sraer J D, Blanc E, Delarue F, Kanfer A, Ardaillou R, Richet G 1979 Effect of calcium and hydrogen ion on the fibrinolytic activity of isolated renal glomeruli from rat. Kidney International 15: 238–245
Angles-Cano E, Sultan Y 1984 A solid phase fibrin immunoassay for the specific detection of monoclonal antibodies against different epitopic determinants of tissue-plasminogen activators. Journal of Immunological Methods 69: 115–127
Angles-Cano E, Balaton A, Sultan Y 1984 Production and immunolocalization of monoclonal antibodies to the high fibrin affinity plasminogen activator of human plasma. Submitted for publication.

89. Plasminogen activator in cultured myocytes and its response to glucocorticoid hormones

M. Mayer, M. Chaouat and Z. Finci

Skeletal muscle cells can be isolated from the hindlegs of newborn rats, grown and maintained in culture for up to 6 days (Mayer et al, 1981). After 3 to 4 days in culture, these cells undergo a morphological differentiation, characterized by fusion of the mononucleated myoblasts to multinucleated myotubes. At about the same time the mitotic activity ceases and a biochemical differentiation takes place, as evident by synthesis of specific muscle proteins such as creatine phosphokinase (CPK), actin and myosin (Senwal, 1979; Kalderon, 1980).

The suggested role of plasminogen activator (PA) in remodelling and differentiation of various tissues and cell types (Ossowski et al, 1975; Ossowski et al, 1979; Isserof et al, 1981) prompted us to determine whether modulation of PA activity is involved in the morphological and/or biochemical differentiation of muscle cells in culture. We found PA activity in the membrane of the myocytes and in Hank's solution conditioned with these cells, but differentiation was not associated with changes in the ability of the cells to secrete PA. In view of the known effects of glucocorticoids on cultured muscle cells (Guerriero & Florini, 1980; Mayer et al, 1981) we also analyzed the effect of dexamethasone on muscle cell differentiation and PA activity.

MATERIALS AND METHODS

Cells: Skeletal muscle cells were obtained from the hindlegs of newborn rats by trypsinization and grown for up to 6 days in serum containing Ham F-10 medium (Mayer et al, 1981). After the growth period the cells were extensively washed and conditioning was performed for the indicated number of hours in serum-free Hank's basal salt solution.

Assay of PA activity: PA in the membranal fraction of the skeletal muscle cells (Desnuelle et al, 1983) and in the conditioned Hank's solution was determined by a functional assay in which the plasminogen-dependent formation of plasmin was monitored. The formed plasmin was measured by its ability to cleave ^{14}C-labelled globin (Mayer et al, 1983). The membranes or conditioned medium (0.4 ml) were first incubated for 90 min with 20 μg plasminogen, prepared according to Deutch & Mertz (1970), followed by a 120 min incubation with 25 μl of ^{14}C-labelled globin, 1.7 mg/ml. Plasminogen-independent globinolysis was subtracted.

Assay of CPK activity: For determination of CPK activity, 1.0ml of phosphate-buffered saline was added to each well containing 1×10^6 cells. The suspension was sonicated, and CPK in the cytosol was assayed with a Seralyzer (Ames Division, Miles Laboratories) utilizing CPK reagent strips according to the manufacturer's instruction.

RESULTS

Figure 89.1 illustrates that 5-day old cultured muscle cells secrete PA activity into the serum-free Hank's conditioning solution in a time-dependent manner (Fig. 89.1A), and that the activity present in the conditioned solution after removal of the cells is proportional to the volume of the aliquot taken for assay (Fig. 89.1B). These observations indicate that differentiated myotubes secrete PA, that the enzyme is stable for several hours and that no PA- or plasmin-inhibitors are secreted into the conditioning solution during incubation with control myotubes. Presence of such inhibitor(s) would have impaired the linear relationship between PA activity and volume of the conditioned solution. Absence of plasmin inhibitor(s) in the solution was also directly confirmed by the finding that the cleavage of ^{14}C-labelled globin by purified, exogenous plasmin was not reduced in presence of the conditioned solution.

Purified membranes obtained from myocytes at various stages of differentiation displayed PA activity and were devoid of plasminogen-independent general proteolytic activity. PA activity of the membranes was 0.43 ± 0.06 μg globin degraded/mg protein.hr^{-1} (mean $\pm$ SEM) in cells harvested before fusion (day 3 of culture), during fusion (day 4 of culture) and afterwards

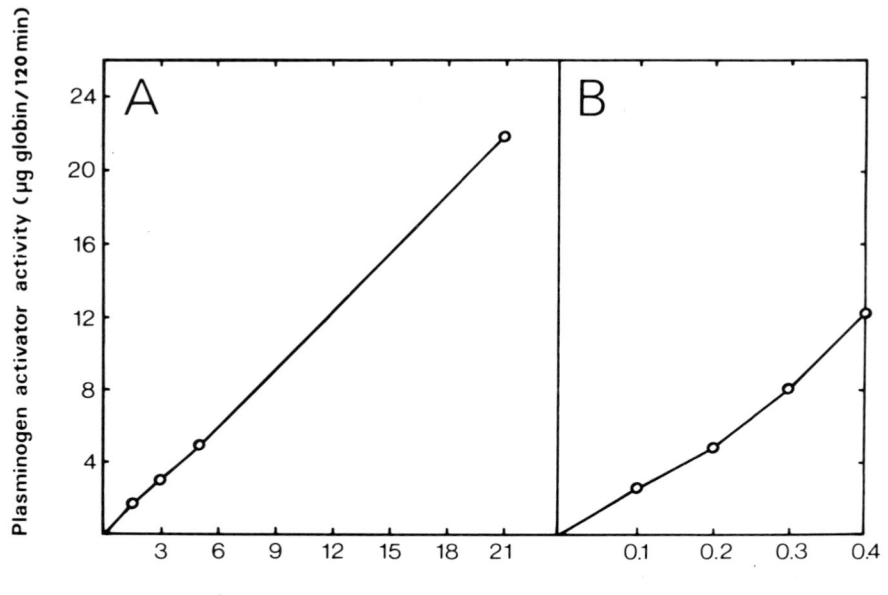

Fig. 89.1 PA activity in Hank's solution conditioned with 5-days old cultured myocytes. A-Effect of conditioning time. B- Açtivity as a function of volume of the conditioned solution.

348

(day 6 of culture), with no difference between activities measured at the different stages of differentiation. A slightly higher specific activity of PA was noticed in 2-day old myotubes, most probably due to the low protein content of these membranes.

When the cells were grown for 5 days in Ham F-10 medium supplemented with 10^{-7}M dexamethasone, the activity of PA subsequently recovered from the conditioning solution was reduced by more than 60%. Similarly, growth in presence of the glucocorticoid markedly reduced CPK activity in the cytosol of the cultured cells, from 46 u/l in controls to 4 u/l in dexamethasone-treated cells. The glucocorticoid did not impair cell viability as measured by release of label from myocytes preloaded with $Na_2^{51}CrO_4$ (Mayer et al, 1981), nor did the hormone inhibit fusion of the myoblasts. Furthermore, dexamethasone added to PA-containing Hank's solution after its conditioning with myocytes had no direct effect on PA activity. These findings suggested that dexamethasone impairs both the ability of the cells to produce active PA and their ability to synthesize specific muscle proteins.

The experiment summarized in Table 89.1 shows that maximal response to the suppressive effect of dexamethasone on secreted and membranal PA activity occurs when the hormone is present for 4 days starting from initiation of the culture. It should be noted that both the biochemical and morphological differentiation of the cells occur during the same period. Thus, during the period of normal differentiation the cells exhibit a dexamethasone-sensitive process that affects their subsequent ability to produce active PA.

Table 89.1 Effect of dexamethasone on secreted and membranal PA activities

Exposure to 5×10^{-7}M dexamethasone		PA in conditioned medium (μg globin/120 min)	PA in membranes (μg globin/mg protein.120 min^{-1})
Beginning on Day	Duration (days)		
—	0	15.3 (100)	1.35 (100)
1	2	13.2 (86)	1.05 (78)
1	4	4.4 (29)	0.43 (32)
1	6	6.4 (42)	0.50 (37)
3	4	8.1 (53)	0.78 (56)
5	1	17.7 (116)	1.29 (96)

Skeletal muscle myocytes were cultured for a total period of 6 days in serum-containing Ham F-10 medium and subsequently incubated in serum-free Hank's conditioning solution for 10 h. PA activity in aliquots of the conditioned solution and in the membranal fraction was determined after the conditioning period. Dexamethasone was added at the specific day of culture and for the number of days as indicated. Numbers in parenthesis indicate percent of activity, with controls in absence of dexamethasone taken as 100%. Globin degrading activity in absence of plasminogen was subtracted, and the results give net values for plasminogen-dependent PA activity. Values are mean of three wells assayed separately.

Modulation of PA activity can occur through formation of a PA-inhibitor complex, and the complex can be dissociated by SDS (Gehlerter et al, 1983; Levine, 1983). It was found that an overnight incubation of the solution conditioned with dexamethasone-treated myocytes with 1% SDS resulted in a complete recovery of the inhibited PA activity to values comparable to those present in solution conditioned with control cells. Thus, the reduction in PA as a result of exposure to the hormone is most probably due to formation of a SDS-sensitive PA-inhibitor complex. In contrast, acidification (pH 3.9) of the conditioned solution did not reverse the dexamethasone-induced reduction in PA activity.

DISCUSSION

The present report indicates than in the course of differentiation of skeletal muscle cells in culture there is a dexamethasone-sensitive process that affects membranal PA activity and reduces the subsequent ability of the cells to secrete PA activity. Since exposure to the hormone also reduces CPK activity but does not inhibit the morphological differentiation (fusion) or viability, we conclude that dexamethasone dissociates between the biochemical and morphological differentiation. It is still unknown whether these two developmental processes are related and sequential or independent and parallel (Sanwal, 1979). The presently observed temporal connection between the sensitivity of PA and CPK to inhibition by dexamethasone suggests that PA is implicated in the biochemical differentiation but not in fusion. The present findings confirm reports that skeletal muscle cells produce PA (Miskin et al, 1978; Festoff et al, 1982) and extend these reports by the observation that a hormone which affects development also regulates the production of PA. The differentiating myocyte is therefore a cell type in which PA appears to play a role in developmental processes. The dexamethasone-induced reduction in PA involves formation of an acid-stable, SDS-sensitive inhibitor. These properties distinguish it from the recently described inhibitor protease-nexin (Baker et al, 1980).

REFERENCES

Baker J B, Low D A, Simmer R L, Cunningham D D 1980 Protease-nexin: A cellular component that links thrombin and plasminogen activator and mediates their binding to cells. Cell 21:37–45
Desnuelle C, Lombet A, Liot D, Marous S, Seràtrice G 1983 Complete monitoring of the purification of the plasma membrane from rabbit skeletal muscle. Biochemical and Biophysical Research Communication 112: 521–527
Deutsch D G, Mertz E T 1970 Plasminogen purification from human plasma by affinity chromatography. Science 170: 1095–1096
Festoff B W, Patterson M R, Romstedt K 1982 Plasminogen activator: The major secreted neutral protease of cultured skeletal muscle cells. Journal of Cellular Physiology 110: 190–195
Gelehrter T, Barouski-Miller P A, Coleman P L, Cwikel B J 1983 Hormonal regulation of plasminogen activator in rat hepatoma cells Molecular and Cellular Biochemistry 53/54: 11–21
Guerriero V, Florini J R 1980 Dexamethasone effects on myoblast proliferation and differentiation. Endocrinology 106: 1198–1202
Isseroff R R, Fusenig N E, Rifkin D B 1983 Plasminogen activator in differentiating mouse keratinocytes. Journal of Investigative Dermatology 80: 217–222
Kalderon N 1980 Muscle cell fusion. In: Gilula N B (ed) Membrane-membrane interactions. Raven Press, New York, pp 99–118
Levin E G 1983 Latent tissue plasminogen activator produced by human endothelial cells in culture: Evidence for an enzyme-inhibitor complex. Proceedings National Academy of Science (USA) 80: 6804–6808
Mayer M, Chaouat M, Hadar R, Nissan S, Lernau O Z 1981 Effect of dexamethasone, Ammonium ions, and serum-deprivation on intracellular proteolysis in cultured muscle cells. Journal of Cellular Physiology 109: 525–533

Mayer M, Chaouat M, Lernau O Z, Nissan S 1983 Hormone-responsive myofibrillar protease activity in cultured rat myoblasts. FEBS Letters 161: 239–242

Miskin R, Easton T G, Reich E 1978 Plasminogen activator in chick embryo muscle cells: Induction of enzyme by RSV, PMA and retinoic acid. Cell 15: 1301–1312

Ossowski L, Quigley J, Reich E 1975 Proteases in biological control. In: Rifkin D, Reich E, Shaw E (eds) Cold Spring Harbor, N.Y., pp 901–913

Ossowski L, Biegel D, Reich E 1979 Mammary plasminogen activator: correlation with involution, hormonal modulation and comparison between normal and neoplastic tissue. Cell 16: 929–940

Sanwal B D 1979 Myoblast differentiation. Trends in Biochemical Science 4: 155–157

90. Single-chain urokinase, a 55 000 MW zymogen precursor of urokinase with fibrin-dependent activation under physiological conditions

V. Gurewich, R. Pannell and P. Kelley

Affinity chromatography using fibrin/Celite is a technique which was originally developed for the purification of tissue plasminogen activator (t-PA) from blood.(1) When this technique was applied to freshly voided urine, a new form of urokinase (UK) was discovered which had a single-chain (SC) structure, resisted inactivation by diisopropylfluoro-phosphate and had a relatively low specific activity on a fibrin plate.(2,3) Further characterization of the SC-UK was hampered by difficulties of obtaining sufficient enzyme from urine to do the experiments. Recently, a transformed human kidney cell line, developed by Collaborative Research Incorporated, Lexington, Massachusetts was identified and used as a source of SC-UK. Relatively large amounts of SC-UK, which appeared identical to that found in urine, could be purified from the spent culture medium of these cells. Using this product in animals, we showed that SC-UK induces thrombolysis more effectively and selectively than UK.(4,5) The following studies were designed to investigate this selective, fibrin-specific mode of action.

METHODS AND MATERIAL

The SC-UK was obtained from Collaborative Research Inc. Two-chain UK was obtained from Serono Laboratories (Randolph, MA. USA) or was made by exposing the SC-UK to sepharose bound plasmin. The SC-UK was labelled with [125]Iodine using the lactoperoxidase reaction (Enzymobeads, Bio-Rad Laboratories). Plasminogen was purified from fresh plasma on Lysine-Sepharose (Pharmacia, Upsalla, Sweden). Bovine trypsin and human plasmin were obtained from Parke-Davis (Ann Arbor, MI) and purified thrombin from Collaborative Research Inc. Reaction products were analyzed by autoradiography of SDS polyacrylamide gels.

Amidolytic assays were performed using S-2444 or S-2251 (Kabi). Fibrin plates for assay of fibrinolytic activity were made up from human fibrinogen (Kabi) enriched with plasminogen. Activities were measured in International Units (IU) relative to the International Reference Preparation as the primary standard.

For DFP treatment, pro-UK and UK were diluted respectively to 0.1 mg/ml (18 μM) in 0.1 M HEPES, pH 7.2, 0.3 mg/ml bovine albumin, 0.15 M NaCl. DFP was diluted into dimethylformamide to a stock concentration of 20 mM.

Treatment was done at 20, 50 and 75 μM DFP on ice for 16 h. after which imidazole was added (10 mM), the solutions brought to room temperature for 2 h. and then stored on ice for 48 h.

Clot lysis experiments were performed with ^{125}I-labelled clots prepared from 1 ml pooled plasma clotted with thromboplastin (10 μl, Sigma). Clots were stored overnight at room temperature and then incubated (37°C) in 4 ml plasma to which the activators were added.

RESULTS AND DISCUSSION

The precursor relationship of pro-UK to UK was established by enzymatic conversion of the single-chain to the two-chain form. When the pro-UK was mixed with plasminogen, plasmin was rapidly generated as indicated by the appearance of a band (the light chain of plasmin) just above the light chain of UK. In the same gels (2nd and 3rd), progressive disappearance of the single chain pro-UK band with emergence of the two chains of UK can be seen (Fig. 90.1). Although a large amount of plasminogen was used in this experiments, catalytic amounts have been shown to cause rapid degradation of pro-UK.

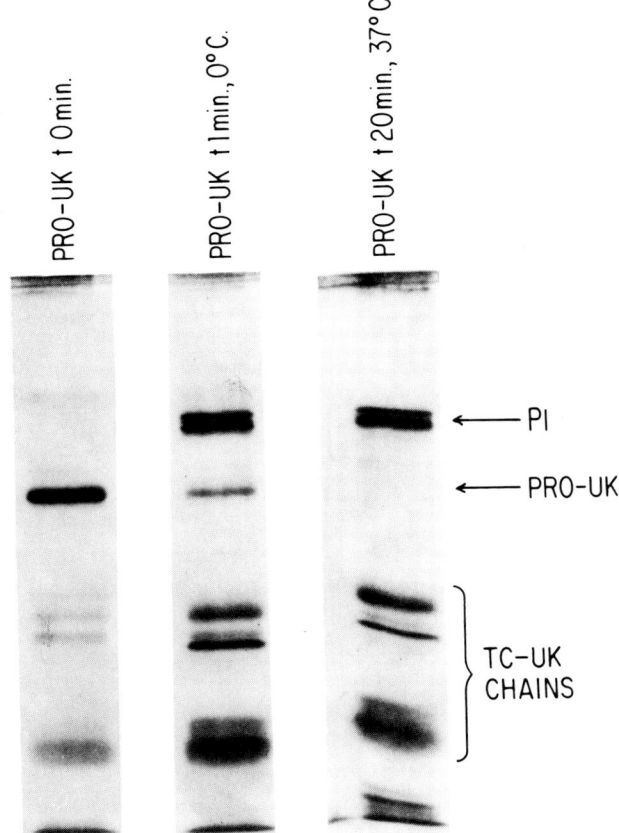

Fig. 90.1 Conversion of pro-UK to HMW-two-chain UK after incubation with plasmin(ogen).

The relationship of the three forms of UK to each other is illustrated (Fig. 90.2). Barlow et al showed that HMW-UK can be converted to UK by relatively large amounts of plasmin (6), whereas catalytic amounts convert pro-UK to HMW-UK.

Three Forms of Urokinase

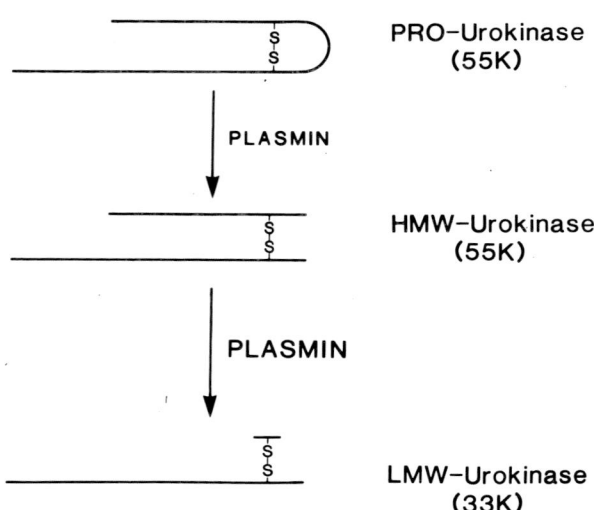

Fig. 90.2 The interrelationship of the 3 forms of UK.

Degradation of pro-UK was also demonstrated with trypsin and crude, bovine thrombin (Parke-Davis) but did not occur with highly purified thrombin (Collaborative Research Inc.) (data not shown).

The degradation of pro-UK was accompanied by activation. A 10-fold increase in amidolytic activity (S-2444) over buffer control was seen within 5 minutes of incubation with plasmin, consistent with a 10% contamination by UK.

After DFP treatment of the pro-UK to inactivate the contaminating UK in the preparation, a 1,000-fold increase in amidolytic activity after incubation with plasmin was observed. It has been previously shown that pro-UK is resistant to inactivation by DFP (3).

On a plasminogen-containing fibrin plate, pro-UK showed a range of lytic activities. An asymptotic increase to a maximum of 100,000 IU/mg was observed as the plasminogen concentration was increased from 0.01–0.2 mg/ml (4).

The effect of fibrin on plasmin elaboration was studied in buffered saline and in plasma. In buffer, fibrin induced only a modest, but repreducible enhancement of plasmin elaboration, consistent with the findings of Lucas et al (7). In plasma, the effect of fibrin was dramatic. Incubation (37°) of pro-UK in plasma or serum for up to three days caused no plasmin elaboration (S-2255), fibrinogenolysis or degradation of the pro-UK. Only after a fibrin clot was added, did plasmin elaboration and fibrinolysis take place. Therefore, in a physiological system, plasmin elaboration by pro-UK was found to be fibrin-dependent.

The fibrinolysis which occurred in the experiments conducted in plasma or serum was not accompanied by any significant fibrinogen degradation, presumably due to the rapid inactivation of UK and plasmin released from the clot surface by inhibitors. The rapid inactivation of free plasmin by α_2-antiplasmin but its resistance to inhibition when plasmin is bound to fibrin (8), probably explains why the activation of pro-UK occurs on the fibrin surface but not in plasma. In blood, active plasmin is probably not found elsewhere than on a clot surface. It is postulated that the activation of pro-UK initiates a chain reaction resulting in the mutual activation of plasminogen and pro-UK. This reaction is apparently confined to the clot surface by the plasma inhibitors (Fig. 90.3). A significant therapeutic potential is evisioned for pro-UK.

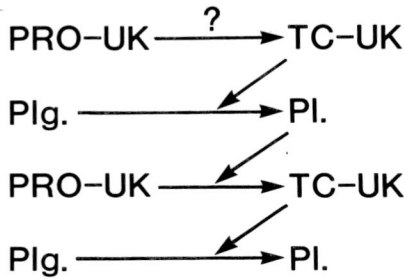

Fig. 90.3 The mutual activation of pro-UK and plasminogen triggered by? the low intrinsic enzymatic activity of pro-UK.

REFERENCES

1. Husain S S, Lipinski B, Gurewich V 1981 Rapid purification of a high-affinity plasminogen activator from human blood plasma by specific adsorption on fibrin/celite. Proceedings of the National Academy of Sciences, USA 78: 4265–4269
2. Husain S S, Gurewich V, Lipinski B 1981 Purification of a new high molecular weight form of urokinase from urine. Thrombosis & Haemostasis 46: 11 (abstract 16)
3. Husain S S, Gurewich V, Lipinski B 1983 Purification and partial characterization of a single-chain, high molecular weight form of urokinase from human urine. Archives Biochemistry and Biophysics 220: 31–38
4. Gurewich V, Pannell R, Louie S, Kelley P, Suddith R L, Greenlee R 1984 Effective and fibrin-specific clot lysis by a zymogen precursor form or urokinase (pro-urokinase). Journal of Clinical Investigation in press
5. Gurewich V, Pannell R, Louie S, Kelley P Fibrin-specific lysis of pulmonary emboli by pro-urokinase (pro-urokinase) in rabbits and dogs. Proceedings of the 7th International Conference on Fibrinolysis. Progress in Fibrinolysis. Churchill Livingstone, Edinburgh
6. Barlow G H, Francis C W, Marder V J 1981 On the conversion of high molecular weight urokinase to the low molecular weight urokinase to the low molecular weight form by plasmin. Thrombosis Research 23: 541–547
7. Lucas M A, Straight D L, Fretlo L J, McKee P A 1983 The effects of fibrinogen and its cleavage products on the kinetics of plasminogen activation by urokinase and subsequent plasmin activity. Journal of Biological Chemistry 258: 12171–12177
8. Lijnen H R, Collen D 1982 Interaction of plasminogen and activators and inhibitors with plasminogen and fibrin. Seminars in Thrombosis and Hemostasis 8: 2–10

91. Studies on the profibrinolytic actions of heparin and its fractions

J. Fareed, M. Walenga, A. Hoppensteadt and L. Messmore

INTRODUCTION

It is generally known that some of the newly developed low molecular weight heparin fractions produce antithrombotic effects without causing any effect on the so-called global anticoagulant tests (6,9,10). More recently, these low molecular weight heparin fractions have been shown to exert antithrombotic actions without producing any effect on routinely performed amidolytic anti Xa assays. This could suggest that besides the antiprotease (anti Xa, anti IIa) in vivo actions these agents may produce their effects by an alternate mechanism (2,4,6,21). In recent years several reports on the fibrinolytic actions of heparin and its fractions have become available (7,8,22). It is believed that these agents may facilitate the release of tissue plasminogen activator which promotes fibrinolysis. The possibility that heparin may facilitate fibrinolysis is of interest since many of the clinical effects of heparin remain unexplained based on the current knowledge of the mechanisms of action.

Table 91.1 depicts some of the mechanisms by which heparin or its low molecular weight fractions may facilitate the fibrinolytic process. Since these agents are heterogenous mixtures of molecularly variant saccharide units, it is possible that some of these components are capable of releasing endogenous plasminogen activator from the endothelial cell linings. Although a definite link between heparin and protein C is not yet established, it may be reasonable to hypothesize that heparin or its fractions may also modulate the activity of protein C. It is known that activated protein C facilitates fibrinolysis via the release of tissue plasminogen activator (5). Since heparin and its fractions are known to influence the metabolic processes on the cellular elements of endothelial cell linings, conceivably this agent may also influence the synthesis of plasminogen

Table 91.1 Possible profibrinolytic actions of heparin and its fractions

1. Direct release of endogenous plasminogen activator from the vessel walls or other cellular elements of blood.
2. Facilitation of the activation of protein C actions promoting the release of plasminogen activator.
3. Effect on the synthesis of plasminogen activators.
4. Impairment of the fibrin monomer polymerization process.
5. Modulation of plasminogen activator inhibitor activity.
6. Modulation of activated protein C activity.

activator (20). Heparin may also impair the fibrin monomer Polymerization, thus altering the stability of clots. Heparin or its derivatives may also modulate the activities of tissue plasminogen activator and protein Ca inhibitor(5). At this time only a limited amount of information is available regarding the fibrinolytic actions of Heparin and its derivatives. In this manuscript we report some of our preliminary results on the possible fibrinolytic actions of heparin and its fractions in humans and a non human primate model.

DESIGN OF THE STUDY

A study was designed to investigate the profibrinolytic actions of heparin and its low molecular weight heparin fractions in humans and a subhuman primate model. Porcine mucosal heparin was obtained from Elkins Sinn Co. (Cherry Hill, NJ) whereas the low molecular weight heparin fractions were obtained from Pharmuka Laboratories; PK 10169 (Gennevilliers, France) and Choay Laboratories; CY 222 (Paris, France). An enzyme linked immunoassay (ELISA) assay method for the measurement of tissue plasminogen activator (t-PA) antigen level was purchased from American Diagnostica (Greenwich, CT), a radioimmunoassay kit for the Bβ 15–42 related peptides (Bβ RPs) from IMCO (Stockholm, Sweden) and an ELISA method for protein C antigen level was obtained from Diagnostica Stago (Asnieres, France). These assays were used to measure the levels of t-PA Bβ RPs and protein C in the plasma of samples obtained from human volunteers and non-human primates. Euglobulin lysis time was determined using a standard laboratory method.

Human Studies

Ten healthy male volunteers were administered with a single dose of 7,500 AXa U/day of heparin or the low molecular weight fractions PK 10169 and CY 222 via the subcutaneous route over 5 days. Blood samples were drawn every day 3 hours after the administration of these agents. Plasma was prepared immediately after the blood draw and frozen at $-70°C$. All tests on the plasma samples were run in batches. In an intravenous study a bolus of 10,000 AXa U/dose of CY 222 was administered to 10 healthy male individuals and blood samples were drawn periodically post injection (1–10 hours). In another intravenous study PK 10169 was administered in a bolus dose to normal healthy volunteers in a dose range of 2,500–12,500 AXa U and blood samples were obtained at varying periods of times post administration. All plasma samples were frozen at $-70°C$ and analyzed in batches.

Primate Studies

In the primate studies a non-human primate model (macaca mulatta) was utilized. An intravenous bolus of 10,000 anti Xa U of a low molecular weight heparin fraction CY 222 was administered every 12 hours for 4 days. Blood samples were drawn every 6 hours. t-PA and protein C levels were measured using immunologic methods.

RESULTS

Figure 91.1 shows the t-PA antigen levels in volunteers treated with a 7 500 AXa U/day subcutaneous dose for 5 days of porcine mucosal heparin. All results

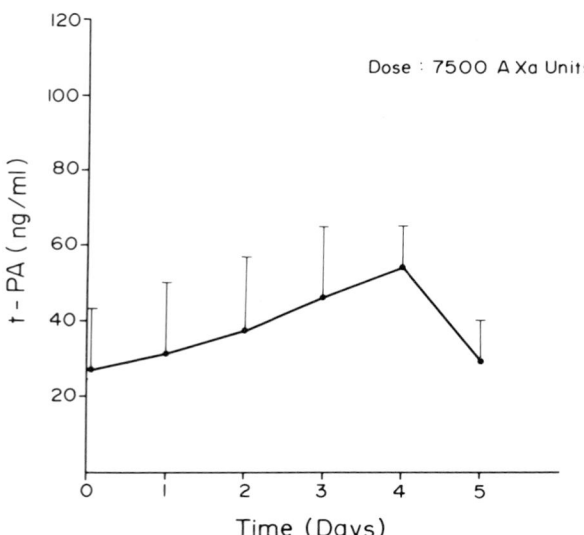

Fig. 91.1 Tissue plasminogen activator antigen (t-PA-A) levels in plasma of human volunteers treated with 7500 AXa U repeated subcutaneous dose of heparin (porcine mucosal heparin Elkius-Sinn, Cherry Hills, NJ, USA). Blood samples were drawn from 10 healthy male volunteers 3 hours after the administration of heparin. Citrated plasma was frozen in aliquots and t-PA-A levels were measured using the ELISA method.

shown in this figure represent a mean of 10 individuals ± 1 S.D. It is evident that up to four days there is a gradual increase in t-PA antigen levels in this group. However, at the fifth day there was a precipitous drop in the t-PA antigen levels.

Figure 91.2 shows the levels of Bβ RPs levels when measured in the same group

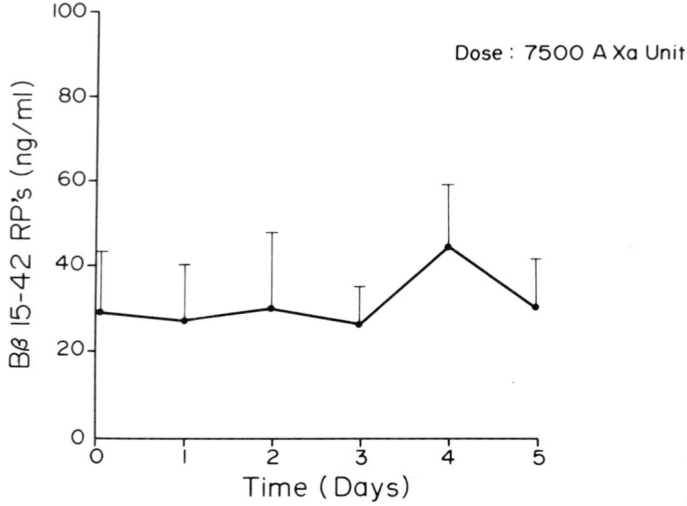

Fig. 91.2 Bβ 15–42 related peptide (Bβ 15–42 RPs) levels in plasma of healthy volunteers treated with 7500 anti Xa repeated subcutaneous dose of heparin (porcine mucosal heparin, Elkius-Sinn, Cherry Hills, NJ, USA). Blood samples were drawn from 10 healthy male volunteers 3 hours after the administration of the heparin. Citrated plasma was frozen in aliquots and Bβ 15–42 RPs levels were measured using an RIA method.

of volunteers. No significant changes were noted in the Bβ RPs levels up to three days. At the fourth day, however, there was an increase in the Bβ RPs levels. On the fifth day the levels reverted to the original values.

Figure 91.3 shows the effect of low molecular weight heparin treatment (7 500 AXa U/day) via the subcutaneous route on the t-PA antigen levels as measured by an ELISA method. Although wide variations in the t-PA levels were observed,

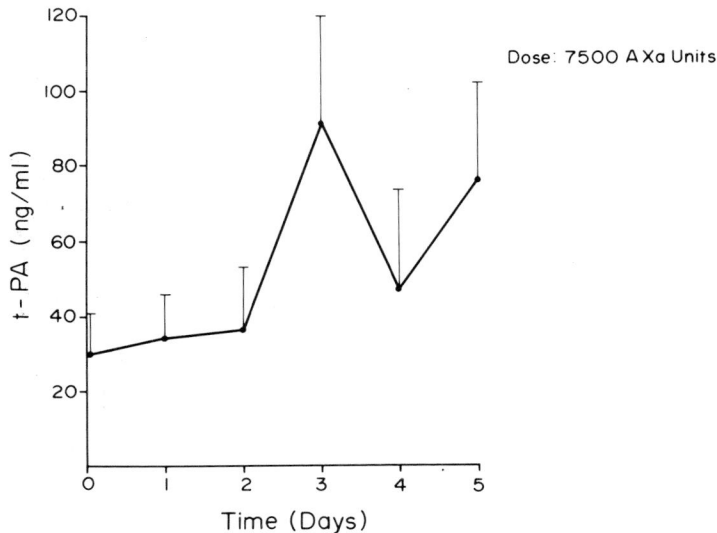

Fig. 91.3 Tissue plasminogen activator antigen (t-PA-A) levels in plasma of human volunteers treated with 7500 AXa repeated subcutaneous dose of a low molecular weight heparin fraction (PK 10169, Pharmuka Laboratories, Gennevilliers, France). Blood samples were drawn from 10 healthy male volunteers 3 hours after the administration of the low molecular weight fraction of heparin. Citrate plasma was frozen in aliquots and t-PA-A levels were measured using an ELISA method.

the data did show a trend. On the third day of treatment a marked increase in the t-PA level was noted. On the fourth day there was a drop, however, the t-PA levels were elevated again on the fifth day. The results depicted on this figure represent a mean of 10 individual determinations ± 1 S.D.

Figure 91.4 shows the Bβ RPs levels in the group treated with a low molecular weight heparin fraction in the same regimen as above. Once again wide variations among the individuals treated were noted. However, it is obvious that after the first day there was a gradual increase in the Bβ RPs levels up to four days, where peak activity was observed, but on the fifth day a precipitous drop in the Bβ RPs levels were noted.

Figure 91.5 shows the results of protein C antigen and t-PA antigen level in eight individuals treated with another low molecular heparin fraction, CY 222. No significant differences were observed in the protein C antigen levels. A gradual increase in the t-PA antigen level was noted during the 2nd–5th days. On the tenth day the t-PA antigen level remained elevated, however no further increase is noted. All results are expressed in this figure as mean ± 1 S.D.

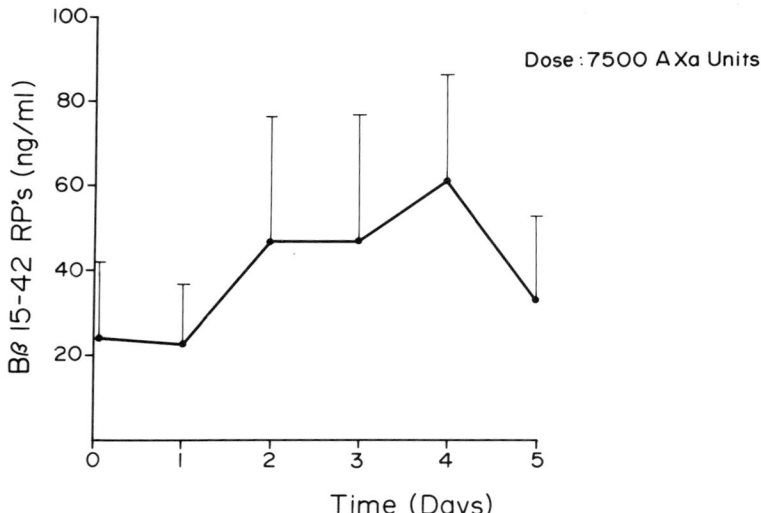

Fig. 91.4 Bβ 15–42 related peptide (Bβ 15–42 RPs) level in plasma of healthy volunteers treated with 7500 AXa U repeated subcutaneous dose of low molecular weight heparin (PK 10169, Pharmuka Laboratories, Gennevilliers, France). Blood samples were drawn from 10 healthy human volunteers 3 hours after the administration of the agent. Citrated plasma was frozen in aliquots. Bβ 15–42 RPs levels were measured using an RIA method.

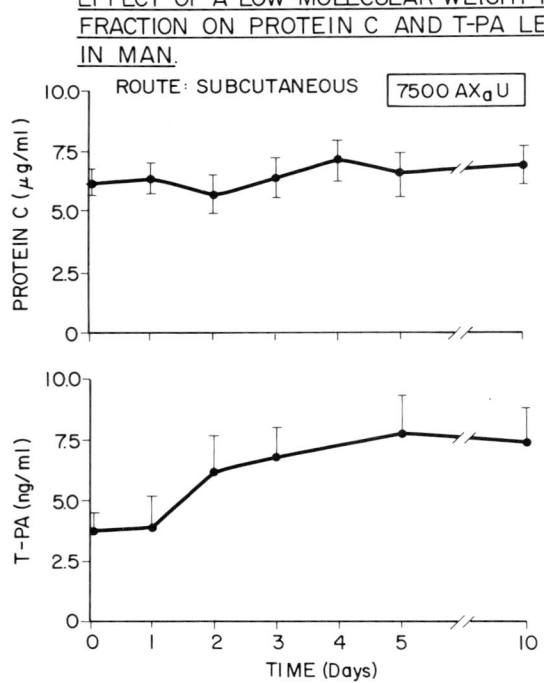

Fig. 93.5 Effect of a low molecular weight heparin fraction (CY 222, Choay Laboratories, Paris, France) on protein C antigen and tissue plasminogen activator levels in man. A repeated dose of this agent was administered via the subcutaneous route. Protein C and t-PA antigen levels were measured using immunologic methods.

Figure 91.6 shows the effect of a low molecular weight heparin fraction, CY 222, on protein C and t-PA levels in man after a 10 000 AXa U bolus injection. No significant changes in the protein C level was noted in this group, however a sizeable increase in the t-PA level was observed one hour after the administration of the low molecular weight heparin. Wide statistical variations were observed among various individuals.

Table 91.2 shows the effect of a bolus intravenous dose of various

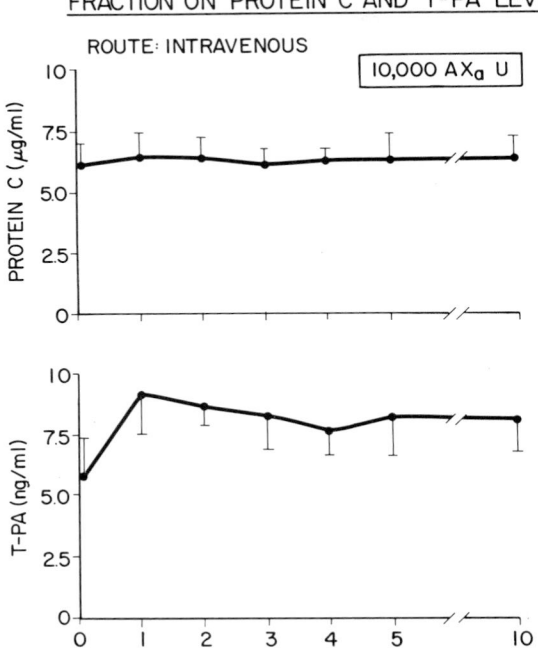

EFFECT OF A LOW MOLECULAR WEIGHT HEPARIN
FRACTION ON PROTEIN C AND T-PA LEVELS.

Fig. 91.6 Effect of a low molecular weight heparin fraction (CY222, Choay Laboratories, Paris, France) on protein C antigen and tissue plasminogen activator levels in man. A single dose of this agent 10 000 AXa U was administered via the intravenous route. Protein C and t-PA antigen levels were measured using immunologic methods.

Table 91.2 Effect of a low molecular weight heparin fraction on the euglobulin lysis time in man

| Dose AXa (U) | Euglobulin Lysis Time | | | |
	0 hr	1 hr	6 hrs	12 hrs
2,500	>180	>180	>180– 90	>180– 70
5,000	>180	>180–60	160 ± 40	>180– 60
7,500	>180	>180–45	140 ± 30	95 ± 17
10,000	>180	>180–60	140–20	80 ± 20
12,500	>180	>180–60	180–60	90 ± 15
Control	>180	—	—	—

All definite results are expressed and represent a mean of 10 individual determinations. The other results are expressed in terms of a range of >180. Varying amounts of a low molecular weight heparin fraction (PK 10169) was administered via the intravenous route. Blood samples were drawn and euglobulin lysis time is measured.

concentrations of a low molecular weight heparin fraction (PK 10169) on euglobulin lysis time (ELT) in 10 individual volunteers. At 0 time all individuals exhibited a euglobulin lysis time (ELT) of > 180 minutes. At one hour no changes were noted in the group treated with 2 500 AXa U, however, in the group treated with 5 000–12 000 AXa U a significant shortening was noted in some of the individuals. Because of the indefinite values mean and standard deviation were not calculated. At 6 hours and 12 hours significant shortening of the ELT was noted in most volunteers, the most pronounced shortening was observed in the volunteers treated with 7 500–12 000 AXa U PK 10169.

Figure 91.7 shows the results of repeated administration of a low molecular weight heparin fraction CY 222 on protein C and t-PA levels in primates treated with a 10 000 AXa U IV bolus of CY 222. These non-human primates were administered with repeated dosage every 12 hours as indicated by the arrows. A gradual increase in the t-PA level was noted over a period of time, however, no significant increase in the protein C level was noted at any time.

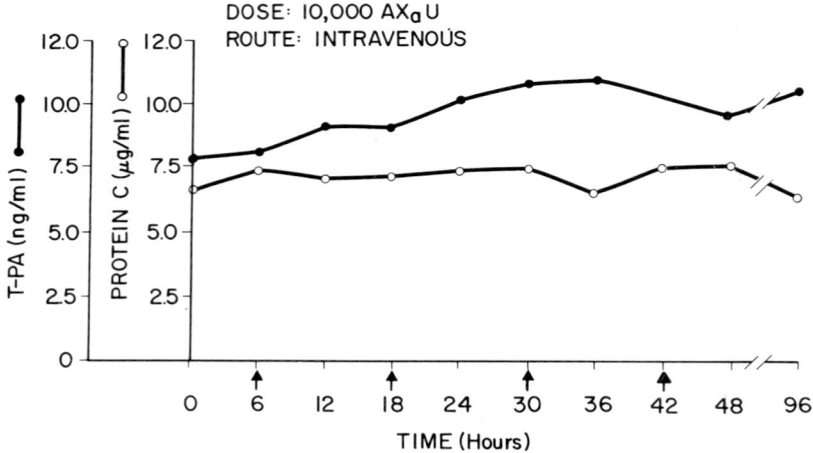

Fig. 91.7 Effect of repeated intravenous administration of a low molecular weight heparin fraction on protein C and tissue plasminogen activator levels in sub-human primates. A single bolus of CY 222 was administered at 10 000 AXa U at 12 hour intervals. Protein C and t-PA levels were measured using immunologic methods.

DISCUSSION

Although numerous reports have recently become available on the profibrinolytic actions of heparin and its fractions, the exact mechanisms of this effect are not clarified (7,8,22). One of the difficulties in these studies is the poor correlation of the in vivo fibrinolytic effect with the in vitro findings on whole blood or plasma (12,13,14,24,25). Additionally most of the conventional in vitro tests have limited value due to drawbacks in methodology or data interpretation. Table 91.3 lists some of the laboratory methods which can be used to study the activation of the fibrinolytic process. The conventional euglobulin lysis time is tedious, semi-physiologic, subjective assay that requires a large amount of test sample. Although reliable methods for the α_2-antiplasmin measurements are available, this inhibitor is only reduced when a major systemic activation of the fibrinolytic

Table 91.3 Laboratory methods to study the profibrinolytic actions of heparin and its derivatives

Method	Comments
1. Euglobulin lysis time	Screening test: Not very reliable.
2. α_2-AP titre	Only reduced in stronger activated states.
3. Plasminogen titre	Only reduced in stronger activated states.
4. Fibrinogen level.	Not reliable. Wide variation.
5. Fibrin split products titre	Not reliable. Nonspecific.
6. Tissue plasminogen activator levels (t-PA titre)	Sensitive marker. Cross reactivity?
7. Bβ 15–42 RPs titre	Sensitive marker. Very short half-life.
8. Plasmin-α_2-AP titre	Reliable. Not available for routine analysis.

process exists. Also it has only a limited value in the evaluation of lytic processes on occurring surfaces and localized sites. Plasminogen levels are reduced at a measurable level only in drug induced fibrinolytic states or during pathologic activation and do not correlate with the localized fibrinolytic process. Thus both α_2-antiplasmin and plasminogen titres are of limited value in the subclinical detection of fibrinolysis. Since the levels of fibrinogen vary widely due to a specific physiologic status, the quantitation of this protein is also of limited value in monitoring the activation of on-site lytic states. Currently, methods available for the measurement of fibrin split products are only sensitive at $>\mu g/ml$ levels and therefore do not provide a reliable index on the subclinical fibrinolytic activation.

Recently many functional and immunologic methods for the evaluation of t-PA have been proposed (3,15,16,17,18,19). The functional methods are somewhat limited in clinical value since the endogenous t-PA inhibitor readily inactivates the t-PA. The immunologic methods for the quantitation of t-PA, on the other hand, provide a reliable tool to quantitate the release of this protein from the endogenous sites. The enzyme linked immunosorbent assay (ELISA) method proposed by Bergsdorf and coworkers is a sensitive method to measure both the bound and unbound t-PA antigen levels (3). This can be particularly useful in the measurement of drug induced release of t-PA, since the functional methods would be limited to measuring only functionally available t-PA. All the complexed t-PA would not be measured resulting in a false low value for total released t-PA.

It can be argued that the endogenously released t-PA can be immediately bound to the site at which a thrombus is formed resulting in low circulating levels of either free or complexed t-PA. The circulating t-PA in healthy individuals can be satisfactorily measured using the ELISA method, however individuals with unhealthy endothelium will bind more t-PA to their vessels and have lower circulating levels. Therefore this method satisfactorily provides a collective t-PA level for release studies, but it should be used with caution when analyzing clinical results. In our studies we utilized the ELISA method to assess the t-PA antigen release in various human volunteers and sub-human primates administered with heparin and its low molecular weight fraction. The antibody to t-PA used in this assay crossreacts with the primate t-PA.

The newly developed assay for Bβ related peptides provides an extremely sensitive tool to measure the activation of the fibrinolytic system (11). We utilized a commercially available radioimmunoassay for the measurement of Bβ RPs in the plasma of human volunteers and primates. The antibody used in this kit crossreacts with both the human and primate antigen. Since the conventional tests have limited sensitivity, in subclinical activation they do not provide reliable data. The Bβ RP assay provides a useful tool to quantitate the subclinical activation of the fibrinolytic system at nanogram/ml levels. However, several problems inherent with this assay are the short half-life of the Bβ 15–42 related peptides and proper sample collection. Even with these limitations, this assay provides a useful marker of the fibrinolytic activation. Plasmin-α_2-antiplasmin complex measurement using an immunologic method can also be used to quantitate the activation of the fibrinolytic system, however, at this time these methods are not available for routine use (18).

In the repeated subcutaneous studies with heparin, the results indicated that a gradual rise in the t-PA antigen was observed in human volunteers up to 4 days. At the 5th day a precipitous drop in the t-PA antigen was observed. This data suggests that heparin is capable of releasing the t-PA like antigen from an endogenous site, however the drop at the 5th day is unexplainable. The Bβ RP level in this heparin treated group did not change for the first 3 days, however, a significant elevation was observed on the 4th day and on the 5th day a reduction of the Bβ RPs was observed. On a statistical basis the results obtained in this study were not significantly different from the base-line values.

In the case of repeated subcutaneous low molecular weight heparin, marked elevation in the t-PA antigen levels was observed on the 3rd and 5th days. After the 4th day of treatment the t-PA antigen levels were lower than the 3rd and 5th days. Although in this group the trend was towards an increased level of t-PA antigen, marked variations were noted in individual results. This may be partly due to endogenous physiologic variations and inconsistency in the blood collection. The Bβ RPs levels in the low molecular weight heparin treated group was increased on the 2nd, 3rd, and 4th days. A marked drop was observed on the 5th day. It is, however, obvious from our results that both the t-PA antigen levels and Bβ RPs are markedly elevated in the group treated with the molecular weight heparin fraction in contrast to heparin.

The variations in our results may be due to many experimental factors. In the human studies, blood was drawn using a routine venipuncture technique. If the venous occlusion technique was performed one would have expected more consistant data. Another problem may be related to the preservation of the blood samples. The samples in this study were not collected in EDTA/Trasylol, rather routine sodium citrate anticoagulant was used. This may be the reason for the variations observed in the Bβ RPs since endogenous protease may modulate these peptides.

In another study with the human volunteers, we measured the protein C and t-PA antigen levels after administering a 7500 AXa total dose of the low molecular weight heparin fractions. No significant changes in the protein C levels were noted over a period of 10 days, however, a marked sustained increase in the t-PA antigen was seen in volunteers treated with this agent. This data is somewhat suggestive of the endogenous release of t-PA after the administration of the low molecular weight heparin fraction and unlike the previous study a constant response was observed.

The same heparin fraction was administered in the intravenous route at a

10 000 AXa bolus injection to man. Over a period of ten hours no change in the protein C level was observed. However, the t-PA antigen levels were significantly increased at one hour after the administration of the low molecular weight heparin. A gradual decrease in the t-PA antigen level was observed over the next 10 hours, however the t-PA levels remain elevated at all times.

We also measured the effect of low molecular weight heparin administration by the euglobulin lysis time. In a dose range of 2 500–12 500 AXa units total dose, the euglobulin lysis time was significantly shortened in a majority of volunteers treated with the low molecular weight heparin fractions.

Since our studies only involved healthy human volunteers we expected a consistent response in the circulating t-PA levels. However, this study may not truly reflect the pathologic lesions and high affinity material (for the t-PA) thrombotic lesions. This may also lead to the wide variations seen in the t-PA levels in various clinical situations. A more pertinent approach may be to study heparin and its fractions with non-invasive in vivo methods such as imaging and other physical diagnostic measures.

Our studies on the primate models were somewhat limited, however, in these studies we were able to demonstrate that the t-PA antigen levels were elevated in primates treated with a 10 000 AXa U/dose of a low molecular weight heparin fraction. This was a large dose since most of the primates are 8–10 kg of weight. The fact that a significant increase in the t-PA antigen levels were seen suggests that this dose of low molecular weight heparin fraction produces release of t-PA. Yet, no significant increase in the protein C levels are noted at any time. The object of this study was to give a supratherapeutic dose of the low molecular weight heparin fraction to produce any possible increase in the t-PA antigen level.

Low molecular weight heparin fractions have been shown to produce antithrombotic actions in limited clinical studies (9,10). It is generally believed that the antithrombotic actions of these agents are primarily due to their anti Xa actions (1,2,3). However, many additional factors may also contribute to their antithrombotic actions (2,4,5,6,20,21). The fact that mini dose heparin is proven to be a clinically effective antithrombotic agent without any major increase in the anti Xa actions is highly suggestive that alternate mechanisms may be involved in the overall antithrombotic effect of these agents. Utilizing sensitive tests for the t-PA and Bβ RPs as markers for the endogenous release of these important activators of fibrinolysis, we have seen that heparin fractions are capable of producing profibrinolytic effects. Additional studies are, however, needed to determine which molecular components of heparin or its fractions produce this effect.

SUMMARY AND CONCLUSIONS

1. Utilizing modified immunochemical methods (ELISA and RIA) tissue plasminogen activator, Bβ 15–42 related peptides and protein C antigen levels were measured in man and a subhuman primate model after subcutaneous and intravenous administration of various low molecular weight heparin fractions.

2. A wide scatter in the data was observed in the t-PA and Bβ 15–42 related peptide levels, however, statistical analysis of the data revealed that certain low molecular weight heparin fractions increased the levels of these endogenous markers of fibrinolysis.

3. No significant alteration in the protein C levels were noted at any time, however a wide scatter in this data was also evident.

4. The profibrinolytic actions of low molecular weight heparin fractions may be related to the release of t-PA which is difficult to measure in plasma since it has strong affinity to endogenous sites (thrombus, surface). This may be the reason for a wide scatter in the data.

5. Most of the results reported in our studies represent data on blood samples which were obtained using the simple venipuncture method. However a proper assessment of the low molecular weight heparin induced firbrinolysis can be adequately made by using the sphygmomanometer.

6. We also find that the intravenous administration of the low molecular weight heparin fractions also caused a shortening of the euglobulin lysis time.

7. Since the low molecular weight heparin fractions are heterogenous in nature, the profibrinolytic actions may be related to one or more of these constituent fragments. Thus the molecular identity of the profibrinolytic component of low molecular fractions remains unknown at this time.

ACKNOWLEDGEMENTS

The authors acknowledge the expert secretarial help of Ms Cher Gurtler and Mrs M. Brauer for the preparation of this manuscript. We are thankful to Drs Francis Toulemonde of Choay Laboratories, Paris, France; Martine Woler of Pharmuka Laboratories, Gennevilliers, France; Austin Daragh of Institute of Clinical Pharmacology, Dublin, Ireland for providing us clinical samples from human volunteers treated with various low molecular weight heparin fractions. We are grateful to Professor M. Samama of Hotel Dieu, Paris, France and Dr John Davidson of Royal Infirmary, Glasgow, Scotland for the helpful advice and encouragement to facilitate these studies.

REFERENCES

1. Aiach M, Schreiber N, Nussas C, Michaud A, Leon M, Leclerc M 1981 An automated amidolytic assay for testing factor X activity. Thromb Res 21: 317–320
2. Barzu T, Molho P, Tobelem G, Petitou M, Caen J P 1984 Binding of heparin and low molecular weight heparin fragments in human vascular endothelial cells in culture. Nouv Rev Fr Hematol 26: 243–247
3. Bergsdorf N, Nilsson T, Wallen P 1983 An enzyme linked immunosorbent assay for determination of tissue plasminogen activator applied to patients with thromboembolic disease. Thromb Hemost 50 (3): 740–744
4. Comp P 1984 Heparin protein C interaction. Nouv Rev Fr Hematol 26: 239–242
5. Comp P C, Esmon C T 1981 Generation of fibrinolytic activity by infusion of activated protein C into dogs. J Clin Inves 68: 1221–1228
6. Fareed J, Kumar A, Walenga J M, Emanuele R M, Williamson K M, Hoppensteadt D 1984 Antithrombotic actions and pharmacokinetics of heparin fractions and fragments. Nouv Rev Fr Hematol 26: 267–275

7. Gaffney P J, Marsh N A, Thomas D P 1982 The influence of heparin and heparin-like substances on the fibrinolytic system in vivo. Haemost 12: 85
8. Halse T 1962 Aktivierung der fibrinolyse und thrombolyse durch polysaccharideschwefsaureester (heparin, heparinoide). Arzneim Forschung 12: 574–582
9. Kakkar V V 1984 Prevention of post operative venous thromboembolism by a new low molecular weight heparin fraction. Nouv Rev Fr Hematol 26, 277–282
10. Kakkar V V, Spinder J, Flute D T, Corrigan T, Fossard D P, Crellin R Q, Wessler S, Yin E T 1972 Efficacy of low doses of heparin in prevention of deep vein thrombosis after major surgery. A double blind trial. Lancet II, pp 101–106
11. Kudry K B, Robinson D, Netre C 1982 Measurement in human blood of fibrinogen/fibrin fragments containing the Bβ 15–42 sequence. Thromb Res 25: 277–291
12. Markwardt F, Klocking H P 1976 Studies on the release of plasminogen activator. Thromb Res 8: 217–223
13. Marsh N A, Gaffney P J 1982 Exercise-induced fibrinolysis — fact or fiction? Thromb Haemostas 48: 201–203
14. Matsuo O, Fijken D C, Collen D 1981 Thrombolysis by human tissue plasminogen activator and urokinase in rabbits with experimental pulmonary embolus. Nature 291: 590–591
15. Ranby M 1982 Tissue plasminogen activator. Isolation, enzymatic properties and assay procedure. Thesis, Umeå University Medical Dissertations. New Series, No 90, Umeå
16. Ranby M, Norrman B, Wallen P 1982 A sensitive assay for tissue plasminogen activator. Thromb Res 27: 743–749
17. Rijken D C, Collen D 1981 Purification and characterization of the plasminogen activator secreted by human melanoma cells in culture. J Biol Chem 256: 7035–7041
18. Rijken D C, Johan-Vague I, Collen D 1983 Complexes between tissue-type plasminogen activator and proteinase inhibitors in human plasma, identified with an immunoradiometric assay. J Lab Clin Med 101: 285–294
19. Rijken D C, Wijngaards G, Welbergen J 1981 Immunological characterization of plasminogen activator activities in human tissues and body fluids. J Lab Clin Med 97: 477–486
20. Rosenberg R D, Fritze L M S, Castellot J J, Karnovsky M J 1984 Heparin like molecules as regulators of alterogenesis. Nouv Rev Fr Hematol 26: 255–260
21. Tollefsen M 1984 Activation of heparin cofactor II by heparin and dermatan sulfate. Nouv Rev Fr Hematol 26: 233–237
22. Vairel E G, Bouty-Boye H, Toulemonde F, Doutremepuich C, Marsh N A, Gaffney P J 1983 Heparin and a low molecular weight fraction enhances thrombolysis and by this pathway exercises a protective effect against thrombosis. Thromb Res 30: 219–224
23. Walenga J M, Fareed J, Messmore H L 1984 Newer avenues in the monitoring of antithrombotic therapy: The role of automation. Sem Thromb Hemost 9(4): 341–354
24. Weimar W, Stibbe J, van Seyen A J, Billiau A, De Somer P, Collen D 1981 Specific lysis of an iliofemoral thrombus by administration of extrinsic (tissue-type) plasminogen activator. Lancet 2: 1018–1020
25. Wiman B, Collen D 1978 Molecular mechanism of physiological fibrinolysis. Nature 272: 549–550

APPENDIX TO SECTION 9

92. Dissociation between plasminogen activator and metastatic potential of experimental tumour cells: biological and pharmacological evidence

L. Mussoni, M.G. Conforti and M.B. Donati

Formation of cancer metastases involves a number of steps which include: detachment from the primary tumour, digestion of the surrounding matrix, entry into the blood stream, transport in the circulation and interaction with various blood constituents, adhesion to the vascular wall and extravasation, arrest in the target organs and proliferation (Fiedler, 1978). It has been proposed that the deposition of fibrin around cancer cells could influence their behaviour in a number of these biological processes (Donati & Poggi, 1980). As a consequence, cancer cell fibrinolytic activity could play an important role in the degradation of fibrin or other substrates surrounding cancer cells, favouring the detachment from the primary and delaying the trapping of the same cells into distant organs (Markus, 1983).

This oversimplified scheme has been challenged by a number of conflicting results obtained in different experimental models of metastases (Poggi et al, 1981). It is the purpose of this brief survey to gather data obtained by our group on the expression of plasminogen activator (PA) by cancer cells metastasizing *spontaneously* from a primary implant. The aim of our work was to obtain an answer to the following questions:

1. Is plasminogen activator expressed differently in cells from the primary tumour and corresponding metastases?
2. Is pharmacological inhibition of fibrinolysis associated with a change in metastatic potential?
3. Is plasminogen activator expressed differently in cells with different metastatic potential?

1. Is plasminogen activator expressed differently in cells from the primary tumour and corresponding metastases?

We have approached this problem on a spontaneously metastasizing tumour, the Lewis Lung Carcinoma (3LL). During growth and metastasis formation of 3LL a low-grade intravascular clotting occurs with increased fibrinogen turnover and fibrin deposition at the tumour site (Poggi et al, 1977). Cancer cells were obtained from primary and from lung nodules and tested either immediately or following an in vitro passage. PA activity was measured by an amidolytic technique. The cells expressed a plasminogen-dependent fibrinolytic activity which did not differ markedly in native or cultured cells. Moreover, an equal amount of PA was produced by cells from the primary and from metastatic nodules. PA activity appeared to be of urokinase-type on the basis of immunological and apparent molecular weight characteristics (Mussoni et al, 1981).

2. Is pharmacological inhibition of fibrinolysis associated with a change in metastatic potential?

In the same 3LL model pharmacological inhibition of fibrinolysis was obtained by treating the animals with tranexamic acid (0.5, 1, 2, g/kg/daily) during the whole tumour development. A dose-dependent inhibition of fibrinolytic activity was obtained in blood of treated mice. Even with the highest dosage which blocked completely the whole blood clot lysis, no change was observed in the primary tumour weight, lung metastasis number and weight, survival time. These observations could be taken as an indication that fibrinolysis does not play any major role in cancer cells-host interactions in the 3LL system. However, it was difficult to obtain a clear-cut evidence that the treatment given was not only affecting host's fibrinolysis *systemically,* but was also *locally* impairing cancer cell PA activity. In vitro experiments showed that indeed PA activity of 3LL cells could be depressed (up to 50%) by incubation with a range of tranexamic acid concentrations. However, cells harvested from animals treated with tranexamic acid expressed the same type and amount of PA activity as cells from control animals. This finding could be ascribed either to poor access of tranexamic acid to the tumor area or to removal of the drug from the vicinity of the cells during the manipulations required for native cell preparation. Whatever their interpretation, these data underline the difficulty of assigning a unequivocal role to some cellular markers on the basis of pharmacological studies (Poggi et al, 1981).

3. Is plasminogen activator expressed differently in cells with different metastatic potential?

In order to overcome the draw-back of pharmacological approaches, which are indirect and not sufficiently specific, we have subsequently studied the expression of PA in cells endowed with different metastatic potential, although deriving from the same parent line. Cells from the benzopyrene-induced fibrosarcoma (mFS6) acquired, following a number of in vitro-in vivo passages, the capacity to metastasize in a markedly different way (95% vs 5% metastatic incidence) (Mantovani, 1978). This model is distinct from most metastatic variants proposed in recent years, since the cells differ in their capacity to give *spontaneous* metastasis following intramuscular implantation not in lung nodules following intravenous injection (Fidler, 1978). No differences were obtained between the amount of PA activity of the parent cell line (metastatic incidence 50%) and of both metastatic sublines. In this model too, the PA was of urokinase-type, of similar molecular weight and immunological characteristic on all three cell lines. It thus appears that, at least in this fibrosarcoma model, PA activity is not selected among the cellular properties strongly associated with the metastatic potential of cancer cells. Interestingly enough, in all mFS6 cell lines PA activity was abolished in vitro by very low concentrations (down to 0.001 u/ml) of purified thrombin (Coen et al, 1983). A similar observation has been made also for the urokinase-type activity expressed by 3LL cells. Both 3LL and mFS6 cells possess procoagulant activity although of different type (direct activator of factor X and tissue thromboplastin, respectively); it is thus conceivable that traces of thrombin, formed by whatever mechanism in the cancer cell microenvironment, would have a regulatory role on PA activity expression. This assumption suggests that cancer cells activities may mutually interact and should be considered together in discussing the role of fibrin in metastases formation.

ACKNOWLEDGEMENTS

Most of the authors' work mentioned in this review was supported by Italian National Research Council (Project 'Oncologia'), by a grant of the Gustavus and Louise Pfeiffer Research Foundation, Los Angeles, California, USA and by 'Associazione italiana per la Ricerca sul Cancro'.
Ivana Garimoldi helped prepare this manuscript.

REFERENCES

Coen D, Bottazzi B, Bini A, Conforti M G, Mantovani A, Mussoni L, Donati M B 1983 Plasminogen activator activity of metastatic variants from a murine fibrosarcoma: effect of thrombin in vitro. International Journal of Cancer 32: 67–70

Donati M B, Poggi A 1980 Malignancy and haemostasis. British Journal of Haematology 44: 173–182

Fidler I J 1978 Tumor heterogeneity and the biology of cancer invasion and metastasis. Cancer Research 38: 2651–2660

Mantovani A 1978 Effects on in vitro tumor growth of murine macrophages isolated from sarcoma lines differing in immunogenicity and metastasizing capacity. International Journal of Cancer 22: 741–746

Markus G 1983 Plasminogen activators in malignant growth. In: Davidson J F, Bachman F, Bouvier C A, Kruithof E K O (eds) Progress in fibrinolysis. Churchill Livingstone, Edinburgh, vol 6, pp 587–604

Mussoni L, Coen D, Balconi G, Delaini F, Donati M B 1981 Plasminogen activator activity of cells from primary and metastases of the Lewis lung carcinoma. In: Davidson J F, Nilsson I M, Astedt B (eds) Progress in fibrinolysis. Churchill Livingstone, Edinburgh, vol 5, p 85–89

Poggi A, Polentarutti N, Donati M B, de Gaetano G, Garattini S 1977 Blood coagulation changes in mice bearing Lewis Lung Carcinoma, a metastasizing tumor. Cancer Research 37: 272–277

Poggi A, Donati M B, Garattini S 1981 Fibrin and cancer cell growth: problems in the evaluation of experimental models. In: Donati M B, Davidson J F, Garattini S (eds) Malignancy and the hemostatic system. Raven Press, New York, pp 89–101

93. Human ovarian carcinoma cells in primary culture: a source of tissue factor and plasminogen activator

L. Mussoni, M.G. Conforti, C. Gambacorti-Passerini, G. Alessio, S. Pepe, M. Vaghi, E. Erba, C. Mangioni, M.B. Donati and N. Semeraro

INTRODUCTION

Human ovarian carcinoma is often associated with thrombohaemorrhagic complications (Astedt et al, 1976). Malignant ovarian tumours possess both procoagulant (PCA) and fibrinolytic activities (FA). These two activities however have been studied separately on different specimens, mainly in tissue extracts or in organ culture (Svanberg, 1975, Astedt & Holmberg, 1976). In these experimental conditions various host cells (macrophages, lymphocytes, fibroblasts, endothelial cells, etc.), besides cancer cells, could contribute to the deposition and/or dissolution of fibrin within the tumour.

In the present study, PCA and FA were evaluated on human ovarian carcinoma cells isolated in primary culture, to avoid interference from contaminating host cells.

MATERIALS AND METHODS

This study was performed on 16 patients (aged between 40–60 yr) with histologically confirmed ovarian carcinoma (FIGO III-IV) of serous-mucinous type. Biopsy material was obtained from primary surgery, from second-look laparotomy or from ascitic fluid after paracentesis under sterile conditions. Tumour cells were isolated as previously described (Morasca et al, 1983) from ascitic fluid (13 cases), from solid tumors (3 cases) and from omental metastasis (1 case). The final cell suspension containing more than 70% viable cells was seeded in culture at 70 000 cells/cm^2 in tissue culture dishes. Culture medium was M-199 supplemented with 15% fetal calf serum. Cells were tested after 5–6 days in culture when the nests of cancer cells became well spread out. In order to evaluate and characterize PCA and FA, the primary cultures were kept overnight in serum free medium. Only the cultures without fibroblast-like cells and with less than 5% macrophages were used.

PCA was measured by a one stage plasma recalcification assay on frozen, then thawed cancer cells (Curatolo et al, 1979). The type of PCA was characterized using human plasma selectively deficient in factors VII, IX and X. PCA was expressed in arbitrary units by comparison with a standard curve of human brain thromboplastin suspension.

FA was determined in cellular extracts obtained with 0.25% Triton X-100 by an amidolytic assay in the presence of fibrin monomers (Ranby & Wallen, 1981). Tumour cell FA was expressed as UK equivalent units/mg of protein, by comparison with a standard urokinase (1st international preparation, coded 66/64, a gift from Dr P.J. Gaffney, London, UK). Plasminogen independent FA was determined by omitting plasminogen in the test mixture. Plasminogen-dependent (PA) fibrinolytic activity was identified using a specific polyclonal antibody against human urokinase (gift from Prof. B. Astedt, University of Lund, Malmo, Sweden) and on the basis of the molecular weight estimation at SDS-PAGE and fibrin overlay (Loskutoff & Mussoni, 1983).

RESULTS AND DISCUSSION

Table 93.1 shows the results of PCA and FA assay on cell preparations from 16 patients. On five occasions more than one sample could be obtained. PCA was detectable in all samples and showed a wide range of activity. The activity was identified in all instances as tissue factor since it required coagulation factor VII, not factor IX, for its expression.

Table 93.1 Amount and type of procoagulant and fibrinolytic activity of human ovarian carcinoma cells. Each value is the mean of duplicate experiments. ND = not detectable

Pat	Cell source	Fibrinolytic activity		Procoagulant activity (u/10 cells)	
		uUK/mg	Inhibition by anti-UK	Normal plasma	F VII-def plasma
1	Ascitic fluid	N.D.	N.D.	34.4	N.D.
2a	Ascitic fluid	0.21	N.D.	134.6	0.50
2b	Ascitic fluid	0.23	N.D.	267.6	0.50
3	Ovary	0.16	Yes	67.0	0.50
4	Ovary	1.90	Yes	206.6	0.50
5	Ascitic fluid	N.D.	N.D.	12.8	0.50
6	Ovary	<0.001	—	358.5	2.15
7a	Ascitic fluid	1.02	Yes	643.4	2.99
7b	Ascitic fluid	1.33	Yes	351.5	1.52
7c	Ascitic fluid	2.05	Yes	1317.4	6.97
8a	Ascitic fluid	2.30	Yes	608.0	2.15
8b	Ascitic fluid	0.50	Yes	564.4	4.79
8c	Ascitic fluid	1.57	Yes	204.1	1.38
9	Ascitic fluid	N.D.	N.D.	659.6	2.83
10	Ascitic fluid	<0.001	—	134.7	4.01
11	Ascitic fluid	<0.001	—	1168.0	31.53
12a	Omentum	<0.001	—	308.5	7.74
12b	Ascitic fluid	<0.001	—	138.5	4.70
13	Ascitic fluid	N.D.	N.D.	230.0	6.28
14	Ascitic fluid	N.D.	N.D.	81.1	0.50
15a	Ascitic fluid	<0.001	—	41.5	0.50
15b	Ascitic fluid	1.33	Yes	58.9	1.36
16	Ascitic fluid	<0.001	—	70.6	0.50

FA was below the detection limit (0.001 uUK/mg) in 8 out of 18 samples tested. The activity varied widely among patients and within the same patient's samples. In all samples but one (pat.3) FA was plasminogen-dependent, suggesting the presence of a plasminogen activator enzyme (PA). Molecular analysis of PA showed a single molecular form of 52 000 daltons, inhibited by an antibody against urokinase. These data confirm on isolated cells the findings of Astedt and Holmberg (1976) that material immunologically identical to urokinase was released from ovarian carcinoma organ cultures.

At variance with previous studies on either PCA or FA activity in tumor cells, this work aimed specifically to investigate the simultaneous expression of FA and PCA on the same clinical material. These two activities were in fact easily demonstrated and characterized here in cells from primary cultures and the possible interference of contaminating host cells was thus ruled out.

PCA and FA, among other factors of cancer cells, have been repeatedly suggested to play a role in fibrin deposition and dissolution in the tumour microenvironment (Donati & Poggi, 1980); however, in the material we studied, no simple correlation could be established between PCA and FA. It must be underlined that most of the patients, at the time of the study, were receiving polychemotherapy. The possibility that such treatment influenced the activities studied here cannot be excluded. It appears premature therefore to speculate about the actual relevance of these tumour cell activities in relation to clinical malignancy before several studies, on larger numbers of patients, become available.

REFERENCES

Astedt B, Svanberg L, Nilsson I M 1971 Fibrin degradation products and ovarian tumours. British Medical Journal 4: 458
Astedt B, Holmberg L 1976 Immunological identity of urokinase and ovarian carcinoma plasminogen activator released in tissue culture. Nature 261: 595–597
Curatolo L, Colucci M, Cambini A L, Poggi A, Morasca L, Donati M B, Semeraro N 1979 Evidence that cells from experimental tumors can activate coagulation factor x. British Journal of Cancer 40: 228–233
Donati M B, Poggi A 1980 Malignancy and haemostasis. British Journal of Haematology 44: 173–182
Loskutoff D J, Mussoni L 1983 Interaction between fibrin and the plasminogen activators produced by cultured endothelial cells. Blood 62: 62–68
Morasca L, Erba E, Vaghi M, Ghelardini C, Mangioni C, Sessa C, Landoni F, Garattini S 1983 Clinical correlates of in vitro drug sensitivities of ovarian cancer cells. British Journal of Cancer 48: 61–68
Ranby M, Wallen P 1981 A sensitive parabolic rate assay for the tissue plasminogen activator. In: Davidson J F, Nilsson I M, Astedt B (eds) Progress in fibrinolysis. Churchill Livingstone, Edinburgh, vol 5, p 233–236
Svanberg L 1975 Thromboplastic activity of human ovarian tumors. Thrombosis Research 6: 307–313

94. Effect of tranexamic acid on spontaneous metastases of Lewis lung carcinoma in mice

L. Mussoni, M.G. Conforti and M.B. Donati

INTRODUCTION

The role of the fibrinolytic system in tumour metastases is still a matter of discussion. Several reports have indicated plasminogen activator (PA) of tumour cells has being associated with malignant transformation and/or cell invasiveness (Markus, 1983). If these indications were correct, antifibrinolytic agents might be potential inhibitors of cancer cell primary growth and metastases. Such drugs as aminocaproic and tranexamic acid have been given to animals implanted with different rodent tumour cells; the various treatments were given with different schedules and for different periods. In most cases an increase in lung colonies after intravenous injection of the cells and a decrease in primary tumour weight after subcutaneous or intramuscular implantation were reported (Peterson, 1977). The aim of the present work was to verify whether treatment with tranexamic acid at doses inhibiting the systemic fibrinolytic activity of tumour bearing animals also affected cancer cell PA and by this means altered the growth and spread of the tumour. The experimental model consisted in Lewis Lung Carcinoma (3LL) cells which we have previously shown to possess PA activity when harvested either from the primary tumour or from lung metastatic nodules (Mussoni et al, 1981).

EXPERIMENTAL SYSTEM

The 3LL was implanted (1×10^5 cells) intramuscularly in male C57 Bl/6 mice. The tumour grows locally and gives metastases selectively to the lungs (Poggi et al, 1977). Primary tumour and lung metastasis growth was assayed as previously described (Donati et al, 1978). Tranexamic acid (t-AMCHA) was dissolved in tap water at dosages of 0.5, 1.0 or 2.0 g/kg b.w. daily and administered in the drinking water. The animals were treated with the drug from the day before tumour cell implantation up to killing. Fibrinolytic activity was evaluated 17–19 days after tumour implantation in the blood and in the extract of primary tumour of the same 3LL bearing mice.

Blood fibrinolytic activity was measured by the diluted blood clot lysis time (DBCLT) on citrated blood taken by cardiac puncture from anesthetized animals

(Poggi et al, 1977). Viable tissue fragments from the primary tumour of the same animal (after removal of the necrotic part) were homogenized and extracted with Triton x-100 (0.25% v/v) before measuring the PA content. PA activity was determined by an amidolytic method (Ranby & Wallen, 1981) in the presence of fibrin monomers. The results were expressed in urokinase (UK) equivalent units by comparison with a standard curve of UK (1st International Standard for urokinase, a kind gift from Dr P.J. Gaffney, London, UK) plotted with each set of experiments. The molecular weight of PA extracted from tumour cells of the primary was determined by fibrin agarose-plates after SDS-PAGE (Coen et al, 1983).

RESULTS AND DISCUSSION

Table 94.1 shows that the doses of tranexamic acid used partially (0.5 g/kg) or completely (1.0, 2.0 g/kg) inhibited the blood fibrinolytic activity of tumour-bearing mice. The PA activity of 3LL cells was well inhibited by in vitro incubation with t-AMCHA (data not shown), but was unaffected by in vivo antifibrinolytic treatment. The molecular type of PA extracted from 3LL of control and treated animals had a similar apparent molecular weight of 45 000 daltons. As shown in Table 94.2, neither the mean survival time nor the primary tumour weight or number of lung metastases were changed by any treatment

Table 94.1 Effect of tranexamic acid on blood fibrinolytic activity and PA activity extracted from the primary tumours of 3LL bearing mice (mean + SE)

Treatment (g/kg/day)	Animals (n)	DBCLT (hours)	Cancer cell PA (u UK/mg protein)
none	20	$5.0 + 0.4$	$0.16 + 0.01$
0.5	20	$10.0 + 0.7$	$0.24 + 0.01*$
1.0	19	>24	$0.20 + 0.01$
2.0	20	>24	$0.19 + 0.1$

Animals were killed on day 17–19 after tumour implantation
* $p < 0.05$ (Dunnett's test).

Table 94.2 Effect of tranexamic acid at different dosages in 3LL-bearing mice (means + SE)

Treatment (g/kg/day)	Animals (n)	MST† (days)	Tumour weight (g)	Lung weight (mg)	Lung metastases number	weight (mg)
none	25	24 (18–29)	$8.3 + 0.4$	$232 + 13$	$21.9 + 1.8$	$135 + 20$
0.5	22	26 (18–31)	$8.3 + 0.3$	$237 + 17$	$20.3 + 2.4$	$128 + 24$
1.0	25	24 (18–29)	$8.6 + 0.3$	$235 + 16$	$19.3 + 1.7$	$151 + 22$
2.0	15	25 (18–31)	$8.4 + 0.3$	$291 + 32*$	$21.1 + 2.7$	$243 + 55*$

Animals were killed on day 21–22 after tumour implantation
† Median survival time (range)
* $p < 0.05$ (Dunnett's test)

378

schedule, whereas the lung weight and the metastasis weight increased with the highest dosage used.

These data indicate that even marked inhibition of *blood* fibrinolysis does not induce major changes in tumour development. On the other hand, no definite proof was obtained in this study of the role of *cancer cell* fibrinolytic activity. The reason why no inhibition of cancer cell PA could be detected ex vivo may be either impaired access of the drug to tumour tissue or to detachment of the drug from its cellular target during the in vitro manipulations required to prepare the tumour extract.

REFERENCES

Coen D, Bottazzi B, Bini A, Conforti M G, Mantovani A, Mussoni L, Donati M B 1983 Plasminogen activator activity of metastatic variants from a murine fibrosarcoma; effect of thrombin in vitro. International Journal of Cancer 32: 67–70

Donati M B, Mussoni L, Poggi A, de Gaetano G, Garattini S 1978 Growth and metastasis of the Lewis lung carcinoma in mice defibrinated with Batroxobin. European Journal of Cancer 14: 343–347

Markus G 1983 Plasminogen activators in malignant growth. In: Davidson J F, Bachman F, Bouvier C A, Kruithof E K O (eds) Progress in fibrinolysis. Churchill Livingstone, Edinburgh, vol 6, p 587–604

Mussoni L, Coen D, Balconi G, Delaini F, Donati M B 1981 Plasminogen ativator activity of cells from primary and metastases of the Lewis lung carcinoma. In: Davidson J F, Nilsson I M, Astedt B (eds) Progress in fibrinolysis. Churchill Livingstone, Edinburgh, vol 5, p 85–89

Peterson H I 1977 Fibrinolytic and antifibrinolytic drugs in the growth and spread of tumors. Cancer treatment reviews 4: 213–217

Poggi A, Polentarutti N, Donati M B, de Gaetano G, Garattini S 1977 Blood coagulation changes in mice bearing the Lewis lung carcinoma, a metastasizing tumor. Cancer Research 37: 272–277

Ranby M, Wallen P 1981 A sensitive parabolic rate assay for the tissue plasminogen activator. In: Davidson J F, Nilsson I M, Astedt B (eds) Progress in fibrinolysis. Churchill Livingstone, Edinburgh, vol 5, p 233–236

379

Index

386

Contemporary Turkish Cooking

FİLİZ ZORLU

Bizim Evde Pişenler

© Çitlembik Publications, March 2007
© Filiz Zorlu, 2007
2nd. EDITION

Translator: Nancy Öztürk
Editors: Defne Orhun, Vanessa Larson
Graphic Design : Esra Pekcan
Photographs: Gökçe Erenmemişoğlu
Food Stylist: Gamze Bursa
Production: Banu Gençoğlu

Printing and Binding: Ofset Yapımevi
Çağlayan Mahallesi Şair Sok. No: 4 Kağıthane
Tel: 0212 295 86 01
Faks: 0212 295 64 55

ISBN: 978-9944-424-16-5

Published by:
Çitlembik Publications
Şeyh Bender Sokak 18/5 Asmalımescit Tünel 34430 İstanbul
Tel: +90 212 292 30 32 / 252 31 63 Fax: +90 212 293 34 66
www.citlembik.com.tr / kitap@citlembik.com.tr

To tell you the truth, it had never occurred to me
to put down in writing the recipes for the dishes I have been cooking
for almost forty years now, dishes I have always enjoyed serving to
my family, friends and acquaintenances.

Two years ago, however, I found myself unable to ignore the prodding
of my two beloved sons, Sarp and Kerem,
so I embarked on this project. It wasn't long before I realized
just how huge a job I had gotten myself into. In the midst of it there
were times when I almost gave up, especially when I saw the food
preparation shows on TV and the rows upon rows of cookbooks on
store shelves. It was only the urging of my sons, who kept insisting
they wanted to have a printed memory of me and my cooking,
that kept me focused on the task at hand.

For years I had augmented the training I had received in the kitchen
of my late mother with new ideas for cooking, exchanging recipes
for meals and teas with friends. I didn't limit my quest to Turkish
cuisine. I borrowed recipes from a number of international cuisines
and modified them to accord with our own food traditions and
tastes. I hope you, too, will enjoy my collection of recipes and that
you will use and modify them to suit your own tastes and those
of your family and friends.

Thank you to each and everyone who had a part in the making
of this book.
I wrote this book for my sons, Sarp and Kerem Tiryakioğlu,
who came up with the idea for it and who stood by me
throughout the entire process.
This is my gift to them.

Fenerbahçe
January 2007

Filiz Zorlu

Our Team:

Standing, from left to right: **Esra Pekcan** (graphic design), **Gökçe Erenmemişoğlu** (photographs),
Gamze Bursa (food styling), **Şerife Yıldırım** (assistant cook)
Seated: **Banu Gençoğlu** (production), **Filiz Zorlu** (author)

Puff

Thanks

To complete this project I worked with a very special team of young people
and found myself energized by their dynamism.
I would like to thank my very beloved daughter, Banu Gençoğlu,
who took on the task of assembling this team and of organizing the entire project.
I also want to convey my gratitude to Gökçe Erenmemişoğlu, who photographed the entire book;
his assistant, Ö. Yurdakul Gündoğdu; food stylist Gamze Bursa;
and designer Esra Pekcan, all of whom did magnificent work.
I have no idea how I could have ever prepared so much food
without the help of my assistant, Şerife Yıldırım.
I would also like to thank Nancy Öztürk for her translations
and the entire Çitlembik Publishing staff
for taking on the job of getting the book printed and distributed.

My husband, Savan, deserves a very special thanks for putting up so amicably
with the absolute chaos that ensued in our house during the long days
of preparing and photographing the dishes.

I would also like to thank my dear friends who not only gave me moral support
during the process of writing and producing the book, but who also so generously
provided their own tablecloths and dishes for the photographs.
They will each find something of their own in this book.

Contents

Soups

Garnishes

Salads

Cold Olive Oil Dishes

Chicken and Meat Dishes

Seafood

Vegetables and Grains

Dough-based Specialties

Rice and Pilafs

Desserts

Teatime

Çorbalar

Soups

Brokoli Çorbası

1 adet soğan
2 diş sarımsak
2 adet orta boy havuç
1 adet kereviz sapı veya 1 adet ufak kök kereviz
1 adet pırasa
1/2 kg brokoli
6 su bardağı tavuk suyu
1 tatlı kaşığı tuzot
1 çay kaşığı kimyon
1/2 çay bardağı süt
1 çorba kaşığı zeytinyağı

1) Soğan, sarımsak, havuç, kereviz ve pırasayı ince olarak kıyıp zeytinyağında çevirin.
2) Sebzelere tavuk suyu, brokoli ve tuzot ilave edip sebzeler iyice pişinceye dek pişirin.
3) Tencerenin altını kapatmaya yakın kimyon ve sütü ilave edin.
4) Hafif soğuyan karışımı blender'dan geçirin.

Broccoli Soup

1 onion
2 cloves garlic
2 medium carrots
1 celery stalk or 1 tablespoon celery root
1 leek
4-5 cups broccoli
6 cups chicken broth
1 teaspoon seasoned salt
1/4 teaspoon cumin
1/4 cup milk
1 tablespoon olive oil

1) Finely dice the onion, garlic, carrot, celery root and leek and sauté lightly in olive oil.
2) Add the chicken broth, broccoli and seasoned salt to the vegetables and cook until soft.
3) Add the cumin and milk shortly before removing the pan from heat.
4) Blend in a blender after the soup has slightly cooled.

Kırmızı Mercimek Çorbası

8 su bardağı tavuk suyu

1 su bardağı kırmızı mercimek

1 kahve fincanı pirinç

1 adet iri havuç

1 tatlı kaşığı tuzot

1) Kaynayan tavuk suyuna yıkanmış mercimek, pirinç, rendelenmiş havuç ve tuzotu ilave edin. Arada bir karıştırarak, kısık ateşte, 1 saat kadar pişirin.
2) Dilerseniz üzerine küp gibi kesilip kızartılmış ekmek serpip servis yapın.

Red Lentil Soup

8 cups chicken broth

1 cup red lentils

1/3 cup rice

1 large carrot

1 teaspoon seasoned salt

1) Bring the chicken broth to a boil and add well-rinsed lentils, rice, grated carrot and seasoned salt.
2) Cook for one hour over low heat, stirring occasionally.
3) If desired, toasted croutons may be sprinkled over the top at serving.

Domatesli Pirinç Çorbası

8 su bardağı tavuk suyu

1 adet tavuk but veya göğüs

3 adet büyük domates

1 çorba kaşığı tuzot

1/2 demet maydanoz

100 gr pirinç

1) Tavuk etini 8 bardak suda haşlayın ve haşladığınız suyu bir kenara ayırın.
2) Haşlanmış tavuk etini kaynayan tavuk suyunda didikleyin. Üstüne rendelenmiş domates, pirinç ve tuzotu ekleyin.
3) 40 dakika kadar pişirin. Ateşten aldığınız çorbaya ince kıyılmış maydanoz serpin.

Tomato Rice Soup

8 cups chicken broth

1 chicken drumstick or breast

3 large tomatoes

1 tablespoon seasoned salt

1/2 bunch parsley

100 gr rice

1) Cook the chicken in 8 cups of water, remove the pieces of meat and reserve the chicken broth for use later.
2) Shred the chicken meat into the broth. Add the minced tomatoes, rice and seasoned salt.
3) Cook for 40 minutes. After removing from heat sprinkle finely chopped parsley over the soup.

Yeşil Mercimek Çorbası

10 su bardağı tavuk suyu

1 su bardağı yeşil mercimek

1 adet domates

1 adet ufak soğan

1 çay bardağı erişte veya ufak kesme makarna

1 çorba kaşığı kuru nane

1 tatlı kaşığı tuzot

1/2 limonun suyu

1) Mercimekleri bol suda hafifçe haşlayıp siyah suyunu süzün.
2) Kaynayan tavuk suyuna mercimek, rendelenmiş domates, ay şeklinde doğranmış soğan ve tuzotu ilave edin. Arada bir karıştırarak, orta ateşte mercimekler yumuşayıncaya dek pişirin.
3) Mercimekler yumuşayınca erişteyi veya makarnayı ilave edin. Erişteler pişince limon suyu ve kuru naneyi de ekleyip ateşi kapatın.

Green Lentil Soup

10 cups chicken broth

1 cup green lentils

1 tomato

1 small onion

1/2 cup fine noodles or homemade noodles cut into tiny squares

1 tablespoon dried mint

1 teaspoon seasoned salt

Juice of 1/2 lemon

1) Cook the lentils lightly in a large pot of water, draining the lentils from the darkened water.
2) Bring the chicken broth to a boil and add the lentils, chopped tomato, the onion cut into crescents, and seasoned salt. Cook until the lentils are soft, stirring occasionally.
3) When the lentils are soft, add the noodles. When the noodles are soft, add the lemon juice and dried mint and remove from heat.

Patates ve Havuçlu Tavuk Çorbası

1 adet tavuk but
1 adet tavuk göğüs
1 adet büyük patates
2 adet havuç
1 çorba kaşığı tuzot
1 adet soğan

1) Tavuk but ve göğsü soğanla birlikte haşlayın.
2) Tavukları haşladığınız sudan 8 bardak kadarını başka bir tencereye alın.
3) Haşlanmış tavukları didikleyin. Patates ve havucu rendeleyin.
4) Kaynayan tavuk suyuna tavuk etlerini, rendelenmiş havuç ve patatesi tuzotla birlikte ekleyip kısık ateşte, 40 dakika kadar pişirin.

Chicken Soup with Potatoes and Carrots

1 chicken leg
1 chicken breast
1 large potato
2 carrots
1 tablespoon seasoned salt
1 onion

1) Boil the chicken leg, breast and onion together in a large pot until all are thoroughly cooked.
2) Remove chicken meat from the broth and reserve at least 8 cups of the broth.
3) Shred the boiled chicken finely. Grate the potato and carrots.
4) Bring the reserved broth back to a boil and add the shredded chicken, grated carrots and potato. Add the seasoned salt and cook for another 40 minutes.

Domatesli Şehriye Çorbası

1/2 kg yumuşak domates

1 adet orta boy soğan

1 adet kereviz sapı

1 diş sarımsak

8 su bardağı tavuk suyu

2 çorba kaşığı domates püresi

1/2 su bardağı arpa veya yıldız şehriye

1 çorba kaşığı tuzot

1 çay kaşığı karabiber

1 çorba kaşığı zeytinyağı

Süs için maydanoz

1) Bir tencerede, soyulmuş domates, dörde bölünmüş soğan, kereviz sapı, ezilmiş sarımsak ve zeytinyağını ağzı kapalı olarak, kısık ateşte 20 dakika kadar pişirin.
2) Pişen sebzeleri blender'dan geçirin ve tekrar tencereye atın.
3) Blender'dan geçen sebzelere domates püresi, şehriye ve tavuk suyunu da ekleyip kaynatın.
4) Çorbanın üstünü ince kıyılmış maydanoz ile süsleyin.

Tomato Noodle Soup

1/2 kg soft tomatoes, peeled

1 medium onion, quartered

1 celery stalk

1 clove garlic

8 cups chicken broth

2 tablespoons tomato purée

1/2 cup orzo or star shaped pasta noodles

1 tablespoon seasoned salt

1/4 teaspoon black pepper

1 tablespoon olive oil

Parsley for garnish

1) Place the peeled tomatoes, quartered onion, celery stalk, crushed garlic, and olive oil in a pot and cook, covered, for 20 minutes over low heat.
2) Blend the cooked vegetables in a blender and return to the pot.
3) Add the tomato purée, noodles and chicken broth to the vegetables and bring the mixture to a boil.
4) Add seasoned salt and pepper to taste.
5) Garnish the soup with finely chopped parsley and serve.

Ekşili Mini Köfte Çorbası

1/2 kg kıyma

1 kahve fincanı pirinç

1 adet havuç

1 adet kereviz sapı

1 adet patates

1 çorba kaşığı tuzot

8 su bardağı su

1 çay kaşığı karabiber

1 dolu yemek kaşığı un

1 limonun suyu

1) Kıymayı pirinçle yoğurup minik köfteler yapın. Derin bir kaba unu ve köfteleri koyup sallayarak unun köftelerin her tarafına bulanmasını sağlayın.
2) Suyu kaynatın. Küp gibi doğranmış havuç, patates, kereviz sapı, unlanmış köfteler, tuzot ve karabiberi ilave edin.
3) 45 dakika orta ateşte kaynatın.
4) Ateşten indirince limon suyunu ekleyin.

Sour Tiny Meatball Soup

1/2 kg ground meat

1/3 cup rice

1 carrot

1 celery stalk

1 potato

1 tablespoon seasoned salt

8 cups water

1/4 teaspoon black papper

1 heaping tablespoon flour

Juice of 1 lemon

1) Knead the rice into the ground meat and shape into tiny meatballs. Put the flour into a deep bowl. Add the meatballs and shake until they are coated with flour.
2) Bring the water to a boil. Add the diced carrot, potato, celery stalk, floured meatballs, seasoned salt and black pepper.
3) Boil for 45 minutes over medium heat.
4) Add the lemon juice after the soup has been removed from heat.

Minestrone Çorbası

10 su bardağı tavuk suyu
1/2 su bardağı kuru fasulye
1 adet soğan
7-8 adet taze fasulye
1 adet patates
1 adet havuç
2 adet kereviz sapı
1 su bardağı beyaz lahana

1 adet pırasa
100 gr aşurelik buğday
1/2 demet maydanoz
2 diş sarımsak
1 çorba kaşığı domates salçası
1 çorba kaşığı tuzot
1 kahve fincanı ufak kesme makarna
50 gr rendelenmiş taze kaşar veya parmesan peyniri

1) Bir gece önceden ıslattığınız buğday ve kuru fasulyeyi ayrı kaplarda iyice yumuşayıncaya dek haşlayın.
2) Kaynayan tavuk suyuna çentilmiş soğan, ince kıyılmış taze fasulye, lahana, pırasa, kereviz sapı, sarımsak, küp şeklinde doğranmış havuç, patates, salça, tuzot, haşlanmış kuru fasulye ve haşlanmış buğdayı ekleyin.
3) Yarım saat kadar pişen sebze karışımına makarnaları ilave edin.
4) Makarnalar pişince ateşten indirip ince kıyılmış maydanozu ekleyin.
5) Rendelenmiş taze kaşar veya parmesan peyniri serpip servis yapın.

Minestrone Soup

23

10 cups chicken broth
1/2 cup white beans
1 onion
7-8 green beans
1 potato
1 carrot
2 stalks celery
1 cup white cabbage

1 leek
100 gr very roughly ground wheat (as for asure/Noah's ark pudding)
1/2 bunch parsley
2 cloves garlic
1 tablespoon tomato paste
1 tablespoon seasoned salt
1/3 cup small pasta pieces
50 gr grated fresh kaseri or parmesan cheese

1) Soak the wheat and beans (if dried) separately overnight and then cook in separate pots until very soft.
2) Bring the chicken broth to a boil and add the grated onion, finely diced green beans, cabbage, leek, celery stalks, garlic, diced carrot, potato, tomato paste, seasoned salt, cooked beans and the cooked wheat.
3) After the vegetable mixture has cooked for approximately 1/2 hour, add the pasta pieces.
4) When the pasta is soft, remove from heat and add the finely chopped parsley.
5) Serve hot with grated fresh kaseri or parmesan cheese.

Havuç ve Kök Ispanak Çorbası

1 paket kök ıspanak

1 adet soğan

2 adet ufak havuç

8 su bardağı tavuk suyu

1 tatlı kaşığı tuzot

1 adet yumurta

1 limonun suyu

1 kahve fincanı un

1 çay bardağı su

1) Kaynayan tavuk suyuna ıspanak kökü, ay şeklinde doğranmış soğan, diyagonal şekilde kesilmiş havuç ve tuzotu koyun.
2) Havuç ve ıspanaklar yumuşayıncaya dek; yaklaşık 25 dakika kaynatın.
3) Yumurta, un ve limon suyunu, 1 çay bardağı suyla çırpın. İnce ince akıtarak çorbaya ekleyin.
4) Karıştırarak 5 dakika daha pişirin.

Carrot and Spinach Root Soup

1 package (1/2 kg) spinach roots (base of the stem)

1 onion

2 small carrots

8 cups chicken broth

1 teaspoon seasoned salt

1 egg

Juice of 1 lemon

1/3 cup flour

1/2 cup water

1) Bring the chicken broth to a boil and add the spinach roots, the onion cut into crescents, the carrots (sliced on the diagonal), and the seasoned salt.
2) Cook until the carrots and spinach roots are soft (approximately 25 minutes).
3) Beat the egg, flour and lemon juice with the 1/2 cup of water. Add the egg mixture to the soup very slowly so as not to curdle.
4) Cook while stirring constantly for 5 more minutes.

Garnitürler

Garnishes

Rus Salatası

5 adet orta boy patates
1 ufak kutu tane mısır
1 adet elma
1 ufak kavanoz mayonez
5 adet kornişon turşu
2 sap kereviz
4 çorba kaşığı iç bezelye
1 adet ufak havuç

1) Haşlanmış patateslerin kabuğunu soyup küp şeklinde doğrayın.
2) Elmayı kabuğuyla birlikte küp şeklinde, kereviz ve turşuyu ise ince ince doğrayın.
3) Bezelyeyi haşlayıp havuçları isteğe göre rendeleyin veya jülyen şekilde doğrayın.
4) Bütün malzemeyi derin bir kaba koyup mayonezle karıştırın.

Russian Salad

5 medium potatoes
1 small (135 gr) can of corn
1 apple
1 small jar (270 gr) mayonnaise
5 gherkin pickles
2 celery stalks
4 tablespoons peas
1 small carrot

1) Peel and dice the boiled potatoes.
2) Dice the unpeeled apple and finely chop the celery and pickles.
3) Boil the peas and either grate or cut the carrot into juliennes.
4) Place all ingredients into a deep bowl and mix with the mayonnaise.

Patlıcan Beğendi

1 1/2 kg patlıcan
2 dolu çorba kaşığı un
1/2 litre süt
2 dolu çorba kaşığı margarin veya tereyağı
1 tatlı kaşığı tuz
1 limonun suyu
100 gr rendelenmiş taze kaşar

1) Patlıcanları ateşte közleyin.
2) Közlediğiniz patlıcanların kabuklarını soyup limon suyunu da eklediğiniz su dolu bir kaba atıp yarım saat bekletin. Daha sonra patlıcanları iyice sıkın. Bıçakla doğrayıp çatal yardımıyla iyice ezin.
3) Süt ve yağı birlikte kaynatın.
4) Blender'a unu ve tuzu koyun. Kaynamış yağlı sütü unun üzerine boşaltıp karıştırarak beyaz sos yapın.
5) Ezilmiş patlıcanları bir tencereye koyup beyaz sosla karıştırın.
6) Karışımı kısık ateşte pişirirken rende peyniri ekleyin. Devamlı karıştırarak peynirler eriyene dek pişirin.
7) Izgara tavuk ya da et yanında sıcak olarak servis yapın.

Eggplant Beğendi

1 1/2 kg eggplant
2 full tablespoons flour
1/2 liter (2 cups) milk
2 full tablespoons margarine or butter
1 teaspoon salt
Juice of 1 lemon
100 gr grated fresh kaseri cheese

1) Roast the eggplants on a gas flame.
2) Peel the roasted eggplants, place in a bowl filled with the lemon juice and water, and allow to sit for half an hour. Then wring out the eggplants well. Dice and mash with a fork.
3) Bring the milk and margarine or butter to a boil.
4) Put the flour and salt in the blender, add the milk and butter mixture and blend into a sauce.
5) Mix the mashed eggplants and the white sauce in a pan.
6) While the mixture is cooking over low heat add the grated cheese. Stir constantly until the cheese has completely melted into the mixture.
7) Serve hot with grilled chicken or meat.

Mektuz (içi doldurulmuş patlıcan)

6 adet küçük patlıcan

200 gr ceviz

6 diş sarımsak

2 adet etli kırmızı biber

3 çorba kaşığı sirke

1 adet limon

1 çorba kaşığı tuz

Zeytinyağı

1) Patlıcanları haşlayıp suyunu sıkın.
2) Biberleri ve sarımsakları ince ince doğrayın.
3) Cevizi çok ince çentin.
4) Biber, ceviz, sarımsak ve tuzu karıştırın.
5) Patlıcanları ortasından yararak, içlerine hazırladığınız karışımdan doldurun.
6) Derin bir kaba veya ufak bir kavanoza patlıcanları yerleştirip, patlıcanların üzerine çıkacak kadar zeytinyağı ve 3 çorba kaşığı sirke ilave edin.
7) En üste dilimlenmiş limonu yerleştirin.
8) 1 hafta - 10 gün sonra patlıcanları istenilen miktarda çıkartıp keskin bir bıçak yardımıyla kesip servis yapın.

Mektuz (Stuffed Pickled Eggplant)

6 small eggplants

200 gr ground walnuts

6 cloves garlic

2 red bell peppers

1 lemon

3 tablespoons vinegar

1 tablespoon salt

Olive oil

1) Boil the eggplants until slightly soft and wring out the excess water.
2) Finely chop the peppers and garlic.
3) Mix the peppers, walnuts, garlic and salt.
4) Make a slash in the eggplants lengthwise and stuff them with the prepared filling mixture.
5) Arrange the eggplants in a small jar and fill to the brim with olive oil and the vinegar.
6) Arrange the sliced lemon on the top.
7) The eggplants will be ready to serve in 1 week - 10 days.

Kabak Beğendi

1 kg kabak

1 ufak demet dereotu

2 çorba kaşığı un

2 çorba kaşığı tereyağı veya margarin

1/2 litreden biraz az süt

1 tatlı kaşığı tuzot

100 gr rendelenmiş taze kaşar veya sert beyaz peynir

1) Kabakları soymadan irice doğrayın. Buharda haşlayın.
2) Kabakları bir kapta çatal yardımıyla iyice ezin.
3) Kabak püresine unu ilave ederek kısık ateşte devamlı karıştırarak pişirin.
4) Sütü yağla birlikte kaynatın ve tuzotu ilave edin. Kaynattığınız sütü ince ince akıtarak kabağa ekleyin.
5) Karışıma rende peyniri ekleyin.
6) Ateşten aldığınız kabağa ince kıyılmış dereotunu da ekleyin.

Izgara tavuk ya da et yanında sıcak olarak servis yapın.

Zucchini Beğendi

1 kg zucchini

1 small bunch dill

2 tablespoons flour

2 tablespoons butter or margarine

A bit less than 1/2 liter milk (less than 2 cups)

1 teaspoon seasoned salt

100 gr grated fresh kaseri cheese

1) Roughly chop the unpeeled zucchinis and steam them.
2) Mash the zucchinis thoroughly with a fork.
3) Add flour to the mashed zucchini and cook, stirring constantly, until thickened slightly.
4) Bring the milk and butter or margarine to a boil and add the seasoned salt. Gradually add this mixture to the cooking zucchini.
5) Add the grated cheese.
6) Remove the zucchini from heat and add the finely chopped dill.
7) Serve hot with grilled chicken or meat.

Humus (Sabbaha)

300 gr nohut
200 gr tahin
1 limonun suyu
2 diş sarımsak
1 çorba kaşığı tuz
1 çay kaşığı kimyon
2 çorba kaşığı zeytinyağı
1 tatlı kaşığı kırmızı pul biber
Süs için 4-5 sap maydanoz

1) Geceden ıslattığınız nohutları düdüklü tencereye koyun ve üzerlerine çıkacak kadar su ilave edin.
2) Tencerenin düdüğü çıktıktan sonra 25 dakika daha pişirin.
3) Nohutların suyunu süzüp, suyu ayırın.
4) Bu sudan azar azar ilave ederek nohutları blender'da çekin.
5) Çekilmiş nohutlara tahin, tuz, limon suyu, kimyon, kırmızı pul biber, zeytinyağı ve dövülmüş sarımsağı ilave edin.
6) Servis tabağına aldığınız humusun üstünü zeytinyağı, birkaç adet haşlanmış nohut ve maydanoz ile süsleyebilirsiniz.

Humus (Sabbaha)

300 gr chickpeas
200 gr tahini
Juice of 1 lemon
2 cloves garlic
1 tablespoon salt
1/4 teaspoon cumin
2 tablespoons olive oil
1 teaspoon red pepper flakes
4-5 parsley sprigs for garnish

1) Soak the chickpeas overnight. The next day add enough water to cover them and cook until soft (may be cooked in a pressure cooker for convenience).
2) Drain the water from the chickpeas and reserve the water.
3) Place the chickpeas in a blender, adding enough of the reserved water to blend smoothly.
4) Add the tahini, salt, lemon juice, cumin, red pepper flakes, olive oil and mashed garlic to the chickpeas.
5) Place the hummus on a serving plate and sprinkle with olive oil. Garnish with a few whole cooked chickpeas and parsley.

fırında Şalgam (Navet)

2 kg şalgam
5 çorba kaşığı margarin veya tereyağı
1 ufak paket çiğ krema
1 su bardağı ekmek kırıntısı
Tuz

1) Şalgamları soyup rendeleyin.
2) Bir süzgece 1 kat şalgam, 1 kat tuz serperek 2 saat bekletin.
3) Şalgamların suyunu elle sıkıp eritilmiş margarinle çevirin. Suyunu çekince kremayı da ekleyip karışımı fırın ısısına dayanıklı bir kaba boşaltın.
4) Fırına vermeden önce üzerini ekmek kırıntıları ile kaplayın. Üstü kızarana dek fırında pişirin.
5) Etin yanında servis yapın.

Roasted Turnips (Navet)

2 kg turnips
5 tablespoons margarine or butter
1 small package heavy cream
1 cup bread crumbs
Salt

1) Peel and grate the turnips.
2) Arrange the turnips in one layer in a large strainer, sprinkle with salt and allow to drain for 2 hours.
3) Wring out any additional liquid from the turnips and sauté lightly in melted margarine. When the turnips have absorbed all the liquid, add the cream and place in an ovenproof baking dish.
4) Sprinkle bread crumbs on the top before baking. Bake until the top is golden brown.
5) Serve with meat.

Ispanak Püresi

1 kg ıspanak

2 çorba kaşığı zeytinyağı

1 tatlı kaşığı tuzot

1 su bardağı süt

2 çorba kaşığı un

1 çorba kaşığı margarin veya tereyağı

1 tatlı kaşığı tuz

100 gr rendelenmiş taze kaşar

1) Geniş bir tavada doğranmış ıspanakları zeytinyağı ve tuzotla ıspanaklar suyunu çekinceye dek kavurun.
2) Sütü yağla birlikte kaynatın.
3) Blender'da un, tuz ve süt karışımını çırpıp beyaz sos yapın.
4) Hazırladığınız beyaz sosu kavrulmuş ıspanaklarla karıştırın.
5) Ispanak püresine rendelenmiş kaşar peyniri ekleyip pişirin.
6) Etin veya tavuğun yanında sıcak olarak servis yapın.

Spinach Purée

1 kg spinach

2 tablespoons olive oil

1 teaspoon seasoned salt

1 cup milk

2 tablespoons flour

1 tablespoon margarine or butter

1 teaspoon salt

100 gr grated fresh kaseri cheese

1) Sauté the spinach in olive oil and seasoned salt in a broad frying pan until the spinach has absorbed all of the liquid.
2) Boil together the milk and butter or margarine.
3) Blend the flour, salt and milk mixture in a blender into a sauce.
4) Mix the white sauce with the sautéed spinach.
5) Add grated kaseri cheese to the spinach purée and cook.
6) Serve hot with meat or chicken.

Çerkez Tavuğu

1 adet bütün tavuk

1/2 kg ince çekilmiş ceviz

2 dilim kenarları kesilmiş bayat ekmek

1 çorba kaşığı tuz

1 adet soğan

2 diş sarımsak

1 tatlı kaşığı kırmızı pul biber

1 tatlı kaşığı tozşeker

1) Tavuğu bol suda, tuz, şeker ve soğanla birlikte haşlayın. Haşlanan tavuğun deri ve kemiklerini ayırıp didikleyin. Tavuğu haşladığınız suyu ayrı bir kaba alın.
2) Ceviz, sarımsak, haşlanmış soğan ve ekmek içini blender'dan geçirin.
3) Karışımı derin bir tencereye alıp üstüne 8 kepçe sıcak tavuk suyu dökün. Koyu bir bulamaç haline gelince didiklenmiş tavuklarla karıştırın.
4) Karışımı 2 dakika kadar hafif ateşte pişirin.

Servis tabağına aldığınız Çerkez tavuğunu kırmızı pul biberle süsleyerek servis yapın.

39

Circassian Chicken

1 whole chicken

1/2 kg finely ground walnuts

2 slices stale bread with their crusts removed

1 tablespoon salt

1 onion

2 cloves garlic

1 teaspoon red pepper flakes

1 teaspoon granulated sugar

1) Boil the chicken in a large quantity of water with the salt, sugar and onion.
2) Drain the chicken, reserving the broth in a separate bowl. Bone and skin the boiled chicken and shred the meat.
3) Blend the walnuts, garlic, boiled onion and crumbled bread in a blender.
4) Pour the walnut mixture into a deep pan, add 8 ladles of broth and begin to cook. When it thickens, add the shredded chicken and continue cooking over low heat for another 2 minutes.
5) Put the Circassian chicken on a serving plate and garnish with red pepper flakes.

Salatalar

Salads

Kısır

250 gr köftelik bulgur

5 sap taze soğan

7-8 adet taze nane yaprağı

1/2 demet maydanoz

2 çorba kaşığı nar ekşisi

1 çay fincanı zeytinyağı

1 tatlı kaşığı tuzot

1 tatlı kaşığı kırmızı pul biber

1 limonun suyu

4-5 adet çeri domates

Yeşil salata

1 adet etli kırmızı biber

1) Bulgurun üstünü ıslatacak kadar kaynar su döküp şişmesini bekleyin.
2) İyice şişen bulgurları ince kıyılmış nane, maydanoz, soğan, yeşil biber, nar ekşisi, limon suyu, zeytinyağı, kırmızı pul biber ve tuzot ilave edip tahta kaşık yardımıyla karıştırın.
3) Servis tabağının dibini salata yapraklarıyla döşeyip kısırı üstüne boşaltın. Kısırın kenarlarını kırmızı biber halkaları ve çeri domateslerle süsleyebilirsiniz.

Kısır

250 gr fine bulgur

5 green onions

7-8 fresh mint leaves

1/2 bunch parsley

2 tablespoons tart pomegranate syrup

1/2 cup olive oil

1 teaspoon seasoned salt

1 teaspoon red pepper flakes

Juice of 1 lemon

4-5 cherry tomatoes

Green leafy lettuce

1 plump bell pepper

1) Pour enough boiling water to cover bulgur and allow bulgur to plump.
2) Once the bulgur is very plump, drain any water remaining and add finely chopped mint, parsley, onions, green pepper, tart pomegranate syrup, lemon juice, olive oil, red pepper flakes and seasoned salt, using a wooden spoon to mix well.
3) Line a serving plate with lettuce leaves and heap the kısır on top. Garnish corners of the plate with sliced bell pepper rounds and cherry tomatoes.

Kalamar Salatası

2 kutu dondurulmuş kalamar

1 adet domates

1 adet salatalık

1 adet sivribiber

1/2 demet dereotu

2 diş sarımsak

1 kahve fincanı zeytinyağı

2 çorba kaşığı sirke

1/2 limonun suyu

1 tatlı kaşığı kırmızı pul biber

1 tatlı kaşığı tuzot

Tuz

1) Kalamarları, 1 çorba kaşığı sirke ve tuzu ilave ettiğiniz bol suda 45 dakika kadar haşlayın.
2) Haşlanmış kalamarları küp şeklinde doğranmış domates, salatalık, ince kıyılmış biber, dereotu ve sarımsakla karıştırın.
3) Zeytinyağı, sirke, limon suyu, kırmızıbiber ve tuzotu çırpıp salatanın üzerine dökün.

Calamari Salad

2 boxes of frozen calamari (350-500 gr packages)

1 tomato

1 cucumber

1 mildly hot, long green pepper

1/2 bunch dill

2 cloves garlic

1/3 cup olive oil

2 tablespoons vinegar

Juice of 1/2 lemon

1 teaspoon red pepper flakes

1 teaspoon seasoned salt

Salt

1) Add 1 tablespoon vinegar and the salt to the calamari and boil for 45 minutes in a large pot of water.
2) Mix the diced tomato, cucumber, finely chopped pepper, dill and garlic with the boiled calamari.
3) Beat the olive oil, vinegar, lemon juice, red pepper flakes and seasoned salt and pour over the salad.

Deniz Mahsulleri Salatası

Haşlanmış karides, tane midye, kalamar, ufak doğranmış ahtapot ve surimi (toplamı 1/2 kg olacak)
1 paket maskolin salata
1 adet göbek salata
1/2 demet roka
6 sap taze soğan
2 limonun suyu
1 çay bardağı zeytinyağı
2 çorba kaşığı balzamik sirke
1 paket fesleğenli hazır salata sosu
1 tatlı kaşığı tuzot

1) Maskolin salata, parçalara bölünmüş göbek salata, ince kıyılmış roka ve taze soğanı deniz mahsulleriyle karıştırıp derin bir kaba alın.
2) Limon suyu, balzamik sirke, zeytinyağı, tuzot ve fesleğenli salata sosunu çırpıp salatanın üstüne dökün.

Seafood Salad

A mixture of boiled shrimp, mussels, octopus, calamari and surimi (total to equal 1/2 kg)
1 package of mesclun (150 gr)
1/2 head iceberg lettuce
1/2 bunch rocket leaves
6 green onions
Juice of 2 lemons
1/2 cup olive oil
2 tablespoons balsamic vinegar
1 package of ready to mix basil salad dressing
1 teaspoon seasoned salt

1) Mix the mesclun, iceberg lettuce torn into pieces, finely chopped rocket leaves and green onions into the seafood and pour into a deep bowl.
2) Beat the lemon juice, balsamic vinegar, olive oil, seasoned salt and basil salad dressing and use this sauce to dress the salad.

Baklalı Bulgur Salatası

250 gr taze iç bakla

250 gr köftelik bulgur

2 adet ufak salatalık

2 adet domates

1 adet kırmızı soğan

250 gr sert beyaz peynir

1 limonun suyu

Birkaç adet taze nane yaprağı

1 tatlı kaşığı tuzot

1 kahve fincanı zeytinyağı

1) Bulgurun üstünü ıslatacak kadar kaynar su döküp şişmesini bekleyin.
2) Taze iç baklayı haşlayıp kabuklarını soyun.
3) Kırmızı soğanı ay şeklinde doğrayın. Tuzla ovun ve yıkayın.
4) Küp şeklinde doğranmış domates, salatalık, beyaz peynir ve ince kıyılmış naneyi bulgur ve baklalarla birlikte karıştırın.
5) Zeytinyağı, tuzot ve limon suyunu çırpıp salatanın üstüne dökün.

Fava and Bulgur Salad

250 gr fresh fava (broad) beans

250 gr fine bulgur

2 small cucumbers

2 tomatoes

1 red onion

250 gr firm Turkish white cheese / feta

Juice of 1 lemon

Several fresh mint leaves

1 teaspoon seasoned salt

1/3 cup olive oil

1) Pour enough boiling water to cover bulgur and allow bulgur to plump.
2) Boil the fresh fava beans and remove skins.
3) Chop the red onion into crescents. Knead with salt and then rinse.
4) Mix in the diced tomato, cucumber, cheese and finely chopped mint and blend well with the bulgur and fava.
5) Beat the olive oil, seasoned salt and lemon juice and pour over the salad.

Domatesli ve Yoğurtlu Patlıcan Salatası

1 kg patlıcan
6 adet çarliston biber
5 diş sarımsak
4 adet iri domates
1 çorba kaşığı tuzot
2 çorba kaşığı sirke
Tuz
Kızartma için yağ

1) İri küpler şeklinde doğranmış patlıcanları yarım saat kadar tuzlu suda bekletin.
2) Çarliston biberlerin çekirdeklerini çıkartıp irice doğrayın.
3) Derin bir tavada, sırasıyla, patlıcan ve biberleri kızartın. Kızaran sebzeleri yağını çekmesi için kâğıt havluya çıkartın.
4) Rendelenmiş domates, sarımsak, tuzot ve sirkeyi yaklaşık 10 dakika pişirin.
5) Patlıcanları derin bir servis tabağına alıp üzerine ılık domates sosunu dökün.
6) Domatesli patlıcan salatasını, yanında yoğurt ile servis yapın.

Tomato and Yogurt Eggplant Salad

1 kg eggplant
6 long sweet green peppers
5 cloves garlic
4 large tomatoes
1 tablespoon seasoned salt
2 tablespoons vinegar
Salt
Oil for frying

1) Allow the roughly diced eggplants to soak for half an hour in salty water.
2) Seed the peppers and chop into rather largish pieces.
3) Fry the eggplants and peppers separately and place on paper towels to drain excess oil.
4) Cook the minced tomato, garlic, seasoned salt and vinegar for approximately 10 minutes.
5) Place the eggplants in a deep serving dish and pour the warm tomato sauce over.
6) Serve the tomato eggplant salad with yogurt on the side.

Fasulye Piyazı

250 gr kuru fasulye

1 adet soğan

2 adet domates

5-6 adet sivribiber

15 adet siyah zeytin

1/2 demet maydanoz

1 çay bardağı sirke

1 çorba kaşığı tuzot

2 adet haşlanmış yumurta

1 çay bardağı zeytinyağı

1) 1 gece önceden bol suda beklettiğiniz fasulyeleri iyice pişene dek haşlayın.
2) Ay şeklinde doğranmış soğanı tuzla ovup yıkayın.
3) Soğan, küp şeklinde doğranmış domates, ince kıyılmış maydanoz ve yeşil biberleri fasulyeye ilave edip karıştırın.
4) Zeytinyağı, sirke ve tuzotu çırpıp fasulyelerin üstüne dökün.
5) Dörde bölünmüş haşlanmış yumurta ve siyah zeytinlerle piyazı süsleyin.

Bean Piyaz

250 gr white (navy) beans

1 onion

2 tomatoes

5-6 long and mildly hot green peppers

15 black olives

1/2 bunch parsley

1/2 cup vinegar

1 tablespoon seasoned salt

2 boiled eggs

1/2 cup olive oil

1) Soak the beans overnight and then cook until soft.
2) Slice the onion into crescents; knead in salt with the hands and then rinse.
3) Add the onion, diced tomatoes, finely chopped parsley and green peppers to the beans, mixing well.
4) Beat the olive oil, vinegar and seasoned salt and pour over the beans.
5) Garnish the piyaz with quartered boiled eggs and black olives.

Kabak Salatası

1 kg kabak
250 gr yoğurt
1 tatlı kaşığı tuzot
3-4 diş sarımsak
2 çorba kaşığı zeytinyağı
1/2 demet dereotu

1) Kabakları bir süzgece rendeleyin. 1 saat kadar suyunun akmasını bekleyin.
2) Tavada zeytinyağını kızdırın. Kabakları suyunu bırakıp çekene dek pişirin.
3) Kabaklar suyunu çekince tuzot ilave edip soğumaya bırakın.
4) Soğuyan kabağa yoğurt, dövülmüş sarımsak ve ince kıyılmış dereotunu ilave edip karıştırın.

Zucchini Salad

1 kg zucchini
250 gr yogurt
1 teaspoon seasoned salt
3-4 cloves garlic
2 tablespoons olive oil
1/2 bunch dill

1) Grate the zucchini into a strainer and allow liquids to drain for one hour.
2) Heat the olive oil in a frying pan and cook until the zucchinis have released and then reabsorbed all of their liquids.
3) When the zucchinis have absorbed their liquids, add the seasoned salt and allow to cool.
4) Add the yogurt, crushed garlic and finely chopped dill to the cool zucchini, mixing well.

Közlenmiş Patlıcan Salatası

3 adet uzun patlıcan

1 limonun suyu

1 tatlı kaşığı tuzot

1 paket sirke ve sarımsaklı hazır salata sosu

1) Közleyip kabuklarını soyduğunuz patlıcanları limonlu suda yarım saat kadar bekletin.
2) İri parçalara böldüğünüz patlıcanları, yan yana gelecek şekilde servis tabağına dizin.
3) Salata sosunu tarifine göre hazırlayıp tuzot ilave edin. Sosu çalkalayıp patlıcanların üzerine dökün.
4) Servis yapmadan önce; 2 saat kadar dinlendirin.

Roasted Eggplant Salad

3 long eggplants

Juice of 1 lemon

1 teaspoon seasoned salt

1 package vinegar and garlic salad dressing mix

1) Roast the eggplants over gas flame, peel, and soak for half an hour in water with the lemon juice added.
2) Cut the eggplants into largish pieces and arrange side by side on a serving plate.
3) Prepare the dressing according to the instructions on the package and add the seasoned salt. Mix the sauce well and pour over the eggplant. Allow to sit for 2 hours before serving.

Kuru Börülce Piyazı

250 gr kuru börülce

1 adet soğan

2 adet domates

5 adet sivribiber

15 adet siyah zeytin

1/2 demet maydanoz

1 çay bardağı sirke

1 çorba kaşığı tuzot

2 adet haşlanmış yumurta

1 çay bardağı zeytinyağı

1) 1 gece önceden bol suda beklettiğiniz börülceleri iyice pişene dek haşlayın.
2) Ay şeklinde doğranmış soğanı tuzla ovup yıkayın.
3) Soğan, küp şeklinde doğranmış domates, ince kıyılmış maydanoz ve yeşil biberleri börülceye ilave edip karıştırın.
4) Zeytinyağı, sirke ve tuzotu çırpıp börülcelerin üstüne dökün.
5) Dörde bölünmüş haşlanmış yumurta ve siyah zeytinlerle piyazı süsleyin.

Black-Eyed Peas Piyaz

250 gr dried black-eyed peas

1 onion

2 tomatoes

5 long and mildly hot green peppers

15 black olives

1/2 bunch parsley

1/2 cup vinegar

1 tablespoon seasoned salt

2 boiled eggs

1/2 cup olive oil

1) Allow the black-eyed peas to soak in water overnight and then boil them until soft.
2) Slice the onion into crescents, knead in salt and then rinse well.
3) Add the onion, diced tomatoes, finely chopped parsley and green peppers to the black-eyed peas and mix well.
4) Beat the olive oil, vinegar and seasoned salt and pour this sauce over the black-eyed peas.
5) Garnish the piyaz with the quartered boiled egg and black olives.

Patates Salatası

1 kg patates
1 çorba kaşığı tozşeker
1 adet soğan
6 sap taze soğan
2 limonun suyu
2 kahve fincanı zeytinyağı
1 tatlı kaşığı hardal
1 kahve kaşığı karabiber
1 çorba kaşığı tuzot
2 adet haşlanmış yumurta
15-20 adet siyah zeytin

1) Haşlayıp kabuklarını soyduğunuz patatesleri iri küpler şeklinde doğrayın.
2) Patatesleri soğutmadan üzerlerine tozşekeri döküp karıştırın. Şekeri çekmesini bekleyin.
3) Ay şeklinde doğranmış soğanları tuzla ovup yıkayın. Şekeri çeken patateslerle karıştırın.
4) Ayrı bir kapta zeytinyağı, hardal, limon suyu, tuzot ve karabiberi çırpıp patateslerin üzerine dökün.
5) 10-15 dakika sonra ince kıyılmış taze soğanları da ilave edin. Salatayı haşlanmış yumurta dilimleri ve siyah zeytin ile süsleyin.

Potato Salad

1 kg potatoes
1 tablespoon granulated sugar
1 onion
6 green onions
Juice of 2 lemons
2/3 cup of olive oil
1 teaspoon mustard
1/2 teaspoon black pepper
1 tablespoon seasoned salt
2 boiled eggs
15-20 black olives

1) Chop the boiled and peeled potatoes into largish cubes.
2) Mix the hot potatoes with the granulated sugar. Allow the potatoes to sit so that they can absorb the sugar.
3) Slice the onion into crescents, knead in salt and then rinse. Mix the onion and the potatoes.
4) Beat together in a separate bowl the olive oil, mustard, lemon juice, seasoned salt and black pepper and then pour this sauce over the potatoes.
5) After allowing the potatoes to sit for 10-15 minutes, add the finely chopped green onions. Garnish the salad with the sliced boiled eggs and black olives.

Patlıcan Salatası

1 kg patlıcan

3 adet domates

2 adet çarliston biber

2 adet yeşil biber

2-3 diş sarımsak

1 limonun suyu

1 tatlı kaşığı tuzot

2 çorba kaşığı zeytinyağı

Süs için 4-5 sap maydanoz

1) Közleyip kabuklarını soyduğunuz patlıcanları limonlu tuzlu suda yarım saat kadar bekletin. Suyunu süzüp iri iri doğrayın.
2) Zeytinyağını kızdırdığınız tavada, közlenen patlıcanları, küp şeklinde doğranmış domates, irice doğranmış biber, ezilmiş sarımsak ve tuzotla birlikte, zeytinyağlı tavada, kısık ateşte, 3 dakika kadar çevirin.
3) Pişen sebzeleri bir servis tabağına alıp üstünü maydanozla süsleyin.
4) Dilerseniz yoğurtla karıştırarak da servis yapabilirsiniz.

Eggplant Salad

1 kg eggplant

3 tomatoes

2 long sweet green peppers

2 green bell peppers

2-3 cloves garlic

Juice of 1 lemon

1 teaspoon seasoned salt

2 tablespoons olive oil

4-5 sprigs of parsley for garnish

1) Place the roasted and peeled eggplants into warm, salted water to which the lemon juice has been added and allow the eggplants to soak for half an hour. Drain the eggplants and chop roughly.
2) Cook the roasted eggplants, diced tomatoes, roughly chopped peppers, crushed garlic, and seasoned salt over low heat in hot olive oil for approximately 3 minutes.
3) Place the cooked vegetables on a serving plate and garnish with the parsley.
4) If desired, beaten plain yogurt may also be mixed into the salad.

Mantar Salatası

1 büyük kavanoz veya 2 orta boy kavanoz konserve mantar

4 sap taze soğan

1 kutu tane mısır

3 adet orta boy domates

3 adet ufak salatalık

4-5 sap maydanoz

1 paket fesleğenli hazır salata sosu

2 limonun suyu

1 kahve fincanı zeytinyağı

1 tatlı kaşığı tuzot

1 tatlı kaşığı hardal

1) Mantarları süzüp derin bir kaba iri halkalar şeklinde doğrayın.
2) Mantarlara, mısır, ince kıyılmış taze soğan, maydanoz, iri doğranmış domates ve salatalığı ilave edin.
3) Hazır sosu limon suyu, zeytinyağı, hardal ve tuzot ile çırpıp mantarların üzerine dökün.

Mushroom Salad

1 large jar or 2 medium size jars of mushrooms

4 green onions

1 can of sweet corn

3 medium tomatoes

3 small cucumbers

4-5 parsley sprigs

1 package basil salad dressing mix

Juice of 2 lemons

1/3 cup olive oil

1 teaspoon seasoned salt

1 teaspoon mustard

1) Drain the mushrooms and slice into thick slices into a deep bowl.
2) Mix the mushrooms, corn, finely chopped green onions, parsley, large diced tomatoes and cucumbers.
3) Mix the dressing mix with the lemon juice, olive oil, mustard and seasoned salt and pour over the mushrooms.

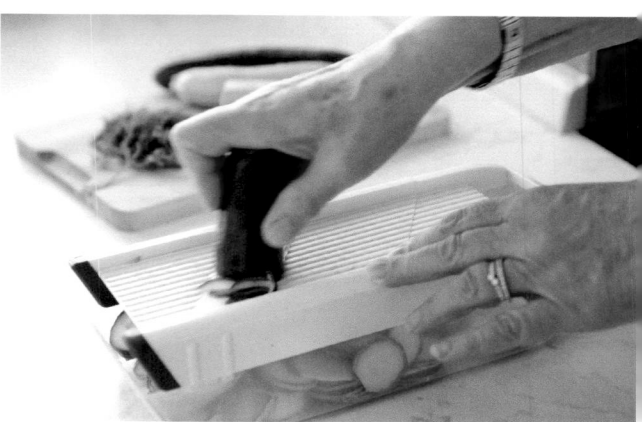

Salatalık ve Kabak Salatası

3 adet salatalık

3 adet körpe kabak

1 demet dereotu

250 gr yoğurt

6 diş sarımsak

1 tatlı kaşığı tuz

1) Yıkanan kabak ve salatalıkları kabuğunu soymadan ince ince dilimleyin.
2) Yoğurdu, ezilmiş sarımsak ve tuzla karıştırın.
3) İnce kıyılmış dereotu, dilimlenmiş kabak ve salatalığı, yoğurtla karıştırıp soğuk olarak servis yapın.

Cucumber and Zucchini Salad

3 cucumbers

3 tender zucchini

1 bunch dill

250 gr yogurt

6 cloves garlic

1 teaspoon salt

1) Finely slice the washed and unpeeled zucchini and cucumber.
2) Mix the crushed garlic and the salt into the yogurt.
3) Mix the yogurt with the finely chopped dill and the sliced zucchini and cucumber and serve.

Tavuk Salatası

1 ufak tavuk

1 adet soğan

1 çorba kaşığı tuzot

250 gr mayonez

1 adet ekşi elma

1/2 demet dereotu

1/2 çay fincanı kuru üzüm

1 çay fincanı iri çentilmiş ceviz

1) Tavuğu soğan ve tuzotla haşlayın. Derisi ve kemiklerini ayırıp ince ince didikleyin ve derin bir kaba alın.

2) Kabuğu soyulup küp şeklinde doğranmış elma, kuru üzüm, ince kıyılmış dereotu, ceviz ve mayonezi tavuğa ilave edip karıştırın.

Chicken Salad

1 small chicken

1 onion

1 tablespoon seasoned salt

250 gr mayonnaise

1 tart apple

1/2 bunch dill

1/4 cup raisins

1/2 cup roughly chopped walnuts

1) Boil the chicken with the onion and the seasoned salt. Remove the bones and skin from the chicken and then cut into small pieces. Place in a bowl.

2) Mix the chicken with the peeled and diced apple, raisins, finely chopped dill, walnuts and mayonnaise and serve.

Yeşil Mercimek ve Lahana Salatası

1 su bardağı yeşil mercimek

5 su bardağı su

1 adet soğan

2 çorba kaşığı zeytinyağı

1 diş sarımsak

1 adet kırmızı soğan

3 su bardağı ince kıyılmış beyaz lahana

1 tatlı kaşığı tuzot

1/2 çay kaşığı karabiber

1 limonun suyu ve kabuğunun rendesi

1) Yeşil mercimeği 5 bardak su ve ay şeklinde doğranmış soğanla birlikte haşlayın.
2) Zeytinyağı koyduğunuz tavada ince kıyılmış kırmızı soğanı, dövülmüş sarımsakla 5 dakika kadar çevirin.
3) Lahanayı da ilave ederek 3-4 dakika daha pişirin.
4) Süzülmüş mercimeklere limon kabuğu rendesi ve limon suyu, tuzot ve karabiberi de ilave edip hepsini karıştırın.
5) Ateşten indirdiğiniz yeşil mercimek ve lahana salatasını ılık veya soğuk olarak servis yapın.

Green Lentil and Cabbage Salad

1 cup green lentils

5 cups water

1 onion

2 tablespoons olive oil

1 clove garlic

1 red onion

3 cups finely chopped cabbage

1 teaspoon seasoned salt

1/8 teaspoon black pepper

Juice and grated rind of 1 lemon

1) Boil the green lentils and onion sliced into crescents in 5 cups of water.
2) Pour the olive oil into a frying pan, add the finely chopped red onion and the crushed garlic and sauté for approximately 5 minutes.
3) Add the cabbage and cook for an additional 3-4 minutes.
4) Drain the lentils and mix in the lemon rind and juice, seasoned salt and black pepper.
5) Add the warm cabbage mixture and serve either warm or cold.

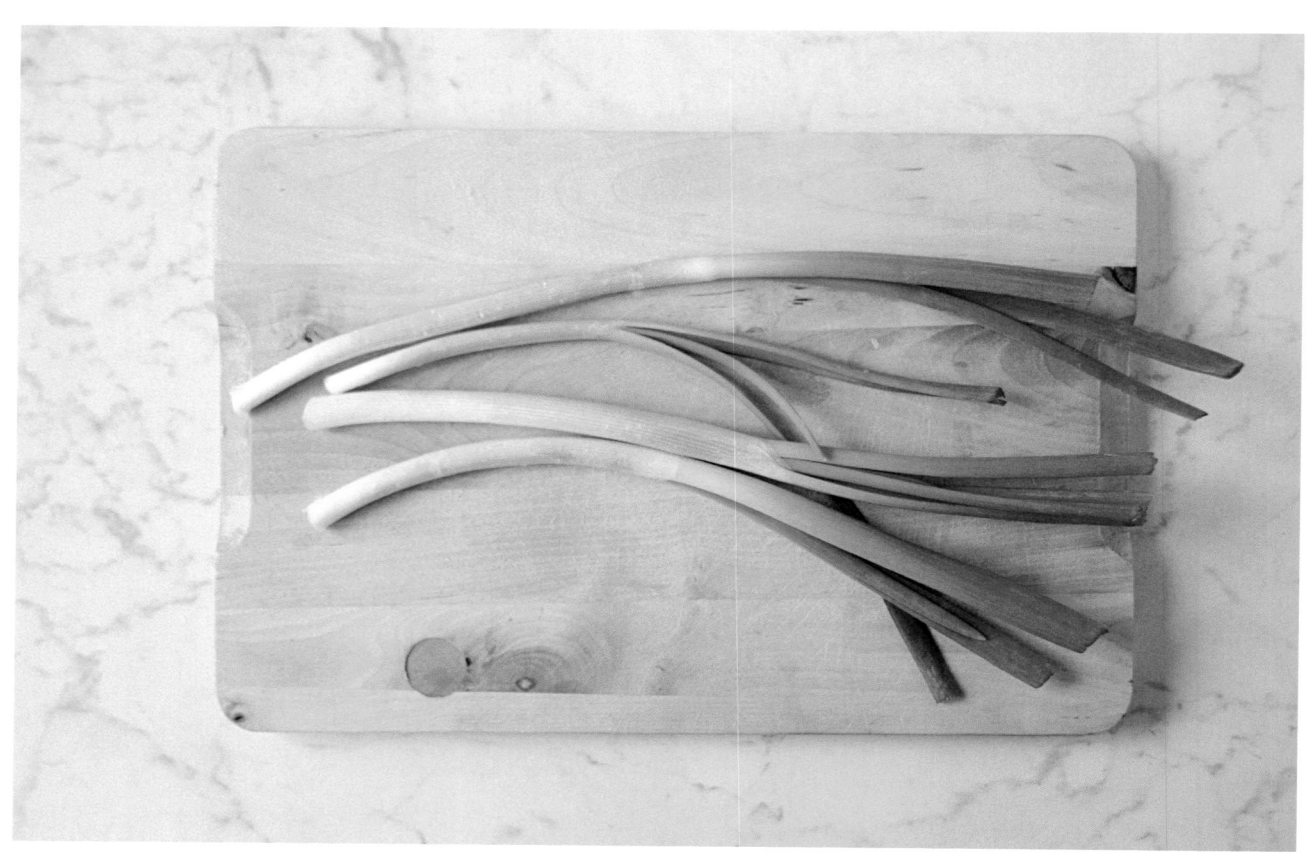

Karnabahar Salatası

3 su bardağı karnabahar

4-5 sap taze soğan

1 kutu tane mısır

1 ufak kavanoz konserve mantar

3 çorba kaşığı yoğurt

3 çorba kaşığı mayonez

1 tatlı kaşığı tuzot

1) Karnabaharların köklerini kesip ufak çiçeklere ayırın.
2) İnce doğranmış taze soğan, mısır, irice doğranmış mantar, tuzot, yoğurt ve mayonezi çiğ karnabaharlarla karıştırıp servis tabağına alın.

Cauliflower Salad

3 cups cauliflower

4-5 green onions

1 can sweet corn

1 small jar of mushrooms

3 tablespoons yogurt

3 tablespoons mayonnaise

1 teaspoon seasoned salt

1) Break the cauliflower into small florets.
2) Add the finely chopped green onions, corn, roughly chopped mushrooms, seasoned salt, yogurt and mayonnaise to the raw cauliflower, mix all well and serve.

Taze Patates ve Semizotu Salatası

1/2 kg taze, ufak patates

1 demet semizotu

10 adet çeri domates

2 sap taze soğan

2 çorba kaşığı ayçekirdeği içi

1/2 paket fesleğenli hazır salata sosu

1 kahve fincanı zeytinyağı

1 limonun suyu

1 tatlı kaşığı tuzot

1) Patatesleri yıkayıp kabuklarıyla birlikte tuzlu suda haşlayın.
2) Semizotunun sadece çiçeklerini ayırıp yıkayın.
3) Derin kaba patates, semizotu, ince kıyılmış taze soğan, çeri domates ve ayçekirdeklerini koyup karıştırın.
4) Limon suyu, fesleğen sosu, zeytinyağı ve tuzotu çırpıp salataya dökün.

New Potato and Purslane Salad

1/2 kg new potatoes

1 bunch purslane

10 cherry tomatoes

2 green onions

2 tablespoons sunflower seeds

1/2 package basil salad dressing mix

1 cup olive oil

Juice of 1 lemon

1 teaspoon seasoned salt

1) Scrub the potatoes well and then boil them in their skins.
2) Stem the purslane and wash the leaves.
3) Mix in a deep bowl the roughly chopped potato, purslane, finely chopped green onions, cherry tomatoes and sunflower seeds.
4) Mix together the lemon juice, basil salad dressing, olive oil and seasoned salt and pour over the salad.

Zeytinyağlılar

Cold Olive Oil Dishes

fava

1/2 kg kuru iç bakla

2 çay bardağı zeytinyağı

2 adet soğan

1 çorba kaşığı tozşeker

1 tatlı kaşığı tuz

Süs için 1/2 demet dereotu

Sıcak su

1) Baklayı geceden ıslatın.
2) Soğanları irice çentip zeytinyağında sararıncaya dek pişirin.
3) Baklaları da ekleyip soğanlarla birlikte çevirin.
4) Tuz ve şekeri ekleyin.
5) Baklaların az üstüne çıkacak kadar su koyup orta ateşte devamlı karıştırarak pişirin.
6) Baklalar pişip suyunu çekince blender'da püre haline getirin.
7) Karışımı bir kalıba döküp üstünü örtün ve 1 gece buzdolabında bekletin.
8) Kalıbı ters çevirin ve etrafını kıyılmış dereotu ile süsleyin.
9) Dilerseniz dereotunun bir kısmını favanın içine de ekleyebilirsiniz.

fava

1/2 kg dried fava beans

1 cup olive oil

2 onions

1 tablespoon granulated sugar

1 teaspoon salt

1/2 bunch dill for garnish

Hot water

1) Soak the fava beans overnight.
2) Roughly chop the onions and sauté in olive oil until golden.
3) Add the fava beans and mix them into the onions.
4) Add the salt and sugar.
5) Add water just to cover the fava beans and cook over medium heat, stirring constantly.
6) When the beans have cooked thoroughly and absorbed all the liquid, blend them into a smooth purée in a blender.
7) Pour the mixture into a mold or deep dish and allow to sit in the refrigerator overnight.
8) Invert the dish onto a serving plate and garnish amply with dill.
9) If desired, some chopped dill can also be added to the mixture before allowing to set.

Zeytinyağlı Lahana Sarması

1 adet esnek ve büyük lahana

3 adet soğan

2 su bardağı pirinç

1 paket dolmalık fıstık

1 paket kuşüzümü

1 su bardağı zeytinyağı

1 tatlı kaşığı kuru nane

1/2 tatlı kaşığı kimyon

1/2 tatlı kaşığı karabiber

1/2 tatlı kaşığı tarçın

1 tatlı kaşığı dolma baharı

2 çorba kaşığı tozşeker

1 tatlı kaşığı tuz

2 1/2 su bardağı ılık su

1/2 limonun suyu

1 su bardağı su

1 adet büyük havuç

1) Lahananın dış yapraklarını kesin. Sıkı olan göbek kısmını çıkarıp ayırın. Lahana yapraklarını haşlayıp süzün.

2) İnce çentilmiş soğanı zeytinyağında; dolmalık fıstıklarla birlikte kavurun. Yıkanmış ve süzülmüş pirinç, rendelenmiş havuç, üzüm, tüm baharat ve şekeri de ekleyerek kavurmaya devam edin.

3) 2 1/2 bardak suyu kavurduğunuz harcın üzerine döküp bir taşım kaynatın ve tencerenin kapağını kapatıp kısık ateşte suyunu çekene dek 15-20 dakika pişirin.

4) Tencerenin altını birkaç tane lahana yaprağıyla döşeyin. El kadar lahana yapraklarının içine harç koyup sıkıca sarın. Üzerine 1 su bardağı su ve limon suyunu dökün. Isıya dayanıklı ufak bir tabağı sarmaların üzerine yerleştirin ve 50 dakika kısık ateşte pişirin.

5) Tencere soğuduktan sonra sarmaları servis tabağına alın.

Cold Stuffed Cabbage

1 fresh and large cabbage

3 onions

2 cups rice

50 gr pine nuts

50 gr currants

1 cup olive oil

1 teaspoon dried mint

1/2 teaspoon cumin

1/2 teaspoon black pepper

1/2 teaspoon cinnamon

1 teaspoon dolma baharı or allspice

2 tablespoons granulated sugar

1 teaspoon salt

2 1/2 cups warm water

Juice of 1/2 lemon

1 cup water

1 large carrot

1) Cut off outer leaves of cabbage and discard. Remove the tight inner leaves and set aside. Boil and drain the green leaves.

2) Sauté the grated onions and pine nuts in the olive oil. Add the washed and drained rice, grated carrot, currants, all the spices and sugar and continue to sauté.

3) Pour 2 1/2 cups of water over the mixture and bring to a boil. When the mixture comes to a boil cover the pot and allow to cook for about 15-20 minutes over low heat until all liquid has been absorbed.

4) Line a large pan with some discarded cabbage leaves and fill each leaf with some of the stuffing and roll firmly. Arrange the stuffed rolls in the pan. Pour the lemon juice and 1 cup of water over the stuffed rolls. Place a small dish over the rolls so they won't rise while cooking and cook for about 50 minutes over low heat.

5) Remove from heat and allow the pot to cool. When the pot is cool, arrange the cabbage rolls on a serving plate.

Zeytinyağlı Yaprak Sarması

1/2 kg yaprak
3 adet büyük soğan
2 su bardağı pirinç
1 paket dolmalık fıstık
1 paket kuşüzümü
1 su bardağı zeytinyağı
1 tatlı kaşığı kuru nane
1/2 tatlı kaşığı kimyon

1/2 tatlı kaşığı karabiber
1/2 tatlı kaşığı tarçın
1 tatlı kaşığı dolma baharı
2 çorba kaşığı tozşeker
1 tatlı kaşığı tuz
2 1/2 su bardağı ılık su
1/2 limonun suyu
1 su bardağı su

1) Yaprakları çok hafif haşlayıp süzün.
2) İnce çentilmiş soğanı zeytinyağında dolmalık fıstıklarla birlikte kavurun. Yıkanmış ve süzülmüş pirinç, üzüm, tüm baharat ve şekeri de ekleyerek kavurmaya devam edin.
3) 2 1/2 bardak suyu kavurduğunuz harcın üzerine döküp bir taşım kaynatın ve tencerenin kapağını kapatıp kısık ateşte suyunu çekene dek 15-20 dakika pişirin.
4) Yaprakların saplarını koparın. Tencerenin altına birkaç tane yaprak döşeyin. Yaprakların içine, parlak tarafları dışarı gelecek şekilde, harç koyup sıkıca sarın. Üzerine 1 su bardağı su ve limon suyunu dökün. Isıya dayanıklı ufak bir tabağı sarmaların üzerine yerleştirin ve 50 dakika kısık ateşte pişirin.
5) Tencere soğuduktan sonra sarmaları servis tabağına alın.

Cold Stuffed Grape Leaves

1/2 kg grape leaves
3 large onions
2 cups rice
50 gr pine nuts
50 gr currants
1 cup olive oil
1 teaspoon dried mint
1/2 teaspoon cumin

1/2 teaspoon black pepper
1/2 teaspoon cinnamon
1 teaspoon dolma baharı or allspice
2 tablespoons granulated sugar
1 teaspoon salt
2 1/2 cups warm water
Juice of 1/2 lemon
1 cup water

1) Lightly boil the grape leaves and drain.
2) Sauté the grated onions and the pine nuts together in the olive oil. Add the washed and drained rice, the currants, all the spices and sugar and continue to sauté.
3) Pour 2 1/2 cups of water over the mixture and bring to a boil. When the mixture comes to a boil, cover the pot and allow to cook for 15-20 minutes until all liquids have been absorbed.
4) Remove the stems from the leaves. Line a large pan with some leaves and, with the shiny side outwards, fill each leaf with some of the stuffing and roll firmly. Arrange the stuffed rolls in the pan. Pour the lemon juice and 1 cup of water over the stuffed rolls. Place a small dish over the rolls so they won't rise while cooking and cook for about 50 minutes over low heat.
5) Remove from heat and allow the pot to cool. When the pot is cool, arrange the stuffed leaves on a serving plate.

Zeytinyağlı Barbunya

1 kg ayıklanmış taze iç barbunya

1 adet soğan

2 adet büyük, olgun domates

5 diş sarımsak

1 adet çarliston biber

1 adet patates

1 adet ufak havuç

1 çorba kaşığı tozşeker

1 tatlı kaşığı tuzot

2 çorba kaşığı zeytinyağı

2 su bardağı ılık su

Süs için 4-5 sap maydanoz

1) Barbunyaları haşlayıp siyah suyunu iyice süzün.
2) Domates, patates ve havuçları küp şeklinde doğrayın. Çarliston biberlerin çekirdeklerini çıkartın ve irice doğrayın.
3) Tencereye haşlanmış fasulye, çentilmiş soğan, domates, çarliston biber, sarımsak, patates, havuç, şeker, tuz ve zeytinyağını koyup karıştırın.
4) Üstüne suyu da ekleyip orta ateşte fasulyeler yumuşayıncaya dek, 50 dakika pişirin.
5) Soğuyan barbunyayı maydanozla süsleyip servis yapabilirsiniz.

Barbunya Beans in Olive Oil

1 kg fresh barbunya beans

(Roman beans can be substituted)

1 onion

2 large, ripe tomatoes

5 cloves garlic

1 long, sweet green pepper

1 potato

1 small carrot

1 tablespoon granulated sugar

1 teaspoon seasoned salt

2 tablespoons olive oil

2 cups warm water

4-5 sprigs of parsley for garnish

1) Cook the beans and drain off the darkened water.
2) Dice the tomatoes, potato and carrots. Seed the peppers and roughly chop.
3) In a pot mix together the softened beans, grated onion, tomatoes, pepper, garlic, potato, carrot, sugar, salt and olive oil.
4) Pour water over and cook for 50 minutes over medium heat until all ingredients are soft and cooked.
5) Garnish the cold barbunya with parsley and serve.

Zeytinyağlı Bamya

1/2 kg taze bamya

1 adet soğan

2 adet domates

1 adet sivribiber

2 çorba kaşığı zeytinyağı

1 tatlı kaşığı tuz

1 çorba kaşığı tozşeker

1 limonun suyu

1 çay bardağı ılık su

1) Bamyaları yıkayıp başlarını külah gibi kesin.
2) Domateslerden birinin kabuklarını soyup küp şeklinde doğrayın.
3) Soğanları küçük parçalar halinde kesin; çentin.
4) Bir tencerede, çekirdekleri çıkarılmış ve ince doğranmış biberlerle, küp domatesleri ve çentilmiş soğanları karıştırın.
5) Bu karışıma zeytinyağı, su, tuz, limon suyu ve şekeri de ilave edip 10 dakika pişirin.
6) Derince bir tencerenin ortasına soyulmamış domatesi yerleştirin. Etrafına taze bamyaları dizin.
7) Pişmiş sosu bu tencereye döküp kapağını kapatın.
8) İlk önce orta, sonra kısık ateşte 25 dakika pişirin.
9) Tencereden çıkartmadan iyice soğuttuğunuz bamyayı bir tabağa ters çevirerek servis yapın.

Okra in Olive Oil

1/2 kg fresh okra

1 onion

2 tomatoes

1 mildly hot long green pepper

2 tablespoons olive oil

1 teaspoon salt

1 tablespoon granulated sugar

Juice of 1 lemon

1/2 cup warm water

1) Wash the okra and cut their stem ends into a cone shape.
2) Peel one of the tomatoes and dice it.
3) Chop the onion into small pieces.
4) Mix in a cooking pot the pepper (seeded and finely chopped), diced tomato and grated onions.
5) Add the olive oil, water, salt, lemon juice and sugar to this mixture and cook for 10 minutes.
6) Place the unpeeled tomato in the center of a deep pot and arrange the okra around the tomato.
7) Pour the cooked sauce over the okra and cook.
8) Cook for 25 minutes, first over medium heat and then over low heat.
9) Cool thoroughly and then invert contents of pan into a serving bowl.

Zeytinyağlı Bakla

1 kg taze bakla

2 çorba kaşığı zeytinyağı

1 çorba kaşığı tozşeker

1/2 limonun suyu

1 adet kuru veya 1 demet taze soğan

1 tatlı kaşığı tuz

1 su bardağı ılık su

1 tatlı kaşığı un

Süs için ince kıyılmış 1/2 demet dereotu

1) Baklaların iki ucunu kesin.
2) Tencereye çentilmiş soğan, bakla, şeker, tuz ve limon suyunu koyup karıştırın.
3) Unu, su içinde eritin.
4) Tencereye zeytinyağı ve unlu suyu da ekleyip orta ateşte baklalar iyice pişinceye kadar pişirin. Eğer düdüklü tencere kullanıyorsanız, düdük çıktıktan sonra 20 dakika daha pişirin.
5) Pişen baklanın üstünü dereotu ile süsleyip yoğurtla servis yapın.

Broad Beans in Olive Oil

1 kg fresh broad (fava) beans

2 tablespoons olive oil

1 tablespoon granulated sugar

Juice of 1/2 lemon

1 onion or one bunch green onions

1 teaspoon salt

1 cup warm water

1 teaspoon flour

1/2 bunch finely chopped dill for garnish

1) Trim the ends off the broad beans.
2) Place and mix in a pot the grated onion, beans, sugar, salt and lemon juice.
3) Dissolve the flour in the water.
4) Add the olive oil and flour-water mixture to the bean mixture and cook over medium heat until soft. If you use a pressure cooker, cook an additional 20 minutes after removing the lid.
5) Serve the cooked broad beans garnished with dill and with yogurt on the side.

Fasulye Pilakisi

2 su bardağı kuru fasulye

1 adet patates

1 adet küçük havuç

1 adet soğan

5 diş sarımsak

1 adet domates

1 çorba kaşığı tuzot

3 çorba kaşığı zeytinyağı

3 su bardağı ılık su

2 çorba kaşığı tozşeker

Süs için 1/2 demet maydanoz

1) Bir gece önceden soğuk suda ıslatılmış fasulyeleri haşlayıp süzün.
2) Tencereye çentilmiş soğan, küp şeklinde doğranmış havuç, patates ve domates, sarımsak, zeytinyağı, tuzot, tozşeker ve fasulyeleri koyup karıştırın.
3) Üstüne ılık su ilave edip orta ateşte fasulyeler yumuşayıncaya dek pişirin.
4) Pişen fasulyenin üzerini maydanozla süsleyip servis yapın.

Bean Pilaki

2 cups white (navy) beans

1 potato

1 small carrot

1 onion

5 cloves garlic

1 tomato

1 tablespoon seasoned salt

3 tablespoons olive oil

3 cups warm water

2 tablespoons granulated sugar

1/2 bunch parsley for garnish

1) Soak the beans in cold water overnight and then cook until semisoft and drain.
2) In a pot mix the grated onion, diced carrot, potato and tomato, garlic, olive oil, seasoned salt, granulated sugar and beans.
3) Poor warm water over and cook over medium heat until beans are very soft.
4) Garnish the pilaki with parsley and serve.

Zeytinyağlı Pırasa

1 kg pırasa

1 adet havuç

1 limonun suyu

1/2 kahve fincanı pirinç

1 çorba kaşığı tuzot

2 çorba kaşığı tozşeker

2 çorba kaşığı zeytinyağı

1 çay fincanı ılık su

1) Pırasaların yeşil uçlarını ve köklerini kesip irice doğrayın. Havuçları diyagonal kesin.
2) Tencereye pırasa, havuç, pirinç, tuzot, şeker, limon suyu, zeytinyağı ve suyu koyup karıştırın.
3) Önce kısık, sonra orta ateşte olmak üzere, arada bir sallayarak pırasalar iyice yumuşayıncaya kadar; 40-45 dakika pişirin.

Leeks in Olive Oil

1 kg leeks

1 carrot

Juice of 1 lemon

1/6 cup rice

1 tablespoon seasoned salt

2 tablespoons granulated sugar

2 tablespoons olive oil

1/3 cup warm water

1) Trim the leeks of their green ends and roots and then cut the remaining edible parts into largish pieces. Slice the carrot diagonally.
2) Mix in a pot the leeks, carrot, rice, seasoned salt, sugar, lemon juice, olive oil and water.
3) Cook initially over low heat and then over medium heat for 40-45 minutes, shaking the pan occasionally, until the leeks are soft.

Zeytinyağlı Kereviz

1 kg kök kereviz
1 adet havuç
1 adet patates
20 adet arpacık soğanı
1 limonun suyu
1 çorba kaşığı tuzot
1 su bardağı ılık su
2 çorba kaşığı zeytinyağı
2 çorba kaşığı tozşeker

1) Soyup küp şeklinde doğradığınız kerevizleri suda bekletin.
2) Tencereye ayıklanmış arpacık soğanı, diyagonal şekilde doğranmış havuç, küp şeklinde doğranmış patates, zeytinyağı, tuzot, tozşeker, limon suyu ve kerevizleri koyup karıştırın.
3) Kerevizlerin üstüne 1 bardak ılık suyu dökün. Birkaç adet körpe kereviz sapı ile birlikte orta ateşte, kerevizler yumuşayıncaya dek pişirin.

Celery Root in Olive Oil

1 kg celery roots
1 carrot
1 potato
20 shallots
Juice of 1 lemon
1 tablespoon seasoned salt
1 cup warm water
2 tablespoons olive oil
2 tablespoons granulated sugar

1) Peel the celery roots, dice and soak in water.
2) In a pot mix the shallots, carrot sliced diagonally, diced potato, olive oil, seasoned salt, granulated sugar, lemon juice and strained celery roots.
3) Pour the cup of water over the celery roots. Add several fresh celery stems if available and cook over medium heat for 45 minutes or until the celery roots are soft.

Zeytinyağlı Enginar

6 adet temizlenmiş taze enginar

36 adet arpacık soğanı

2 çorba kaşığı zeytinyağı

1 tatlı kaşığı tuz

2 çorba kaşığı tozşeker

2 su bardağı su

1 limon

Süs için 1/2 demet dereotu

1) Enginarları yarım limonla ovup tencereye yerleştirin.
2) Her bir enginarın üstüne ayıklanmış arpacık soğanlarını koyun.
3) Bir bardak suda şeker, tuz ve zeytinyağını çırpıp enginarların üstüne dökün.
4) Kalan 1 bardak su ile limon suyunu da dökün.
5) Enginarlar yumuşayıncaya kadar; kısık ateşte 45-50 dakika pişirin.
6) Servis tabağına aldığınız enginarları kıyılmış dereotu ile süsleyip servis yapın.

Artichokes in Olive Oil

6 cleaned and trimmed fresh artichokes

36 shallots

2 tablespoons olive oil

1 teaspoon salt

2 tablespoons granulated sugar

2 cups water

1 lemon

1/2 bunch dill for garnish

1) Rub the artichokes with lemon halves and arrange in a pan.
2) Arrange the trimmed shallots over each artichoke.
3) Mix the sugar, salt and olive oil into 1 cup of water and pour over the artichokes.
4) Mix the remaining 1 cup of water with the lemon juice and pour over.
5) Cook over low heat for 45-50 minutes until the artichokes are soft.
6) Place the artichokes on a serving plate and garnish with dill.

Mini Patlıcanlı İmambayıldı

10 adet mini patlıcan

4 adet domates

2 adet soğan

1/2 demet maydanoz

5 diş sarımsak

1 çorba kaşığı tozşeker

1 çorba kaşığı zeytinyağı

1 tatlı kaşığı tuz

1 çay fincanı su

Kızartma için zeytinyağı

1) Sapları kesilmiş patlıcanları kızgın yağda kızartın ve yağını çekmesi için kâğıt havluya alın.
2) Küp şeklinde doğranmış domates, ay şeklinde çentilmiş soğan ve ortadan ikiye kesilmiş sarımsakları zeytinyağında, domates suyunu çekene dek pişirin.
3) Ateşten aldığınız harca ince kıyılmış maydanozları ekleyin.
4) Patlıcanların ortasını yarıp harç malzemesi ile doldurun.
5) Şeker ve tuzu suda eritip, tencereye dizdiğiniz patlıcanların üstünde gezdirin.
6) Orta ateşte, 15 dakika kadar pişirin.

Mini Eggplant İmambayıldı

10 tiny eggplants

4 tomatoes

2 onions

1/2 bunch parsley

5 cloves garlic

1 tablespoon granulated sugar

1 tablespoon olive oil

1 teaspoon salt

1/3 cup water

Olive oil for frying

1) Trim the stems off the eggplants, fry in the hot oil and then allow excess oil to drain on paper towels.
2) Cook the diced tomatoes, onions chopped into crescents, and the chopped garlic in the 1 tablespoon olive oil until the tomato juice has been absorbed.
3) After removing from heat, add the finely chopped parsley to the mixture.
4) Cut a slit in the eggplants lengthwise and fill this slit amply with the mixture.
5) Dissolve the sugar and salt in water and pour over the eggplants.
6) Cook over medium heat for 15 minutes.

Zeytinyağlı Çalı Fasulye

1 kg çalı fasulye

5 diş sarımsak

1 adet soğan

2 adet olgun domates

2 çorba kaşığı zeytinyağı

1 çorba kaşığı tozşeker

1 tatlı kaşığı tuzot

1 su bardağı ılık su

1) Fasulyelerin kılçıklarını ayıkladıktan sonra ortadan, uzunlamasına kesin.
2) Tencereye fasulye, çentilmiş soğan, çok ufak doğranmış domates, sarımsak, tozşeker, tuzot ve zeytinyağını koyup karıştırın.
3) Fasulyelerin üstüne ılık suyu döküp orta ateşte, fasulyeler yumuşayıncaya dek pişirin. Eğer düdüklü tencere kullanıyorsanız su eklemeyin. Düdük çıktıktan 20 dakika sonra ateşi kapatın.

String Beans in Olive Oil

1 kg string beans

5 cloves garlic

1 onion

2 ripe tomatoes

2 tablespoons olive oil

1 tablespoon granulated sugar

1 teaspoon seasoned salt

1 cup warm water

1) Trim the beans and halve them lengthwise.
2) In a pot mix the beans, grated onion, finely diced tomatoes, garlic, granulated sugar, seasoned salt and olive oil.
3) Pour the warm water over the bean mixture and cook over medium heat for 1 hour. If you use a pressure cooker, continue to cook conventionally for an additional 20 minutes after you have removed the lid.

Zeytinyağlı Kabak

1 kg kabak

1 adet soğan

1 adet domates

1 kahve fincanı bulgur

2 yemek kaşığı zeytinyağı

1 tatlı kaşığı tuzot

Süs için 1/2 demet dereotu

3 diş sarımsak

1) Kabakları uzunlamasına 4'e bölüp iri dikdörtgenler şeklinde doğrayın.
2) Soğanları ay şeklinde doğrayın. Domatesleri küp şeklinde doğrayın ve sarımsakları kıyın.
3) Tencereye soğan, kabak, domates, sarımsak, zeytinyağı, tuzot ve bulguru koyun.
4) Sebzeleri hiç su eklemeden, kısık ateşte, arada bir sallayarak, kabaklar yumuşayıncaya kadar pişirin.
5) Ateşten aldıktan sonra üstünü dereotu ile süsleyebilirsiniz.
6) Tercihe göre sıcak ya da soğuk servis yapın.

Zucchini in Olive Oil

1 kg zucchini

1 onion

1 tomato

1/3 cup bulgur

2 tablespoons olive oil

1 teaspoon seasoned salt

3 cloves garlic

1/2 bunch dill for garnish

1) Quarter the zucchinis lengthwise and then cut into large rectangular pieces.
2) Slice the onion into crescents. Dice the tomatoes and grind the garlic.
3) Mix in a pot the onion, zucchini, tomatoes, garlic, olive oil, seasoned salt and bulgur.
4) Without adding any water, cook this mixture over low heat, shaking the pot occasionally, until the zucchinis are soft.
5) Remove from heat and garnish with sprigs of dill.
6) May be served hot or cold as desired.

Tavuk ve Et Yemekleri

Chicken and Meat Dishes

Peynirli Tavuk But

8 adet derisi çıkartılmış tavuk kalça şiş

1 çorba kaşığı hardal

3 çorba kaşığı beyaz şarap

1 tatlı kaşığı tuzot

1 çay kaşığı karabiber

1 su bardağı rendelenmiş taze kaşar

1 su bardağı ekmek kırıntısı

4 çorba kaşığı eritilmiş tereyağı

1) Hardal, beyaz şarap, tuzot ve karabiberi bir kapta karıştırın. Tavukları bu karışıma bulayıp 2 saat kadar buzdolabında bekletin.
2) Tavukları sırasıyla yağa ve ekmek kırıntısına bulayıp rulo yapın ve fırın ısısına dayanıklı bir kaba dizin.
3) Tavukların üzerine rendelenmiş kaşar peyniri serpin ve orta ısılı fırında, üstü kızarana dek pişirin.

Chicken Rolls with Cheese

8 skinned chicken thighs beaten into fillets

1 tablespoon mustard

3 tablespoons white wine

1 teaspoon seasoned salt

1/4 teaspoon black pepper

1 cup grated fresh kaseri cheese

1 cup bread crumbs

4 tablespoons melted butter

1) Mix the mustard, white wine, seasoned salt and black pepper in a bowl. Put the chicken pieces into this marinade and refrigerate for 2 hours.
2) Dip the chicken pieces into first the butter and then the bread crumbs. Roll and arrange in an ovenproof baking dish.
3) Sprinkle grated kaseri cheese over the chicken and roast in moderately hot (220-230 °C) oven until golden brown.

Sebzeli Tavuk

8 adet kemiksiz tavuk but
1 adet büyük domates
20 adet arpacık soğanı
1 adet havuç
1 adet patates
2 adet kereviz sapı
1/2 demet maydanoz
1 çorba kaşığı tuzot
1 tatlı kaşığı kekik
2 diş sarımsak

1) Tavuk butlarını tencereye dizin. Üzerine, rendelenmiş domates, ayıklanmış arpacık soğanı, dilimlenmiş havuç, küp şeklinde doğranmış patates, kereviz, tuzot, kekik ve sarımsağı ilave edin.
2) Orta ateşte, 45 dakika kadar pişirin. Üzerine ince kıyılmış maydanoz serpip servis yapın.

Chicken with Vegetables

8 boneless chicken thighs
1 large tomato
20 shallots
1 carrot
1 potato
2 celery stalks
1/2 bunch parsley
1 tablespoon seasoned salt
1 teaspoon thyme
2 cloves garlic

1) Arrange chicken thighs in a pan. Over them add the minced tomato, shallots, sliced carrot, diced potato, chopped celery, seasoned salt, thyme and garlic.
2) Cook over medium heat for 45 minutes. Top with finely chopped parsley and serve.

Tavuklu Tart

Tart hamuru için:

125 gr yumuşatılmış margarin

2 çorba kaşığı yoğurt

10 çorba kaşığı un

1 adet yumurta

1/2 paket kabartma tozu

1 çay kaşığı tuz

Tavuklu harç için:

1 adet tavuk but

1 adet tavuk göğüs

1/2 kavanoz konserve mantar

2 çorba kaşığı un

1 çay kaşığı tuz

1 çay kaşığı karabiber

1 çorba kaşığı margarin

1) Tavuk parçalarını haşlayın. Haşlanan sudan 2 su bardağı kadarını ayırın.
2) Tavukları didikleyip ince doğranmış mantarları ilave edin.
3) Un, tuz ve karabiberi kaynamış 2 bardak tavuk suyuyla blender'da çırpın ve tavuklara ilave edin.
4) Hamur malzemesinin hepsini karıştırıp kıvama gelinceye dek yoğurun. Daha sonra hamuru 1/4 ve 3/4 olmak üzere iki parçaya ayırın.
5) Büyük parçayı merdane yardımıyla açıp, yağlanmış yuvarlak bir kalıba yerleştirin.
6) Hazırlanan iç malzemeyi hamurun içine döşeyin.
7) Kalan hamuru açıp üstünü kapatın. Kenarları birleştirerek fazlalıkları kesin.
8) Orta dereceli fırında, üstü kızarana dek 1 saat pişirin.

Chicken Tart

Dough:

125 gr margarine

2 tablespoons yogurt

10 tablespoons flour

1 egg

1/2 package baking powder

1/4 teaspoon salt

Chicken filling:

1 chicken leg

1 chicken breast

1/2 jar mushrooms

2 tablespoons flour

1/4 teaspoon salt

1/4 teaspoon black pepper

1 tablespoon margarine

1) Boil the chicken until cooked, reserving 2 cups of the broth.
2) Shred the chicken and add the finely diced mushrooms.
3) Blend the reserved broth, flour, salt and black pepper in a blender and add chicken to this mixture.
4) Knead all the dough ingredients until dough has reached the right consistency. Divide the dough into two unequal pieces (one 1/4 and and the other 3/4 of the total).
5) Roll out the large piece on a floured surface and arrange into a greased tart pan.
6) Arrange the prepared filling on top of the dough in the pan.
7) Roll out the remaining dough and use it to cover the chicken. Cut off any dough hanging over the side.
8) Bake in moderately hot (220-230 °C) oven until golden brown.

Bademli Tavuk

1 adet kemikleri ve derisi çıkartılmış tavuk

1 adet ufak havuç

1 adet kabak

1 adet soğan

5 sap taze soğan

100 gr haşlanmış ve kabukları soyulmuş badem

1/2 kırmızı ve sarı etli biber

1 adet dolmalık yeşil biber

1 çorba kaşığı mısır nişastası

1 tatlı kaşığı tuzot

1 su bardağı su

1 çorba kaşığı sıvıyağ

2 çorba kaşığı soya sosu

1) Wok tarzı tavada sıvıyağı kızdırın. İri doğranmış soğan ve küp şeklinde doğranmış tavukları, tavuklar suyunu bırakana dek devamlı karıştırarak pişirin.
2) Diyagonal şekilde kesilmiş havuç ve kabak ile ince şeritler halinde kesilmiş biberleri ilave edin.
3) Mısır nişastasını 1 bardak suda eritin. İçine tuzot ve soya sosunu da ilave edip karıştırın. Tavuğa yavaşça ilave edin ve 10 dakika kadar pişirin.
4) Az sıvıyağda kavurduğunuz badem ve ince kıyılmış taze soğanları tavuğa ilave edip karıştırın. Ateşten alıp servis yapın.

Chicken with Almonds

1 boneless and skinned chicken

1 small carrot

1 zucchini

1 onion

5 green onions

100 gr boiled and peeled almonds

1/2 red or yellow bell pepper

1 green bell pepper

1 tablespoon cornstarch

1 teaspoon seasoned salt

1 cup water

1 tablespoon hazelnut or other vegetable oil

2 tablespoons soy sauce

1) Heat hazelnut oil in a wok or other similar pan. Cook the roughly chopped onion and diced chicken until the chicken has released its juices.
2) Add the carrot and zucchini cut into diagonal strips, and the peppers cut into fine strips.
3) Dissolve the cornstarch in 1 cup of water. Add the seasoned salt and soy sauce and mix. Slowly add to the chicken and cook for an additional ten minutes.
4) Sauté the almonds in a small quantity of vegetable oil and add to the chicken, along with the finely chopped green onions. Remove from heat and serve.

Tavuklu Bamya

1/2 kg taze bamya

1/2 kg kuşbaşı tavuk

2 çorba kaşığı zeytinyağı

1 adet soğan

2 adet olgun domates

1 adet sivribiber

1/2 limonun suyu

1 tatlı kaşığı tuzot

1) Bamyaların başlarını külah gibi kesin.
2) Ay şeklinde doğranmış soğanları rengi pembeleşinceye dek zeytinyağında çevirin.
3) Soğanlara küp şeklinde doğranmış domates, çekirdekleri çıkartılıp ince kıyılmış biber, tuzot, limon suyu ve tavuk parçalarını ekleyin. Orta ateşte, 20 dakika kadar pişirin.
4) Tavuklara bamyayı ekleyin. Arada bir sallayarak 25 dakika daha pişirin. Sıcak olarak servis yapın.

Chicken with Okra

1/2 kg fresh okra

1/2 kg cubed chicken

2 tablespoons olive oil

1 onion

2 ripe tomatoes

1 mildly hot, long green pepper

Juice of 1/2 lemon

1 teaspoon seasoned salt

1) Cut the stem end of the okras into a cone shape.
2) Slice the onion into crescents and sauté in the olive oil until their color turns slightly pink.
3) To the onions add the diced tomatoes, seeded and finely chopped pepper, seasoned salt, lemon juice and chicken pieces and cook over medium heat for 20 minutes.
4) Add the chicken to the okra. Cook for 25 more minutes, shaking the pan occasionally.
5) Serve hot.

Etli Pazı Sarması

1/2 kg kıyma
1 adet soğan
1/2 demet maydanoz
1/2 demet dereotu
1 adet domates
2 demet iri yapraklı pazı

1 adet etli kırmızı biber
1 çay kaşığı karabiber
1 çay kaşığı kırmızı pul biber
1 çay kaşığı kimyon
1 çorba kaşığı tuzot
1 su bardağı ılık su

1) Domates, soğan ve kırmızı etli biberi robottan geçirin. Bu karışımı kıyma, ince kıyılmış maydanoz, dereotu, karabiber, kırmızı pul biber, kimyon ve tuzotla yoğurun.

2) Pazıların saplarını kesip hafifçe haşlayın. Haşladığınız yaprakları ikiye bölün. Yaprakların parlak tarafları dışarı gelecek şekilde harçla doldurup sıkıca sarın.

3) Tencereye dizdiğiniz sarmaların üstüne 1 su bardağı ılık su döküp orta ateşte 50 dakika kadar pişirin. Yoğurtla servis yapın.

Meat-Stuffed Chard Rolls

1/2 kg ground meat
1 onion
1/2 bunch parsley
1/2 bunch dill
1 tomato
2 bunches large leaf chard

1 red bell pepper
1/4 teaspoon black pepper
1/4 teaspoon red pepper flakes
1/4 teaspoon cumin
1 tablespoon seasoned salt
1 cup warm water

1) Process the tomato, onion and red bell pepper in a food processor. Add the ground meat, finely chopped parsley, dill, black pepper, red pepper flakes, cumin and seasoned salt and knead.

2) Remove the chard stems and lightly boil. Cut each boiled leaf into two equal pieces. Hold the leaf so the shiny part will be outside, stuff with a small amount of filling, and roll up tightly.

3) Arrange the rolls in a pan and pour 1 cup warm water over. Cook over medium heat for 50 minutes. Serve with yogurt.

Mantarlı Kuzu Eti

1 kg kuşbaşı kuzu eti
1 adet soğan
2 adet domates
2 adet sivribiber
1 küçük kavanoz konserve mantar
1 çorba kaşığı tuzot
1 tatlı kaşığı kekik

1) Eti ay şeklinde doğranmış soğanlarla orta ateşte, devamlı karıştırarak suyunu bırakana dek pişirin.
2) Et suyunu salınca, küp şeklinde doğranmış domates, ince kıyılmış sivribiber, suyu süzülmüş ve dilimlenmiş mantar ve tuzotu ekleyip kısık ateşte 40-45 dakika kadar pişirin.
3) Üstüne kekik serpip servis yapın.

Lamb with Mushrooms

1 kg cubed lamb meat
1 onion
2 tomatoes
2 mildly hot, long green peppers
1 small jar mushrooms
1 tablespoon seasoned salt
1 teaspoon thyme

1) Sauté the meat with the onion, cut into crescents.
2) After the meat has released its juices, add the diced tomatoes, finely chopped green peppers, drained and sliced mushrooms and seasoned salt and cook for 40-45 minutes over low heat.
3) Sprinkle with thyme and serve.

Yoğurtlu Kuzu Eti

1 kg kuşbaşı kuzu eti

1 adet soğan

3 adet olgun domates

2 su bardağı yoğurt

1 çorba kaşığı un

1 tatlı kaşığı tuzot

1 tatlı kaşığı kekik

1 çay kaşığı tarçın

1 çay kaşığı karabiber

1) Eti, soğanla birlikte 10 dakika kadar kavurun.
2) Küp şeklinde doğranmış domates, tuzot, tarçın ve karabiberi ilave edip etler suyunu çekene dek pişirin.
3) Üzerine kekik serptiğiniz etleri fırın ısısına dayanıklı bir kaba alın. Yoğurt ve unu çırpıp etin üstüne dökün.
4) Orta ısılı fırında, yarım saat kadar pişirin.

Lamb in Yogurt

107

1 kg cubed lamb meat

1 onion

3 ripe tomatoes

2 cups yogurt

1 tablespoon flour

1 teaspoon seasoned salt

1 teaspoon thyme

1/4 teaspoon cinnamon

1/4 teaspoon black pepper

1) Sauté the meat and the onion together for 10 minutes.
2) Add the diced tomatoes, seasoned salt, cinnamon and black pepper and cook until the meat broth has been absorbed.
3) Sprinkle the meat with thyme and place in an ovenproof baking dish. Mix together the yogurt and flour and pour over the meat.
4) Bake in moderately hot (220-230 °C) oven for half an hour.

Taze Patatesli Kuzu But

1 adet yağları alınmış ve kemiği kırdırılmış kuzu but

2 adet soğan

3 diş sarımsak

1 tatlı kaşığı kırmızı pul biber

1 tatlı kaşığı kekik

1 tatlı kaşığı biberiye

1 çorba kaşığı tuzot

1/2 kg patates

1) Ay şeklinde doğranmış soğan, pul biber, tuzot, kekik ve biberiyeye bulanmış kuzu budunu birkaç yerinden delip içine sarımsakları yerleştirin. 1 gece buzdolabında dinlendirin.

2) Kuzu budunu derin bir tencereye alın. Kapağı kapalı olarak, çok kısık ateşte, arada bir çevirerek 3 saat kadar pişirin.

3) Suyunu salmış olan ete, taze patatesleri ilave edin. Kısık ateşte 1 saat kadar daha pişirin.

4) Servis yapmadan önce üzerine bol kekik serpin.

Leg of Lamb with Potatoes

109

1 boneless and defatted leg of lamb

2 onions

3 cloves garlic

1 teaspoon red pepper flakes

1 teaspoon thyme

1 teaspoon rosemary

1 tablespoon seasoned salt

1/2 kg potatoes

1) Dip the lamb into a mixture of the onions sliced into crescents, the red pepper flakes, seasoned salt, thyme, and rosemary. Poke several small holes into the leg and insert garlic cloves. Allow the lamb smothered with spices and vegetables to sit in the refrigerator overnight.

2) The next day place the leg of lamb into a deep pot. Cook tightly covered for three hours over very low heat. Remember to turn the lamb occasionally as it cooks.

3) Add the potatoes to the pot and turn in the meat broth. Cook over low heat for another hour.

4) Sprinkle with thyme and serve.

Kuru Köfte

1 kg kıyma
3 dilim bayat ekmek
1 adet soğan
1 adet yumurta
1 çorba kaşığı tuzot
1 çay kaşığı kimyon
1 çay kaşığı karabiber
Kızartma için bol sıvıyağ

1) Ekmek dilimlerinin kabuklarını kesin ve çok hafif ıslatın.
2) Rendelenmiş soğan ve ekmek dilimlerine kıyma, yumurta, tuzot, kimyon ve karabiberi ilave edip yoğurun.
3) Harçtan ufak parçalar alıp parmak şeklinde yuvarlayın.
4) Bol kızgın yağda kızartıp yağını çekmesi için kâğıt havlu üzerine çıkartın.

Dry Meatballs

1 kg ground meat
3 slices stale bread
1 onion
1 egg
1 tablespoon seasoned salt
1/4 teaspoon cumin
1/4 teaspoon black pepper
Vegetable oil for frying

1) Remove the crusts from the bread and moisten bread lightly.
2) Mix the grated onion and crumbled bread with the ground meat, egg, seasoned salt, cumin and black pepper and knead.
3) Form finger-size rolls with your hands.
4) Fry the rolls in a large quantity of oil and then place on paper towels to drain off excess oil.

Kuru Köfteli Tortellini

1 kg dana kıyma

1 adet soğan

3 dilim kenarları kesilmiş bayat ekmek

1 çorba kaşığı tuzot

1 tatlı kaşığı karabiber

1 tatlı kaşığı kekik

1 tatlı kaşığı kimyon

2 paket peynirli tortellini

4 adet olgun iri domates

2 adet sivribiber

1/2 demet maydanoz

2 çorba kaşığı zeytinyağı

1) Derin bir kapta kıyma, rendelenmiş soğan ve ekmek, tuzot, kimyon ve karabiberi yoğurun.
2) Minik köfteler yapıp, yağlı kâğıt serilmiş ve bol kekik serpilmiş fırın tepsisine dizin.
3) Orta ısılı fırında, arada bir sallayarak, köfteler kızarana dek pişirin.
4) Sivribiberlerin çekirdeklerini çıkartıp ince kıyın. Zeytinyağı, küp gibi doğranmış domates ve biberleri tuzotla, suyunu çekene dek pişirin.
5) Paketteki tarife göre haşladığınız tortellinilerin üzerine domates sosunu dökün.
6) Üstüne fırında pişirdiğiniz mini köfteleri yerleştirin. Üzerine ince kıyılmış maydanoz serpip sıcak olarak servis yapın.

Dry Meatball Tortellini

1 kg ground veal

1 onion

3 slices stale bread with crusts removed

1 tablespoon seasoned salt

1 teaspoon black pepper

1 teaspoon thyme

1 teaspoon cumin

2 packages cheese tortellini

4 large ripe tomatoes

2 mildly hot, long green peppers

1/2 bunch parsley

2 tablespoons olive oil

1) In a deep bowl knead together the ground veal, grated onion, crumbled bread, seasoned salt, cumin and black pepper.
2) Make tiny meatballs and arrange on a pan lined with greased paper and sprinkled with a large quantity of thyme.
3) Cook in moderately hot (220-230 °C) oven until meatballs are cooked, shaking pan occasionally.
4) Seed the long peppers and dice finely.
5) Cook the olive oil, diced tomatoes and peppers with seasoned salt until all the juices are absorbed.
6) Cook the tortellini according to the directions on the package and pour the tomato sauce over.
7) Arrange the meatballs cooked in the oven over the tortellini mixture. Top with finely chopped parsley and serve hot.

Izgara Bütün Bonfile

1 adet sinirleri ve yağları alınmış bütün bonfile (1,5 kg)

1 tatlı kaşığı kırmızı pul biber

1 çorba kaşığı tuzot

1 tatlı kaşığı kekik

1 tatlı kaşığı biberiye

1 adet soğan

1 diş sarımsak

1 kahve fincanı sıvıyağ

1) Bonfileyi ay şeklinde doğranmış soğan, biberiye, pul biber, tuzot, çentilmiş sarımsak, sıvıyağ ve kekiğe bulayıp 1 gece buzdolabında bekletin.
2) Elektrikli ızgarayı 5 dakika kızdırdıktan sonra bonfileyi koyun.
3) Her 10 dakikada bir çevirerek, iyi pişmiş bonfile için 75, orta pişmiş bonfile için 60 dakika pişirin.
4) Bonfileyi dilimleyerek, sebze ve fırında patates ile servis yapın. Dilerseniz kömür ızgarada da pişirebilirsiniz.

Grilled Whole Sirloin

1 whole sirloin steak (about 1.5 kilos), with any fat and suet removed

1 teaspoon red pepper flakes

1 tablespoon seasoned salt

1 teaspoon thyme

1 teaspoon rosemary

1 onion

1 clove garlic

1 /2 cup vegetable oil

1) Marinate the whole steak in a mixture of the onion sliced into crescents, the rosemary, pepper flakes, seasoned salt, crushed garlic, vegetable oil and thyme and allow to sit in the refrigerator overnight.
2) Preheat the electric grill for 5 minutes and then place the steak on the grill.
3) Turn every 10 minutes. Cook 75 minutes for well-done and 60 minutes for medium.
4) Slice the steak and serve it with vegetables and a baked potato on the side. The steak can also be cooked over charcoal.

Mantarlı Bonfile

8 parça az dövülmüş bonfile

1 adet soğan

1 tatlı kaşığı tuzot

1 tatlı kaşığı kırmızı pul biber

1 çay kaşığı biberiye

1 çay kaşığı kekik

200 gr konserve mantar

1 paket hazır kuşkonmaz veya kremalı mantar çorbası (90 gr)

2 çorba kaşığı tereyağı

2 su bardağı su

1) Bonfileleri ay şeklinde doğranmış soğan, biberiye, pul biber, tuzot ve kekikle ovup 1 gece buzdolabında bekletin.
2) Tereyağını kızdırıp bonfilelerin iki tarafını da kızartın.
3) Mantarları irice doğrayın. Paket çorbayı 2 bardak suda eritin.
4) Mantarları ve çorbayı bonfilelerin üzerine döküp, etler yumuşayıncaya kadar; 30 dakika pişirin.

Mushroom Steak

8 pieces slightly flattened steak fillet

1 onion

1 teaspoon seasoned salt

1 teaspoon red pepper flakes

1/4 teaspoon rosemary

1/4 teaspoon thyme

1 small jar mushrooms

1 package dry soup mix (preferably asparagus or cream of mushroom)

2 tablespoons butter

2 cups water

1) Marinate the steak in a mixture of the onion sliced into crescents, the rosemary, pepper flakes, seasoned salt and thyme and allow to sit in the refrigerator overnight.
2) Heat the butter and brown the steaks on each side.
3) Dice the mushrooms into large pieces. Dissolve the soup mix in 2 cups of water.
4) Pour the mushrooms and soup over the meat and allow to cook for 30 minutes, until soft.

Izgara Köfte

1 kg dana kıyma

1 adet orta boy soğan

3 dilim kenarları kesilmiş bayat ekmek

6-7 sap ince kıyılmış maydanoz

1 tatlı kaşığı kekik

1 tatlı kaşığı tuzot

1 tatlı kaşığı karabiber

1 tatlı kaşığı kimyon

1 adet yumurta

1/2 kahve fincanı sıvıyağ

1) Derin bir kaba kıyma, rendelenmiş ekmek ve soğan, maydanoz, kekik, tuzot, karabiber ve kimyonu koyup yoğurun.
2) Köfte harcını 1 saat kadar buzdolabında bekletin.
3) Elinizde şekillendirdiğiniz köftelerin iki tarafına fırça yardımıyla sıvıyağ sürün. Kızdırılmış teflon tavada veya ızgarada pişirin.

Grilled Meatballs

1 kg ground veal

1 medium onion

3 slices stale bread with crusts removed

6-7 sprigs finely chopped parsley

1 teaspoon thyme

1 teaspoon seasoned salt

1 teaspoon black pepper

1 teaspoon cumin

1 egg

1/2 cup vegetable oil

1) Into a deep bowl place the ground veal, crumbled bread, grated onion, parsley, thyme, seasoned salt, black pepper and cumin and knead until homogenous.
2) Place the mixture in the refrigerator and allow to sit for 1 hour.
3) Form into oval rounds with the hands and brush vegetable oil on each side. Fry in a nonstick frying pan or on a grill.

Fırında Hindi But

2 adet derisi çıkarılıp ikiye bölünmüş hindi but

1 adet soğan

1 çorba kaşığı tuzot

1 tatlı kaşığı biberiye

1 tatlı kaşığı kırmızı pul biber

2 çorba kaşığı sıvıyağ

Kekik

1) Derin bir kapta butları, tuzot, biberiye, kırmızı pul biber ve ay şeklinde doğranmış soğanla ovun. 1 gece buzdolabında dinlendirin.
2) Çelik bir tencerede butları 2 çorba kaşığı sıvıyağda çevirerek kızartın.
3) Tenceredeki tüm yağı süzün ve tencerenin ağzını kapayarak 1 saat kadar kısık ateşte arada bir çevirerek pişirin. Bu arada et suyunu salacaktır.
4) Fırın ısısına dayanıklı bir kaba butları yerleştirin. Üstüne tenceredeki tüm et suyunu dökün.
5) Orta ısılı fırında, arada bir kaşık yardımıyla suyunu üstünde gezdirerek 1 saat kadar pişirin.
6) Bütün veya didiklenmiş olarak, üstüne kekik serpip servis yapın.

Roast Turkey Leg

2 skinned turkey legs divided into two pieces

1 onion

1 tablespoon seasoned salt

1 teaspoon rosemary

1 teaspoon red pepper flakes

2 tablespoons vegetable oil

Thyme

1) Place the turkey legs in a deep bowl and knead into them a mixture of seasoned salt, rosemary, red pepper flakes and crescent-shaped sliced onions. Allow the turkey smothered with the vegetables and spices to sit in the refrigerator overnight.
2) Sauté the turkey in a steel pot in 2 tablespoons vegetable oil until fried golden.
3) Drain off all the oil in the pan, cover the pan tightly and allow meat to cook for 1 hour over very low heat, turning over occasionally. The meat will release its juices during this cooking.
4) Arrange the turkey legs in an ovenproof baking dish and pour all the accumulated juices over.
5) Roast in moderately hot (220-230 °C) oven, basting occasionally, for one hour.
6) Either remove the meat from the bone or serve as whole pieces. Sprinkle with thyme and serve.

Deniz Ürünleri

Seafood

Çingene Palamudu Pilakisi

4 adet çingene palamudu

2 adet soğan

3 adet domates

3 adet sivribiber

1 adet patates

1 adet havuç

2 adet kereviz sapı

1 çorba kaşığı tuzot

1/2 limonun suyu

1 demet maydanoz

2 çorba kaşığı zeytinyağı

1. Ay şeklinde doğranmış soğanı, sararıncaya dek zeytinyağında çevirin. Soğana küp şeklinde doğranmış domates, patates, havuç ve kereviz sapıyla birlikte ince kıyılmış biberleri ekleyin.
2. Arada bir karıştırarak 15 dakika kadar pişirin.
3. Ateşten indirdiğiniz sosa tuzot, limon suyu ve kıyılmış maydanozu ekleyip karıştırın.
4. Fırın ısısına dayanıklı bir kaba sosun yarısını yayıp üstüne balık filetolarını yerleştirin.
5. Kalan sosu balıkların üzerine dökün. Önceden ısıtılmış fırında 45 dakika pişirin.

Bonito with Veggie Stew

4 bonito fish

2 onions

3 tomatoes

3 mildly hot, long green peppers

1 potato

1 carrot

2 celery stalks

1 tablespoon seasoned salt

Juice of 1/2 lemon

1 bunch parsley

2 tablespoons olive oil

1) Sauté the onions sliced into crescents in a little olive oil until golden. Add the diced tomatoes, potato, carrot and celery stalks and the finely chopped peppers to the onion.
2) Cook all the vegetables for 15 minutes, stirring occasionally.
3) After removing from heat stir in the seasoned salt, lemon juice and finely chopped parsley.
7) Place half this sauce in an ovenproof baking dish and arrange the fish fillets on top.
8) Pour the remaining sauce on top of the fish and cook in preheated oven for 35-40 minutes.

Fırında Bademli Balık

1 kg beyaz etli balık filetosu
1 tatlı kaşığı tuzot
1 çay kaşığı kırmızıbiber
1/2 limonun suyu
1/4 su bardağı erimiş tereyağı
1/2 su bardağı ince kıyılmış çiğ badem
2 çorba kaşığı tereyağı
1/4 su bardağı limon suyu

1) Fırın ısısına dayanıklı bir kabı alüminyum folyo ile kaplayıp eritilmiş tereyağının birazını folyoya sürün.
2) Balık filetolarını tuzot ve kırmızıbiberle ovun. Balıkları folyoya yerleştirip üzerine limon suyu gezdirin.
3) Balıkları önceden ısıtılmış fırında 25 dakika kadar pişirin.
4) Balık pişerken, erimiş 2 çorba kaşığı tereyağında, bademleri pembeleşinceye kadar çevirin.
5) Bademleri fırından çıkardığınız balıkların üstüne serpin.
6) Bademleri çevirdiğiniz tereyağını 1/4 su bardağı limon suyu ile karıştırıp sıcak olarak balıkların üstüne döküp hemen servis yapın.

Baked Fish with Almonds

1 kg white meat fish fillets
1 teaspoon seasoned salt
1/4 teaspoon paprika
Juice of 1/2 lemon
1/4 cup melted butter
1/2 cup finely chopped raw almonds
2 tablespoons butter
1/4 cup lemon juice

1) Line an ovenproof baking dish with aluminum foil and spread some of the melted butter on top of the foil.
2) Knead the seasoned salt and paprika into the fish fillets. Arrange the fillets over the foil in the baking dish and lightly pour the lemon juice over.
3) Bake the fish in preheated oven for 25 minutes.
4) While the fish is baking, lightly sauté the almonds in the 2 tablespoons of butter.
5) After you have removed the fish from the oven, sprinkle the almonds on top.
6) Stir 1/4 cup lemon juice into the butter in the pan (in which you sautéed the almonds), heat and pour over fish as you serve.

Karides Kokteyli

1 kg haşlanmış karides

1/2 su bardağı kereviz sapı

2 adet haşlanmış yumurta

1/2 su bardağı mayonez

1 çorba kaşığı ketçap

1/4 çay kaşığı Tobasco acı sos

1/2 limonun suyu

1 adet domates veya birkaç adet çeri domates

Yeşil salata yaprakları

1) Karidesleri limon suyu ile ıslatın.
2) Küp şeklinde doğranmış kereviz sapı, mayonez, ketçap, Tobasco sos ve haşlanmış yumurta dilimlerini karideslerle karıştırın.
3) Servis tabağını salata yaprakları ile döşeyin ve karışımı üstüne yerleştirin.
4) Etrafını dilimlenmiş domates veya çeri domateslerle süsleyip servis yapın.

Shrimp Cocktail

1 kg boiled shrimp

1/2 cup celery stalks

2 boiled eggs

1/2 cup mayonnaise

1 tablespoon catsup

1/8 tsp of hot Tabasco sauce

Juice of 1/2 lemon

1 tomato or several cherry tomatoes

Lettuce leaves

1) Wet the shrimp with the lemon juice.
2) Mix into the shrimp the diced celery stalks, mayonnaise, catsup, Tabasco sauce and sliced boiled eggs.
3) Line a serving dish with the lettuce leaves and arrange the shrimp mixture on top.
4) Garnish with the sliced tomato or the cherry tomatoes and serve.

Fırında Levrek

8 parça deniz levreği filetosu

1 çorba kaşığı tereyağı

1 ufak kavanoz konserve mantar

2 adet sivribiber

3 adet domates

1/2 su bardağı beyaz şarap

2 çorba kaşığı çiğ krema

2-3 adet defne yaprağı

1 tatlı kaşığı tuzot

1 çay kaşığı karabiber

1/2 limon

1) Tereyağını erittiğiniz geniş bir tavada ince kıyılmış sivribiber ve mantarları, küp gibi doğranmış domatesleri, tuzot ve karabiberi pişirin.
2) Sebze karışımına beyaz şarabı ilave edip 2-3 dakika daha pişirin.
3) Ateşten aldığınız sebzeleri çiğ krema ile karıştırın.
4) Fırın ısısına dayanıklı bir kaba balık filetolarını dizin ve üstüne hazırladığınız sosu dökün.
5) Limon dilimleri ve defne yaprakları ile süsleyip önceden ısıtılmış, orta dereceli fırında 45 dakika pişirin.

Baked Sea Bass

8 fillets sea bass

1 tablespoon butter

1 small jar of mushrooms

2 mildly hot, long green peppers

3 tomatoes

1/2 cup white wine

2 tablespoons heavy cream

2-3 bay leaves

1 teaspoon seasoned salt

1/4 teaspoon black pepper

1/2 lemon

1) Melt the butter in a large frying pan and sauté in it the finely chopped green peppers and mushrooms, the diced tomatoes, seasoned salt and black pepper.
2) Add the white wine to the vegetable mixture and cook for an additional 2-3 minutes.
3) Remove from heat and mix in the cream.
4) Arrange the fillets in an ovenproof baking dish and pour the sauce over.
5) Garnish with slices of lemon and bay leaves and bake at medium heat for 45 minutes.

Ispanaklı Levrek

8 parça deniz levreği filetosu

1 paket ıspanak

1/2 kg süt

2 çorba kaşığı margarin

2 çorba kaşığı un

1 tatlı kaşığı tuz

100 gr rendelenmiş taze kaşar

1) Ispanakları irice doğrayıp tuzlu suda haşlayın.
2) Sütü margarinle kaynatın. Süt, un ve tuzu blender'da çırpın.
3) Beyaz sosu ıspanaklarla karıştırın.
4) Fırın ısısına dayanıklı bir kaba sosun yarısını yayıp üstüne balık filetolarını yerleştirin.
5) Kalan beyaz sosu balıkların üzerine dökün ve üstünü rendelenmiş taze kaşar ile örtün.
6) Orta ısılı fırında peynirler kızarıncaya dek; 45 dakika pişirin.

Spinach Sea Bass

8 fillets sea bass

1 package spinach (750 gr)

1/2 liter milk

2 tablespoons margarine

2 tablespoons flour

1 teaspoon salt

100 gr grated fresh kaseri cheese

1) Roughly chop the spinach and cook in salted water.
2) Boil the milk and margarine in a saucepan and then blend the milk mixture, flour and salt in a blender.
3) Mix the white sauce into the spinach.
4) Pour half the white sauce into an ovenproof baking dish and arrange the fish fillets on top.
5) Pour the remaining white sauce over the fish and cover with the grated fresh kaseri cheese.
6) Bake at medium heat until the cheese browns, approximately 45 minutes.

Karidesli Brokoli ve Karnabahar

2 çorba kaşığı haşlanmış karides

1 çorba kaşığı soya sosu

1 tatlı kaşığı mısır nişastası

2 çorba kaşığı sıvıyağ

4 sap taze soğan

1 adet kırmızı biber

1 diş sarımsak

250 gr karnabahar

250 gr brokoli

1 çay bardağı su

Tuz ve karabiber

Süs için 50 gr tuzsuz badem

1) Mısır nişastası ve soya sosunu suyla karıştırıp bekletin.
2) Wok tarzı tavada sıvıyağı kızdırıp, haşlanıp kabukları çıkarılmış bademleri kavurun. Kavrulan bademleri kepçe yardımıyla dışarıya alın.
3) Wok'ta kalan yağda karides, ince kıyılmış taze soğan, kırmızı biber ve sarımsağı 1 dakika çevirin.
4) Küçük çiçeklere ayrılmış brokoli ve karnabaharı ekleyip 2 dakika karıştırarak pişirin.
5) Tavaya mısır nişastalı sosu, tuz ve biberi de ilave edip ağzı kapalı olarak 2 dakika daha pişirin.
6) Tabağa aldığınız karışımı kavrulmuş bademlerle süsleyip hemen servis yapın.

Shrimp with Broccoli and Cauliflower

2 large spoonfuls boiled shrimp

1 tablespoon soy sauce

1 teaspoon cornstarch

2 tablespoons vegetable oil

4 green onions

1 red pepper (paprika)

1 clove garlic

250 gr cauliflower

250 gr broccoli

1/2 cup water

Salt and pepper

50 gr unsalted almonds for garnish, blanched and skinned

1) Mix the soy sauce and cornstarch with the water and put aside.
2) Heat the oil in a wok or similar pan and sauté the almonds. Remove from oil when golden.
3) In the same oil lightly sauté the shrimp, finely chopped green onions, pepper and garlic for 1 minute.
4) Add the cauliflower and broccoli broken into small florets and cook, stirring, for 2 more minutes.
5) Add the soy sauce mixture, salt and pepper, cover the pot and allow to cook for 2 minutes.
6) Pour into a serving dish and garnish with the almonds.

Fırında Sarımsak ve Tereyağlı Balık

1 kg beyaz etli balık filetosu

1 tatlı kaşığı tuzot

1 çay kaşığı karabiber

1 limonun suyu

2 çorba kaşığı erimiş tereyağı

1 diş sarımsak

1) Fırın ısısına dayanıklı bir kabı alüminyum folyo ile kaplayıp eritilmiş tereyağının birazını folyoya sürün.
2) Balık filetolarını tuzot ve karabiberle ovun. Limon, erimiş tereyağı, karabiber, ezilmiş sarımsak ve tuzotu çırpıp balıkların üstünde gezdirin.
3) Önceden ısıtılmış fırında 35 dakika kadar pişirin.

Baked Fish with Garlic and Butter

1 kg white meat fish fillet

1 teaspoon seasoned salt

1/4 teaspoon black pepper

Juice of 1 lemon

2 tablespoons melted butter

1 clove garlic

1) Line an ovenproof baking dish with aluminum foil and pour some of the melted butter on top of the foil.
2) Knead the seasoned salt and pepper into the fish fillets and arrange the fillets in the dish. Mix the lemon juice, the rest of the melted butter, black pepper, crushed garlic and seasoned salt and pour over the fish.
3) Cook in preheated oven for 35 minutes.

Somonlu Krep Pastası

10 adet krep
2 paket (400 gr) labne peynir
4 paket füme somon
1/2 demet dereotu
3 adet közlenmiş kırmızı biber

1) Labne peynir ve kıyılmış dereotunu karıştırın.
2) Kreplerin üzerine bu karışımdan sürdükten sonra somon fümeleri yerleştirin. Bu işlemi krepler bitinceye dek tekrarlayın.
3) Közlenmiş kırmızı biberleri ince şeritler halinde kesin.
4) Üst üste dizdiğiniz kreplerin kenarlarını bu şeritlerle kapatın. Kalan şeritlerle pastanın üstünü süsleyebilirsiniz.

Salmon Crepe Pastry

10 crepes
1 package (400 gr) labne cheese (soft cream cheese)
4 packages of smoked salmon (400 gr)
1/2 bunch dill
3 roasted paprika peppers

1) Mix the labne (or soft cream cheese) and finely chopped dill and spread on the crepes. Top with the salmon. Continue until you have used up all the crepes.
2) Cut the roasted paprika peppers into thin strips.
3) Layer the crepes on top of one another and use the pepper strips to close their edges. Garnish the top with any leftover pepper strips.

Karides Güveç

1 kg karides
1 adet soğan
1 diş sarımsak
2 adet domates
2 adet sivribiber
1 ufak kavanoz konserve mantar
2 çorba kaşığı tereyağı
100 gr rendelenmiş taze kaşar
1 çay kaşığı karabiber
1 tatlı kaşığı tuzot
1/2 limonun suyu

1) Tereyağını erittiğiniz bir tavada, rendelenmiş sarımsak, soğan ve karidesleri devamlı çevirerek 5 dakika kadar pişirin.
2) Küp şeklinde doğranmış domates, ince kıyılmış biber ve mantarlara tuzot, karabiber ve limon suyunu ekleyin. Domatesler suyunu çekene dek, karideslerle birlikte pişirin.
3) Karidesleri, yağlanmış, fırın ısısına dayanıklı bir kaba veya ufak güveçlere yerleştirip üstüne rendelenmiş peyniri serpin.
4) Orta ısılı bir fırında, peynirler eriyip kızarıncaya dek pişirin.

Shrimp Casserole

1 kg shrimp
1 onion
1 clove garlic
2 tomatoes
2 mildly hot, long green peppers
1 small jar of mushrooms
2 tablespoons butter
100 gr grated fresh kaseri cheese
1/4 teaspoon black pepper
1 teaspoon seasoned salt
Juice of 1/2 lemon

1) Melt the butter in a frying pan, add the minced garlic, grated onion, and shrimp and cook for 5 minutes, stirring constantly.
2) Add the diced tomatoes, finely chopped peppers and mushrooms, seasoned salt, black pepper and lemon juice. Cook the shrimp until the tomatoes have absorbed all of their juices.
3) Arrange the shrimp mixture in a greased, ovenproof baking dish and sprinkle the grated cheese on top.
4) Cook in moderately hot oven until the cheese has melted and turned golden.

Balık Buğulama

8 adet balık fileto (levrek, mezgit, fener balığı vb.)

1 adet soğan

1 adet limon

1 adet iri domates

1 adet patates

2 adet sivribiber

1 çorba kaşığı tuzot

1 çay kaşığı karabiber

1 çorba kaşığı mısır nişastası

1 su bardağı su

1 çorba kaşığı tereyağı

1) Geniş bir tencereye sırasıyla, yuvarlak kesilmiş soğan, patates, balık fileto, dilimlenmiş ve çekirdekleri alınmış domates, dörde bölünmüş sivribiber, yarım limonun dilimleri ve ufak parçalar halinde tereyağını yerleştirin.
2) Kalan yarım limonun suyunu ve mısır nişastasını tuzot ve karabiberle birlikte tencerenin üzerinde gezdirin.
3) Kaynamaya başladıktan sonra 30 dakika daha pişirin.
4) Balık buğulamayı üzerine ince kıyılmış maydanoz serperek servis yapın.

Steamed Fish

8 fish fillets (sea bass, whiting, angler, etc.)

1 onion

1 lemon

1 large tomato

1 potato

2 mildly hot, long green peppers

1 tablespoon seasoned salt

1/4 teaspoon black pepper

1 tablespoon cornstarch

1 cup water

1 tablespoon butter

1) Place in layers in a wide pan: the sliced onion, potato, fish fillets, tomato (sliced and seeds removed), peppers cut into quarters, half of the lemon, sliced, and butter cut into small pieces.
2) Sprinkle on top the juice from the remaining half lemon and the cornstarch mixed with the seasoned salt and black pepper.
3) Boil for 30 minutes after the mixture has come to a boil.
4) Garnish with finely chopped parsley and serve.

Bademli Karides

1/2 kg karides
1 su bardağı ince kıyılmış çiğ badem
3 çorba kaşığı tereyağı
1/2 çay kaşığı tuz
1 çay kaşığı kırmızıbiber
2 çorba kaşığı kıyılmış maydanoz
Servis için melba tost

1) Karidesleri haşlayın.
2) Tereyağını eritin. Karidesleri badem, tuz ve karabiberi ekleyip 5 dakika kadar çevirerek pişirin. Ateşten alın, kıyılmış maydanozu ilave edin.
3) Melba tostların üzerine sürüp sıcak servis yapın.

Shrimp with Almonds

1/2 kg shrimp
1 cup finely chopped raw almonds
3 tablespoons butter
1/8 teaspoon salt
1/4 teaspoon paprika
2 tablespoons finely chopped parsley
Melba toast

1) Boil the shrimp.
2) Heat the butter. Add the shrimp, almonds, salt and paprika. Cook for about 5 minutes stirring all the time. Remove from heat and add the parsley.
3) Spread over melba toast pieces and serve hot.

füme Somonlu Kiş

200 gr füme somon
100 gr rendelenmiş taze kaşar
1 su bardağı kıyılmış ıspanak
1/2 su bardağı kıyılmış etli kırmızı biber
1/2 su bardağı çentilmiş soğan
2 çorba kaşığı un
4 adet yumurta
1 su bardağı süt
3 damla Tobasco acı sos

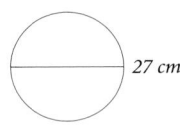

27 cm

1) Bir kapta ufak parçalara bölünmüş somon, taze kaşar, haşlanmış ıspanak, soğan, kırmızı biber ve unu karıştırın.
2) Önceden yağlanmış, 27 cm'lik bir tart kalıbına bu karışımı yayın.
3) Yumurta, süt ve Tobasco sosu çırpıp somon karışımının üstüne dökün.
4) Orta ısılı fırında 45 dakika kadar pişirin.
5) Piştikten sonra, 10 dakika bekletip servis yapın.

Smoked Salmon Quiche

200 gr smoked salmon
100 gr grated fresh kaseri cheese
1 cup finely chopped boiled spinach
1/2 cup finely chopped red bell pepper
1/2 cup grated onion
2 tablespoons flour
4 eggs
1 cup milk
3 drops of hot Tabasco sauce

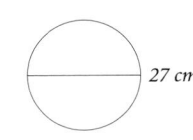

27 cm

1) Mix in a bowl the salmon cut into small pieces, the fresh kaseri cheese, boiled spinach, onion, red pepper and flour.
2) Arrange this mixture in a greased 27 cm tart pan.
3) Beat the eggs, milk and Tabasco sauce and pour over the fish mixture.
4) Bake at medium heat for 45 minutes.
5) After removing from oven let sit 10 minutes before serving.

Izgara Balıklar için Sos

Izgara yapılacak tüm balıkları
bu sosta 1 saat beklettikten sonra pişirebilirsiniz.

2 adet büyük soğan

1 çay fincanı sıvıyağ

5-6 adet defne yaprağı

10 adet tane karabiber

1 tatlı kaşığı tuz

1) Soğanı çentin ve rondo'da su gibi oluncaya dek çekin.
2) Sıvıyağ, tane karabiber, tuz ve defne yaprağı ile karıştırın.

Sauce for Grilled fish

Keep the fish in this sauce for 1 hour and then grill.
You can use this sauce for all grilled fish.

2 onions
1/2 cup sunflower oil
5-6 bay leaves
10 peppercorns
1 teaspoon salt

1) Grate or process the onions until liquid.
2) Mix with the oil, bay leaves, peppercorns and salt.

Sebze ve Tahıl Yemekleri

Vegetables and Grains

Sebze Sote

1/2 baş karnabahar
20 adet brüksellahanası
1 adet orta boy patates
1 adet havuç
2 adet kabak
1 adet yeşil biber

1/2 kırmızı biber
1/2 sarı biber
10 ufak parça brokoli
1 ufak kavanoz konserve mantar (150 gr)
1 çorba kaşığı tuzot
Sıvıyağ

1) Karnabaharların köklerini kesip iri parçalara ayırın.
2) Kabakları iri küp, havuçları diyagonal, patatesleri küp şeklinde doğrayın.
3) Mantarların suyunu süzüp kırmızı biberleri şeritler halinde kesin.
4) Sıvıyağla hafifçe ıslattığınız tavayı kızdırın ve sırasıyla sebzeleri sote edin.
5) Sebzelerin yağını çekmesi için kâğıt havlu üzerine çıkarın.
6) Bütün sebzeleri tuzotla karıştırıp sıcak servis yapın.
7) Sebze soteyi önceden hazırlayacaksanız, servis yapmadan önce 20 dakika fırında ısıtın.

Vegetable Sauté

1/2 head of cauliflower
20 Brussels sprouts
1 medium potato
1 carrot
2 zucchinis
1 green pepper

1/2 red pepper
1/2 yellow pepper
10 small pieces broccoli
1 small jar mushrooms (150 gr)
1 tablespoon seasoned salt
Vegetable oil

1) Stem the cauliflowers, break into florets and halve if very large.
2) Roughly dice the zucchinis, slice the carrot on the diagonal, and dice the potato.
3) Drain the mushrooms and cut the peppers into thin strips.
4) Dribble the vegetable oil lightly into the frying pan and sauté all the vegetables, one after the other.
5) Drain the vegetables on paper towels to remove excess oil.
6) Mix the whole vegetables with seasoned salt and pour into a serving bowl. Serve hot.
7) If you have prepared the vegetables ahead of time, reheat in an oven for 20 minutes before serving.

Sote Sultani Bezelye

1/2 kg sultani bezelye
2 çorba kaşığı margarin veya tereyağı
5 bardak su
1 kahve kaşığı karbonat
1 tatlı kaşığı tuz

1) Bezelyeleri yıkayın. İki ucunu ve yanlarını sıyırıp kesin.
2) Bir tencerede su, tuz ve karbonatı kaynatın.
3) Bezelyeleri bu suya atıp 15 dakika haşlayın.
4) Bezelyeleri süzüp bir tavada tereyağı veya margarinle sote edin.
5) Sıcak olarak servis yapın.

Snow Peas Sauté

1/2 kg fresh snow peas
2 tablespoons margarine or butter
5 cups water
1/2 teaspoon bicarbonate of soda
1 teaspoon salt

1) Wash the peas and snip off the ends and sides.
2) Bring the salted water, to which you have also added the bicarbonate of soda, to boil in a pot.
3) Add the peas to the boiling water and cook for 15 minutes.
4) After draining the peas, lightly sauté them in a frying pan in butter or margarine.
5) Serve hot.

Yumurtalı Taze Fasulye

1 kg ayşekadın fasulye

1 adet soğan

1 diş sarımsak

3 adet yumurta

1 kahve fincanı süt

1 adet domates

1 çay fincanı rendelenmiş taze kaşar

1 tatlı kaşığı tuzot

2 çorba kaşığı sıvıyağ

1) Fasulyeleri yıkayıp ufak ufak doğrayın.
2) Soğan ve sarımsağı rendeleyin.
3) Fasulye, soğan ve sarımsağı yağda devamlı çevirerek kavurun.
4) Rendelenmiş domatesi fasulyeye ekleyin.
5) Yumurtaları süt ve tuzot ile çırpın, rendelenmiş peyniri ilave edin.
6) Bu karışımı fasulyenin üstüne döküp karıştırın ve düzeltin.
7) Tavanın üstünü kapatıp 10 dakika pişirin.

Green Beans with Eggs

1 kg tender green beans

1 onion

1 clove garlic

3 eggs

1/3 cup milk

1 tomato

1/2 cup grated fresh kaseri cheese

1 teaspoon seasoned salt

2 tablespoons vegetable oil

1) Wash and sort the beans and chop into small pieces.
2) Grate the onion and garlic.
3) Sauté the beans, onion and garlic in the oil, stirring constantly.
4) Add the minced tomato to the beans.
5) Beat the eggs with the milk and seasoned salt. Add the grated cheese to this mixture.
6) Pour this mixture over the beans, stir it and arrange it nicely in a pan.
7) Cover and cook for 10 minutes.

Ispanak Yemeği

1 1/2 kg ıspanak (2 paket)

1 adet domates

1 adet soğan

1 tatlı kaşığı tuzot

2 çorba kaşığı zeytinyağı

1/2 kahve fincanı bulgur

1) Ispanakları yıkayıp ince ince doğrayın. Soğanları ay gibi, domatesleri ise küp şeklinde doğrayın.
2) Ispanak, domates, soğan, tuzot ve bulgura zeytinyağını ilave edip karıştırın.
3) Tencerenin kapağını kapatarak önce kısık, sonra orta ateşte, ıspanaklar suyunu salıp tekrar çekene dek; 1 saat kadar pişirin.
4) Son 15 dakika tencerenin kapağını açarak fazla suyun uçmasını sağlayın.

Spinach

1.5 kg of fresh spinach (2 packages)

1 tomato

1 onion

1 teaspoon seasoned salt

2 tablespoons olive oil

1/2 cup bulgur

1) Wash and chop the spinach and slice the onion into crescent shapes. Dice the tomato.
2) Mix the spinach, tomato, onion, seasoned salt, bulgur and olive oil and place all in a pan.
3) Cover the pan and cook (first over low heat and then over medium heat) until the spinach has released and then reabsorbed all its liquids; this will take approximately one hour.
4) Uncover during the last 15 minutes, allowing any extra liquids to cook away.

Semizotu Yemeği

1 kg semizotu
1 adet soğan
1 adet domates
1 tatlı kaşığı tuzot
2 çorba kaşığı zeytinyağı
1/2 kahve fincanı pirinç veya bulgur

1) Semizotlarının köklerini kesip yıkayın ve doğrayın.
2) Domatesleri küp, soğanları ise ay şeklinde doğrayın.
3) Bir tencereye semizotu, soğan, domates, zeytinyağı, tuzot, pirinç veya bulguru koyup karıştırın.
4) Hiç su eklemediğiniz tencerenin kapağı kapalı olarak 45 dakika, ağzı açık olarak da 15 dakika pişirin.

Purslane

1 kg purslane
1 onion
1 tomato
1 teaspoon seasoned salt
2 tablespoons olive oil
1/2 cup rice or bulgur

1) Cut off and discard the roots, wash well and chop.
2) Dice the tomato and chop the onion into crescent shapes.
3) In a pan place the purslane, onion, tomato, olive oil, seasoned salt, and washed rice or bulgur and mix.
4) Add no water. Cover and cook for 45 minutes, leaving pan uncovered for the last 15 minutes.

Mantar Graten

500 gr konserve mantar

1/2 litre süt

2 dolu çorba kaşığı un

100 gr rendelenmiş taze kaşar

1 çorba kaşığı margarin veya tereyağı

1 tatlı kaşığı kırmızı pul biber

1 tatlı kaşığı tuzot

1) Mantarların suyunu süzüp dilimleyin.
2) Sütü yağla birlikte kaynatın.
3) Blender'a un ve tuzot koyun. Kaynamış yağlı sütü unun üzerine boşaltıp çırpın.
4) Hazırladığınız beyaz sosa mantarları da ekleyerek karıştırın.
5) Karışımı fırına dayanıklı bir kaba boşaltın. Üstüne rendelenmiş kaşar ve pul biber serpip orta ısılı fırında, üstü kızarıncaya kadar 50 dakika pişirin.

Mushrooms au Gratin

500 gr mushrooms

1/2 liter (2 cups) milk

2 full tablespoons flour

100 gr grated fresh kaseri cheese

1 tablespoon margarine or butter

1 teaspoon red pepper flakes

1 teaspoon seasoned salt

1) Drain and slice the mushrooms.
2) Bring the milk and margarine or butter to a boil.
3) Put the flour and seasoned salt in a blender. Pour in the boiling milk and butter mixture and blend.
4) Add the mushrooms to this white sauce.
5) Pour the mixture into an ovenproof baking dish. Sprinkle the grated cheese and pepper flakes on the top and bake in moderately hot (220-230 °C) oven for about 50 minutes or until top is golden brown.

Nohut Yemeği

2 su bardağı nohut

3 adet domates

2 adet sivribiber

1 adet soğan

1 tatlı kaşığı tuzot

1 tatlı kaşığı acı biber salçası

1 bardak su

2 çorba kaşığı sıvıyağ

1) Nohutları 1 gece suda bekletin.
2) Soğanları ay, domatesleri küp şeklinde doğrayın. Sivribiberlerin tohumlarını çıkartıp ufak ufak kesin.
3) Nohut, soğan, domates, tuzot, sıvıyağ, acı biber salçası, sivribiber ve 1 bardak suyu düdüklü tencerede karıştırın.
4) Tencerenin düdüğü çıktıktan sonra, kısık ateşte 20 dakika pişirin.

Chickpeas

2 cups dried chickpeas

3 tomatoes

2 mildly hot, long green peppers

1 onion

1 teaspoon seasoned salt

1 teaspoon hot pepper sauce

1 cup water

2 tablespoons vegetable oil

1) Allow the chickpeas to soak overnight in a large quantity of water.
2) Chop the onion into crescent shapes, dice the tomatoes, remove the seeds from the peppers and chop finely.
3) Cook the chickpeas, onion, tomatoes, peppers, seasoned salt, vegetable oil, hot pepper sauce and 1 cup of water in a pressure cooker or in a heavy pot.
4) If you are using a pressure cooker, cook for 20 additional minutes after you have removed the lid.

Türlü

1/2 kg kuşbaşı tavuk, dana veya kuzu eti

1 adet soğan

2 adet kabak

1 adet havuç

1 adet patlıcan

1 adet iri patates

150 gr taze bamya

250 gr ayşekadın fasulye

2 adet domates

3 adet sivribiber

1 çorba kaşığı margarin

1 çorba kaşığı tuzot

1/2 bardak su

1 çorba kaşığı kekik

1) Orta boy, toprak bir güvecin içini margarinle sıvayın.
2) Patlıcanları alaca soyup yuvarlak dilimleyin. Tuzlu suda 15 dakika bekletin.
3) Domates, patates, kabak, soğan, sivribiber ve havuçları dilimleyin. Bamyaların başlarını külah gibi soyup, fasulyeleri ortadan ikiye bölün.
4) Yağlanmış güvece sırasıyla soğan, et, patates, havuç, fasulye, bamya, patlıcan, kabak, domates ve sivribiberleri dizin. En üste domates dilimlerini yerleştirin.
5) Suyu kekik ve tuzotla karıştırıp domateslerin üzerinde gezdirin. Güvecin kapağını kapatıp kısık ateşte 2 saat pişirin.

Vegetable Medley

1/2 kg cubed chicken, veal or lamb meat

1 onion

2 zucchinis

1 carrot

1 eggplant

1 large potato

150 gr fresh, small okras

250 gr tender green beans

2 tomatoes

3 mildly hot, long green peppers

1 tablespoon margarine

1 tablespoon seasoned salt

1/2 cup water

1 tablespoon thyme

1) Grease the inside of a medium, clay casserole with the margarine.
2) Partially peel the eggplants (leaving some strips of skin) and slice. Allow to sit in salty water for 15 minutes to release any bitter flavors.
3) Slice the tomatoes, potato, zucchinis, onion, long peppers and carrot. Cut the stem ends of the okra into cones; snap the beans into halves.
4) In the greased casserole place in layers the onion, meat, potato, carrot, beans, okra, eggplant, zucchini, tomatoes and long peppers. Arrange the tomato slices on top.
5) Mix the water, thyme and seasoned salt and pour over the vegetables. Cover and bake at low heat for 2 hours.

Patates Köftesi

1 kg patates

1 adet soğan

1 diş sarımsak

1 çorba kaşığı maydanoz

2 sap taze soğan

2 adet yumurta

1 çorba kaşığı un

1 çay kaşığı karabiber

Kızartma için sıvıyağ

1) Patates ve soğanı bir süzgece iri rendeleyip, 1 saat kadar suyunu akıtmasını bekleyin.

2) Derin bir kapta dövülmüş sarımsak, ince kıyılmış maydanoz, taze soğan, yumurta, un, tuz ve biberi patatesle karıştırın.

3) Karışımı kaşıkla dökerek kızgın yağda kızartın.

4) Kızaran köfteleri bir kâğıt havluya çıkartarak yağını çektirdikten sonra sıcak servis yapın.

Potato Rissoles

1 kg potatoes

1 onion

1 clove garlic

1 tablespoon parsley

2 green onions

2 eggs

1 tablespoon flour

1/4 teaspoon black pepper

Vegetable oil for frying

1) Roughly grate the potatoes and onion into a strainer over a bowl and allow to drain for 1 hour.

2) In a deep bowl mix the grated potatoes and onion with the mashed garlic, finely chopped parsley, green onions, eggs, flour, salt and pepper.

3) Drop the mixture in spoonfuls into hot oil and fry.

4) Drain the fried potato rissoles on sheets of paper towels before serving hot.

Patlıcan-Biber Kızartması

1 kg patlıcan
6 adet çarliston biber
4 adet büyük domates
5 diş sarımsak
1 tatlı kaşığı tuz
1 çorba kaşığı sirke
Kızartma için sıvıyağ

1) Patlıcanları enlemesine, ortadan ikiye kesin.
2) Her yarım patlıcanı ister yuvarlak, ister boyuna dilimleyip tuzlu suda bekletin.
3) Çarliston biberleri ortadan ikiye bölüp çekirdeklerini çıkarın.
4) Bol yağ içinde biber ve patlıcanları kızartın.
5) Tavadan aldığınız patlıcan ve biberlerin yağını kâğıt havluya çektirdikten sonra servis tabağına alın.
6) Rendelenmiş domates ve ezilmiş sarımsakları, tuz ile birlikte, domatesler suyunu çekene dek pişirin.
7) Pişen domates karışımına sirkeyi ilave edin. Domates karışımını patlıcan ve biberlerin üstüne döküp servis yapın.

Fried Eggplants & Peppers

1 kg eggplant
6 long, sweet green peppers
4 large tomatoes
5 cloves garlic
1 teaspoon salt
1 tablespoon vinegar
Vegetable oil for frying

1) Cut each eggplant in half through the middle.
2) Either cut the eggplant into round slices or slice the long way. Place in salted water to draw out any bitter flavors.
3) Halve the peppers and seed them.
4) Fry the peppers and eggplants in a large quantity of vegetable oil.
5) Drain the fried vegetables on paper towels, pat dry and then arrange on a serving plate.
6) Sauté the chopped tomatoes and mashed garlic with the salt until the liquids are all absorbed.
7) Add the vinegar to the cooked tomato mixture. Pour the mixture over the fried vegetables and serve.

Etli Ayşekadın Fasulye

1 kg ayşekadın fasulye

1/2 kg kuşbaşı dana eti veya 250 gr kıyma

2 adet olgun domates

1 adet soğan

2 bardak ılık su

1 tatlı kaşığı tuzot

1) Çentilmiş soğan, küp şeklinde doğranmış domates, et veya kıymayı suyunu bırakıp çekene dek pişirin.

2) Ortadan ikiye kesilmiş fasulyeleri, domates sosuyla birlikte tuzotu da ekleyip kısık ateşte ağzı kapalı olarak, 15 dakika pişirin.

3) Fasulyelerin üzerine suyu da ekleyip fasulyeler iyice yumuşayıncaya kadar pişirin.

Green Beans with Meat

1 kg tender green beans

1/2 cubed veal meat or 250 gr ground veal

2 ripe tomatoes

1 onion

2 cups warm water

1 teaspoon seasoned salt

1) Sauté the grated onion, diced tomatoes, and the cubed or ground veal until all liquids have been absorbed.

2) Snap the beans into halves and cook in a covered saucepan with the tomato sauce mixture and seasoned salt over low heat for 15 minutes.

3) Add the water and continue cooking until the beans are soft.

Sebzeli Kiş

Hamur için:

300 gr un

1 su bardağı erimiş
margarin-sıvıyağ karışımı

1 adet yumurta

1 çay kaşığı tuz

Harç için:

1 adet kabak

1 adet havuç

1/2 kırmızı etli biber

1/2 yeşil etli biber

125 gr konserve mantar

1/2 demet dereotu

1 tatlı kaşığı kekik

3 adet yumurta

1 su bardağı süt

100 gr rendelenmiş taze kaşar

1 çorba kaşığı zeytinyağı

27 cm

1) Un, yağ karışımı, yumurta ve tuzu yoğurun.
2) Yağlanmış tart kalıbına hazırlamış olduğunuz hamuru elinizle bastırarak döşeyin.
3) Kabak ve havucu rendeleyin. Mantar ve biberleri ince doğrayarak 1 kaşık yağda, sebzeler suyunu çekene dek çevirin.
4) Sebze karışımına kekik ve dereotunu da ekleyip tart hamurunun üstüne yerleştirin.
5) Yumurtaları sütle çırpıp tartın üstüne dökün.
6) 1 saat bekledikten sonra kişin üstüne rendelenmiş peyniri serpip orta ısılı fırında üstü kızarana dek; 1 saat kadar pişirin.

Vegetable Quiche

Dough:

300 gr flour

1 cup melted
margarine-vegetable oil mixture

1 egg

1/4 teaspoon salt

Filling:

1 zucchini

1 carrot

1/2 red bell pepper

1/2 green bell pepper

125 gr jar of mushrooms

1/2 bunch dill

1 teaspoon thyme

3 eggs

1 cup milk

100 gr grated fresh kaseri cheese

1 tablespoon olive oil

27 cm

1) Knead the flour, oil mixture, egg and salt together.
2) Place the dough into a greased tart pan and pat it down with the hands.
3) Grate the zucchini and carrot. Finely chop the mushrooms and peppers and, stirring constantly, sauté lightly in the oil until the vegetables have absorbed all the liquids.
4) Add the thyme and dill to the vegetable mixture and arrange over the dough in the pan.
5) Beat the eggs with the milk and pour over the vegetables.
6) Allow to sit for 1 hour, then sprinkle with the grated cheese and bake for approximately 1 hour in moderately hot (220-230 °C) oven, until top is golden brown.

Fırında Mücver

750 gr kabak
6-7 adet ince taze soğan
1/2 demet maydanoz
1 demet dereotu
3 adet yumurta
3 çorba kaşığı un
100 gr ufalanmış beyaz peynir
1 tatlı kaşığı tuzot

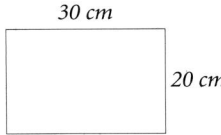

30 cm

20 cm

1) Fırın ısısına dayanıklı bir kabı yağlayıp buzluğa koyun.
2) Kabakları bir süzgece rendeleyip, 1 saat kadar suyunu akıtmasını bekleyin.
3) Derin bir kapta kabak, ince doğranmış taze soğan, dereotu, maydanoz, ufalanmış beyaz peynir, un, tuzot ve yumurtaları tahta bir kaşıkla iyice karıştırın.
4) Buzluktan çıkardığınız kaba bu karışımı döküp orta ısılı bir fırında, üstü kızarana dek; 1 saat kadar pişirin.

163

Baked Mücver (Zucchini Pancakes)

750 gr zucchini
6-7 thin green onions
1/2 bunch parsley
1 bunch dill
3 eggs
3 tablespoons flour
100 gr shredded white cheese (feta)
2 teaspoons seasoned salt

30 cm

20 cm

1) Grease an ovenproof baking dish and place in the freezer compartment of your refrigerator.
2) Grate the zucchini and place in a strainer over a bowl. Allow to drain for 1 hour.
3) In a deep bowl use a wooden spoon to mix the zucchini, finely diced green onions, dill, parsley, shredded white cheese, flour, seasoned salt and eggs.
4) Pour the mixture into the cold baking dish and bake in moderately hot oven for 1 hour, or until top is golden brown.

Mercimek Köftesi

1 su bardağı kırmızı mercimek
1 su bardağı ince, köftelik bulgur
1 adet soğan
1/2 çay bardağı zeytinyağı
2 çorba kaşığı domates salçası
1 tatlı kaşığı kimyon

1 tatlı kaşığı tuzot
1 tatlı kaşığı kırmızı pul biber
1/2 demet maydanoz
6 sap taze soğan
1 adet kıvırcık salata

1) Mercimekleri, üstüne çıkacak kadar suyla haşlayın. Haşlama sırasında oluşan köpükleri bir kevgir yardımıyla alın.
2) Ateşi kapatıp mercimekleri haşladığınız tencereye bulguru ekleyip tencerenin kapağını kapatın.
3) Bir tavada çentilmiş soğanları, renkleri sararıncaya kadar zeytinyağında çevirin.
4) Soğanlara domates salçasını da ekleyip bir müddet pişirin.
5) Ateşten aldığınız karışıma tuzot, kimyon ve kırmızı pul biberi ilave edip karıştırın.
6) Bu karışımı mercimek ve bulgura ekleyin.
7) Karışım soğumaya başlayınca ince kıyılmış maydanoz ve yeşil soğanı da ilave edip yoğurun ve uzun köfte şekli verin.
8) Mercimek köftelerini salata yaprakları üzerinde servis yapabilirsiniz.

Lentil Rissoles

1 cup red lentils
1 cup finely ground bulgur
1 onion
1/2 cup olive oil
2 tablespoons tomato paste
1 teaspoon cumin

1 teaspoon seasoned salt
1 teaspoon red pepper flakes
1/2 bunch parsley
6 green onions
1 bunch leaf lettuce

1) Boil the lentils in water that just covers them. Use a skimmer to remove any foam that appears during cooking.
2) Remove from heat, add the bulgur to the cooked lentils and cover the pan.
3) In a frying pan, sauté the finely grated onions until their color changes to a pale yellow.
4) Add the tomato paste to the onions and cook a while longer.
5) Remove from heat and add the seasoned salt, cumin and red pepper flakes.
6) Add the lentils and bulgur to this mixture.
7) As the mixture begins to cool add the finely chopped parsley and green onions, knead well and shape into long, oblong rolls.
8) Serve the rissoles on the lettuce leaves.

Bulgur Köftesi

Köfte için:

250 gr köftelik bulgur

1/2 kg yağsız kıyma

1 çorba kaşığı tuzot

1 tatlı kaşığı pul biber

3 çorba kaşığı tatlı biber salçası

2-3 çorba kaşığı un

Sos için:

3 diş sarımsak

3 çorba kaşığı sıvıyağ

2 adet domates

1 çorba kaşığı biber salçası

2 çorba kaşığı nar ekşisi

1) Bulgurun üstüne kaynar su döküp şişmesini bekleyin.
2) Şişen bulguru kıyma, biber salçası, tuzot ve pul biberle yoğurun.
3) Ceviz büyüklüğünde parçalardan yuvarlak köfteler yapıp ortalarına basarak bir çukur oluşturun.
4) Köfteleri unlanmış bir tepsiye koyun. Sallayarak una bulayın.
5) Unlanmış köfteleri kaynayan suda haşlayın. Kepçeyle alıp derin bir tabağa yerleştirin.
6) Sos için sıvıyağda rende domates, dövülmüş sarımsak ve biber salçasını pişirin.
7) Ateşten indirdiğiniz sosa nar ekşisi ilave edip köftelerin üstüne sıcak olarak dökün.
8) Dilerseniz yoğurtla servis yapabilirsiniz.

Bulgur Rissoles

Rissoles:

250 gr finely ground bulgur

1/2 kg lean ground meat

1 tablespoon seasoned salt

1 teaspoon red pepper flakes

3 tablespoons paprika paste

2-3 tablespoons flour

Sauce:

3 cloves garlic

3 tablespoons vegetable oil

2 tomatoes

1 tablespoon paprika paste

2 tablespoons unsweetened pomegranate syrup

1) Pour boiling water over the bulgur and allow to soften and swell.
2) Knead the softened bulgur with the ground meat, paprika paste, seasoned salt and pepper flakes.
3) Roll into rissoles the size of large walnuts and use your finger to make a small hole in the middle.
4) Arrange the rissoles on a floured baking sheet. Shake the rissoles on the sheet so they are floured.
5) Boil the floured rissoles in boiling water. Remove from the water with a strainer and place in a deep bowl.
6) For the sauce, sauté the chopped tomatoes, mashed garlic and paprika paste in vegetable oil.
7) Remove from heat, stir in the pomegranate syrup and pour the hot mixture over the rissoles.
8) The rissoles in sauce may also be served with yogurt.

Acılı Taze Patates

1/2 kg ufak, taze patates

3-4 sap taze soğan

1-2 adet acı kırmızı biber

3 diş sarımsak

2 çorba kaşığı soya sosu

1 çorba kaşığı tuz

2 çorba kaşığı sıvıyağ

Süs için 1 çorba kaşığı kavrulmuş susam

1) Taze patatesleri ovarak iyice yıkayın ve kabuklarını soymadan irice doğrayıp dirice kalacak şekilde tuzlu suda haşlayın.
2) Taze soğanları doğrayın.
3) Wok tarzı tavada sıvıyağı kızdırıp kurulanmış patatesleri 2-3 dakika kızartın.
4) Patateslere kıyılmış taze soğan, sarımsak ve kırmızı biberi de ilave edip 1-2 dakika daha pişirin.
5) Soya sosunu ekleyip 1 dakika daha pişirin.
6) Patateslerin üzerini kavrulmuş susam ile süsleyip sıcak servis yapın.

Spicy New Potatoes

1/2 kg small, new potatoes

3-4 green onions

1-2 hot red peppers

3 cloves garlic

2 tablespoons soy sauce

1 tablespoon salt

2 tablespoons vegetable oil

1 tablespoon roasted sesame seeds for garnish

1) Scrub and thoroughly wash the new potatoes. Dice them in rather large pieces (without peeling) and boil them in salted water.
2) Finely chop the green onions.
3) Heat the vegetable oil in a wok or similar pan and fry the dry potatoes for 2-3 minutes.
4) Add the chopped onions, garlic and red peppers to the potatoes and continue cooking for 1-2 minutes more.
5) Add the soy sauce to the potatoes and cook for 1 more minute.
6) Garnish the potatoes with roasted sesame seeds and serve warm.

Kuru fasulye

2 su bardağı kuru fasulye

3 adet domates

1 adet soğan

1 çorba kaşığı tuzot

1 tatlı kaşığı acı biber salçası

2 çorba kaşığı sıvıyağ

1 su bardağı su

1) Fasulyeleri 1 gece önceden soğuk suda ıslatın.
2) Suyunu süzdüğünüz fasulyeleri bol suda hafifçe haşlayın. Üstünde oluşan köpükleri alın ve süzün.
3) Düdüklü tencereye çentilmiş soğan, domates, tuzot, biber salçası, sıvıyağ, fasulye ve suyu koyup karıştırın.
4) Ateşe koyduğunuz tencerenin düdüğü çıktıktan sonra, 15 dakika daha pişirin.

White Beans

2 cups white (navy) beans

3 tomatoes

1 onion

1 tablespoon seasoned salt

1 teaspoon hot pepper paste

2 tablespoons vegetable oil

1 cup water

1) Soak the beans in cold water overnight.
2) Drain the beans and then cook them in a large quantity of water until partially cooked. Use a spoon to remove and discard any foam that appears during the cooking process.
3) To a pressure cooker or heavy pot add the grated onion, tomatoes, seasoned salt, pepper paste, vegetable oil, beans and water.
4) If cooking in a pressure cooker, continue to cook for 15 minutes after you have removed the lid.

Bakla ve Mantar Sote

6 çorba kaşığı tavuk suyu

1 çay kaşığı mısır nişastası

2 çorba kaşığı sıvıyağ

3 sap taze soğan

2 diş sarımsak

125 gr konserve mantar

250 gr taze iç bakla

Tuz ve karabiber

1) Tavuk suyu ve mısır nişastasını karıştırıp bekletin.
2) Wok tarzı tavada yağı kızdırın. Taze soğan, sarımsak ve kıyılmış mantarları 2 dakika yağda çevirin.
3) Tavuk suyu, bakla, tuz ve karabiberi ilave edip 3 dakika daha pişirin.
4) Sıcak olarak hemen servis yapın.

Fava Beans and Mushroom Sauté

6 tablespoons chicken broth

1/4 teaspoon cornstarch

2 tablespoons vegetable oil

3 green onions

2 cloves garlic

125 gr canned mushrooms

250 gr fresh fava beans

Salt and black pepper

1) Mix the chicken broth and cornstarch and allow to sit.
2) Heat the oil in a wok or similar pan. Sauté the green onions, garlic and chopped mushrooms for 2 minutes in the oil.
3) Add the chicken broth, fava beans, salt and black pepper to the mushroom mixture and cook for an additional 3 minutes.
4) Serve hot.

Kıymalı Taze Patates

1 kg taze patates

250 gr kıyma

2 adet domates

1 adet soğan

3 adet sivribiber

2 su bardağı su

1 çorba kaşığı tuzot

2 çorba kaşığı sıvıyağ

1) Kıyma, küp şeklinde doğranmış domates, çentilmiş soğan ve ince kıyılmış biberleri suyunu salıp tekrar çekinceye dek pişirin.
2) Patatesleri 4'e bölüp kızgın sıvıyağda kavurun.
3) Patateslere kıyma, su ve tuzotu da ilave edip karıştırın.
4) Orta ateşte patatesler yumuşayıncaya dek pişirin.

One-Dish Ground Meat and New Potatoes

1 kg new potatoes

250 gr ground meat

2 tomatoes

1 onion

3 mildly hot, long green peppers

2 cups water

1 tablespoon seasoned salt

2 tablespoons vegetable oil

1) Sauté the ground meat, diced tomatoes, grated onion and finely chopped peppers until all their liquids are reabsorbed.
2) Quarter the potatoes and sauté in the hot vegetable oil.
3) Add to the sautéed potatoes the ground meat, water and seasoned salt and mix.
4) Cook over medium heat until the potatoes are soft.

Patlıcan Musakka

1 kg patlıcan
1 adet soğan
500 gr kıyma
2 adet domates
2 adet sivribiber
1 çay bardağı su
1 tatlı kaşığı tuz

1) Kıymayı, küp şeklinde doğranmış domates, çentilmiş soğan ve ince kıyılmış biberle birlikte suyunu salıp çekinceye dek pişirin.
2) Patlıcanları alaca soyup kalınca dilimleyip yarım saat kadar tuzlu suda bekletin. Suyunu süzüp sıkın.
3) Tencereye bir sıra patlıcan, bir sıra kıyma koyarak patlıcan sırasıyla bitirin.
4) Patlıcanlar pişinceye dek; 45 dakika pişirin.

Eggplant Moussaka

1 kg eggplant
1 onion
500 gr ground meat
2 tomatoes
2 mildly hot, long green peppers
1/2 cup water
1 teaspoon salt

1) Sauté together the ground meat, diced tomatoes, grated onion and finely chopped peppers until all liquids are absorbed.
2) Partially peel the eggplants (leaving strips of skin), slice and allow to soak for half an hour in salted water to draw out any bitter flavors.
3) In a pan layer the rinsed eggplant and the ground meat mixture, finishing with an eggplant layer on the top.
4) Cook for approximately 45 minutes, until the eggplants are cooked.

Mücver Kızartma

1 kg kabak
1 demet ince taze soğan
1/2 demet maydanoz
1 demet dereotu
3 adet yumurta
3 çorba kaşığı un
2 tatlı kaşığı tuzot
Kızartma için sıvıyağ

1) Kabakları bir süzgece rendeleyip 1 saat kadar suyunu salmasını bekleyin.
2) Derin bir kapta kabak, ince doğranmış taze soğan, dereotu, maydanoz, un, tuzot ve yumurtaları tahta bir kaşıkla iyice karıştırın.
3) Kızgın yağa, hazırladığınız harçtan bir kaşık döküp hafifçe bastırın.
4) İki tarafı da kızardıktan sonra kâğıt havluya çıkartıp yağını çektirin.
5) Sıcak olarak servis yapın.

Fried Mücver (Zucchini Pancakes)

1 kg zucchini
1 bunch thin green onions
1/2 bunch parsley
1 bunch dill
3 eggs
3 tablespoons flour
2 teaspoons seasoned salt
Vegetable oil for frying

1) Grate the zucchini into a strainer and allow to drain into a bowl for 1 hour.
2) In a deep bowl use a wooden spoon to mix the zucchini, finely diced green onions, dill, parsley, flour, seasoned salt and eggs.
3) Drop ample spoonfuls into a frying pan of hot oil and press them down lightly.
4) Fry on both sides and then allow any excess oil to drain off on layers of paper towels.
5) Serve hot.

Havuç Kızartması

1 kg iri havuç

5 kahve fincanı un

5 kahve fincanı su

1 tatlı kaşığı tuz

250 gr yoğurt

5 diş sarımsak

Kızartma için sıvıyağ

1) Havuçları kazıyarak soyun ve bol suda, az yumuşayıncaya dek haşlayın. Haşlanmış havuçları keskin bir bıçakla uzunlamasına dilimleyin.
2) Un, su ve tuzu karıştırarak koyuca bir bulamaç yapın.
3) Bulamaca batırdığınız havuç dilimlerini derin bir tavada kızartın. Kızaran havuçları yağını bırakması için kâğıt havluya çıkarın.
4) Sarımsakları ezip yoğurtla karıştırın.
5) Kızarmış havuçları sarımsaklı yoğurt ile servis yapın.

Fried Carrots

1 kg large carrots

1 2/3 cups of flour

1 2/3 cups water

1 teaspoon salt

250 gr yogurt

5 cloves garlic

Vegetable oil for frying

1) Peel the carrots and boil in a large quantity of water until almost soft. Slice the boiled carrots the long way.
2) Mix the flour, water and salt into a thick mixture.
3) Dip the carrots into the flour mixture and fry in a deep frying pan. Drain the fried slices on paper towels to remove any excess oil.
4) Mash the garlic and mix into the yogurt.
5) Serve the fried carrots with the garlic yogurt.

Fırında Patates

1 kg patates

2 su bardağı süt

1 diş sarımsak

2 çorba kaşığı sıvıyağ

2 çorba kaşığı un

1 tatlı kaşığı tuzot

1 tatlı kaşığı tuz

1 çay kaşığı karabiber

100 gr rendelenmiş taze kaşar

1) Süt, sarımsak ve yağı birlikte kaynatın.
2) Süt karışımına, ayıklanıp yuvarlak dilimlenmiş patatesleri, tuzot ve karabiberi de ekleyip 15 dakika pişirin.
3) Patatesleri ayırıp, yağlanmış yuvarlak bir kalıba muntazam döşeyin.
4) Blender'da un, tuz ve kaynamış süt karışımını çırpın.
5) Hazırladığınız beyaz sosu patateslerin üzerine döküp üstünü rendelenmiş kaşar peyniri ile sıvayın.
6) Önceden ısıtılmış orta ısıdaki fırında, üstü kızarana dek; 15 dakika kadar pişirin.

Baked Potatoes

1 kg potato

2 cups milk

1 clove garlic

2 tablespoons vegetable oil

2 tablespoons flour

1 teaspoon seasoned salt

1 teaspoon salt

1/4 teaspoon black pepper

100 gr grated fresh kaseri cheese

1) Boil the milk, garlic and oil together.
2) Add the potatoes (peeled and sliced into rounds), the seasoned salt and the black pepper to the milk mixture and cook for 15 minutes.
3) Remove the potatoes and arrange neatly in a greased, round baking dish.
4) Blend the flour, salt and boiled milk mixture in a blender.
5) Pour this white sauce over the potatoes and top with grated kaseri cheese.
6) Bake in preheated oven at medium heat for 15 minutes or until golden.

Sebzeli Çin Makarnası

250 gr Çin makarnası

3 çorba kaşığı sıvıyağ

4 sap taze soğan

1 diş sarımsak

1 adet havuç

1 adet salatalık

125 gr yeşil fasulye

125 gr konserve mantar

1/4 sarı, 1/4 kırmızı, 1/4 yeşil ve 1/4 turuncu etli biber

1 su bardağı tavuk suyu

2 çorba kaşığı soya sosu

1 çorba kaşığı mısır nişastası

Tuz ve karabiber

1) Çin makarnasını (egg noodle) paketin üzerindeki dakika bilgisine göre suda haşlayın.
2) Wok tarzı tavada 2 çorba kaşığı sıvıyağı kızdırın. İçine ince kıyılmış soğan, havuç, salatalık, yeşil fasulye ve dövülmüş sarımsağı koyup 2 dakika çevirerek pişirin.
3) Sebze karışımına dilimlenmiş mantarları ilave edip 1 dakika daha çevirin.
4) Tavuk suyuna mısır nişastası, soya sosu, tuz ve biberi ilave edip karıştırın.
5) Hazırladığınız sosu sebzelere ilave ederek koyulaşıncaya dek pişirin.
6) Süzülmüş makarnaları sebzelere katıp karıştırın.
7) Sıcak olarak servis yapın.

Vegetables & Noodles

250 gr egg noodles

3 tablespoons vegetable oil

4 green onions

1 clove garlic

1 carrot

1 cucumber

125 gr green beans

125 gr canned mushrooms

1/4 each of a yellow, a red, a green and an orange bell pepper

1 cup chicken broth

2 tablespoons soy sauce

1 tablespoon cornstarch

Salt and black pepper

1) Boil the egg noodles according to the directions on the package.
2) Place 2 tablespoons vegetable oil in a wok or similar pan and heat thoroughly. Add the finely chopped onions, carrot, cucumber, green beans and mashed garlic and sauté all for 2 minutes.
3) Add the sliced mushrooms to the vegetable mixture and sauté for 1 minute more.
4) Mix the chicken broth with the cornstarch, soy sauce, salt and pepper.
5) Add the prepared sauce to the vegetables and cook until the mixture thickens.
6) Drain the noodles and stir into the vegetables.
7) Serve hot.

Karnıyarık

6 adet ufak boy patlıcan

250 gr kıyma

1 adet soğan

3 adet domates

6 adet yeşil biber

2 tatlı kaşığı tuzot

1 çay fincanı su

Kızartma için sıvıyağ

1) Patlıcanları boylamasına ortadan yarın ve tuzlu suda bekletin.
2) Kıyma, küp şeklinde doğranmış domates, ince kıyılmış yeşil biber ve çentilmiş soğana 1 tatlı kaşığı tuzot ekleyerek suyunu çekinceye dek pişirin.
3) Bol sıvıyağda, patlıcanların iki tarafını da kızartın ve yağını çekmesi için kâğıt havluya alın.
4) Patlıcanların içini kıyma ile doldurun ve fırına dayanıklı bir kaba dizin.
5) Her bir patlıcanın üstüne bir dilim domates ve yarım yeşil biber yerleştirin.
6) Suyu 1 tatlı kaşığı tuzot ile karıştırıp patlıcanların üzerine dökün.
7) Karnıyarıkları orta ısılı fırında, üstündeki domatesler yumuşayıncaya kadar; 30 dakika pişirin.

Karnıyarık (Stuffed Eggplant)

6 small eggplants

250 gr ground meat

1 onion

3 tomatoes

6 green peppers

2 teaspoons seasoned salt

1/2 cup water

Vegetable oil for frying

1) Halve the eggplants the long way and allow to soak in salted water to draw out any bitter flavors.
2) Cook together the ground meat, diced tomatoes, finely chopped green peppers, grated onion and 1 teaspoon seasoned salt until all liquids are absorbed.
3) Fry the eggplants on both sides in a large quantity of vegetable oil and allow to drain on paper towels.
4) Cut a slash in the middle of the eggplants and stuff the ground meat mixture into this slash. Arrange the stuffed eggplants in an ovenproof baking dish.
5) Place slices of tomatoes and half of a green pepper on the top of each eggplant.
6) Mix the water with 1 teaspoon seasoned salt and pour over the eggplants.
7) Bake the stuffed eggplants at medium heat for 30 minutes, or until tops are roasted and tomatoes are soft.

Mısır, Mantar ve Pırasa Üçlemesi

3 adet pırasa

2 diş sarımsak

200 gr bebek mısır

150 gr konserve mantar

2 çorba kaşığı soya sosu

1 tatlı kaşığı mısır nişastası

1 çay fincanı su

1 çay kaşığı karabiber

2 çorba kaşığı sıvıyağ

1) Wok tarzı tavada diyagonal kesilmiş pırasa ve çentilmiş sarımsakları kızgın yağda 2 dakika çevirin.
2) Mantar ve bebek mısırları irice doğrayın. Pırasalara ilave edip 2 dakika daha pişirin.
3) Su, soya sosu ve mısır nişastasını karıştırıp sebzelerin üstüne dökün.
4) Kıvamı koyulaşınca sebzelere karabiberi de ekleyip sıcak olarak servis yapın.

Corn, Mushroom and Leek Medley

3 leeks

2 cloves garlic

200 gr baby corn (canned)

150 gr canned mushrooms

2 tablespoons soy sauce

1 teaspoon cornstarch

1/2 cup water

1/4 teaspoon black pepper

2 tablespoons vegetable oil

1) Heat the oil until hot in a wok or similar pan and sauté the leeks (cut on the diagonal) and the mashed garlic for 2 minutes.
2) Roughly chop the mushrooms and baby corn. Add them to the leeks and sauté for 2 minutes.
3) Mix the water, soy sauce and cornstarch and pour over the vegetables.
4) When the mixture thickens, add black pepper to the vegetables and serve hot.

Hamur İşleri

Dough-based Specialties

Börek Harçları

Ispanaklı veya Pazılı Harç

1 kg ıspanak veya pazı

1 adet soğan

1 tatlı kaşığı tuzot

1 çay kaşığı karabiber

1) Soğanları ay şeklinde doğrayın.
2) Ispanak ya da pazıyı iyice yıkayıp suyunu süzdükten sonra ince ince doğrayın.
3) Ispanak ya da pazıyı, soğanlarla birlikte tuzot ve karabiberi de ekleyerek kavurun.
4) Suyunu iyice çektikten sonra soğumaya bırakın.

Kıymalı Harç

1/2 kg kıyma

1 adet soğan

1 adet domates

2 adet sivribiber

1 tatlı kaşığı tuzot

1) Soğanları ay şeklinde doğrayın.
2) Kıymayı, soğanı, küp şeklinde doğranmış domatesleri ve ince kıyılmış biberleri tuzot ile kavurun.
3) Suyunu iyice çektikten sonra soğumaya bırakın.

Peynirli Harç

250 gr beyaz peynir

1/2 demet maydanoz

1) Çatalla ezdiğiniz beyaz peyniri ince kıyılmış maydanoz ile karıştırın.

Peynirli-Patatesli Harç

150 gr beyaz peynir

3 adet orta boy patates

1 tatlı kaşığı kırmızı pul biber

1) Patatesleri haşlayıp çatalla ezin.
2) Ezilmiş peynir, patates ve pul biberi karıştırın.

Börek fillings

Spinach or Chard filling

1 kg spinach or chard

1 onion

1 teaspoon seasoned salt

1/4 teaspoon black pepper

1) Chop the onions into crescent shapes.
2) Wash the spinach or chard well, drain and then finely chop.
3) Sauté the spinach or chard with the onions, seasoned salt and black pepper.
4 After the mixture has absorbed all the liquids, remove from heat and allow to cool.

Ground Meat filling

1/2 kg ground meat

1 onion

1 tomato

2 mildly hot, long green peppers

1 teaspoon seasoned salt

1) Chop the onions into crescent shapes.
2) Sauté the ground meat with the onions, diced tomatoes, finely chopped peppers and seasoned salt.
3 After the mixture has absorbed all the liquids, remove from heat and allow to cool.

Cheese filling

250 gr white cheese (feta cheese)

1/2 bunch parsley

1) Mash the cheese with a fork and mix it with the parsley.

Cheese-Potato filling

150 gr white cheese (feta cheese)

150 gr potatoes

1 teaspoon red pepper flakes

1) Boil the potatoes and mash with a fork.
2) Mix the mashed cheese, potato and pepper flakes.

Kıymalı-Peynirli Tepsi Böreği

5 adet yufka
1/2 su bardağı sıvıyağ
1 su bardağı süt
1 adet yumurta
1/2 kg kıyma
1 adet ufak soğan
1 adet domates

1 adet sivribiber
1/2 kg beyaz peynir
1/2 demet maydanoz
1 tatlı kaşığı tuzot
1 çay kaşığı karabiber
Süs için çörekotu

95 cm

45 cm

1) Bir tavada, küp şeklinde doğranmış domates, ince kıyılmış sivribiber ve soğanları, tuzot ve karabiberi de ekleyerek kıyma ile birlikte kavurun.
2) Bir çatal yardımıyla ezdiğiniz beyaz peyniri ince kıyılmış maydanozla birlikte karıştırın.
3) Süt ve sıvıyağı ayrı bir kapta çırpın.
4) Fırın tepsisini yağlayın. Birinci yufkayı yayıp üstünde yağ-süt karışımını gezdirin. Yufkanın kenarlarını kapatın.
5) İkinci yufkayı da koyup yağ-süt karışımı ile ıslatın.
6) Kıyma ve peynir harçlarını ikiye bölün. Tepsinin yarısına kıymalı, diğer yarısına da peynirli harcı döşeyin.
7) Aralarını yağ-süt karışımı ile ıslatarak iki yufka daha döşeyin. Harcın diğer yarısını da bu katın üstüne yayın. Kalan son yufkayı en üste koyup kenarlarını kapatın.
8) Son olarak kalan yağ-süt karışımını yumurta ile çırpıp böreğin üstüne döküp çörekotu ile süsleyin.
9) Orta ısılı fırında üstü kızarana dek; 1 saat kadar pişirin.

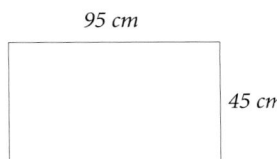

Meat-Cheese Tray Börek

5 yufka (phyllo dough sheets)
1/2 cup vegetable oil
1 cup milk
1 egg
1/2 kg ground meat
1 small onion
1 tomato

1 mildly hot, long green pepper
1/2 kg white cheese (feta cheese)
1/2 bunch parsley
1 teaspoon seasoned salt
1/4 teaspoon black pepper
Black cumin for garnish

(Note: a baking sheet measuring approximately 95 x 45 cm (37"x 18")
is recommended, or use a baking sheet that is approximately
the same size as the dough you will be using.)

1) Sauté the ground meat with the diced tomato, finely chopped green pepper and onion, seasoned salt and black pepper in a frying pan.
2) Mix the white cheese (mashed with a fork) and the finely chopped parsley.
3) Beat the milk and vegetable oil in a separate bowl.
4) Grease the baking sheet. Arrange the first sheet of dough on the baking sheet and brush with some of the milk/oil mixture. Turn up any corners of dough hanging over the side of the pan.
5) Add the second sheet of dough over the first, and brush on additional milk and oil mixture.
6) Divide the ground meat and cheese mixtures into two equal portions. Put half of the ground meat mixture on half of the sheet and half of the cheese mixture on the other half.
7) Add two more sheets of dough, brushing each with the milk/oil mixture. Add the remaining ground meat and cheese fillings in the same manner as above. Cover with the last sheet of dough and press the edges together.
8) Beat the egg into the remaining milk/oil mixture and brush on the top. Garnish with black cumin seeds.
9) Bake in moderately hot (220-230 °C) oven until the top is golden, approximately 1 hour.

Patates Böreği

5-6 adet küp şeklinde doğranmış çiğ patates

1 su bardağı yoğurt

1/2 su bardağı sıvıyağ

3 çorba kaşığı un

1 paket kabartma tozu

1 çay kaşığı tuz

1 1/2 çay kaşığı kırmızıbiber

1 çay kaşığı karabiber

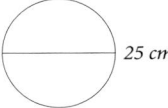

25 cm

1) Tüm malzemeyi karıştırın ve yağlanmış yuvarlak bir tepsiye dökün.
2) Orta dereceli fırında patatesler yumuşayıncaya dek pişirin.
3) Sıcak olarak servis yapın.

Potato Börek

5-6 diced potatoes

1 cup yogurt

1/2 cup vegetable oil

3 tablespoons flour

1 package baking powder

1/4 teaspoon salt

3/8 teaspoon red pepper

1/4 teaspoon black pepper

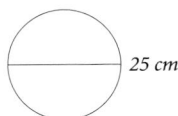

25 cm

189

1) Mix all the ingredients and pour into a greased, round baking pan.
2) Cook in moderately hot (220-230 °C) oven until potatoes are soft.
3) Serve hot.

Telkadayıflı Börek

300 gr telkadayıf
4 adet yumurta
3 su bardağı süt
100 gr erimiş tereyağı
Taze kaşar-dil peyniri karışımı

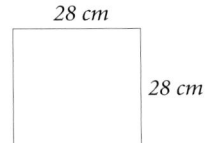

28 cm

28 cm

1) Erimiş tereyağını telkadayıfa yedirin.
2) Telkadayıfın yarısını, yağlanmış, orta boy, dört köşe bir fırın kabına döşeyin.
3) Üstüne rendelenmiş peynir karışımını döşeyin.
4) Kalan telkadayıf ile böreğin üstünü kapatın.
5) Süt ve yumurtayı çırpıp böreğin üstüne dökün.
6) 1 gece buzdolabında bekletin.
7) Orta dereceli fırında üstü kızarana dek pişirin.

Shredded Wheat Börek

300 gr telkadayıf (shredded wheat)
4 eggs
3 cups milk
100 gr melted butter
Fresh kaseri-string cheese mixture

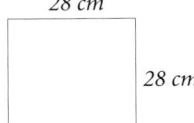

28 cm

28 cm

1) Pour the melted butter over the shredded wheat.
2) Pour half of the shredded wheat mixture into a medium-size, greased, square baking pan.
3) Sprinkle the grated cheese mixture over the shredded wheat.
4) Cover with the remaining shredded wheat.
5) Beat the milk and eggs together and pour over the mixture.
6) Allow to rest overnight in the refrigerator.
7) Bake in moderately hot (220-230 °C) oven until the top is golden brown.

Zeytinli Börek

125 gr erimiş margarin

2 adet yumurta

250 gr un

1/2 su bardağı yoğurt

100 gr çekirdekleri çıkartılmış siyah zeytin

3 adet taze soğan

2-3 sap maydanoz

2-3 sap nane

1 çay kaşığı tuz

1/2 paket kabartma tozu

1) Un, bir yumurta, yağ, yoğurt, tuz ve kabartma tozunu yoğurarak yumuşak bir hamur yapın.
2) İnce kıyılmış taze soğan, zeytin, nane ve maydanozu karıştırın.
3) Hamurdan ceviz büyüklüğünde parçalar alarak elinizle açın.
4) Elinizde açtığınız hamur parçalarına 1 tatlı kaşığı kadar zeytinli harçtan koyup kapatın.
5) Zeytinli hamur bohçalarını tepsiye dizin ve üstüne çırpılmış bir yumurta sürüp fırına verin.
6) Üstü kızarana dek, 50 dakika pişirin.

Olive Börek

125 gr melted margarine

2 eggs

250 gr flour

1/2 cup yogurt

100 gr seeded black olives

3 green onions

2-3 sprigs parsley

2-3 sprigs mint

1/4 teaspoon salt

1/2 package baking powder

1) Mix the flour, one egg, margarine, yogurt, salt and baking powder into a soft dough.
2) Mix the finely chopped green onions, olives, mint and parsley.
3) Take walnut size rounds of dough and pat them out into rounds with your hands.
4) Add 1 teaspoon of olive filling to the rounds and close into halves.
5) Arrange the olive-filled pastries on a tray and brush with a beaten egg.
6) Bake for approximately 50 minutes, or until golden.

Ispanaklı Börek

3 adet yufka

1 paket ıspanak

1 adet soğan

1 tatlı kaşığı tuz

1 çay kaşığı karabiber

1/2 lt süt

3 adet yumurta

100 gr taze kaşar

Sıvıyağ

1) Ispanakları yıkayıp ince ince doğrayın. Ay şeklinde doğranmış soğanı tuz ve karabiber ile birlikte suyunu iyice çekene dek pişirin.
2) 3 yufkayı, aralarına sıvıyağ sürerek birbirine yapıştırın.
3) Üstte kalan yufkayı da yağladıktan sonra ıspanaklı harcı üstüne döşeyin.
4) Yufkaları, üstündeki ıspanak harcı ile birlikte, bir uçtan başlayarak sıkı bir rulo haline getirin.
5) Hazırladığınız ruloyu iki parmak kalınlığında dilimlere ayırın.
6) Dilimleri fırın ısısına dayanıklı bir kaba yerleştirip üstüne yumurta-süt karışımını dökün.
7) Buzdolabında bir gece bekletin.
8) Buzdolabında beklettiğiniz dilimlerin üzerine taze kaşarı rendeleyip orta ısılı fırında, üstü kızarana dek pişirin.

Spinach Börek

3 yufka (sheets of phyllo dough)

1 package spinach

1 onion

1 teaspoon salt

1/4 teaspoon black pepper

1/2 liter (2 cups) milk

3 eggs

100 gr fresh kaseri cheese

Vegetable oil

1) Finely chop the spinach and wash well. Sauté with the onion sliced into crescent shapes, the salt and the black pepper until all the liquids have been absorbed.
2) Layer 3 sheets of dough, brushing with the vegetable oil between each layer.
3) Layer the spinach evenly over the top of the third greased sheet of dough.
4) Starting at one end, roll up the yufka and spinach into a tight roll.
5) Slice the roll into slices as thick as two fingers.
6) Arrange the slices in an ovenproof baking dish. Beat the milk and eggs together and pour over all.
7) Allow to sit in the refrigerator overnight.
8) Top the slices with fresh grated kaseri cheese and bake in moderately hot (220-230 °C) oven until the top is golden brown.

Muskaböreği

3 adet yufka
1 çay bardağı sıvıyağ
1 adet yumurtanın sarısı
Börek harçlarından herhangi biri
Süs için çörekotu

1) Yufkaları 3 parmak genişliğinde şeritler halinde kesip her bir şeride sıvıyağ sürün.
2) Şeritlerin ucuna börek harcından koyup muska şeklinde sarın. Uçlarını suyla yapıştırıp kapatın.
3) Börekleri tepsiye dizip üzerlerine yumurta sarısı sürün ve çörekotu ile süsleyin.
4) Börekleri bir gece buzlukta bekletin.
5) Buzluktan çıkardığınız börekleri orta ısıdaki fırında, üstü kızarıncaya dek; 1 saat kadar pişirin.

Muska (amulet) Börek

3 yufka (sheets of phyllo dough)
1/2 cup vegetable oil
1 egg yolk
Black cumin for garnish
Any of the above börek fillings

1) Cut the phyllo dough into strips as wide as three fingers and brush each strip with vegetable oil.
2) Add a small quantity of filling on the edge of each strip and then roll up in the shape of an amulet. Close the edges of the strip with a small bit of water.
3) Arrange the boreks on a baking sheet, brush with beaten egg yolk and garnish with black cumin.
4) Allow the boreks to sit overnight in the refrigerator.
5) Bake the boreks in moderately hot (220-230 °C) oven until golden brown, for approximately 1 hour.

Kolböreği

3 adet yufka
1 kahve fincanı sıvıyağ
Börek harçlarından herhangi biri
1 adet yumurta

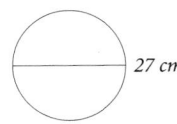

27 cm

1) Her bir yufkayı ikiye katlayın ve üstüne bir fırça yardımıyla sıvıyağ sürün.
2) Yufkanın geniş kısmına harçtan bir miktar koyun ve rolu halinde sarın.
3) Yuvarlak bir tepsiye, ortadan başlayarak çevire çevire döşeyin.
4) Bir yufkanın bittiği yerden diğer yufkayı başlatarak 3 yufkayı da döşeyin.
5) Yumurtayı çırpıp üstüne sürün.
6) Orta ısılı fırında 1 saat pişirin.

197

Kol (arm) Börek

3 yufka (sheets of phyllo dough)
1/3 cup vegetable oil
Any of the above börek fillings
1 egg

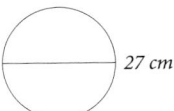

27 cm

1) Fold each piece of dough into two and brush with the vegetable oil.
2) Put the filling across the wide end of the dough and roll up into a tight roll.
3) Roll the dough, snail-like, round and round in a round baking sheet.
4) Continue to create the spiral with the other rolls of dough.
5) Beat the egg and brush over the top of the börek.
6) Bake for 1 hour in moderately hot (190-200 °C) oven.

Krep (10 adet)

3 adet yumurta
1 1/2 su bardağı süt
1 çay kaşığı tuz
3 çorba kaşığı un

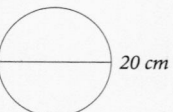 20 cm

1)   Un, tuz ve yumurtayı iyice çırpın. Üstüne sütü ilave edip yarım saat dinlendirin.
2)   Ufak teflon bir tavayı yağlayın.
3)   Tava kızınca içine bir kepçe karışımdan dökün.
4)   İki tarafını da pişirdiğiniz kreplere, isteğe göre tatlı ya da tuzlu karışımlardan sürüp rulo haline getirin.

Tatlı karışımlar için:

Her çeşit marmelat
Çikolata sosu
Kestane püresi

Tuzlu karışımlar için:

Labne peynir ve füme somon
Krem peynir ve jambon
Beyaz sosla karıştırılmış ince tavuk dilimleri
Beyaz sosla karıştırılmış kavrulmuş ıspanak

Beyaz Sos

1 su bardağı süt
2 çorba kaşığı margarin
2 çorba kaşığı un
1 tatlı kaşığı tuz

1)   Sütü margarin ile birlikte kaynatın.
2)   Blender'a unu ve tuzu koyun. Üstüne kaynar süt ve yağ karışımını döküp çırpın.

Crepes (makes 10)

3 eggs
1 1/2 cups milk
1/4 teaspoon salt
3 tablespoons flour

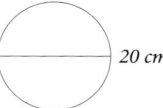

20 cm

1) Beat the eggs with the flour. Add the milk and salt and allow to sit for half an hour.
2) Grease a small nonstick frying pan.
3) When the pan is hot use a ladle to pour in enough mixture for one crepe.
4) When both sides are cooked they may be filled with either sweet or savory fillings and then rolled up.

for sweet fillings:

All varieties of jams or marmalades
Chocolate sauce
Puréed chestnuts

for savory fillings:

Labne (soft cream cheese) and smoked salmon
Cream cheese and ham
Strips of cooked chicken mixed with white sauce
Sautéed spinach mixed with white sauce

199

White Sauce

1 cup milk
2 tablespoons margarine
2 tablespoons flour
1 teaspoon salt

1) Bring the milk and margarine to a boil.
2) Place the flour and salt in the blender. Pour in the hot milk and margarine mixture and blend.

Domatesli Kuskus

1 1/2 su bardağı kuskus

2 adet domates

2 çorba kaşığı zeytinyağı

1 adet sivribiber

1 çorba kaşığı tuzot

1/2 çay kaşığı karabiber

1) Kuskusu bol suda haşlayın.
2) Küp şeklinde doğranmış domates ve ince doğranmış biberleri tuzot ve karabiberi de ekleyerek zeytinyağıyla pişirin.
3) Süzülmüş kuskuslara sosu ekleyip 2-3 dakika daha pişirin.
4) Kuskusu yağlanmış, ufak kaplara doldurun. Tabağa ters çevirerek koyun.
5) Et veya tavuk yanında servis yapın.

Tomato Couscous

1 1/2 cups couscous

2 tomatoes

2 tablespoons olive oil

1 mildly hot, long green pepper

1 tablespoon seasoned salt

1/2 teaspoon black pepper

1) Boil the couscous in a large quantity of water.
2) Sauté in olive oil the diced tomatoes and finely diced pepper, along with the seasoned salt and black pepper.
3) Add the mixture to the well-drained couscous and continue cooking for another 2-3 minutes.
4) Pack the couscous into greased, small bowls. Invert these bowls onto each plate, making sure to retain the neat and rounded shape.
5) Serve alongside meat or chicken.

Fesleğen Soslu Tagliatelle

1/2 paket tagliatelle

2 diş sarımsak

1 su bardağı taze fesleğen

1 kahve fincanı ceviz

1/2 paket labne peynir

1 tatlı kaşığı tuzot

1/2 çay kaşığı karabiber

1) Sarımsak, fesleğen, ceviz ve peyniri robottan geçirin. Karabiberi ekleyin.
2) Tagliatelle'yi tuzot eklediğiniz suda haşlayın.
3) Haşlanan makarnayı hemen sosla karıştırıp sıcak olarak servis edin.

Tagliatelle with Fresh Basil

1/2 package tagliatelle

2 cloves garlic

1 cup fresh basil leaves

1/3 cup walnuts

1/2 package labne (soft cream cheese)

1 teaspoon seasoned salt

1/8 teaspoon black pepper

1) Process the garlic, basil, walnuts and cheese in a food processor or grind well.
   Add the black pepper
2) Boil the tagliatelle in water to which the seasoned salt has been added.
3) Drain the pasta, stir in the sauce and serve hot.

Yalancı Suböreği

3 adet yumurta

1 çay bardağı su

3 adet yufka

250 gr beyaz peynir

1/2 demet maydanoz

100 gr eritilmiş margarin

1) Margarini eritin.
2) Yumurta, margarin ve suyu derin bir kapta çırpın.
3) Beyaz peyniri kıyılmış maydanozla ezin.
4) Yufkaları ufak parçalara bölün ve yumurta karışımıyla karıştırın.
5) Orta boy, teflon bir tavaya yufka karışımının yarısını yayıp üstüne peyniri yerleştirin.
6) Kalan yufkayı peynirin üstüne kapatın.
7) Kısık ateşte, altı kızarana dek çevirerek pişirin.
8) Bir tabak yardımıyla ters çevirip altını da pişirin.

Easy Boiled Börek

3 eggs

1/2 cup water

3 yufka (sheets of phyllo dough)

250 gr white cheese (feta)

1/2 bunch parsley

100 gr margarine

1) Melt the margarine.
2) Beat the eggs, margarine, and water in a deep mixing bowl.
3) Mash the white cheese with the finely chopped parsley.
4) Cut the yufka into small pieces and mix with the egg mixture.
5) In a medium-size, nonstick frying pan arrange half of the yufka mixture and then sprinkle with the cheese.
6) Arrange the remaining dough over the cheese filling.
7) Cook on over low heat, turning the pan constantly, until the bottom is golden.
8) Using a plate, invert the börek, return it to the frying pan and cook the other side in a similar fashion as above.

Pilavlar

Rice and Pilafs

Arpa Şehriye Pilavı

500 gr arpa şehriye

3 çorba kaşığı sıvıyağ

1 adet domates

1 adet kırmızı etli biber

2 adet sivribiber

1 tatlı kaşığı tuzot

3 su bardağı su

1) Arpa şehriyeyi pembeleşinceye kadar sıvıyağda kavurun.
2) Üstüne soğuk su, zar şeklinde doğranmış biber, rendelenmiş domates ve tuzotu ilave edip karıştırın.
3) Su kaynayınca altını kısıp yarım saat pişirin.
4) Ateşi kapattıktan sonra pilavın üstünü bir bez veya bir kâğıt havluyla kapatıp yarım saat kadar dinlendirin.

Orzo Noodle Pilaf

500 gr orzo noodles

3 tablespoons vegetable oil

1 tomato

1 red bell pepper

2 mildly hot, long green peppers

1 teaspoon seasoned salt

3 cups water

1) Sauté the orzo noodles in vegetable oil until slightly golden.
2) Pour the cold water, diced peppers, chopped tomato and seasoned salt over the noodles and begin cooking.
3) When the water comes to a boil, reduce heat to low and cook for half an hour.
4) Remove from heat. Cover with a clean cloth or thick paper towels and allow to sit for half an hour before serving.

Domatesli Pilav

2 su bardağı baldo pirinç

3 adet olgun domates

2 su bardağı tavuk suyu

2 çorba kaşığı tereyağı veya margarin

2 çorba kaşığı sıvıyağ

2 tatlı kaşığı tuzot

1) Küp şeklinde doğranmış domatesleri sıvıyağla pişirin.
2) Pişen domateslere tavuk suyu, tuzot ve tereyağını ilave edin. Kaynayınca, yıkanmış pirinci koyup karıştırın.
3) Su kaynayınca altını kısıp yarım saat pişirin.
4) Pilavı karıştırın. Ateşi kapattıktan sonra pilavın üstünü bir bez veya bir kâğıt havluyla kapatıp yarım saat kadar dinlendirin.

Tomato Pilaf

2 cups baldo or arborio rice

3 ripe tomatoes

2 cups chicken broth

2 tablespoons butter or margarine

2 tablespoons vegetable oil

2 teaspoons seasoned salt

1) Sauté the diced tomatoes in the vegetable oil.
2) When the tomatoes are soft add the chicken broth, seasoned salt and butter.
3) When this mixture comes to a boil add the well-rinsed rice; mix well.
4) After the mixture has come to a boil, reduce heat to low and cook for half an hour more.
5) Remove from heat and stir the rice. Cover with a clean cloth or thick paper towels and allow to sit for half an hour before serving.

Portakallı Pilav

2 su bardağı baldo pirinç

1 adet soğan

3 çorba kaşığı tereyağı veya margarin

1/2 su bardağı portakal suyu

2 1/2 su bardağı tavuk suyu

1 adet iri portakal kabuğu rendesi

2 tatlı kaşığı tuzot

1 çay kaşığı karabiber

1) Soğanları rendeleyip tereyağında hafifçe kavurun. Yıkanmış pirinci de koyup kavurmaya devam edin.
2) Kavurduğunuz pirince tavuk suyu, portakal suyu, portakal kabuğu rendesi, tuzot ve biberi ilave edin.
3) Su kaynadıktan sonra ateşi kısıp yarım saat pişirin.
4) Pilavı karıştırın. Ateşi kapattıktan sonra pilavın üstünü bir bez veya bir kâğıt havluyla kapatıp yarım saat kadar dinlendirin.

Orange Pilaf

2 cups baldo or arborio rice

1 onion

3 tablespoons butter or margarine

1/2 cup orange juice

2 1/2 cups chicken broth

Grated rind of 1 orange

2 teaspoons seasoned salt

1/4 teaspoon black pepper

1) Grate the onion and sauté lightly in butter. Add the well-rinsed and drained rice and continue to sauté.
2) Add the broth, orange juice, grated orange rind, seasoned salt and pepper.
3) After the mixture has come to a boil, reduce heat and cook for half an hour.
4) Remove from heat and stir the rice. Cover with a clean cloth or thick paper towels and allow to sit for half an hour before serving.

Sade Pilav

2 su bardağı baldo pirinç

3 su bardağı tavuk suyu

2 tatlı kaşığı tuzot

2 çorba kaşığı tereyağı veya margarin

2 çorba kaşığı sıvıyağ

1) Su, tuzot, sıvıyağ, tereyağı veya margarini karıştırıp kaynatın. Pirinci ilave edin.
2) Bir taşım kaynatıp ateşin altını kısın ve yarım saat pişirin.
3) Pilavı karıştırın. Ateşi kapattıktan sonra pilavın üstünü bir bez veya bir kâğıt havluyla kapatıp yarım saat kadar dinlendirin.

Plain Cooked Rice

2 cups baldo or arborio rice

3 cups chicken broth

2 teaspoons seasoned salt

2 tablespoons butter or margarine

2 tablespoons vegetable oil

1) Mix the chicken broth, seasoned salt, vegetable oil, and butter or margarine and bring to a boil. Add the rice.
2) After the mixture has come to a boil reduce heat and cook for half an hour.
3) Remove from heat and stir the rice. Cover with a clean cloth or thick paper towels and allow to sit for half an hour before serving.

Taskebaplı Pilav

1 kg kuşbaşı kuzu eti

1 adet büyük, olgun domates

1 adet soğan

1 adet sivribiber

2 su bardağı baldo pirinç

2 tatlı kaşığı tuzot

3 çorba kaşığı tereyağı veya margarin

3 su bardağı su

Süs için 3-4 sap maydanoz

1) Kuzu etini ay gibi doğranmış soğan, domates ve çekirdekleri çıkartılıp ince kıyılmış biberle, suyunu salıp çekinceye dek pişirin.
2) Isıya dayanıklı ufak bir kaba (pyrex bir kâseye) bu karışımı bastırarak doldurun. Daha sonra bu kabı pilavı pişireceğiniz tencerenin ortasına, ters çevirerek oturtun.
3) Kâseyi elinizle bastırarak tencereye suyu yavaşça dökün. 2 tatlı kaşığı tuzot ve yağı ilave edip ateşi açın.
4) Kaynayan suya yıkanmış pirinci ilave edip bir kaşık yardımıyla her tarafa yayın.
5) Ateşin altını kısıp yarım saat pişirin.
6) Ateşi söndürüp pişen pilavın üstünü bir bez ya da kâğıt havluyla kapatıp yarım saat kadar dinlendirin.
7) Etin kabını çıkartıp büyük bir servis tabağına tencereyi ters çevirin.
8) Etin üstünü ince kıyılmış maydanozla süsleyip servis yapın.

Taskebap Pilaf (Pilaf with Cubed Meat)

1 kg cubed lamb meat

1 large, ripe tomato

1 onion

1 mildly hot, long green pepper

2 cups baldo or arborio rice

2 teaspoons seasoned salt

3 tablespoons butter or margarine

3 cups water

3-4 sprigs parsley for garnish

1) Sauté the lamb meat, crescent-shaped sliced onion, tomato and seeded, finely chopped pepper until all liquids have been absorbed.
2) Press this mixture into a small ovenproof baking dish or bowl. Then carefully invert the bowl into the middle of the pan in which the pilaf will cook.
3) Hold the bowl in place as you slowly add the water, seasoned salt and butter or margarine.
4) When the water in the pan comes to a boil, add the rice, making sure that the rice is arranged evenly around the bowl.
5) After the rice and water again come to a boil, reduce heat to low and cook for half an hour.
6) Remove from heat. Cover with a clean cloth or thick paper towels and allow to sit for half an hour before serving.
7) Remove the bowl and invert the rice and meat mixture onto a serving platter.
8) Garnish the meat with finely chopped parsley and serve.

Patlıcanlı Pilav

3 adet patlıcan	1 çay kaşığı tarçın
2 su bardağı baldo pirinç	1 çay kaşığı karabiber
1 adet soğan	2 adet kesmeşeker
1 adet büyük, olgun domates	1 çay bardağı zeytinyağı
2 tatlı kaşığı tuzot	3 su bardağı su
1 çay kaşığı dolma baharı	Kızartma için 1/2 su bardağı zeytinyağı

1) Patlıcanları alaca soyup iri kareler şeklinde doğrayın. Bol tuzlu suda yarım saat kadar bekletin.
2) Patlıcanları kızgın yağda kızartın ve yağını çekmesi için kâğıt havluya alın.
3) Rendelenmiş soğanı zeytinyağında pembeleşinceye dek çevirin. Üzerine rendelenmiş domates, tarçın, karabiber, dolma baharı, tuzot, şeker ve suyu ilave edin.
4) Karışım kaynayınca pirinci ilave edin. Kaynayınca altını kısın. Yarım saat sonra altını kapattığınız tencereye patlıcanları da ilave edip karıştırın.
5) Üstünü bir bez ya da kâğıt havluyla kapatıp yarım saat kadar dinlendirin.
6) Ilık veya soğuk olarak servis yapın.

Eggplant Pilaf

3 eggplants	1/4 teaspoon cinnamon
2 cups baldo or arborio rice	1/4 teaspoon black pepper
1 onion	2 sugar cubes
1 large ripe tomato	1/2 cup olive oil
2 teaspoons seasoned salt	3 cups water
1/4 teaspoon mixed stuffing spices	1/2 cup olive oil for frying

1) Peel the eggplants (leaving half the peel intact) and roughly cube. Allow to soak in heavily salted water for half an hour.
2) Fry the eggplants in hot oil and place on paper towels to absorb excess oil.
3) Lightly sauté the grated onion until golden. Add the minced tomato, cinnamon, black pepper, mixed spices, seasoned salt, sugar and water.
4) When the mixture comes to a boil add the rice, reduce heat, and cook for half an hour. Remove from heat and stir in the eggplant.
5) Cover the mixture with a cloth or thick paper towels and allow to steam off the heat for half an hour.
6) Serve warm or cold.

Tel Şehriyeli Pilav

2 su bardağı baldo pirinç

1 su bardağı tel şehriye

3 çorba kaşığı sıvıyağ

3 çorba kaşığı tereyağı veya margarin

2 tatlı kaşığı tuzot

4 su bardağı tavuk suyu

1) Tel şehriyeleri sıvıyağda, rengi kahverengileşinceye dek, devamlı karıştırarak kavurun.
2) Şehriyelere tavuk suyu, tuzot ve tereyağını ilave edin.
3) Su kaynayınca yıkanmış pirinçleri de ilave edip karıştırın.
4) Ateşin altını kısıp yarım saat pişirin.
5) Ateşi kapatıp pişen pilavı karıştırın. Üstünü bir bez ya da kâğıt havluyla kapatıp yarım saat kadar dinlendirin.

Fine Noodle Pilaf

2 cups baldo or arborio rice

1 cup fine noodles (tel şehriye)

3 tablespoons vegetable oil

3 tablespoons butter or margarine

2 teaspoons seasoned salt

4 cups chicken broth

1) Sauté the noodles in the vegetable oil, stirring constantly, until nicely golden.
2) Add the chicken broth, seasoned salt and butter to the noodles.
3) When the water comes to a boil add the well-rinsed and drained rice and mix.
4) After the pilaf again comes to a boil, reduce heat to low and cook for half an hour.
5) Remove from heat and stir the rice. Cover with a clean cloth or thick paper towels and allow to sit for half an hour before serving.

Nohutlu Pilav

2 su bardağı baldo pirinç

3 su bardağı tavuk suyu

1/2 su bardağı nohut

3 çorba kaşığı tereyağı veya margarin

1 tatlı kaşığı tuzot

1) Bir gece önceden ıslattığınız nohudu bol suda haşlayıp suyunu süzün.
2) Tavuk suyu, tuzot ve yağı birlikte kaynatın. Kaynayan suya yıkanmış pirinç ve nohutları ilave edin.
3) Ateşin altını kısıp yarım saat pişirin.
4) Ateşi kapatıp pişen pilavı karıştırın. Üstünü bir bez ya da kâğıt havluyla kapatıp yarım saat kadar dinlendirin.

Chickpea Pilaf

2 cups boldo or arborio rice

3 cups chicken broth

1/2 cup chickpeas

3 tablespoons butter or margarine

1 teaspoon seasoned salt

1) Soak the chickpeas overnight and then cook in a large quantity of water until soft.
2) Bring the chicken broth, seasoned salt and butter or margarine to a boil. Slowly add the well-rinsed and drained rice and the chickpeas to the boiling water.
3) After the pilaf again comes to a boil, reduce heat to low and cook for half an hour.
4) Remove from heat and stir the rice. Cover with a clean cloth or thick paper towels and allow to sit for half an hour before serving.

Mercimekli Bulgur Pilavı

1 1/2 su bardağı bulgur

1 çay bardağı yeşil mercimek

1 adet soğan

3 sap taze soğan

1 tatlı kaşığı tuzot

2 adet olgun domates

2 adet sivribiber

3 su bardağı tavuk suyu

1 kahve fincanı zeytinyağı

1 tatlı kaşığı kuru nane

1) Mercimekleri haşlayıp suyunu süzün.
2) Ay şeklinde doğranmış soğanları sararıncaya dek zeytinyağında çevirin. Üzerine küp şeklinde doğranmış domates ve çekirdekleri çıkartılıp ince kıyılmış biberleri ekleyip pişirin.
3) Pişen karışıma bulguru ilave edip tahta bir kaşık yardımıyla 5 dakika kadar kavurun.
4) Bulgura tavuk suyu, tuzot ve haşlanmış mercimekleri ekleyip karıştırın.
5) Bir taşım kaynatıp ateşin altını kısın. Yarım saat pişirin.
6) Pişen pilava ince kıyılmış taze soğanları da ekleyip karıştırın. Üstünü bir bez ya da kâğıt havluyla kapatıp yarım saat kadar dinlendirin.
7) Üstüne kuru nane serpip servis yapın.

Lentil and Bulgur Pilaf

1 1/2 cups bulgur

1/2 cup green lentils

1 onion

3 green onions

1 teaspoon seasoned salt

2 ripe tomatoes

2 mildly hot, long green peppers

3 cups chicken broth

1/3 cup olive oil

1 teaspoon dried mint

1) Boil the lentils and drain.
2) Sauté the crescent-shaped sliced onions in the olive oil until golden. Add the diced tomatoes and seeded, finely chopped peppers and continue to sauté.
3) Add the bulgur to the vegetable mixture and continue sautéing, stirring with a wooden spoon, for five minutes.
4) Add the chicken broth, seasoned salt and cooked lentils and bring to a boil. Reduce heat to low and cook for half an hour.
5) Remove from heat, add the finely chopped green onions and mix. Cover with a clean cloth or thick paper towels and allow to sit for half an hour before serving.
6) Sprinkle dried mint on the top of the pilaf and serve.

İç Pilav

2 su bardağı baldo pirinç

2 çorba kaşığı sıvıyağ

3 su bardağı tavuk suyu

2 çorba kaşığı margarin veya tereyağı

1/2 demet dereotu

6 adet taze soğan

100 gr çamfıstığı

100 gr kuşüzümü

1 tatlı kaşığı tuzot

1) Tencereye sıvıyağı koyup fıstıklar pembeleşinceye kadar kavurun. Kepçeyle fıstıkları bir kenara alın.
2) Tencereye tavuk suyu, üzüm, margarin ve tuzotu koyup kaynatın.
3) Kaynayınca, yıkanmış pirinç ve kavurduğunuz fıstığı ekleyin.
4) Bir taşım kaynatıp ateşin altını kısın. Yarım saat pişirin.
5) Dereotu ve soğanı ince kıyın. Altı kapatılmış pilava ilave edip karıştırın ve üstünü kâğıt havlu ile kapatarak yarım saat dinlendirin.

Stuffing Pilaf

2 cups baldo or arborio rice

2 tablespoons vegetable oil

3 cups chicken broth

2 tablespoons butter or margarine

1/2 bunch dill

6 green onions

100 gr pine nuts

100 gr currants

1 teaspoon seasoned salt

1) Sauté the the pine nuts in the vegetable oil until golden. Remove from the oil with a slotted spoon.
2) Add the broth, currants, margarine and seasoned salt to the pot and bring to a boil.
3) When it boils add the rinsed rice and sautéed pine nuts.
4) When mixture comes to a rolling boil, reduce heat and allow to cook for half an hour.
5) Remove the rice mixture from heat and mix in the finely chopped dill and onions. Cover with a cloth or paper towels and allow to sit for half an hour before serving.

Tatlılar

Desserts

Çikolatalı Sıcak Kek

250 gr bitter çikolata

100 gr tozşeker

125 gr tereyağı

2 adet yumurta

2 yumurtanın sarısı

3 çorba kaşığı un

(Not: Fırından çıkan bu keklerin dışları katı, içleri akışkan olacaktır.)

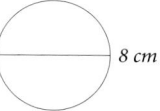

8 cm

1) Ufak sufle kaplarının içini margarinle yağlayıp buzlukta bekletin.
2) Bir kapta çikolatayı tereyağıyla birlikte eritin.
3) İki yumurta ve iki yumurta sarısını tozşekerle çırpın.
4) Tereyağıyla eriyen çikolataya yumurta karışımını ve unu ekleyip karıştırın.
5) Soğuyan kapların içini unlayın ve çikolata karışımını kaplara bölüştürün. Keki hemen pişirmeyecekseniz buzdolabında birkaç saat bekletebilirsiniz.
6) Önceden ısıtılmış çok sıcak fırında 10 dakika kadar pişirin.
7) Fırından çıkarınca ters çevirip üstüne kakao eleyin. Yanında sade dondurma ile servis yapın.

Chocolate Hot Pudding Cupcakes

250 gr bitter chocolate

100 gr granulated sugar

125 gr butter

2 eggs

2 egg yolks

3 tablespoons flour

(Note: While the outside of these cupcakes will be firm, the inside will be soft and pudding-like.)

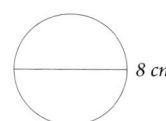

8 cm

1) Grease the insides of cupcake molds and place in the freezer to cool.
2) Melt the chocolate and butter together in a saucepan.
3) Beat the two eggs and two egg yolks with the granulated sugar.
4) Add the egg mixture and flour to the melted butter and chocolate and mix well.
5) Pour the mixture into the cooled and floured molds.
6) Bake in preheated, hot (220-230 °C) oven for 10 minutes. If you are not planning to bake the cupcakes immediately, you may allow them to sit in the refrigerator for several hours, but they should be brought back to room temperature before baking.
7) After removing from the oven invert the cupcakes on a serving plate and dust with cocoa. Serve with vanilla or plain ice cream on the side.

Karışık Meyve Tatlısı

Meyve harcı için:

2 adet elma

2 adet armut

2 portakalın suyu

6 çorba kaşığı tozşeker

250 gr dondurulmuş vişne

250 gr dondurulmuş frambuaz

Hamur için:

75 gr yumuşatılmış margarin

75 gr file fındık

100 gr tozşeker

20 gr un

33 cm

1) Elma ve armutları soyup bir tencereye dilimleyin. Şeker ve portakal suyuyla birlikte, ağzı kapalı olarak kaynatın.
2) Yumuşayan meyvelere frambuaz ve vişneyi de ekleyip hafif sulu kalıncaya dek pişirin.
3) Pişen meyveleri fırın ısısına dayanıklı bir kaba boşaltın.
4) Hamur malzemelerini karıştırın. Hazırladığınız hamuru meyvelerin üstüne ufalayın. Üstünü file fındık ile kaplayın.
5) Orta ısılı fırında, hamurlar kızarıncaya dek; 45-50 dakika pişirin.

Mixed Fruit Delight

Fruit mixture:

2 apples

2 pears

Juice of 2 oranges

6 tablespoons granulated sugar

250 gr frozen sour cherries

250 gr frozen raspberries

Dough:

75 gr soft margarine

75 gr sliced hazelnuts

100 gr granulated sugar

20 gr flour

33 cm

1) Peel the apples and pears and slice into a saucepan. Add the sugar and orange juice, cover and bring to a boil.
2) When the fruit is soft add the raspberries and sour cherries and cook until the mass is slightly juicy.
3) Pour the fruit mixture into an ovenproof baking dish.
4) Mix the dough ingredients and knead slightly. Crumble this dough over the fruit. Cover all with the sliced hazelnuts.
5) Bake for 45-50 minutes in moderately hot (190-200 °C) oven until the top is golden.

Bademli Muhallebi

1 lt süt

5 çorba kaşığı pirinç unu

8 çorba kaşığı şeker

200 gr ayıklanmış ve çekilmiş çiğ badem

1/2 su bardağı su

1) Pirinç unu, şeker ve 100 gr bademi bir kapta karıştırın.
2) Üstüne sırasıyla su ve sütü ilave ederek iyice karıştırın.
3) Tencereye aldığınız karışımı, orta ateşte devamlı karıştırarak pişirin.
4) Soğuyan muhallebiyi kalan 100 gr bademle süsleyerek servis yapın.

Almond Pudding

1 liter milk

5 tablespoons rice flour

8 tablespoons sugar

200 gr crushed almonds

1/2 cup water

1) Mix the rice flour, sugar and 100 gr almonds in a bowl.
2) Add the water and milk and beat well.
3) Pour the mixture into a saucepan and cook over medium heat, stirring constantly.
4) Pour into serving bowls and allow to cool. Garnish the pudding with the remaining 100 gr almonds.

Kabak Tatlısı

1 kg dilimlenmiş balkabağı
800 gr tozşeker
Süs için 250 gr çekilmiş ceviz

1) Kabakları yıkayıp süzün. Çelik bir tencereye dizin.
2) Üstüne şekeri boşaltın.
3) Tencerenin kapağını kapatıp kısık ateşte, suyunu bırakana kadar pişirin.
4) Kabaklar köpüklenmeye başlayınca tencerenin kapağını açın ve köpükleri bir kepçe yardımıyla toplayın.
5) Kabaklar suyunu çekip ağdalaşıncaya dek kapağı açık bir şekilde pişirin.
6) İnce çekilmiş cevizle süsleyip servis yapın.

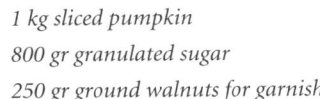

Pumpkin Sweet

1 kg sliced pumpkin
800 gr granulated sugar
250 gr ground walnuts for garnish

1) Wash and drain the pumpkin slices and arrange them in a stainless steel pan.
2) Pour the sugar over the slices.
3) Cover the pan and cook over low heat until the pumpkin has released its juices.
4) When the pumpkin begins to foam, uncover and use a large spoon to remove the foam.
5) Cook uncovered until the pumpkin has absorbed all the juices and thickened.
6) Serve with finely ground walnuts.

Ayva Tatlısı

8 adet ayva
Tozşeker
1/2 çay bardağı su
Ayvaların çekirdekleri
Kaymak

1) Ayvaların kabuklarını soyup ikiye bölün. Ortasını bıçakla alıp çekirdeklerini ayrı bir kaba ayırın.
2) Ayvaları derin bir tencereye, oyuk kısımları üste gelecek şekilde yerleştirin. Her bir parçanın ortasına 3 çorba kaşığı tozşeker koyun.
3) Suyu ayvaların üstünde gezdirin ve aralarına yıkanmış çekirdekleri serpin.
4) Tencerenin kapağını kapatıp kısık ateşte, şekerler eriyinceye kadar pişirin.
5) Tencerenin kapağını açıp ayvaları arada bir çevirerek jöle kıvamına gelinceye dek pişirin.
6) Ayvaları soğuk olarak, kaymakla servis yapın.

Quince Sweet

8 quinces
Granulated sugar
1/4 cup water
Quince seeds
Thick whipping or clotted cream

1) Peel and halve the quinces. Remove the seeds with a knife and reserve the seeds in a small bowl.
2) Place the quinces into a deep pot, with the hollowed out sides facing upwards. Place 3 tablespoons granulated sugar into each hollow.
3) Sprinkle the water over the quinces and then sprinkle the washed seeds among them.
4) Cover the pot and cook over low heat until the sugar has dissolved.
5) Uncover the pot, turning the quinces occasionally; cook until the quinces are a jelly-like consistency.
6) Serve the quinces cold, topped with a dollop of Turkish kaymak or thick whipping or clotted cream.

Aşure

1/2 kg aşurelik buğday
1 su bardağı nohut
1 su bardağı kuru fasulye
3 su bardağı tozşeker
15 su bardağı su

8 adet kuru kayısı
6 adet kuru incir
1 çay bardağı kuru üzüm
50 gr haşlanıp soyulmuş ve iri çentilmiş tuzsuz badem
Süs için ceviz, fındık ve nar taneleri

1) Buğday, nohut ve kuru fasulyeleri bir gece önceden, ayrı kaplarda ıslatın.
2) Nohut, kuru fasulye ve buğdayları haşlayın. Nohudun kabuklarını hafifçe ovalayarak çıkarın.
3) Ayıklanmış nohut, fasulye ve sulu haldeki buğdayı büyük bir tencereye aktarıp üzerine suyu koyun. Orta ateşte, arada bir karıştırarak kaynatın.
4) Yarım saat kadar kaynattıktan sonra ince kıyılmış kuru incir, kuru kayısı, üzüm ve bademleri de ilave edin. 15 dakika kadar kaynatın.
5) Tozşekeri de ilave edin. Sık sık karıştırarak yarım saat kadar daha kaynatın.
6) Ateşten aldığınız aşureyi ufak kâselere bölüştürün. İyice soğuduktan sonra üzerini ceviz, fındık ve nar taneleri ile süsleyin.

Aşure (Noah's Ark Pudding)

1/2 kg finely chopped wheat
1 cup chickpeas
1 cup white (navy) beans
3 cups granulated sugar
15 cups water

8 dried apricots
6 dried figs
1/2 cup raisins
50 gr blanched, peeled and coarsely chopped unsalted almonds
Walnuts, hazelnuts and pomegranate seeds for garnish

1) Soak the wheat, chickpeas and beans overnight in separate bowls.
2) Cook the chickpeas, beans and wheat separately until done. Drain the beans and chickpeas and, rubbing the chickpeas in your hands, remove their skins.
3) Pour the skinless chickpeas, beans and wheat, with its water, into a large cooking pot. Add the 15 cups water. Cook over medium heat, stirring occasionally.
4) After cooking for half an hour add the finely chopped dried figs, dried apricots, raisins and blanched almonds. Cook for an additional 15 minutes.
5) Add the granulated sugar. Cook for another half hour, stirring frequently.
6) Remove from heat and pour into individual serving bowls. After cooling, garnish the aşure with walnuts, hazelnuts and pomegranate seeds.

Profiterol

Hamur için:
150 gr un
80 gr tereyağı
1 su bardağı su ve süt karışımı
1 çay kaşığı tozşeker
1 çay kaşığı tuz
4 adet yumurta

Krema için:
1/2 lt süt
150 gr tozşeker
80 gr un
1 adet yumurta
2 adet yumurtanın sarısı
1 limon kabuğu rendesi
1/2 limonun suyu
50 gr tereyağı

Sos için:
2 paket hazır çikolata sosu
100 gr çiğ antepfıstığı

1) Tencerede yağ, süt, su, tuz ve şekeri kaynatın.
2) Ateşi kısıp unu ilave edip 6-7 dakika daha devamlı karıştırarak pişirin.
3) Ateşten indirdiğiniz tencerenin içine yumurtaları teker teker ekleyip yedirin. Bir yumurtayı hamura yedirmeden ikincisini kırmayın.
4) Geniş bir tepsiye yağlı kâğıt döşeyin. Hamuru sıkma poşetine koyup ufak toplar halinde sıkın.
5) Önceden ısıtılmış fırında, üstü pembeleşinceye dek pişirin.
6) Fırını kapattıktan sonra soğuyuncaya dek topları fırında tutun. Hemen çıkardığınız takdirde toplar sönecektir.
7) Fırından çıkardığınız topları birbirinden ayırmadan, ortadan ikiye bölün.
8) Krema için sütü kaynatın.
9) Ayrı bir kapta şeker ve yumurtaları çırpın. Limon rendesi ve unu ilave edip karıştırın.
10) Bu karışımı ufak bir tencereye alıp üzerine kaynar sütü yavaşça boşaltın. Muhallebi kıvamına gelene dek devamlı karıştırarak pişirin.
11) Ortadan kesilmiş topların içini bol krema ile doldurun.
12) Çikolata soslarını paketteki tarife göre hazırlayın. Yarısını kremalı topların üzerine dökün. Diğer yarısını ise servis esnasında kullanmak üzere bir sosluğa koyun.
13) Profiterolü çiğ antepfıstığıyla süsleyip servis yapın.

Profiterol (Cream Puffs)

Dough:
150 gr flour
80 gr butter
1 cup equal parts water and milk
1/4 teaspoon granulated sugar
1/4 teaspoon salt
4 eggs

Filling:
1/2 liter milk
150 gr granulated sugar
80 gr flour
1 egg
2 egg yolks
Grated rind of 1 lemon
Juice of 1/2 lemon
50 gr butter

Sauce:
2 packages chocolate sauce mix (130 gr each)
100 gr unsalted pistachios

1) Bring the butter, milk, water, salt and sugar to a boil in a saucepan.
2) Lower heat, add the flour and cook, stirring constantly, 6-7 minutes more.
3) Remove from heat and add the eggs, one by one, mixing well after each addition and ensuring that the dough is completely homogenous before adding an additional egg.
4) Line a large baking sheet with greased paper. Use a pastry bag to drop out small balls of dough onto the sheet.
5) Bake in preheated oven until golden.
6) Turn off the oven but do not remove the puffs until they have cooled. The puffs will collapse if removed from the hot oven before they have cooled down.
7) Once you have removed the puffs from the oven, slice them open, but do not separate the halves completely.
8) Boil the milk for the cream filling.
9) In a separate pan beat the sugar and eggs. Add the lemon rind and flour and beat well.
10) Slowly pour the boiling milk into this mixture. Stirring constantly, cook until the mixture is of pudding consistency.
11) Fill the puffs with an ample amount of cream filling and arrange them on a large serving plate.
12) Prepare the chocolate sauce according to the package directions. Pour half of the sauce over the cream puffs. Reserve the other half to add at serving.
13) Garnish the puffs with the pistachios.

Çikolatalı Muhallebi

Muhallebi için:

200 gr margarin

1 su bardağı un

1 lt süt

1 su bardağı tozşeker

1-2 parça damlasakızı

Süs için file badem

Çikolata sos için:

25 gr margarin

3 çorba kaşığı tozşeker

1 adet çırpılmış yumurta

3 tatlı kaşığı kakao

30 cm

20 cm

1) 200 gr erimiş margarini unla birlikte biraz kavurun. Soğuk süt, şeker ve dövülmüş damlasakızını ekleyin.
2) Devamlı karıştırarak, koyulaşıncaya kadar pişirin. Koyulaşan muhallebiyi ateşten alıp 15-20 dakika kadar mikser ile çırpın.
3) Muhallebiyi dikdörtgen bir kaba döküp soğutun.
4) Çikolatalı sos için, 25 gr margarini eritin. Üstüne 3 çorba kaşığı şeker, çırpılmış yumurta ve kakaoyu ekleyip karıştırarak pişirin.
5) Sosun kıvamı koyulaşınca soğumuş muhallebi üzerine dökün. 2 saat buzlukta bekletin.
6) Buzluktan çıkardığınız muhallebiyi file bademle süsleyin.

Chocolate Pudding

Pudding:

200 gr margarine

1 cup flour

1 liter milk

1 cup granulated sugar

1-2 pieces mastic

Sliced almonds for garnish

Chocolate Sauce:

25 gr margarine

3 tablespoons granulated sugar

1 beaten egg

3 teaspoons cocoa

30 cm

20 cm

1) Whisk together the 200 gr melted margarine and flour over low heat. Add the cold milk, sugar and crushed mastic.
2) Stirring constantly, cook until pudding thickens. Remove from heat and beat the thick pudding for 15-20 minutes with an electric mixer.
3) Pour the pudding into a rectangular dish and allow to cool.
4) Melt 25 gr margarine for the chocolate sauce. Add 3 tablespoons sugar, the beaten egg and cocoa and cook, stirring constantly.
5) When the sauce has reached the desired consistency, pour it over the cold pudding and allow to cool in the freezer for 2 hours.
6) Remove the pudding from the freezer and garnish with the sliced almonds.

Pekmez Kavurması

1 1/2 su bardağı un
100 gr tereyağı
1 su bardağı ılık su
1 su bardağı üzüm pekmezi
100 gr çekilmiş ceviz
Süs için 8 adet yarım ceviz

1) Yağ ve unu, un sararıncaya dek, kısık ateşte kavurun.
2) Kavurduğunuz una su ve pekmezi ilave edip suyunu çekene kadar, devamlı karıştırarak pişirin.
3) Çekilmiş cevizleri pekmez karışımına ilave edip karıştırın.
4) Servis tabağına aldığınız pekmez kavurmasının üstünü yarım cevizlerle süsleyin.

Pekmez (Molasses Treat)

1 1/2 cups flour
100 gr butter
1 cup warm water
1 cup grape pekmez or dark molasses
100 gr crushed walnuts
8 half walnuts for garnish

1) Over low heat whisk together the butter and flour until the flour turns golden.
2) Add the water and pekmez and continue to cook, stirring constantly, until the liquids are absorbed.
3) Add the crushed walnuts to the pekmez mixture.
4) Pour the pekmez mixture on a serving plate and garnish with the half walnuts.

Çilek Soslu Sakızlı Muhallebi

Muhallebi için:

1 1/2 lt süt

1 su bardağından 1 parmak kadar az tozşeker

2 iri parça dövülmüş damlasakızı

4 dolu çorba kaşığı buğday nişastası

1 dolu çorba kaşığı mısır nişastası

Çilek sosu için:

1 kg taze veya dondurulmuş çilek

4 çorba kaşığı pudraşeker

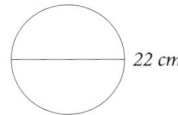

22 cm

1) 1 litre sütü şeker ve sakızla birlikte kaynatın.
2) Ayrı bir kapta buğday ve mısır nişastasını 1/2 litre sütle eritin.
3) Kaynayan sütün içine nişastalı sütü ip gibi akıtıp devamlı karıştırarak koyulaşıncaya dek pişirin.
4) Isıya dayanıklı bir kabı soğuk suyla ıslatın. Muhallebiyi bu kaba döküp 2 saat kadar buzlukta tutun. Buzluktan aldığınız muhallebiyi bir gece buzdolabında bekletin.
5) Çilekleri pudraşeker ile birlikte, blender'ın düşük seviyesinde çırpın. Eğer dondurulmuş çilek kullanıyorsanız blender'dan geçirmeden önce çileklerin buzunu çözün.
6) Muhallebiyi porsiyonlara bölüp çilek sosuyla birlikte servis yapın.

Mastic Pudding with Strawberry Sauce

Pudding:

1 1/2 liters milk

1 slight cup granulated sugar

2 large pieces crushed mastic

4 heaping tablespoons wheat starch

1 heaping tablespoon cornstarch

Strawberry sauce:

1 kg fresh or frozen strawberries

4 tablespoons powdered sugar

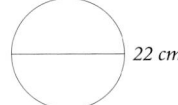

22 cm

1) Boil together 1 liter milk, the sugar and mastic.
2) In a bowl dissolve the wheat and corn starches in 1/2 liter milk.
3) Pour the starch-milk mixture into the boiling milk in a slow but steady stream, stirring constantly and continuing to cook until thick.
4) Wet an ovenproof round baking dish with cold water. Pour the pudding into this dish and allow to cool in the freezer for 2 hours. Remove the pudding from the freezer, place in the refrigerator and leave overnight.
5) Blend the strawberries with the powdered sugar at low speed in a blender. If using frozen strawberries, make sure they are thawed before placing in blender.
6) Divide the pudding into individual servings and serve with the strawberry sauce.

Kırıntılı Elma

200 gr un
100 gr tozşeker
75 gr yumuşatılmış margarin
1 1/2 kg ekşi elma
1 çorba kaşığı tarçın
2 çorba kaşığı tozşeker
2 çorba kaşığı limon suyu
100 gr tuzsuz badem
1 ufak kutu çiğ krema

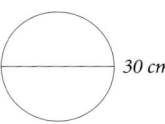

30 cm

1) Kabukları soyulmuş elmaları dilimleyin. Fırın ısısına dayanıklı, yağlanmış bir kalıba çok sıkı bir şekilde yerleştirin.
2) Üstüne sırasıyla 2 çorba kaşığı limon suyu, 2 çorba kaşığı tozşeker ve 1 çorba kaşığı tarçını serpin.
3) Ayrı bir kapta un, 100 gr tozşeker ve margarini yoğurun. Elde ettiğiniz hamuru elmaların üzerine ufalayın.
4) Sıcak suda bekletilerek kabukları soyulmuş bademleri, bütün olarak hamurun üstüne yerleştirin.
5) Orta ısılı fırında, üstü kızarıncaya dek; 50 dakika pişirin.
6) Ilık olarak çiğ krema ile servis yapın.

Apple Crumble

200 gr flour
100 gr granulated sugar
75 gr softened margarine
1 1/2 kg tart apples
1 tablespoon cinnamon
2 tablespoons granulated sugar
2 tablespoons lemon juice
100 gr unsalted almonds
1 small box of whipping cream (200 ml)

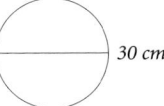

30 cm

1) Slice the peeled apples into an ovenproof, greased baking dish and arrange snuggly.
2) Over the apples sprinkle first the lemon juice, then 2 tablespoons granulated sugar and then the cinnamon.
3) Knead the flour, 100 gr granulated sugar and margarine together in a mixing bowl. Crumble this mixture over the apples.
4) Blanch the almonds in hot water and peel. Arrange them whole over the dough.
5) Bake for 50 minutes in moderately hot (190-200 °C) oven until top is golden.
6) Serve warm with whipped cream.

İrmik Helvası

1/2 kg irmik
1 kahve fincanı sıvıyağ
100 gr tereyağı
100 gr çamfıstığı
3 su bardağı tozşeker
2 su bardağı süt
2 su bardağı su
100 gr tuzsuz badem

1) Fıstıkları, sıvıyağda rengi hafif pembeleşinceye dek kavurun.
2) İrmiği ve tereyağını da ilave edip kısık ateşte 40-45 dakika daha kavurun.
3) Ayrı bir kapta, süt ve su karışımını kaynatıp irmiğe ilave edip karıştırın. İrmiğin çekmesini bekleyin.
4) Daha sonra tozşekeri ilave edin ve hiç karıştırmadan kısık ateşte 10 dakika kadar bekletin.
5) Sonra karıştırın ve biraz daha ateşte tutun.
6) Ateşten alıp karıştırdığınız irmik helvasını, sıvıyağda kavrulmuş bademlerle süsleyin.

Semolina Dessert

1/2 kg semolina
1/3 cup vegetable oil
100 gr butter
100 gr pine nuts
3 cups granulated sugar
2 cups milk
2 cups water
100 gr unsalted almonds

1) Sauté the pine nuts in the vegetable oil until they are slightly golden.
2) Add the semolina and butter and sauté for 40-45 minutes over low heat.
3) Mix the milk and water and bring to a boil in a saucepan. Mix this liquid into the semolina and, continuing to cook, allow the semolina to absorb all the liquids.
4) Add the granulated sugar and continue to cook over low heat without stirring.
5) After 10 minutes stir and cook for a little while longer.
6) Remove from heat and garnish the semolina with the almonds you have roasted in oil.

Vişneli Muhallebi

Muhallebi için:

1 lt süt

1/2 su bardağı tozşeker

100 gr haşlanıp ince çentilmiş çiğ badem

1 kahve fincanı un

Vişne sosu için:

1/2 su bardağı tozşeker

1 çorba kaşığı mısır nişastası

1 kutu dondurulmuş vişne

1 ufak kutu vişne suyu (125 ml)

1) Şeker ve unu sütle çırpın. Orta ateşte tahta kaşık yardımıyla karıştırarak pişirin.
2) Sütün kıvamı koyulaşınca ateşten alın ve isteğe göre dikdörtgen bir kap veya kâselerin yarısına kadar doldurun.
3) İnce çentilmiş bademleri, muhallebi ılıkken üzerine yerleştirin ve donmasını bekleyin.
4) Donmuş vişneleri bir gece önceden bir süzgece koyup suyunu bir kapta toplayın.
5) Vişnelerin kendi suyu, mısır nişastası, 1 küçük kutu vişne suyu ve şekeri karıştırıp kaynatın.
6) Kıvamı koyulaşan sosa vişne tanelerini de ekleyip muhallebinin üzerine yayın.

Sour Cherry Pudding

Pudding:

1 liter milk

1/2 cup granulated sugar

100 gr blanched and finely chopped raw almonds

1 1/3 cups flour

Sour cherry sauce:

1/2 cup granulated sugar

1 tablespoon cornstarch

1 package frozen sour cherries (500 gr)

1 small box of sour cherry juice (125 ml)

```
          30 cm
┌──────────────────────┐
│                      │ 20 cm
└──────────────────────┘
```

1) Beat together the sugar, flour and milk. Stir with a wooden spoon while cooking over medium heat.
2) When the milk has reached pudding consistency, remove from heat and half fill a rectangular serving dish or individual serving bowls.
3) When the pudding is still warm, top with the chopped almonds and allow to cool and set.
4) One night before serving, place the frozen sour cherries in a strainer and allow the juices to flow into a bowl.
5) Mix the juice from the sour cherries, cornstarch, 1 small box of sour cherry juice and the sugar and bring to a boil.
6) When this mixture thickens, add the sour cherries and serve over the pudding.

Pekmezli Sütlaç

1 1/2 lt süt
2 çay bardağı pirinç
4 su bardağı su
500 gr pekmez
2 çorba kaşığı buğday nişastası

1) Sütü 1 çay fincanı pirinçle kaynatın. Pirinçler yumuşayınca az su içinde erittiğiniz 1 çorba kaşığı buğday nişastasını süte ilave edin. Kıvamı koyulaşıncaya dek orta ateşte, devamlı karıştırarak pişirin.
2) Kâselerin yarısına kadar bu hazırladığınız şekersiz sütlacı bölüştürün.
3) 4 bardak suyu, kalan 1 çay fincanı pirinçle kaynatın. Pirinçler yumuşayınca pekmez ve az su içinde erittiğiniz 1 çorba kaşığı buğday nişastasını suya ilave edin. Koyulaşıncaya dek orta ısılı ateşte devamlı karıştırarak pişirin.
4) Pekmezli karışımı, donmuş olan sade sütlaçların üzerine bölüştürüp soğutun.

Pekmez (molasses) Rice Pudding

247

1 1/2 liters milk
1 cup rice
4 cups water
500 gr pekmez or dark molasses
2 tablespoons wheat starch

1) Boil the milk with 1/2 cup of rice. Dissolve 1 tablespoon of starch in a small amount of water and, when the rice is soft, add this to the milk and rice mixture. Cook over medium heat, stirring constantly, until it is of pudding consistency.
2) Half fill individual serving bowls with this sugarless pudding.
3) Boil the remaining 1/2 cup of rice in 4 cups of water. Dissolve the remaining 1 tablespoon of starch into a small amount of water. When the rice is soft add the pekmez and starchy water and continue cooking, stirring constantly, until of pudding consistency.
4) Pour the pekmez pudding over the cold, firm rice pudding and allow to cool.

Armut Tatlısı

6 adet uzun saplı armut

1 lt portakal suyu

6 tatlı kaşığı neskafe

8 çorba kaşığı tozşeker

2 tatlı kaşığı konyak

1 kutu çiğ krema

1 tatlı kaşığı mısır nişastası

1) Yıkanmış armutların dik durması için altlarını kesin ve derin bir tencereye yerleştirin.
2) Üstüne şeker, neskafe ve konyağı dökün.
3) Portakal suyunun 1 su bardağı kadarını ayırıp kalanını armutların üzerine dökün.
4) Orta ateşte, armutlar hafif yumuşayıncaya dek, arada bir kaşıkla suyunu üzerinde gezdirerek pişirin.
5) Armutları servis tabağına alın.
6) Artan portakal suyu ve mısır nişastasını tenceredeki suya ilave edip hafif koyulaşıncaya dek kaynatın.
7) Sosu armutların üzerine döküp yanında çiğ krema ile servis yapın.

Pear Sweet

6 long-stemmed pears

1 liter orange juice

6 teaspoons instant coffee granules

8 tablespoons granulated sugar

2 teaspoons cognac

1 box heavy cream

1 teaspoon cornstarch

1) Wash the pears and cut a tiny slice off of their bottoms so they will stand up straight. Stand the pears in a deep pot.
2) Sprinkle the pears with sugar, instant coffee granules and cognac.
3) Reserve 1 cup of the orange juice and then pour the remaining juice over the pears.
4) Cook over medium heat until the pears are slightly soft, basting occasionally with the juices.
5) Place the pears on a serving plate.
6) Stir the remaining orange juice and the cornstarch into the juices left in the saucepan and boil until slightly thick.
7) Pour the sauce over the pears. Serve with thick or clotted cream.

Yoğurt Tatlısı

3 adet yumurta

3 dolu çorba kaşığı yoğurt

1/2 kahve fincanı sıvıyağ

1 paket kabartma tozu

1 1/2 kahve fincanı şeker

5 kahve fincanı un

1 limon kabuğu rendesi

Şurup için

4 su bardağı su

3 su bardağı şeker

28 cm

28 cm

1) Yumurta ve şekeri iyice çırpın.
2) Yoğurt, sıvıyağ, limon kabuğu rendesi, kabartma tozu ve unu da ekleyerek tahta kaşıkla karıştırın.
3) Karışımı kare bir kaba dökün.
4) Önceden ısıtılmış fırında, üstü kızarana dek 20-25 dakika pişirin.
5) Şurup için şeker ve suyu kaynatın, ardından soğutun.
6) Fırından aldığınız yoğurt tatlısını karelere kesin ve soğuk şerbeti üstüne boşaltın.
7) Tatlı soğuduktan sonra servis yapın.

(Not: Kekin sıcak, döktüğünüz şurubun ise soğuk olmasına dikkat edin.)

Yogurt Sweet

3 eggs

3 heaping tablespoons yogurt

1/6 cup vegetable oil

1 tablespoon baking powder

1/2 cup sugar

1 2/3 cups flour

Grated rind of 1 lemon

Syrup:

4 cups water

3 cups sugar

28 cm

28 cm

1) Beat the eggs and sugar together.
2) Add the yogurt, oil, lemon rind, baking powder and flour and stir well with a wooden spoon.
3) Pour the mixture into a square baking dish.
4) Bake in preheated oven for 20-25 minutes, or until golden.
5) Boil the sugar and water together for the syrup and then cool.
6) After removing from the oven, cut the yogurt sweet into squares and pour the cold syrup over evenly.
7) Serve cold.

(Note: Make sure that the cake is hot and the syrup cold when pouring the syrup over the cake.)

Tahinli Yalancı Baklava

1 adet yufka

1 çay bardağı tahin

1/2 çay bardağı eritilmiş margarin

1 çay bardağı tozşeker

1 çay bardağı dövülmüş ceviz

1 adet yumurta sarısı

Pudraşeker

1) Yufkayı masaya yayın.
2) Margarin ve tahini, sırasıyla yufkanın her yerine yayın.
3) Tozşeker ve cevizi karıştırıp yufkanın üstüne serpin.
4) Yufkayı bir ucundan başlayarak sıkı sıkı sarın.
5) Ruloyu verevine iri parçalara bölün. Üstüne çırpılmış yumurta sarısını sürün.
6) Yağlı kâğıt döşenmiş bir fırın tepsisine koyup önceden ısıtılmış orta dereceli fırında 50 dakika pişirin.
7) Fırından çıktıktan sonra soğumasını bekleyip üstüne pudraşeker serpin.

(Not: 1 adet yufkadan 13-14 parça baklava çıkıyor.)

Easy Tahini Sweet

255

1 sheet of yufka dough or 2 or more sheets of phyllo dough

1/2 cup tahini

1/4 cup melted margarine

1/2 cup granulated sugar

1/2 cup ground walnuts

1 egg yolk

Powdered sugar

1) Spread the yufka on the table or counter (if using the smaller phyllo dough, lay 2 sheets side by side, making sure they overlap a bit to form one piece).
2) Spread the margarine and tahini, one after the other, evenly across the dough.
3) Mix the granulated sugar and walnuts and sprinkle them on top of the dough.
4) Starting at one end, roll up tightly.
5) Cut the roll diagonally into largish pieces. Brush the beaten egg yolk over the tops of the pieces.
6) Line a baking sheet with greased paper, arrange the pieces at even intervals and bake in moderately hot (190-200 °C) for 50 minutes.
7) After removing from oven, allow to cool and then sprinkle with powdered sugar.

(Note: Each yufka yields 13-14 pieces.)

Kuru İncir Tatlısı

1/2 kg kuru incir
1 su bardağı iri çentilmiş ceviz
5 çorba kaşığı tozşeker
1 çorba kaşığı tereyağı
1 su bardağı su
Kaymaklı dondurma

1) Kuru incirleri elinizle ovarak yumuşatın.
2) Cevizleri 2 çorba kaşığı tozşekerle karıştırın.
3) İncirlerin ortasını keskin bir bıçakla kesin ve içini ceviz-şeker karışımı ile doldurup sıkıca bastırıp kapatın.
4) Bir tavada tereyağını eritip incirlerin iki tarafını da kızartın.
5) Kalan tozşekeri incirlerin üzerine serpip suyu ekleyin. Kısık ateşte incirler iyice pişene dek pişirin.
6) İncirleri ılık olarak, yanında dondurma ile servis yapın.

Dried Fig Sweet

1/2 kg dried figs
1 cup coarsely chopped walnuts
5 tablespoons granulated sugar
1 tablespoon butter
1 cup water
Vanilla ice cream

1) Soften the figs by rubbing them in your hands.
2) Mix the walnuts with 2 tablespoons granulated sugar.
3) Use a sharp knife to slice the figs open. Stuff the opening with the walnut-sugar mixture and press firmly to close.
4) Melt the butter and brown the figs on both sides.
5) Sprinkle the remaining granulated sugar over the figs and add the water. Cook over low heat until the figs are well cooked.
6) Serve the figs warm, with a dollop of vanilla or plain ice cream on the side.

Sütlaç

1 1/2 lt süt
1 çay fincanı pirinç
1 su bardağı tozşeker
1 çay kaşığı tuz
2 çorba kaşığı buğday nişastası

1) Kaynayan 1 litre süte pirinci ilave edin.
2) Pirinçler iyice yumuşayınca şekeri ve, tuz ve nişasta ile çırpılmış 1/2 litre sütü ip gibi akıtarak ilave edin.
3) Devamlı karıştırarak koyulaşıncaya dek pişirin.
4) Dilerseniz, ısıya dayanıklı kâselere boşalttığınız sütlaçların üstünü fırında kızartın.

Rice Pudding

1 1/2 liters milk
1/3 cup rice
1 cup granulated sugar
1/4 teaspoon salt
2 tablespoons wheat starch

1) Add the rice to 1 liter boiling milk.
2) Mix the starch into the remaining 1/2 liter milk.
3) When the rice is soft, add the sugar and salt and then pour in the starch-milk mixture in a slow but steady stream.
4) Cook, stirring constantly, until the mixture is of pudding consistency.
5) If you would like a browned surface, pour the pudding into ovenproof serving dishes and brown briefly using the broiler in your oven.

Çay Saati

Teatime

Elmalı Pay

5 adet iri ekşi elma
200 gr yumuşatılmış margarin
3 bardak un
7 çorba kaşığı su
1/2 çay kaşığı tuz
6 çorba kaşığı tozşeker
4 tatlı kaşığı tarçın
Kaymaklı dondurma veya çiğ krema

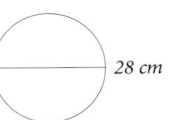

28 cm

1) Yağ, tuz, su ve unu karıştırarak yumuşak bir hamur yapın.
2) Elmaları soyup ince ince dilimleyin.
3) Hamuru 1/4 ve 3/4 olmak üzere ikiye bölün.
4) Büyük parçayı unlu bir zeminde, merdane yardımıyla yuvarlak olacak şekilde açın ve yağlanmış bir tart kalıbına döşeyin.
5) Elmaların yarısını, gelişigüzel şekilde hamurun üstüne dizin. Üzerine 3 kaşık şeker ve 2 kaşık tarçın serpin.
6) Kalan elmalarla ikinci bir kat daha yapın; üzerine tekrar 3 kaşık şeker ve 2 kaşık tarçın dökün.
7) Kalan ufak parça hamuru açıp tartın üstünü kapatın. Yandan taşan hamuru bıçakla kesin. Hamurun kenarlarını muntazam aralıklarla çimdikleyerek iki hamuru birbirine yapıştırın.
8) Üstüne biraz tozşeker serpip hamuru 4-5 yerinden delin.
9) Orta dereceli fırında üzeri kızarıncaya dek; 1 saat pişirin.
10) Kaymaklı dondurma veya çiğ krema ile, ılık olarak servis yapın.

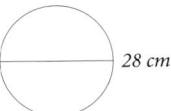

Apple Pie

5 large tart apples
200 gr softened margarine
3 cups flour
7 tablespoons water
1/8 teaspoon salt
6 tablespoons granulated sugar
4 teaspoons cinnamon
Vanilla ice cream or whipped or clotted cream

28 cm

1) Cut the margarine, salt, and water into the flour and knead only until it forms a soft dough.
2) Peel the apples and slice thinly.
3) Divide the dough into 2 uneven portions, 1/4 and 3/4 of the total.
4) Put the larger ball of dough on a floured surface and roll out into a circle with a rolling pin. Position the dough into a round and greased tart pan.
5) Spread half of the apples over the dough. Sprinkle 3 tablespoons of sugar and 2 teaspoons of cinnamon over the apples.
6) Add the remaining apples and sprinkle the remaining sugar and cinnamon over the apples.
7) Roll out the remaining dough and position over the apples. Cut away any dough hanging from the top of the pan with a knife. Pinch the edges of the dough together neatly at regular intervals.
8) Sprinkle the top of the tart with a little granulated sugar and punch 4-5 holes in the top to release steam.
9) Bake at medium heat for about an hour or until the top is nicely browned.
10) Serve with vanilla ice cream or whipped or clotted cream.

Perişan

1 su bardağı tozşeker
2 adet yumurta
250 gr erimiş margarin
4 su bardağı un
1 su bardağı kuru sarı üzüm
1 su bardağı iri çentilmiş fındık
1/2 paket kabartma tozu
1 portakal kabuğu rendesi

1) Yumurtalar ve şekeri mikserde çırpın. Diğer malzemeleri de ilave edip karıştırın.
2) Hazırladığınız karışımı, yağlı kâğıtla kaplanmış tepsiye bir kaşıkla ufak toplar halinde dökün.
3) Orta ısılı fırında, toplar kızarıncaya dek pişirin.

Perişan

1 cup granulated sugar
2 eggs
250 gr melted margarine
4 cups flour
1 cup yellow raisins
1 cup coarsely chopped hazelnuts
1 teaspoon baking powder
Grated rind of 1 orange

1) Beat the eggs and sugar with a mixer. Gradually add all the remaining ingredients and mix.
2) Line a baking dish with greased paper. Make small spoonfuls of dough and place them on the paper.
3) Bake at medium heat until the balls have nicely browned.

Kuru Kayısılı Tart

1/2 kg kuru kayısı

2 çorba kaşığı tozşeker

250 gr un

100 gr yumuşatılmış tereyağı veya margarin

1 adet yumurta

100 gr tozşeker

1 paket çiğ krema

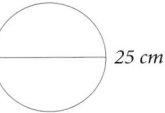
25 cm

1) Kuru kayısıları bir gece önceden bol suda bekletin. Daha sonra suyunu süzün.
2) Fırın ısısına dayanıklı bir kabı 1 tatlı kaşığı tereyağı ile yağlayın ve buzlukta bekletin.
3) Un, 100 gr şeker, yumurta ve yumuşak margarini yoğurun.
4) Buzluktan aldığınız kalıba 2 çorba kaşığı tozşeker serpin. Suyunu süzdüğünüz kayısıları muntazam olarak kalıba yerleştirin.
5) Hamuru merdane yardımıyla, kalıbın çapından biraz geniş açıp kayısıların üstüne yerleştirin. Kenarlarını bıçakla kesip düzeltin.
6) Önceden ısıtılmış, orta dereceli fırında, üstü kızarana dek; 1 saat kadar pişirin.
7) Fırından aldığınız tart ılıyınca bir bıçak yardımıyla hamurun kenarlarını açın. Servis tabağına ters olarak çıkarın.
8) Yanında çiğ krema ile, ılık olarak servis yapın.

Dried Apricot Tart

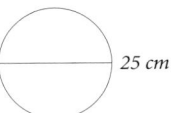

269

1/2 kg dried apricots

2 tablespoons granulated sugar

250 gr flour

100 gr softened butter or margarine

1 egg

100 gr granulated sugar

1 package whipping cream

25 cm

1) Soak the dried apricots overnight in a large measure of water and then drain.
2) Grease an ovenroof baking dish with 1 teaspoon butter and put in freezer.
3) Knead together the flour, 100 gr sugar, egg and softened margarine.
4) Remove baking dish from freezer and sprinkle 2 tablespoons granulated sugar into it. Neatly arrange the apricots in the bottom of the dish.
5) Use a rolling pin to roll out the dough just a bit larger than the circumference of your baking dish, place the dough in the dish, and cover the apricots with it. Cut off any extra dough hanging over the sides.
6) Bake in preheated, moderately hot (220-230 °C) oven until the top is golden brown, approximately 1 hour.
7) When it has cooled somewhat, use a knife to help remove the tart from the dish. Invert the tart (apricots up) onto a serving plate.
8) Serve warm topped with whipped cream.

Tarçınlı Elmalı Kek

1 su bardağından 1 parmak az tozşeker

3 adet yumurta

2 çorba kaşığı tarçın

1 adet elma

1 çay fincanı çentilmiş ceviz

1 su bardağı un

1/2 paket kabartma tozu

Süs için pudraşeker

1) Şeker ve yumurtayı mikserde çırpın. İçine tarçın, ceviz, kabuğu soyulup küp şeklinde doğranmış elma, un ve kabartma tozunu ilave edin. Karıştırarak koyu bir bulamaç haline getirin.
2) Karışımı ortası delik, yağlanmış bir kalıba dökerek orta dereceli fırında 50 dakika pişirin.
3) Kek ılıyınca ters çevirin. Üstünü pudraşeker ile süsleyin.

Cinnamon-Apple Pound Cake

7/8 cup sugar

3 eggs

2 tablespoons cinnamon

1 apple

50 gr finely chopped walnuts

1 cup flour

1 teaspoon baking powder

Powdered sugar for decoration

1) Peel and dice the apple.
2) Beat the sugar and eggs with a mixer. Add the cinnamon, apples, flour, walnuts and baking powder. Stir until it becomes thick and creamy.
3) Pour into a greased Bundt pan and bake at medium heat for about an hour.
4) When somewhat cool, turn the cake over onto a serving plate. Sprinkle powdered sugar over the cake and serve.

Çikolata ve fındıklı Pasta

300 gr siyah çikolata

200 gr tereyağı

150 gr un

200 gr tozşeker

6 adet yumurta

100 gr ikiye bölünmüş iç fındık

7 çorba kaşığı süt

1 paket hazır çikolatalı sos

1) Çikolatayı sütle, çok kısık ateşte eritin. İçine yağı da ekleyin. Biraz karıştırdıktan sonra ateşi kapatın.
2) Şeker ve yumurta sarılarını iyice çırpın.
3) Ayrı bir kapta yumurta beyazlarını kar kıvamına gelene dek çırpın.
4) Yumurta sarıları, çikolatalı süt, yumurta beyazları ve unu karıştırıp yağlanmış, kelepçeli bir kalıba dökün.
5) Orta ısılı fırında 50-60 dakika kadar pişirin.
6) Dilerseniz üstünü tarifine göre hazırlanmış çikolatalı sosla sıvayıp, tane fındıklarla süsleyerek servis yapın.

Chocolate and Hazelnut Cake

300 gr dark chocolate

250 gr butter

150 gr flour

200 gr granulated sugar

6 eggs (separated)

100 gr hazelnuts, halved

7 tablespoons milk

1 package (130 gr) chocolate sauce mix

1) Melt the chocolate in the milk over very low heat. Add the butter and after stirring for a short time, remove from heat.
2) Cream well the sugar and egg yolks.
3) Beat the egg whites in a separate bowl until snowy soft.
4) Mix together the egg yolk and sugar mixture, the chocolate mixture, the halved hazelnuts, the flour and the egg whites and pour into a greased springform pan.
5) Bake at medium heat for 50-60 minutes.
6) If desired, chocolate sauce can be poured over the top and then garnished with the hazelnuts.

Vişneli Pay

700 gr vişne
75 gr tereyağı
125 gr un
4 adet yumurta
90 gr tozşeker
1 su bardağı süt
Pudra şekeri veya çiğ krema

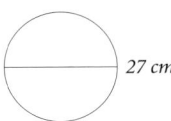

27 cm

1) Vişnelerin saplarını ayıklayıp yıkayın ve kâğıt havluyla kurulayın.
2) Fırın ısısına dayanıklı bir kabı 2 çorba kaşığı tereyağıyla yağlayın.
3) Yağlanmış kalıba, her tarafına gelecek şekilde, 2 çorba kaşığı tozşeker serpin.
4) Vişneleri yağlanmış ve şekere bulanmış kaba, tek sıra halinde dizin.
5) Tereyağının geri kalanını eritin. Un, yumurta, süt ve kalan şekerle erimiş tereyağını mikserde çırpın. Hazırladığınız bu karışımı yavaşça vişnelerin üzerine dökün.
6) Önceden ısıtılmış, orta dereceli fırında üstü pembeleşinceye kadar pişirin.
7) İsteğe göre üstüne pudraşeker veya çiğ krema dökerek servis yapın.

Sour Cherry Pie

273

700 gr sour cherries
75 gr butter
125 gr flour
4 eggs
90 gr granulated sugar
1 cup milk
Powdered sugar or whipping cream

27 cm

1) Grease an ovenproof baking dish with 2 tablespoons of butter.
2) Sprinkle 2 tablespoons of granulated sugar evenly over the entire surface of the pan.
3) Arrange the sour cherries in one layer in the buttered and sugared pan.
4) Melt the remaining butter. Beat the flour, eggs, milk, remaining sugar and melted butter with a mixer. Slowly pour this mixture over the sour cherries.
5) Bake in preheated, moderately hot oven until the top is nicely browned.
6) Sprinkle the top with powdered sugar or serve with whipped cream.

Yulaflı Diyet Muffin

2 1/4 su bardağı yulaf kepeği

1/3 su bardağı tozşeker

1 paket kabartma tozu

1/3 su bardağı kuru üzüm

2 adet yumurtanın akı

1 1/4 su bardağı yağsız süt

2 çorba kaşığı sıvıyağ

1) Yumurta akı, süt, kabartma tozu ve yağı çırpın. Kuru malzemenin üzerine döküp karıştırın.
2) 12'lik muffin kaplarına, yarısı dolacak şekilde dökün.
3) Orta ısıdaki fırında pişirin.

Oat Bran Diet Muffins

2 1/4 cups oat bran

1/3 cup granulated sugar

1 tablespoon baking powder

1/3 cup raisins

2 egg whites

1 1/4 cups fat-free milk

2 tablespoons vegetable oil

1) Beat the egg whites with the milk, baking powder and oil. Pour over the dry ingredients and mix.
2) Pour mixture into a 12-muffin tin, filling halfway.
3) Bake in moderately hot (220-230 °C) oven until muffins rise and harden.

Muzlu Kek

8 çorba kaşığı yumuşatılmış margarin

1 su bardağı tozşeker

2 adet yumurta

3 adet olgun muz

1 çorba kaşığı süt

1 su bardağı çentilmiş ceviz

2 su bardağı un

1 çay kaşığı tuz

1/2 paket kabartma tozu

22 cm

12 cm

1) Margarin ve şekeri çırpın. Yumurtaları teker teker ilave edip çırpmaya devam edin.
2) Muzları bir kâsede çatalla ezin. Süt ve cevizleri de ekleyip karıştırın.
3) Ayrı bir kapta un, tuz ve kabartma tozunu karıştırın.
4) Çırpılmış yağ ve şeker karışımına sırasıyla muz ve un karışımını ilave edip karıştırın.
5) Hazırladığınız karışımı dikdörtgen bir kek kalıbına dökün. Önceden ısıtılmış, orta dereceli fırında 1 saat kadar pişirin.

Banana Cake

8 tablespoons softened margarine

1 cup granulated sugar

2 eggs

3 ripe bananas

1 tablespoon milk

1 cup finely chopped walnuts

2 cups flour

1/4 teaspoon salt

1 teaspoon baking powder

1) Cream the margarine and sugar. Add the eggs one by one, beating well after each addition.
2) Use a fork to pulp the bananas. Add the milk and walnuts and mix well.
3) In a bowl mix the flour, salt and baking powder.
4) Alternate adding the wet banana mixture with the dry ingredients to the dough and blend well.
5) Pour the prepared mixture into a rectangular, greased cake pan and bake in preheated, moderately hot (220-230 °C) oven for one hour.

Meyveli Kek

3 adet yumurta

1 su bardağı tozşeker

1 su bardağı süt

1 su bardağı eritilmiş margarin (1/2 bardak eritilmiş margarin, 1/2 bardak sıvıyağ da olabilir)

3 su bardağı un

1 su bardağı dolusu kuru meyve (çentilmiş fındık, çentilmiş ceviz, kuru kayısı ve kuru üzüm karışımı)

1 paket kabartma tozu

1) Yumurta ve şekeri çırpın. Üzerine süt, yağ, kabartma tozu ve unu ilave edin.
2) Bütün malzemeyi iyice karıştırdıktan sonra kuru meyveleri ilave edip karıştırın.
3) Hazırladığınız karışımı dikdörtgen bir kek kalıbına dökün. Önceden ısıtılmış, orta dereceli fırında 50 dakika kadar pişirin.

30 cm

12 cm

Pound Cake with fruit

3 eggs

1 cup granulated sugar

1 cup milk

1 cup melted margarine

3 cups flour

1 full cup of a mixture of finely chopped hazelnuts, walnuts, dried apricots and raisins

1 tablespoon baking powder

1) Cream the eggs and sugar. Add the milk, margarine, flour and baking powder.
2) After blending all the ingredients add the dried fruit and nuts and mix well.
3) Pour the mixture into a rectangular, greased cake pan. Bake in preheated moderately hot (220-230 °C) oven for 50 minutes.

30 cm

12 cm

Kakaolu Vişneli Kek

2 su bardağı kekun

2 adet yumurta

1/2 su bardağı erimiş margarin

1 su bardağı tozşeker

1/2 su bardağı kakao

3 çorba kaşığı yoğurt

1 küçük kavanoz vişne kompostosu

2 tatlı kaşığı vişne likörü

1 paket krem şanti

1 su bardağı süt

1 poşet hazır çikolata sosu

Süs için rendelenmiş bitter çikolata

23 cm

1) Yumurtaların beyazı ve sarısını ayırın. Yumurta sarılarını şekerle çırpın.
2) Yağ, yoğurt, un ve kakaoyu ilave edip karıştırın.
3) Ayrı bir kapta yumurta beyazlarını çırpıp bu karışıma ilave edin.
4) Hazırladığınız karışımı yağlanmış, kelepçeli bir kalıba dökün. Orta ısılı fırında 50 dakika pişirin.
5) Soğuyan pastayı eninden, ortadan ikiye bölün.
6) 1 paket krem şantiyi sütle çırpın.
7) Parçaları vişne likörü ile ıslatın. İki parçaya da 1 su bardağı sütle çırpılmış krem şanti sürün.
8) Vişnelerin çekirdeklerini çıkarıp pastanın alt kısmına döşeyin.
9) Diğer parçayı üstüne kapatın. Pastanın üstünü poşetindeki tarifte belirtilen şekilde hazırlanmış çikolata sosu ile kaplayın.
10) Rende çikolata ile süsleyip servis yapın.

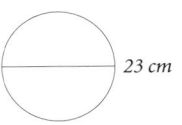

Pound Cake with Cocoa and Sour Cherries

2 cups cake flour

2 eggs

1/2 cup melted margarine

1 cup granulated sugar

1/2 cup cocoa

3 tablespoons yogurt

1 small jar (300 gr) sour cherries

2 teaspoons sour cherry liqueur

100 gr whipped cream

1 package (130 gr) chocolate sauce mix

Grated dark chocolate for garnish

23 cm

1) Separate the eggs and beat the yolks with the sugar.
2) Add the margarine, yogurt, flour and cocoa and beat well.
3) Beat the egg whites in a separate bowl and fold them into the mixture.
4) Pour the mixture into a greased cake pan, preferably a springform pan. Bake at medium heat for about 50 minutes.
5) Slice the cooled cake in half, lengthwise.
6) Dribble the sour cherry liqueur over each of the cut sides. Frost the tops of both halves with the whipped cream.
7) Pit the sour cherries and arrange on top of the bottom layer of the cake. (If using frozen cherries, thaw before using.)
8) Put the top layer over the cherries. Pour the chocolate sauce over the top.
9) Garnish with grated chocolate and serve.

Siyah Üzümlü Kek

1 1/2 kahve fincanı kuru siyah üzüm

200 gr sıvıyağ

3 kahve fincanı pudraşeker

1 kahve fincanı mısır nişastası

1 çay kaşığı rendelenmiş limon kabuğu

4 adet yumurta

1 1/2 su bardağı un

2 kahve fincanı süt

2 kahve fincanı tozşeker

1 paket vanilya

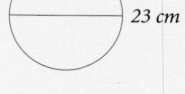 23 cm

1) Kuru üzümleri 1 saat önce, ılık suda ıslatın.
2) Yağ, pudraşeker, nişasta, vanilya ve limon kabuğunu karıştırın.
3) Yumurtaların beyazı ve sarısını ayırıp sarılarını teker teker bulamaca ilave edin.
4) Yumurta aklarını tozşekerle çırpın.
5) Sırasıyla üzüm ve yumurta aklarını, süt ve unu limon kabuklu bulamaca ilave edin.
6) Hazırladığınız karışımı yağlanmış, tercihen yandan kelepçeli bir kalıba dökün. Orta ısılı fırında üstü kızarana dek; 50 dakika kadar pişirin.

Raisin Pound Cake

1 1/2 cups raisins

200 gr vegetable oil

1 cup powdered sugar

1/3 cup cornstarch

1/4 teaspoon grated lemon rind

4 eggs

1 1/2 cups flour

1/2 cup milk

1/2 cup granulated sugar

1 tablespoon vanilla

23 cm

1) Soak the raisins in warm water for 1 hour before preparing cake.
2) Mix the oil, powdered sugar, cornstarch, and lemon rind.
3) Separate the eggs and add the yolks, one by one, to the mixture, beating well after each addition.
4) Beat the egg whites with the granulated sugar until stiff but not dry.
5) One by one, add the raisins, egg whites, milk and flour to the mixture.
6) Pour the mixture into a greased cake pan (preferably a springform pan) and bake in moderately hot oven for 50 minutes or until baked.

Hurmalı Kek

300 gr hurma
200 gr çentilmiş ceviz
200 gr tozşeker
150 gr un
5 adet yumurta
Biraz likör

22 cm
12 cm

1) Hurmaların çekirdeklerini çıkartıp çatalla ezin.
2) Bir kapta ceviz, un, şeker ve hurmaları karıştırın. Yumurta ve likörü ilave edin.
3) Hazırladığınız karışımı dikdörtgen bir kalıba dökün. Orta ısılı fırında üstü kızarana dek pişirin.

Date Pound Cake

279

300 gr dates
200 gr finely chopped walnuts
200 gr granulated sugar
150 gr flour
5 eggs
A small amount of liqueur

22 cm
12 cm

1) Remove seeds from dates and mash with a fork.
2) Mix the walnuts, flour, sugar and dates. Add the eggs and liqueur.
3) Pour the mixture into a greased, rectangular baking dish. Bake at medium heat until golden.

Cevizli Üzümlü Kek

250 gr çentilmiş ceviz
250 gr kuru sarı üzüm
6 adet yumurta
3 çorba kaşığı un
3 çorba kaşığı tozşeker

20 cm
12 cm

1) Bir kâsede ceviz, üzüm, un, şeker ve yumurtaları karıştırın.
2) Hazırladığınız karışımı yağlanmış, dikdörtgen bir kalıba dökün. Orta ısılı fırında 20-25 dakika kadar pişirin.

Walnut-Raisin Pound Cake

250 gr finely chopped walnuts
250 gr yellow raisins
6 eggs
3 tablespoons flour
3 tablespoons granulated sugar

20 cm
12 cm

1) In a bowl mix the walnuts, raisins, flour, sugar and eggs.
2) Pour the mixture into a greased, rectangular baking dish. Bake at medium heat for 20-25 minutes.

Peynirli Toplar

125 gr eritilmiş margarin
1 çorba kaşığı yoğurt
200 gr beyaz peynir
1 1/2 su bardağı kekun
1 adet yumurta sarısı
Susam

1) Margarin, ezilmiş peynir, yoğurt ve unu yoğurup ufak toplar şekline sokun.
2) Bir tepsiye yağlı kâğıt serip topları üzerine dizin.
3) Yumurtanın sarısını çırpın.
4) Topların üstüne yumurta sürüp susam serpin.
5) Orta dereceli fırında 50 dakika pişirin.

Cheese Balls

125 gr melted margarine
1 tablespoon yogurt
200 gr white cheese (feta cheese)
Sesame seeds
1 egg yolk (beaten)
1 1/2 cups cake flour

1) Line a dish with greased paper.
2) Knead together the margarine, mashed cheese, yogurt and flour and form into small balls.
3) Place the balls on the paper and brush with the egg yolk.
4) Sprinkle with sesame seeds.
5) Bake at medium heat for about 50 minutes or until golden.

Havuçlu Kek

2 su bardağı ince rendelenmiş havuç

2 su bardağı un

1 1/2 su bardağı tozşeker

3 adet yumurta

1/2 su bardağı çentilmiş ceviz

1/2 su bardağı kuru sarı üzüm

1 paket kabartma tozu

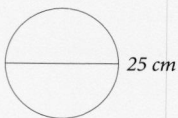

25 cm

1) Şeker ve yumurtaları çırpın. En son ceviz ve üzüm gelecek şekilde tüm malzemeyi ilave edin.

2) Hazırladığınız karışımı yağlanmış, tercihen yandan kelepçeli bir kalıba dökün. Orta ısılı fırında 50 dakika kadar pişirin.

Carrot Pound Cake

2 cups finely grated carrots

2 cups flour

1 1/2 cups granulated sugar

3 eggs

1/2 cup finely chopped walnuts

1/2 cup yellow raisins

1 tablespoon baking powder

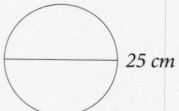

25 cm

1) Beat the sugar and eggs. Add the other ingredients, ending with the walnuts and raisins.

2) Pour the mixture into a greased baking pan (preferably a springform pan) and bake at medium heat for 50 minutes or until golden.

Brownie

100 gr yumuşak margarin
1 2/3 su bardağı tozşeker
3 adet yumurta
1 su bardağından biraz fazla un
1 çay kaşığı kabartma tozu
1 çimdik tuz
1/2 su bardağı kakao
1 1/2 su bardağı çentilmiş ceviz

1) Şekerle yağı, krema kıvamına gelene dek çırpın. Yumurtaları teker teker ekleyerek karışıma yedirin.
2) Kalan malzemeyi de ilave edip kare bir kalıba dökün. Orta ısılı fırında, 35-40 dakika kadar pişirin.

Brownies

100 gr softened margarine
1 2/3 cups granulated sugar
3 eggs
1 slightly rounded cup flour
1/4 teaspoon baking powder
1 pinch salt
1/2 cup cocoa
1 1/2 cups finely chopped walnuts

1) Beat the sugar and margarine until creamy. Add the eggs one by one, beating well after each addition.
2) Add the remaining ingredients and pour into a greased, square pan.
3) Bake at medium heat for 35-40 minutes.

Çikolatalı Muffin

2 adet yumurta

150 gr tozşeker

200 gr un

100 gr erimiş margarin veya tereyağı

100 gr damla çikolata

1/2 paket kabartma tozu

3 çorba kaşığı yoğurt

1) Yumurtaları mikserde çırpın. Üzerine şeker, yağ ve yoğurdu ekleyip çırpmaya devam edin.
2) Damla çikolata, kabartma tozu ve unu da ilave edip karıştırın.
3) Karışımı muffin kalıplarının yarısını dolduracak şekilde bölüştürün. Önceden ısıtılmış orta dereceli fırında, 20-25 dakika kadar pişirin.

Chocolate Chip Muffins

2 eggs

150 gr granulated sugar

200 gr flour

100 gr melted margarine or butter

100 gr chocolate chips

1 teaspoon baking powder

3 tablespoons yogurt

1) Beat the eggs well and beat in the sugar, margarine and yogurt, beating well after each addition.
2) Mix in baking powder and flour and add the chocolate chips.
3) Half fill greased muffin forms.
4) Bake in preheated, moderately hot oven for 20-25 minutes.

Mısır Unlu Tuzlu Kek

2 su bardağı fırınlanmış mısır unu
1 su bardağı beyaz un
1 su bardağı süt
1/2 su bardağı sıvıyağ
1 paket kabartma tozu
1 adet tavuk bulyon
1 çay kaşığı tuz
1 çay kaşığı şeker
250 gr ufalanmış beyaz peynir
1/2 demet maydanoz
Süs için çörekotu

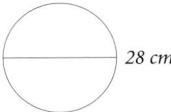 28 cm

1) Ufak bir fırın tepsisini yağlayıp üstüne bolca çörekotu serpin. Tepsiyi buzlukta bir saat bekletin.
2) Tüm malzemeyi karıştırıp yoğurun ve buzluktan çıkardığınız çörekotlu tepsiye döşeyin.
3) Orta dereceli fırında, üzeri kızarıncaya dek pişirin. Ilıkken ters çevirip servis yapın.

Salty Corn flour Loaf

2 cups oven-toasted corn flour
1 cup flour
1 cup milk
1/2 cup vegetable oil
1 tablespoon baking powder
1 chicken bouillon cube
1/4 teaspoon salt
1/4 teaspoon sugar
250 gr white cheese (feta cheese), crumbled with fingers
1/2 bunch parsley
Black cumin for garnish

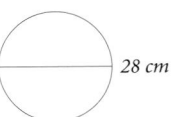 28 cm

1) Grease a small baking dish and sprinkle amply with black cumin.
2) Allow dish to sit in freezer for 1 hour.
3) Mix together all ingredients, knead, and pour batter into the cold dish.
4) Bake at medium heat until the top is golden. Invert and serve.

Soğanlı Kiş

100 gr margarin
1 1/2 su bardağı un
4 çorba kaşığı su
1 çay kaşığı tuz
2 adet soğan
1 su bardağı süt
3 adet yumurta
200 gr rendelenmiş taze kaşar veya gravyer peyniri

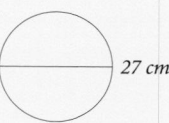
27 cm

1) Margarin, un, su ve tuzu hamur kıvamına gelene dek karıştırın. Hamuru unlu bir zeminde açıp tart kalıbına yerleştirin.
2) Halka şeklinde doğranmış soğanları biraz margarinle az pişirin.
3) Soğanları hamurun üzerine yayın.
4) Ayrı bir kapta süt ve yumurtaları çırpın.
5) Soğanların üzerine dökün. Üstüne rendelenmiş peynirleri serpin. Bir gece buzdolabında bekletin.
6) Orta ısılı fırında üstü kızarana dek; 1 saat kadar pişirin.

Onion Quiche

100 gr softened margarine
1 1/2 cups flour
4 tablespoons water
1/4 teaspoon salt
2 onions
1 cup milk
3 eggs
200 gr grated fresh kaseri or Gruyère cheese

27 cm

1) Mix margarine, flour, water and salt until it forms a ball of dough. Roll out on a floured surface and arrange in a tart pan.
2) Lightly sauté the onions sliced into half rounds in a little margarine.
3) Arrange the onions over the dough.
4) Beat together the milk and eggs. Pour the milk and egg mixture over the onions. Sprinkle the top with the grated cheese.
5) Allow to sit overnight in the refrigerator.
6) Bake at medium heat for 1 hour or until top is golden.

Limonlu Cheesecake

Tart için:

2 adet yumurta sarısı

175 gr yumuşatılmış margarin

1 1/2 su bardağı kekun

3 çorba kaşığı pudraşeker

Limonlu krema için:

1 su bardağı toz limon jölesi

6 çorba kaşığı tozşeker

1 su bardağı su

1 kutu krem beyaz peynir

1 adet limon kabuğu rendesi

1/2 limon suyu

1 paket krem şanti

1 su bardağı süt

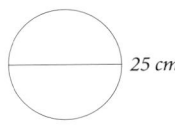

25 cm

1) Tart malzemesinin hepsini yoğurup kelepçeli bir tart kalıbına elinizle döşeyin. Orta dereceli fırında, üstü kızarana dek pişirin.
2) Krema için, jöleyi suyla ezip şekeri ekleyin. Kısık ateşte, şekerler eriyinceye dek kaynatın.
3) Ilıyan jöle karışımına limon kabuğu rendesi, limon suyu ve peyniri ilave edip blender'dan geçirin.
4) 1 paket krem şantiyi sütle çırptıktan sonra karışıma ilave edip karıştırın.
5) Tart kalıbının altını alüminyum folyo ile kapatın.
6) Hazırladığınız karışımı tart kalıbına dökün ve üstünü kapatıp bir gece buzdolabında dinlendirin.

Lemon Cheesecake

Dough:

2 egg yolks

175 gr softened margarine

1 1/2 cups cake flour

3 tablespoons powdered sugar

Lemon cream filling:

1 cup powdered lemon gelatin

6 tablespoons granulated sugar

1 cup water

200 gr cream cheese

Grated rind of 1 lemon

Juice of 1/2 lemon

1 package whipped cream mix (75 gr)

1 cup milk

25 cm

1) Knead together all of the tart dough ingredients and spread dough in a springform pan. Bake at medium heat until golden.
2) To prepare the cream filling, mix the gelatin in the water, add the sugar and cook over low heat until the sugars dissolve.
3) Add the grated lemon rind, lemon juice and cheese to the cooled gelatin mixture and blend in a blender.
4) Beat the package of whipped cream mix with the milk and add to the gelatin mixture, beating well.
5) Line the bottom of the tart form with aluminum foil.
6) Pour the mixture into the prepared tart pan and allow to sit for one night in the refrigerator.

Poğaça

Hamur için:

1 su bardağı eritilmiş margarin

1/2 su bardağı sıvıyağ

Sarısı ve beyazı ayrılmış 1 adet yumurta

1 paket kabartma tozu

1 çay kaşığı tuz

4 su bardağı un

Süs için çörekotu

Peynirli iç için:

250 gr beyaz peynir

6 sap ince kıyılmış maydanoz

Kıymalı iç için:

250 gr kıyma

1 adet ufak soğan

1 adet domates

1 adet sivribiber

1 çay kaşığı tuz

1) Margarin, sıvıyağ, yumurta beyazı, kabartma tozu, tuz ve unu yoğurarak yumuşak bir hamur yapın.
2) Peynirli poğaçalar için, beyaz peyniri ezip ince kıyılmış maydanozla karıştırın.
3) Kıymalı poğaçalar için, çentilmiş soğan, küp şeklinde doğranmış domates, ince kıyılmış sivribiber ve tuzu, suyunu çekene dek pişirin.
4) Poğaça hamurundan ceviz büyüklüğünde parçalar alıp elinizle açın. İçine istediğiniz malzemeyi koyup kenarlarını bastırarak kapatın.
5) Üzerine yumurta sarısını sürüp çörekotu ile süsleyin. Orta ısılı fırında üstü kızarana dek pişirin.

Poğaça (Turkish Savory Biscuits)

Dough:

1 cup melted margarine

1/2 cup vegetable oil

1 egg, separated

1 tablespoon baking powder

1/4 teaspoon salt

4 cups flour

Black cumin for garnish

Cheese filling:

250 gr white cheese (feta cheese)

6 sprigs finely chopped parsley

Meat filling:

250 gr finely ground meat

1 small onion

1 tomato

1 mildly hot, long green pepper

1/4 teaspoon salt

1) Lightly knead the margarine, oil, egg white, baking powder, salt and flour into a soft dough.
2) For cheese poğaças: Mash the cheese well and add the finely chopped parsley.
3) For meat poğaças: Mix the ground meat, finely grated onion, finely diced tomato, diced green pepper and salt and cook until all liquid is absorbed.
4) Roll the dough into walnut-size pieces and then open with your hands. Fill with desired filling and close into half rounds, making sure to press edges together.
5) Brush with the egg yolk and garnish with black cumin. Bake at moderate heat until golden.

Zeytinli Kek

4 adet yumurta

2 su bardağı yoğurt

1 su bardağı sıvıyağ

1 paket kekun

1 su bardağı çekirdekleri çıkartılmış siyah zeytin

1 adet domates

3-4 adet sivribiber

2 çorba kaşığı kekik

1 tatlı kaşığı tuzot

25 cm

1) Domatesleri küp gibi kesip biberlerin çekirdeklerini çıkartıp ince kıydıktan sonra tüm malzemeyi karıştırın.
2) Malzemeyi kelepçeli bir kalıba döküp orta dereceli fırında üstü kızarana dek pişirin.

Olive Loaf

4 eggs

2 cups yogurt

1 cup vegetable oil

1 package (350 gr) cake flour

1 cup pitted black olives

1 tomato

3-4 mildly hot, long green peppers

2 tablespoons thyme

1 teaspoon seasoned salt

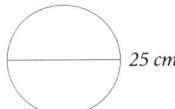

25 cm

1) Dice the tomato. Seed the peppers and chop finely. Mix all ingredients.
2) Pour mixture into a small baking pan and bake at moderate heat until golden.

Scone

2 dolu çorba kaşığı yumuşak margarin

8 çorba kaşığı un

1/2 paket kabartma tozu

1 çorba kaşığı tozşeker

3 çorba kaşığı kuru üzüm

7 çorba kaşığı süt

Üstüne sürmek için süt

1) Tüm malzemeyi derin bir kaba koyup yumuşak hamur kıvamına gelinceye dek karıştırın.
2) Unlanmış bir zeminde merdane ile açıp bir çay fincanı ağzıyla yuvarlak kalıplar halinde kesin.
3) Yağlı kâğıt serilmiş bir fırın tepsisine yerleştirin. Bir fırça yardımıyla üzerlerine süt sürün.
4) Önceden ısıtılmış orta dereceli fırında 25 dakika kadar pişirin.
5) Ilık olarak, yanında reçelle servis yapın.

Scones

2 full tablespoons softened margarine

8 tablespoons flour

1 teaspoon baking powder

1 tablespoon granulated sugar

3 tablespoons raisins

7 tablespoons milk

Milk to brush on top

1) Put all ingredients into a deep bowl and stir into a soft dough.
2) Roll out on a floured surface and cut out small circles.
3) Line a baking pan with greased paper and arrange the scones on the pan. Brush with milk.
4) Bake in preheated oven at medium heat for 25 minutes.
5) Serve warm with jams or preserves.

Taze İncirli Tart

Tart hamuru için:

1 1/2 su bardağı un

1/2 çay kaşığı tuz

1 çay kaşığı tozşeker

8 çorba kaşığı tereyağı

2-3 çorba kaşığı su

İç malzeme için:

12-16 adet taze incir

1 adet yumurta sarısı

1 ufak kutu çiğ krema

1 1/2 çorba kaşığı esmer tozşeker

1) Un, tuz ve şekeri bir kapta karıştırın. Üzerine tereyağı ve suyu ekleyip yoğurun.
2) Hamurun üstünü streç film ile kapatıp buzdolabında 15 dakika kadar dinlendirin.
3) Dinlenmiş hamuru unlanmış bir zeminde açıp tercihen yandan kelepçeli bir tart kalıbına yayın.
4) Kalıbı 15 dakika buzlukta tuttuktan sonra önceden ısıtılmış fırında 20-25 dakika kadar pişirin.
5) Yıkanmış taze incirlerin saplarını kesip, kabuklarını soymadan ikiye bölün.
6) İncirleri iç kısımları dışa gelecek şekilde tart kalıbına yerleştirin.
7) Ayrı bir kapta yumurta sarısı, çiğ krema ve esmer şekeri çırpın. Bu karışımı yavaşça incirlerin üzerine dökün.
8) Orta dereceli fırında 30 dakika kadar pişirin. Ilık olarak servis yapın.

Fresh Fig Tart

Tart dough:

1 1/2 cups flour

1/8 teaspoon salt

1/4 teaspoon granulated sugar

8 tablespoons butter

2-3 tablespoons water

Filling:

12-16 fresh figs

1 egg yolk

1 small box heavy cream

1 1/2 tablespoons brown sugar

1) Mix the flour, salt and sugar in a bowl. Knead in the butter and water.
2) Cover with plastic wrap and allow to sit in refrigerator for 15 minutes.
3) Roll dough out on a floured surface to fit your tart pan (preferably a springform pan) and spread dough in pan.
4) Place pan in freezer for 15 minutes and then place in preheated oven and bake for 20-25 minutes.
5) Remove the stems from the washed fresh figs and cut into two (without peeling).
6) Arrange on the tart crust with the insides of the figs facing up.
7) In a separate bowl beat the egg yolk, heavy cream and brown sugar. Slowly pour this mixture over the figs.
8) Bake at medium heat for 30 minutes and serve warm.

Üç Peynirli Tart

Tart hamuru için.

1 su bardağı kekun

1/2 su bardağı un

1 adet yumurta

1 çay kaşığı tuz

125 gr eritilmiş margarin

Peynirli harç için:

1 su bardağı süt

3 adet yumurta

300 gr rendelenmiş gravyer, taze kaşar ve dil peyniri karışımı

Süs için çörekotu

1) Kekun, yumurta, un, tuz ve margarini karıştırıp hamur haline getirin.
2) Hamuru yağlanmış bir tart kalıbına döşeyin.
3) Peynir karışımını hamurun üstüne serpin. 1 su bardağı süt ve üç yumurtayı karıştırıp peynirlerin üzerine dökün.
4) Tartı bir gece buzdolabında dinlendirin.
5) Üstüne çörekotu serpip orta dereceli fırında 1 saat kadar pişirin.

Three-Cheese Tart

Tart dough:

1 cup cake flour

1/2 cup flour

1 egg

1/4 teaspoon salt

125 gr melted margarine

Cheese filling:

1 cup milk

3 eggs

A mixture of 300 gr grated Gruyère, fresh kaseri and string cheese

Black cumin for garnish

1) Mix together the cake flour, egg, flour, salt and margarine into a dough.
2) Spread the dough in a greased tart pan.
3) Sprinkle the cheese mixture over the dough. Mix together the milk and 3 eggs and pour over the cheese.
4) Allow tart to sit in refrigerator overnight.
5) Sprinkle black cumin on top and bake at medium heat for 1 hour.

Mısır Unu Pastası

3 adet yumurta
1 su bardağı yoğurt
1 su bardağı sıvıyağ
1 paket kabartma tozu
3 su bardağı fırınlanmış mısır unu
1 su bardağı un
1 su bardağı ılık su
2 su bardağı tozşeker

1) Bütün malzemeyi, en son ılık suyu ekleyerek karıştırın.
2) Hazırladığınız karışımı ufak, kâğıttan kek kalıplarına döküp orta ısılı fırında, üstü kızarana dek; 1 saat kadar pişirin.

Corn Flour Muffins

3 eggs
1 cup yogurt
1 cup vegetable oil
1 tablespoon baking powder
3 cups oven-toasted corn flour
3 cups flour
1 cup warm water
2 cups granulated sugar

1) Mix all ingredients together, adding the warm water last.
2) Pour the mixture into small paper cups and bake at medium heat for 1 hour until tops are golden.

Ispanaklı Kiş

Hamur için:
100 gr margarin
4 çorba kaşığı su
1/2 çay kaşığı tuz
1 1/2 su bardağı un

Ispanaklı harç için:
1 kg ıspanak
1 adet soğan
100 gr rendelenmiş taze kaşar
1 çay kaşığı karabiber
1 tatlı kaşığı tuz

Beyaz sos için:
1 su bardağı süt
2 çorba kaşığı un
1 çorba kaşığı margarin
1 çimdik tuz

1) Ispanağı, ay şeklinde doğranmış soğanı, hiç su eklemeden, tuz ve karabiberle birlikte suyunu çekene dek kavurun.
2) Hamur malzemesinin hepsini karıştırıp yoğurun ve yağlanmış bir tart kalıbına yayın.
3) Beyaz sos için, sütü yağla birlikte kaynatın. Blender'da un, tuz ve yağlı süt karışımını çırpın.
4) Hazırladığınız beyaz sosu ıspanakla birlikte karıştırıp tart hamurunun üstüne yerleştirin.
5) Üzerine rendelenmiş peyniri de serpip orta ısılı fırında, peynirler kızarana dek pişirin.

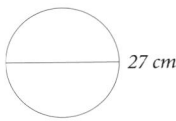 27 cm

303

Spinach Quiche

Dough:
100 gr margarine
4 tablespoons water
1/4 teaspoon salt
1 1/2 cups flour

Spinach filling:
1 kg spinach
1 onion
100 gr grated fresh kaseri cheese
1/4 teaspoon black pepper
1 teaspoon salt

White sauce:
1 cup milk
2 tablespoons flour
1 tablespoon margarine
1 pinch salt

1) Sauté the spinach, onion sliced into crescents, salt and pepper (without adding any water) until all juices have been absorbed.
2) Knead the dough ingredients together and spread dough in a greased tart pan.
3) To make the white sauce, boil the milk and margarine together and mix the flour, salt, and milk mixture in a blender.
4) Mix the white sauce with the spinach mixture and spread onto the dough.
5) Sprinkle with grated cheese and bake at medium heat until the cheese is golden brown.

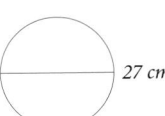 27 cm

Çilek Soslu Cheesecake

Tart için:

3 çorba kaşığı yumuşatılmış tereyağı

3 çorba kaşığı tozşeker

1 adet yumurtanın sarısı

1 su bardağı un

1/2 çay kaşığı kabartma tozu

1/2 çay kaşığı tuz

1/2 bardak çentilmiş tuzsuz badem

Krema için:

900 gr krem beyaz peynir (4 1/2 kutu)

1 çay kaşığı limon suyu

4 adet yumurta

1 su bardağı tozşeker

Çilekli sos için:

500 gr taze veya dondurulmuş çilek

1 adet portakalın suyu ve kabuğunun rendesi

3 çorba kaşığı tozşeker

1) Tereyağ ve şekeri mikserde krema haline gelinceye kadar çırpın. Yumurta sarısını ekleyip karıştırın.
2) Haşlanmış bademleri robottan geçirin.
3) Başka bir kâseye tüm kuru malzemeyi koyun ve tereyağ-şeker karışımını ilave edip yoğurun.
4) Hamuru, tercihen kelepçeli bir kalıba elinizle döşeyin.
5) Krema için, krem beyaz peyniri çırpın. Yavaşça şeker, limon suyu ve yumurta ilave edin. Hepsini karıştırdıktan sonra kalan üç yumurtayı teker teker ilave edin.
6) Tart kalıbının altını alüminyum folyo ile kapatın.
7) Bu karışımı tart hamurunun üstüne döküp orta ısılı fırında, üstü kızarana dek pişirin.
8) Fırından çıkan tartı soğumaya bırakın. Kalıptan çıkarmadan 1 gece buzdolabında bekletin.
9) Çilekli sos için bütün malzemeyi orta ateşte pişirip 3 dakika kadar kaynatın.
10) Soğuyan sosu blender'dan geçirin ve buzdolabında soğutun.
11) Kalıptan çıkardığınız keki dilimlere ayırın. Dilimlerin üzerine çilekli sos dökerek servis yapın.

Cheesecake with Strawberry Sauce

Dough:

3 tablespoons softened butter

3 tablespoons granulated sugar

1 egg yolk

1 cup flour

1/8 teaspoon baking powder

1/8 teaspoon salt

1/2 cup finely chopped unsalted almonds

Cream filling:

900 gr cream cheese

1/4 teaspoon lemon juice

4 eggs

1 cup granulated sugar

Strawberry sauce:

500 gr fresh or frozen strawberries

Juice and grated rind of one orange

3 tablespoons granulated sugar

1) Beat the butter and the 3 tablespoons sugar in a mixer until thick and creamy. Add the egg yolk and mix.
2) Pulverize the boiled almonds in a food processor.
3) Mix the dry ingredients in a separate bowl and knead with the butter-sugar mixture.
4) Spread the dough in a pan (preferably a springform pan).
5) To prepare the cream filling, beat the cream cheese and then slowly add the sugar, lemon juice and 1 egg. Then add the remaining 3 eggs, one by one, beating well after each addition.
6) Pour this mixture over the dough, cover with aluminum foil and bake at medium heat for about one hour or until golden.
7) Allow the cheesecake to cool before placing in refrigerator. Allow to sit in the fridge overnight without removing from the pan.
8) Place all strawberry sauce ingredients into a saucepan, bring to a boil and boil for three minutes (if using frozen strawberries thaw before using).
9) Blend the cool sauce in a blender and allow to cool in refrigerator.
10) Using a sharp knife, cut around the edges and, after removing from the form, slice the cheesecake into serving sizes. Pour the sauce over and serve.

Karamelli Cheesecake

1 su bardağı tozşeker

3 çorba kaşığı su

1/2 su bardağı tozşeker

1/3 su bardağı süt

500 gr taze ricotta peyniri veya tuzsuz lor peyniri

1/2 limon kabuğu rendesi

1/2 portakal kabuğu rendesi

6 adet yumurta

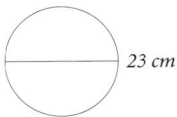

23 cm

1) 1 su bardağı şeker ve 3 çorba kaşığı suyu bir tencerede eritip sarı-kahve renk alıncaya dek kaynatın.
2) Bir tart kalıbına döküp kalıbın her tarafına yayın.
3) 1/2 su bardağı şeker ve sütü birlikte kaynatın.
4) Peyniri bir kaba koyup sıcak sütü üstüne yavaşca dökün. Limon ve portakal kabuğu rendesini ilave edin.
5) Yumurtaları teker teker bu bulamaca ilave edip tel yardımıyla devamlı çırpın.
6) Hazırladığınız karışımı karamelli kalıba yavaşca dökün.
7) Önceden ısıtılmış orta dereceli fırında 1 saat kadar pişirin.
8) Fırından çıkan keki 20 dakika kadar soğutun. Servis tabağına ters çevirerek alın.

Caramel Cheesecake

1 cup granulated sugar

3 tablespoons water

1/2 cup granulated sugar

1/3 cup milk

500 gr fresh ricotta cheese or unsalted lor (farmer's) cheese

Grated rind of 1/2 lemon

Grated rind of 1/2 orange

6 eggs

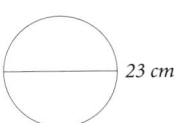

23 cm

1) Dissolve 1 cup sugar in 3 tablespoons water in a pan and boil until the mixture reaches a golden brown color.
2) Carefully pour the mixture evenly over the bottom of a springform pan.
3) Boil the 1/2 cup sugar and milk together.
4) Put the cheese in a bowl and slowly pour the hot milk mixture over. Add the lemon and orange rind.
5) Add the eggs one by one and beat with a whisk until thick and creamy.
6) Slowly pour the mixture over the caramel in the pan.
7) Bake for one hour in preheated, moderately hot oven.
8) After removing from oven allow to cool for 20 minutes. Invert onto a serving plate and serve slightly warm.

Vişneli Cheesecake

1 1/2 paket Eti Burçak bisküvi

125 gr tereyağı

150 gr şeker

800 gr labne peyniri

3 adet yumurta

2 çorba kaşığı un

1 paket dondurulmuş vişne

1 ufak kutu vişne suyu

1 çorba kaşığı mısır nişastası

23 cm

1) Dondurulumş vişneleri bir gece önceden süzgece koyup suyunu bir kapta toplayın.
2) Bisküvileri robottan geçirip iyice ufalayın. Tereyağını eritip bisküvilerle yoğurun.
3) Bisküvileri, tercihen kelepçeli bir kalıba elinizle bastırarak döşeyin ve buzluğa koyup bekletin.
4) Şeker ve peyniri mikserde çırpın. Yumurta ve unu da ilave edip çırpmadan karıştırın.
5) Buzluktan aldığınız kalıba bu karışımı dökün ve önceden ısıtılmış fırında, üstü kızarana dek pişirin.
6) Pişen kekin üstünü kapatıp bir gece buzdolabında dinlendirin.
7) Vişne tanelerini kekin üzerine dizin.
8) Vişnelerin saldığı su, hazır vişne suyu ve mısır nişastasını karıştırın. Koyulaşıncaya dek, kısık ateşte, devamlı karıştırarak pişirin.
9) Karışımı vişnelerin üzerine dökün.

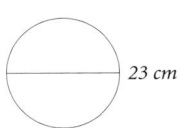

Sour Cherry Cheesecake

1 1/2 packages (1 package equals 165 gr) Eti Burçak cookies or graham crackers

125 gr butter

150 gr sugar

4 packages labne (soft cream cheese)

3 eggs

2 tablespoons flour

500 gr frozen sour cherries

100 ml sour cherry juice

1 tablespoon cornstarch

23 cm

1) Place the frozen cherries into a strainer over a bowl and let stand overnight. Reserve the juice.
2) Crumble the cookies or graham crackers in a food processor. Melt the butter and knead into the crumbs.
3) Press the crumbs into a springform pan with the hands and allow to sit in the freezer for half an hour.
4) Beat the sugar and cheese. Cut in the eggs and flour, but do not beat.
5) Remove the pan from the freezer and pour this mixture over. Bake in preheated oven until top is golden.
6) Cover the cake and allow to sit overnight in refrigerator.
7) Neatly arrange the sour cherries over the cake.
8) Mix the juice drained from the sour cherries, the 100 ml sour cherry juice and the cornstarch and cook over low heat, stirring constantly, until slightly thick.
9) Pour this mixture over the sour cherries on the cake.

İncir Pastası

Pasta için:

250 gr kuru incir

3 paket kakaolu bisküvi

2 paket krem şanti

1 1/2 bardak süt

Çentilmiş ceviz

Sos için:

1 1/2 su bardağı tozşeker

1 su bardağı süt

2 çorba kaşığı kakao

3 parça bitter çikolata

 20 cm

1) Bisküvileri robottan geçirin. İncirleri doğrayıp ceviz ve bisküvilerle karıştırın.
2) 2 paket krem şantiyi sütle çırpıp bisküvili karışıma yedirin.
3) Çukur bir kabı yağlı kâğıtla döşeyin. Karışımı kaba döküp üstünü kaşıkla düzeltin. Üstünü streç filmle kapatıp bir gece buzdolabında bekletin.
4) Katılaşan karışımı servis tabağına ters çevirip çıkartın.
5) Sos malzemelerinin hepsini ufak bir tencerede karıştırın. Kısık ateşte muhallebi kıvamına gelene dek pişirin.
6) Sos ılıyınca pastanın üzerine döküp soğuk olarak servis yapın.

Fig Cake

Dough:

250 gr dried figs

3 1/2 packages chocolate cookies

(1 package equals 175 gr)

2 packages whipped cream mix

(1 package equals 75 gr)

1 1/2 cups milk

100 gr finely chopped walnuts

Sauce:

1 1/2 cups granulated sugar

1 cup milk

2 tablespoons cocoa

80 gr bitter chocolate

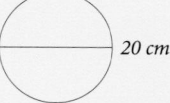 20 cm

1) Grind the cookies until finely crumbed.
2) Mix together the diced figs, walnuts and cookie crumbs.
3) Prepare the whipped cream by beating the mix with the milk and mix into the cookie mixture.
4) Line a deep baking dish with greased paper. Pour the mixture into the dish and smooth with a spoon. Cover with plastic wrap and allow to sit in the refrigerator overnight.
5) Turn over the now hardened mixture upside-down onto a serving dish.
6) Mix all the sauce ingredients in a small saucepan and cook over low heat until the sauce comes to pudding consistency.
7) Pour the cooled sauce over the cake and serve cold.

Fırına girecek bütün kalıpları yumuşak bir margarinle yağlayıp 30 dakika buzlukta tutun. Hazırladığınız karışımları buzluktan çıkmış kalıba döküp hemen fırına verin. Böylece kek ve pastaların yapışmadan kolayca çıkmasını sağlarsınız.

Grease cake pans with soft margarine and keep in the freezer for about 30 minutes. When the cake batter is ready, take the pan out of the freezer and pour in the batter; put into oven immediately. This way you can take out the cakes easily without sticking.